BIOLOGY

Acknowledgments

Grateful acknowledgment is given to the authors, artists, photographers, museums, publishers, and agents for permission to reprint copyrighted material. Every effort has been made to secure the appropriate permission. If any omissions have been made or if corrections are required, please contact the Publisher.

Photographic Credits
Front Cover: Krishan Lad/EyeEm/Getty Images.
Back Cover: Yuhko Okada/EyeEm/Getty Images

Acknowledgments and credits continue on page 592.

For product information and technology assistance, contact us at Customer & Sales Support, **888-915-3276**

For permission to use material from this text or product, submit all requests online at **www.cengage.com/permissions**

Further permissions questions can be emailed to **permissionrequest@cengage.com**

National Geographic Learning |Cengage
200 Pier 4 Blvd., Suite 400
Boston, MA 02210

National Geographic Learning, a Cengage company, is a provider of quality core and supplemental educational materials for the PreK-12, adult education, and ELT markets. Cengage is a leading provider of customized learning solutions with employees residing in nearly 40 different countries and sales in more than 125 countries around the world. Find your local representative at **NGL.Cengage.com/RepFinder**.

Visit National Geographic Learning online at **NGL.Cengage.com**.

ISBN: 978-0-357-85914-8

Printed in the United States of America

Print Number: 01
Print Year: 2022

CONTENTS IN BRIEF

PROGRAM CONSULTANTS

CATHERINE WORKMAN, PH.D.
Vice President of Science
National Geographic Society
Washington, D.C.

Dr. Catherine Workman develops and oversees the implementation and execution of the science components of the National Geographic Society's strategy and leads the science team. Trained as an evolutionary anthropologist, Catherine has extensive experience in the policy, strategy, management, metrics, and communication of biodiversity conservation, international grant-making, and combating wildlife trafficking. She collaborates with colleagues and partners to engage a range of audiences and stakeholders including nonscientific, underrepresented, and youth groups. Prior to joining National Geographic, Catherine worked in the Conservation Biology department at Denver Zoo and was a 2014–2015 AAAS Science & Technology Policy Fellow at the United States Agency for International Development (USAID), where she helped address issues from unsustainable fishing to illegal logging. Catherine has a Ph.D. in evolutionary anthropology from Duke University.

CATHERINE L. QUINLAN, ED.D.
Assistant Professor of Science Education
School of Education, Howard University
Washington, D.C.

Dr. Catherine L. Quinlan has over two decades of science-teaching experience in the K–12 and university settings, sixteen years of which were teaching high school biology. She holds a B.A. in English from Barnard College (premed), and an Ed.D. in Science Education from Teachers College, Columbia University. In her current position at Howard University School of Education, Dr. Quinlan prepares preservice teachers in science methods and education foundations for the K–12 classroom. Her research uses multidisciplinary and interdisciplinary approaches to look at the impact of cognitive, social, cultural, and historical factors on representation, and on Black students' persistence in STEM. Her research focuses on creating and evaluating a culturally representative science curriculum, with a pilot funded by the National Science Foundation (NSF). Dr. Quinlan continues to bridge theory and practice with her representative chapter book series for children, Keystone Passage, which grounds the realities of science, history, and culture in light fantasy. Her Twitter handle is @ProfQuinlan.

PROGRAM REVIEWERS

CONTENT REVIEWERS

NADIA BAZIHIZINA, PH.D.
Research Fellow
University of Florence
Florence, Italy

SHANE CAMPBELL-STATON, PH.D.
Assistant Professor
Department of Ecology and Evolutionary Biology
Princeton University
Princeton, New Jersey

ELAINE Y. HSIAO, PH.D.
De Logi Associate Professor of Biological Sciences
Department of Integrative Biology and Physiology
University of California, Los Angeles
Los Angeles, California

ERICA SMITH, PH.D.
Biology Education Consultant
Chicago, Illinois

LAB REVIEWERS

TRICIA KERSHNER
Hilliard Davidson High School
Hilliard, Ohio

SARA E. LAHMAN, PH.D.
Associate Professor of Biology
University of Mount Olive
Mount Olive, North Carolina

ELIZABETH LUCAS
Hilliard Davidson High School
Hilliard, Ohio

TEACHER CONSULTANTS

JEFF BAIER
Webster Thomas High School
Webster, New York

CAMERON BREWSTER
Cleveland State Community College
Cleveland, Tennessee

ALISSA BURSE
Rocky River High School
Mint Hill, North Carolina

LAURIE FREE
Affton High School
St. Louis, Missouri

JEREMY MOHN
Blue Valley Northwest High School
Overland Park, Kansas

DANIELLE TOWNS-BELTON
Glencliff High School
Nashville, Tennessee

NERY VALDERRAMA
Nova High School
Davie, Florida

NATIONAL GEOGRAPHIC EXPLORERS

KATIE AMATO
Biological anthropologist

DIVA AMON
Deep-sea biologist

CHRISTOPHER C. AUSTIN
Biologist

CARTER CLINTON
Biological anthropologist

NICOLE COLÓN CARRIÓN
Biologist, ecologist

CAMILA ESPEJO
Veterinarian

HOLLY FEARNBACH
Zoologist

ANDRIAN GAJIGAN
Biochemist

PABLO GARCIA BORBOROGLU
Marine biologist and penguin
conservationist

STANLEY GEHRT
Urban wildlife researcher

SHANE GERO
Marine biologist

DAVID GRUBER
Marine biologist

FEDERICO KACOLIRIS
Biologist

HEATHER KOLDEWEY
Marine biologist and
environmentalist

BRENDA LARISON
Biologist

HEATHER J. LYNCH
Quantitative ecologist

EMILY OTALI
Primatologist

ROBERT A. RAGUSO
Biologist

KRISTEN RUEGG
Biologist

PARDIS SABETI
Computational biologist

ÇAĞAN ŞEKERCIOĞLU
Ornithology professor

ANUSHA SHANKAR
Biologist

DANIEL STREICKER
Infectious disease ecologist

VARUN SWAMY
Ecologist

GERARD TALAVERA
Evolutionary biologist

ROSA VÁSQUEZ ESPINOZA
Chemical biologist, Amazon
conservationist

BRANWEN WILLIAMS
Oceanographer and climate
scientist

KIM WILLIAMS-GUILLÉN
Conservationist

ROBERT WOOD
Roboticist

RAE WYNN-GRANT
Carnivore ecologist

CONTENTS

| UNIT 1 |

RELATIONSHIPS IN ECOSYSTEMS 28

ABOUT THE COVER Jellyfish have been a part of Earth's marine ecosystems for hundreds of millions of years. Hundreds of different species are found all over the world, from just below the ocean surface to the deep sea.

Jellyfish such as these sea nettles drift with the current, sometimes propelling themselves with jets of water. These beautiful and prolific carnivores catch food in their tentacles, which are lined with special toxin-producing cells.

CHAPTER 1

INTRODUCTION
TO BIOLOGY

An adult female sperm whale, named Aurora by researchers, swims with two calves from her social unit. This type of whale has the biggest brain of any animal known to have lived.

1.1 THE STUDY OF LIFE

1.2 CONSTRUCTING EXPLANATIONS ABOUT THE
NATURAL WORLD

1.3 USING BIOLOGY TO DEVELOP SOLUTIONS

Scientists study organisms such as sperm whales from many different perspectives. While some scientists may study the communication and ecological roles of sperm whales, others explore their physiological or genetic characteristics to better understand these animals.

Chapter 1 supports the NGSS Performance Expectations **HS-ETS1-1** and **HS-ETS1-2**.

CASE STUDY
PROJECT CETI: DECODING WHALE CODAS WITH ARTIFICIAL INTELLIGENCE

HOW DO WE STUDY THE NATURAL WORLD?

Sperm whales lead complex social lives. At the highest level, their society is organized into different clans, each numbering in the hundreds or thousands. They communicate with one another in short, patterned series of clicks called codas. Marine biologist and National Geographic Explorer Dr. Shane Gero has observed and analyzed thousands of codas from sperm whales around Dominica, an island country in the Caribbean. He has determined that different clans "speak" in different dialects just like American, Australian, and British are different dialects of English. Gero and others have shown that individual whales use specific click patterns to identify themselves as if by name. As calves, whales appear to babble-click much as human babies learn language by mimicking the sounds they hear at home.

Although plenty of animals communicate, the general consensus among scientists is that only humans use true language. Gero and another National Geographic Explorer, marine biologist Dr. David Gruber, are challenging this view. They want to leverage the latest advances in artificial intelligence (AI) to translate codas into something humans can understand. One day, we might even be able to talk to whales directly.

As an initial test of this idea, Gruber sent Gero's recordings to a team of computer scientists who specialize in machine learning, a subfield of artificial intelligence. The team applied AI techniques to Gero's recordings and trained a computer to recognize sperm whale clans based on their codas. The computer was able to correctly identify a whale's clan more than 93 percent of the time.

Excited by the result, Gruber founded Project CETI (**Ce**tacean **T**ranslation **I**nitiative) with a team of scientists to build on Gero's work. (Cetaceans are whales, dolphins, and porpoises.) Along with Gero, the team includes another National Geographic Explorer, roboticist Dr. Robert Wood, as well as experts in linguistics, machine learning, and camera engineering.

Ask Questions *In this chapter, you will learn about the practices scientists and engineers use to study the natural world. As you read, generate questions about how you think scientists and engineers work—including how they are similar and different.*

FIGURE 1-1
A sperm whale makes sound by snapping together two lip-like structures, called phonic lips, inside its head near the blowhole. The sound travels through the spermaceti organ, from the distal air sac to the frontal air sac near the whale's skull. From there, the sound reflects forward through an oil-filled organ, called the junk, to emerge from the front of the whale's head and travel through the water.

▶ **VIDEO 1-1** Go online to learn more from National Geographic Explorer Dr. Shane Gero about how families of sperm whales communicate.

adaptation
biology
evolution
genome
genus
species
taxonomy

THE STUDY OF LIFE

On your way to school, maybe you pass by a grassy field, or walk under a tree, or step over weeds growing in a cracked sidewalk. No matter where you are, living things are all around you, on you, and even within you.

Describe *What living things can you think of that you observe or interact with regularly? Describe at least four different types of living things you are familiar with. What do they have in common? How are they different?*

The Diversity of Life

Life is incredibly diverse. A **species** is a group of closely related living things. On Earth, there are an estimated 8.7 million different species of plants and animals, and scientists have described only about 1.2 million of them. If you consider microbes, some scientists estimate that there may be as many as one trillion different species!

While some species are easy to find and observe, others are incredibly tiny and require special tools to see, and some can only be studied in the place where they live. Sometimes that place is difficult to reach, whether it is at the bottom of the ocean or inside another organism. **Biology** is the scientific study of living organisms. In this chapter and throughout this book, we will explore hundreds of organisms and learn how scientists study the world. Unit 1 explores the many ways in which organisms interact with each other and with their environment.

Defining Life Life has nested levels of organization. Cells are the building blocks of life. Cells include many parts that work together. These parts are made of molecules, and molecules are made up of atoms, which are the building blocks of all matter. A living organism consists of one or more cells. Some cells live and reproduce independently. Other cells live as part of a multicellular organism. Unit 2 describes cells and how they function, and Unit 3 explores how whole organisms are organized.

Classifying Life Each time a new species is discovered, it is named and classified, a practice called **taxonomy**. Taxonomy organizes organisms with shared characteristics into a series of eight progressively narrower categories, starting with the domains of life, then kingdoms, all the way down to species (**Figure 1-2**; see also Appendix E). Although biologists have used many of the same categories for over two centuries, taxonomy continually changes as scientific advances reveal increasingly detailed information about the similarities and differences between species. The largest category, the domain, emerged when advances in genetic technologies enabled scientists to classify all species into three groups based on molecular-level distinctions.

Each species is given a unique two-part scientific name. The first part of a scientific name is the **genus**, which is defined as a group of species that share a unique set of features. The second part of a scientific name is the name of the species. When both parts are combined, a scientific name identifies one unique organism. **Figure 1-3** shows only a tiny sample of the diversity of life found on Earth. The common name and scientific name are indicated for each species.

Go Online SIMULATION

FIGURE 1-3 Go online to begin exploring the Diversity of Life on Earth.

Domain
Kingdom
Phylum
Class
Order
Family
Genus
Species

FIGURE 1-2
Moving from the top to the bottom of the pyramid, each taxonomic level becomes more specific and includes fewer organisms.

FIGURE 1-3 ▽
The diversity of living organisms is demonstrated by these organisms: Australian-spotted jellyfish, Grandidier's baobab, salmonella, water bear, Philippine tarsier, and peacock spider.

Phyllorhiza punctata

Adansonia grandidieri

Salmonella typhimurium

phylum **Tardigrada**

Tarsius syrichta

Maratus volans

transcription → translation

DNA   RNA   protein

DNA and Genetic Variation

Every organism on Earth has a genome that is contained in each of its cells. A **genome** is the complete set of instructions that makes each organism different from other organisms. The genome is a sequence of DNA (deoxyribonucleic acid) that encodes the information for making RNA (ribonucleic acid) and protein molecules that perform all the functions required for life (**Figure 1-4**). The genome in each cell of an organism programs development and growth. It also guides ongoing activities that sustain an organism throughout its lifetime. Unit 4 details how genetic material codes for processes and characteristics that make each organism distinct.

Inheritance Inheritance, the passing of DNA and the traits it encodes from parent to offspring, occurs during reproduction. All organisms inherit their DNA from one or more parents. Individuals of the same species are alike in most aspects of body form, function, and behavior because their DNA is very similar. Humans look and act like humans and not like sunflowers because they inherited human DNA, which differs from sunflower DNA in the information it carries.

Genetic Variation Look at **Figure 1-3** and think about other organisms you know about. Organisms of different species have different sizes and shapes, and they use a variety of mechanisms and behaviors to survive and reproduce. However, these diverse organisms are unified by the four-base DNA code that all living organisms share. Each organism's unique genome sequence encodes information that leads to their particular characteristics.

In addition to the often obvious physical differences between species, individuals of almost every natural population (a group composed of a single species) also vary—just a little bit—from one another. For example, one human has green eyes, the next has brown eyes, and so on. Such variation arises from small differences in the sequences of DNA molecules. As you will learn in Units 4 and 5, differences among individuals of a species are the raw material of evolutionary processes.

SEP **Construct an Explanation** *Identify one physical trait that you and all of your classmates share, and another that differs between individual classmates. Explain why some traits are common to all individuals within a species, while others vary from one individual to another.*

Evolution and Adaptation

You and every organism in this book are the result of millions of years of evolution. **Evolution** describes the ways in which a population of a species changes through time, over many generations. The variation in DNA among individuals is what enables species to evolve. Every time organisms reproduce, their offspring potentially inherit minor changes in DNA.

Some changes in DNA result in molecular- and cellular-level differences that lead to an advantage that helps an organism thrive in its environment. These inheritable advantages that are passed from generation to generation are called **adaptations**. For example, the kangaroo rat shown in **Figure 1-5** lives in the hot, dry deserts of North America. It has an unusual ability to extract water from the seeds it eats and can survive without drinking water because of its specialized kidneys. You will encounter examples of adaptations throughout this book. Unit 5 describes the mechanisms and evidence of evolution in detail.

FIGURE 1-5
Many adaptations are observable as an organism's physical characteristics or behaviors. This kangaroo rat moves at night to conserve water, and it has large hind legs and feet to help it escape predators.

CCC **Structure and Function** *Consider the variety of adaptations described for the kangaroo rat. Now look back at* **Figure 1-3**. *Can you identify any possible adaptations that might relate to how those organisms live in their habitats?*

1.1 REVIEW

1. **Sequence** List these terms by level of organization from simplest to most complex.

   • atoms
   • cells
   • molecules
   • organisms

2. **Describe** How could a population of a species change over a long period of time?

3. **Identify** What categories are used in taxonomy to name unique organisms? Select all correct answers.

   A. DNA
   B. genus
   C. species
   D. genome complexity
   E. number of adaptations

4. **Define** What is a genome?

EXTRACTING DNA FROM FRUIT

SEP **Constructing Explanations** What are some observable properties of DNA?

DNA is the basis of all living things. It is important to the study of life, which includes exploring such things as the structure and function of organisms and the systems in which they live. In this activity, you will use everyday materials to extract DNA from strawberries.

Strawberry fruits turn red when they ripen.

Materials

- strawberries (3)
- knife
- small seal-top plastic bag
- transparent cups or 250-mL beakers (3)
- dish soap, 10 mL
- salt, 1 g
- water, 100 mL
- small stirrer
- filter paper
- alcohol, 50 mL (pure ethanol or 91% isopropyl alcohol)
- paper towels

Safety

Procedure

1. Use the knife to cut away any leaves from the strawberries. Then chop the strawberries into cubes. *CAUTION: Be careful when using sharp objects.*

2. Place the strawberries in the seal-top bag. Remove as much air from the bag as possible and seal it. Then gently knead the strawberries with your hand. Do not apply too much pressure, which can cause the bag to rupture. Continue until the strawberries are a fine paste.

3. In a cup, mix 100 mL of water with 1 g of salt and 10 mL of dish soap. Stir with the stirrer.

4. Open the seal-top bag and pour in the dish soap–salt solution. Seal the bag and gently mash it so that the solution and the strawberry puree are mixed well. Again, be careful not to rupture the bag. Continue kneading the mixture for at least two minutes.

5. Place the filter paper partially inside a cup. You can fold the extra paper outside the cup and hold it if necessary.

6. Open the seal-top bag. Carefully pour the mixture into the filter to filter out the solids. Dispose of the filter and the remaining strawberry mixture in the trash.

7. Pour 50 mL of alcohol into another cup. Tilt the cup with the strawberry mixture, then slowly pour the alcohol down the inside of the cup. There should be a thin layer of alcohol floating on top of the strawberry mixture.

8. The white substance that forms (precipitates) below the alcohol is the strawberry DNA. Gently wrap the white substance around the stirrer and remove from the cup.

9. Once you are done, clean up and return unused materials to the materials station.

Results and Analysis

1. **Describe** Describe the appearance of the DNA sample.

2. **Analyze** Does the DNA appear as you expected? Why or why not?

3. **Evaluate** Why did you need to observe a very large sample of DNA rather than a sample from a single cell? How would your observations differ if you could investigate at the microscopic level?

CONSTRUCTING EXPLANATIONS ABOUT THE NATURAL WORLD

You have likely used scientific thinking in your everyday life. Suppose you wanted to tend to an ailing houseplant. Was it getting too much sunlight or too little? Had it been watered too much or not enough? Could there be a problem with the soil? You could decide on one thing to change and observe the result. Biologists perform these types of activities all the time. Using an orderly, consistent approach to answer questions about the natural world helps assure that their conclusions are meaningful and reliable and can be verified by others.

Explain *Describe a question that you answered using scientific thinking. Explain the process you used to reach your conclusions.*

Using Scientific Thinking to Answer Questions

The author Vladimir Nabokov once said, "I cannot separate the aesthetic pleasure of seeing a butterfly and the scientific pleasure of knowing what it is." You have probably seen butterflies at some point or another in your life. Perhaps you have even wondered about their movements around the planet. National Geographic Explorer Dr. Gerard Talavera (**Figure 1-6**) studies exactly this question: Where does the vibrant, multicolored painted lady butterfly (*Vanessa cardui*) of Northern Europe migrate when the weather turns cold? What are its migration patterns?

FIGURE 1-6 ▽
Dr. Gerard Talavera surveys butterfly populations in southern Ghana.

The painted lady butterfly is found on nearly every continent. The species cannot survive for long in cold temperatures and is unable to hibernate, so it must migrate in response to seasonal changes. Scientists have debated how painted lady butterflies from as far north as Scandinavia are able to make the journey to warmer climates in Africa and back each year. Some argued that a single butterfly, with a life cycle of only 4–5 weeks (**Figure 1-7**), could not make so long a journey. They proposed that multiple generations of butterflies—perhaps up to 10—must take part in completing a single annual migratory circuit.

Talavera studies the migratory patterns of butterflies. A trip from Northern Europe to Africa includes a flight across the Mediterranean Sea, a distance of hundreds of kilometers over open water. When the butterflies reach Africa, they seek food and a safe place to rest. From this point they complete another incredibly long journey over Earth's largest hot desert, the Sahara. The butterflies reach their final destination, the lush African savanna, during the end of the rainy season. Is it possible that a single generation can complete this trip of more than 4000 kilometers? Based on field observations, Talavera hypothesized this was the case.

Talavera and the team he works with needed to develop a plan to investigate the migration phenomenon. They came up with multiple ways to test their predictions. One method was to use the pollen carried by individual butterflies to identify the plant species they visited and map the butterflies to specific regions along a migratory path. Another method was to analyze the chemistry of the butterflies' wings to model their migration patterns based on the regional chemical makeup of the food sources they would have eaten as caterpillars. Talavera also modeled the butterflies' ecological niches to predict their preferred breeding grounds over multiple generations. In addition, he used genetic information to understand the relationships between different populations and how these populations migrate all over the world. This effort required the collection of hundreds of specimens out in the field along the migratory path.

FIGURE 1-7
Vanessa cardui goes through four life stages: egg (a), caterpillar (b), chrysalis (c), and butterfly (d). Caterpillars are herbivores, so a large number of caterpillars hatching in an area can have an impact on the ecosystem in which they live.

 VIDEO

VIDEO 1-2 Go online to observe painted lady butterflies at different stages of life.

FIGURE 1-8
This map illustrates the journey taken by painted lady butterflies as they migrate from Europe and Northern Africa to central Africa in the fall, and vice versa in the spring. The butterfly's range extends across nearly this entire map, with the exception of the Sahara (and other desert regions), which the butterflies fly over. The Sahel is a transition region between the Sahara desert and the tropical savanna region to the south.

The scientists compared the data across multiple groups of butterflies to determine their migratory origins and destinations. Based on this evidence, Talavera and other scientists were able to model the migration patterns of painted lady butterflies on a map (**Figure 1-8**). They argued that the butterflies can indeed make the southward trans-Mediterranean journey in a single generation, flying from Northern Europe to the African savanna over one lifetime.

Researchers think the butterflies make use of patterns in wind gusts to move across long passages of the journey, sometimes flying as fast as 50 kilometers per hour at altitudes as high as 500 meters. Once they reach the African savanna, the butterflies produce several generations of offspring. These offspring progressively migrate further south, toward the tropics. When the land gets dry and food resources are in short supply, the butterflies migrate north again, reaching the Mediterranean in early spring.

The butterflies making the return journey to Northern Europe may be several generations removed from the original painted ladies that flew southward across the Mediterranean. Both of these long journeys, revealed by the work of Talavera and his colleagues, suggests that the butterflies' migration is truly remarkable from a human perspective.

Investigating the migratory patterns of *Vanessa cardui* and other butterflies is both fascinating and essential. Butterflies are important pollinators, helping plants to reproduce by spreading their pollen. Studying their behaviors and movements across continents increases our understanding of how pollinators sustain many other types of life on Earth.

CCC **Patterns** *Talavera was able to identify patterns in butterfly behavior and support his arguments using evidence. When have you observed a pattern and used it to draw a conclusion?*

The Practices of Science

The central purpose of all science, including biology, is the gathering and sharing of information. For this information to be meaningful and reliable, scientists must approach their research as objectively as possible and with a shared set of values and practices. There are eight central practices of scientific inquiry.

Asking Questions Scientists ask questions about how the natural world works. Scientific questions can be investigated through observation and measurement. Scientists must aim to establish what is already known and determine what questions have not been answered. Scientists also ask questions to clarify the ideas of others. Scientists use this information to develop hypotheses to test.

Planning and Carrying Out Investigations Scientists plan and carry out investigations to test hypotheses in the field or laboratory. They must clearly identify all meaningful data and determine the variables and parameters they will set to obtain these data. Scientists use standardized methods, procedures, and measurement systems to minimize error and make valid comparisons between results.

Analyzing and Interpreting Data The data that result from scientific investigations must be interpreted to identify patterns and trends. Data can be qualitative, involving descriptions, or quantitative, involving measurements consisting of numbers and units. Scientists must identify sources of error in results.

Developing and Using Models A **model** is a tool for representing an idea or an explanation of observed phenomena. Models help scientists formulate questions as they proceed to a fuller understanding of the behavior of the world. A model can be a diagram, drawing, physical replica, mathematical representation, or computer simulation.

Constructing Explanations Scientists use evidence to construct explanations that fit their observations. New explanations are accepted when they are better able to explain phenomena than previous ideas.

Engaging in Argument from Evidence Scientists use evidence to defend and critique claims and explanations about the natural world. Scientists engage in argumentation at all stages of the scientific process.

Using Mathematics and Computational Thinking Scientists use mathematics to represent variables and their relationships. Mathematical models and computational tools help scientists make and test predictions. Statistical methods help scientists identify data patterns and correlations.

Obtaining, Evaluating, and Communicating Information Scientists must be able to communicate their findings clearly and persuasively. Information can be presented in a variety of ways, both written and oral. Scientists critique ideas to evaluate the validity of arguments from a variety of sources.

These eight practices show that science is a process, not a single set of facts or ideas. Scientists engage in all of the practices of science at different stages of their research, often more than one practice at a time, and not necessarily in any specific order. As scientists gain greater knowledge about the world, they use the evidence they gather to make further inferences. An inference is an interpretation of data based on information that is already known.

The red circles indicate five sites where Talavera and colleagues captured and analyzed butterflies. At each of these locations, butterflies with a common chemical composition were identified. These butterflies were considered to be one group in the study.

The scale and colors on the map approximately show the predicted probability of birthplace regions for the butterflies in this group. The darkest areas on the map represent the most likely birthplaces.

Adapted from Talavera, et al. 2018.

Models and Systems It is often easier to interpret data when they can be visualized using a model. A simple diagram can help you understand the structure of a cell. A graph can help correlate data, revealing a pattern or trend. Scientists often work with large sets of data that can only be analyzed using computer models. Working with other scientists, Talavera modeled the origins and movements of butterflies across the globe by interpreting chemical data he collected and correlating the data with locations on a map. These data have been simplified for **Figure 1-9**.

Another way that scientists model information is by defining and analyzing systems. We can define a system as the part of the universe on which a scientist's attention is focused when making observations. A **system** consists of components that may interact, though the system as a whole may behave very differently from each of its components. A scientist carefully defines the boundary of the system they are studying. For example, a cell biologist might choose to focus on a single cell as a system. Meanwhile, an ecologist might study an entire population of organisms and their environment as a single system.

In addition to the behavior of a system's parts, scientists are often interested in the cycling of matter and flow of energy into and out of the system across its boundaries. These are called the inputs and outputs of the system. For example, oxygen is an input to the cardiovascular system, and carbon dioxide is an output. **Feedback** is the process by which outputs from a system influence the behavior of the system—for example, a person's heart rate may increase due to feedback in the presence of excess carbon dioxide.

FIGURE 1-9 ▲
Talavera sampled the chemical composition of butterfly wings from many locations at different times of year. Combining these data with wind patterns and other observations, he was able to identify several groups of butterflies that shared probable birthplace regions. These regions have vegetation with a matching chemical composition, and the butterflies ate this vegetation as caterpillars. This map (simplified from a figure published in a peer-reviewed journal) models data for one of those butterfly groups, demonstrating how far those butterflies had traveled since their birth.

A system can be part of a larger system or consist of smaller systems. Thinking in terms of a clearly defined system helps scientists organize and analyze their observations. One type of system that biologists often analyze is an ecosystem. An *ecosystem* consists of one or more communities of different species interacting with one another and with their nonliving environment. You will learn more about ecosystems in Unit 1.

SEP **Systems and System Models** *Consider a model of your home or school as a system. How would you define the system's boundaries? What are some inputs and outputs of the system?*

Science Is a Human Endeavor

Despite all efforts to standardize the practices of science and view data with objectivity, it is still a human endeavor, or activity. It is susceptible to human error, biases, and misinterpretation. This is why it is important that scientists actively engage in communicating and evaluating information. Scientific theories once thought flawless are proved wrong as our understanding of the universe increases. The entire scientific community benefits when their work is viewed with both impartiality and skepticism.

CONNECTIONS

DEVELOPING SCIENTIFIC EXPERIMENTS

Experimental and observational studies are key to the practice of science. To gather evidence and construct explanations, scientists must develop hypotheses and plan experiments with carefully controlled variables.

A researcher who wants to perform an experiment will first read about what others have discovered on the topic. They will then make a hypothesis, which is a testable explanation for a natural phenomenon. Next, they will test the hypothesis.

Some predictions are tested by systematic observation. Others require experimentation. Experiments are tests designed to determine whether a prediction is valid. If working directly with an object or event is not possible, experiments may be performed on a model system. For example, animal diseases are often used as models of similar human diseases.

A typical experiment explores a cause-and-effect relationship using variables. A variable is something that can differ, such as a characteristic that differs among individuals or an event that differs over time. An independent variable is defined or controlled by the person performing the experiment. A dependent variable is a factor that is influenced by the independent variable.

Biological systems are complex because they involve many interdependent variables. It can be difficult to study one variable separately from the rest. Because of this complexity, biology researchers often test two groups of individuals at the same time. For example, an experimental group may be a set of individuals

that have a certain characteristic or receive a certain treatment. This group is tested side by side with a control group, which is identical to the experimental group except for one independent variable. Any differences in experimental results between the two groups is likely to be an effect of changing the independent variable.

Experimental results—data—offer a quantifiable way of evaluating a hypothesis. Data that validate the prediction are evidence in support of the hypothesis. Data that show the prediction is invalid are evidence that the hypothesis is flawed and should be revised.

National Geographic Explorer Dr. Rosa Vásquez Espinoza examines a sample gathered in the field. Learn more about her research in Chapter 5.

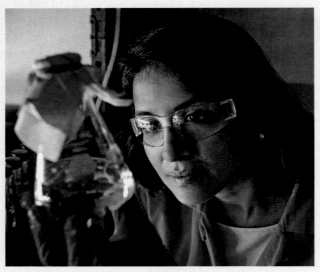

A key skill for scientific communication is the ability to provide and receive criticism in a clear, professional, and constructive manner. Scientific critique identifies how methods and procedures could be improved or gives a rationale for a different interpretation of results. All scientists should be prepared to receive critique openly and use this information to refine their processes and ideas.

Scientists are always updating and refining their ideas. Sometimes they disagree. These disagreements are ultimately healthy for science, as they force us to examine our preconceived notions and further advance our knowledge. For example, the COVID-19 pandemic exposed the public to an evolving set of interpretations about how the virus was spread. As scientists began to better understand the virus, our ability to protect ourselves and others increased.

We should also be aware of the limitations of science. Ethical issues often cannot be resolved using science. Misinformation and the misapplication of scientific facts have occasionally resulted in actions that have done harm to society or the environment. At the same time, scientists should not be afraid to stand firmly behind their principles.

Engaging with science is important for you as a student completing coursework. Beyond school, being a curious and well-informed member of society will help you when making decisions, some as basic as the products you buy, and others as exceptional as how you choose to view the world. Everyone benefits from a broad understanding of science and its practices, and the ability to use scientific thinking to solve problems both big and small.

SEP **Argue From Evidence** *Describe a time when you had to persuade another person using evidence that you could provide. How were you able to change their mind?*

1.2 REVIEW

1. **Analyze** Identify the practice(s) of science represented in each part of an investigation. There may be more than one practice for each part.

   - A researcher models migration patterns based on empirical data.

   - A science team comes up with multiple ways to test their predictions.

   - A scientist wonders where butterflies go when the weather turns cold.

   - Several scientists debate how European butterflies make the annual journey to Africa.

   - Scientists make sense of a statistical comparison of specimens taken from multiple locations.

   - At a national meeting, scientists share the evidence they collected in their investigation about butterfly migration.

   - Scientists publish a scientific journal article describing how butterflies make use of wind patterns to enable their migration.

2. **Justify** Describe the ways in which an ecosystem meets the criteria of a system.

3. **Describe** Use an example to support the claim that because science is a human endeavor, scientific disagreement is healthy for science.

ON ASSIGNMENT After months of tracking by National Geographic photographer Thomas Peschak, a full moon illuminates this pangolin that has just emerged from its burrow in the Tswalu Kalahari Reserve, South Africa. Pangolins are one of the most common victims of illegal trafficking. Their scales, blood, meat, and skin are all sought after for traditional medicine, culinary, or fashion purposes.

biological engineer
constraint
criterion
engineering
trade-off

USING BIOLOGY TO DEVELOP SOLUTIONS

Have you ever considered the origins of various objects in your life? Who came up with them? What decisions went into their design? How were they made? What are they made from?

Even the simplest objects you interact with every day are the results of decisions, revisions, and improvements made over time. More sophisticated technologies require even greater thought and experimentation. In this section we will explore **engineering**, the application of science to design solutions to real-world problems.

Describe *Take a look around you and find a human-designed object. Describe how it is used and how its design suits its purpose.*

CASE STUDY
PROJECT CETI: DECODING WHALE CODAS WITH ARTIFICIAL INTELLIGENCE

Ask Questions *Generate questions about engineering approaches that could help scientists in decoding sperm whale communication.*

The Practices of Engineering

Scientists and engineers have many things in common, but often their goals are different. Scientists tend to seek explanations for the world around them, whereas engineers are concerned with using science to develop solutions. Instead of asking questions as a scientist would, an engineer identifies problems and tries to solve them using scientific knowledge. A **biological engineer**, or bioengineer, uses the principles of biology in particular to develop solutions. Bioengineers participate in a wide range of occupations, including the development of new drugs and medicinal therapies, improvements to agriculture, the design of safety equipment, and a host of other applications.

Consider, for example, the fact that many manufactured medicines and other useful compounds originated from naturally derived sources (**Figure 1-10**). A biologist might approach this fact and ask questions such as:

- What chemicals in this substance make it function as a medicine?
- Is its usefulness as a medicine due to a single chemical or a combination of chemicals?
- Can the organism that this substance is derived from be sustainably harvested?
- How does the drug work in the body?

The scientist is asking questions to construct explanations. An engineer faced with the same set of facts might ask questions such as:

- How can we improve the effectiveness of this medicine?
- Is there an easier way to obtain the compound(s) responsible for its usefulness as a medicine?
- Can the substance be synthesized in a lab setting?
- Are there better ways of storing or administering this medicine?

In order to answer any of these questions, it is important for the engineer to very clearly define the problem and the goals of its solution.

Defining a Problem Now consider the real-world problem of designing a prosthetic leg for amputees. An engineer's goal is to make the best possible prosthesis that is reasonably achievable. However, simply stating that the goal is "to make a functional prosthetic leg" is somewhat ambiguous. It is much easier to imagine the requirements that the prosthesis will need to meet if we think about who it is being designed for and its intended purpose. Is it simply for walking on flat surfaces? Is it being designed for athletic activity? A carefully defined engineering problem allows engineers to develop and compare different solutions in a measurable way.

Suppose now that the prosthesis is being designed for a runner. This quickly gives us a much better picture of the user's requirements. The prosthesis should definitely be lightweight. It should be able to withstand high impact forces. It should probably be flexible, too. These requirements that a solution must meet are called criteria. A singular requirement is a **criterion**. Criteria are most easily compared when they are defined in a quantifiable way. Rather than saying the prosthesis should be lightweight, we could say the prosthesis must weigh no more than 1.5 kg. We could also say that it must be able to bear the force of a 73-kg (161-lb) person running at full speed while remaining flexible.

Once we have a clearer picture of the solution's criteria, we can also begin to think about its **constraints**, or the limitations that an engineer needs to consider when designing a solution. Constraints often include limiting factors such as cost, availability of materials, safety, aesthetics, and possible social, cultural, and environmental impacts. For the prosthetic leg, costs, safety, and the availability of materials are constraints we will have to take into account. Aesthetics might also be worth considering but probably is not as much of an issue.

FIGURE 1-10 ▲

Penicillium chrysogenum (a) is a source of antibiotics. Compounds from *Streptomyces coelicoflavus* (b) have shown promise as treatments for diabetes. The Madagascar periwinkle (c) produces substances that are used to treat cancer. Horseshoe crab (d) blood is used in tests to detect toxins.

FIGURE 1-11 ▶
Sprinters compete at the Tokyo 2020
Paralympic Games.

Developing Possible Solutions Once the problem is clearly defined and the solution's criteria and constraints are considered, engineers begin to brainstorm solutions. Brainstorming should be a judgment-free collaborative activity where new ideas are developed and shared. At this point, no idea should be off-limits. The goal is to come up with as many ideas as possible. Sometimes what seems like an impossible idea can help point in the direction of an even better solution.

With a set of possible solutions in mind, we can begin to compare how well they meet the criteria we have defined. This often requires balancing multiple criteria for the solution against one another while also keeping in mind its constraints.

BIOTECHNOLOGY FOCUS

TURNING TO NATURE FOR INSPIRATION Modern high-tech running blades were originally designed by American biomedical engineer Van Phillips, who was an amputee himself. Prior prosthesis designs were stiff and not useful for running. Inspired by the mechanics of cheetahs' legs, Phillips came up with a curved, springy design that allows users to run and jump. Running blades are made from carbon fiber, which is lightweight, flexible, and strong. The curved design stores the energy from a runner's stride and releases it like a spring, propelling the runner forward.

Some prosthetic devices take inspiration from nature.

In the case of a prosthetic running leg such as in **Figure 1-11**, we might select a material that is a little more costly but is more lightweight. We might need to design the prosthesis with less flexibility but more ability to withstand the forces exerted on it while running. This prioritization of one criterion over another is called making a **trade-off**.

Optimizing the Solution Engineering design is an iterative process. This means that engineers will repeat the steps of the process over and over, gradually refining the solution each time. Sometimes a solution that seemed promising simply will not work and the engineers will have to go back to the drawing board. New criteria may come to light as solutions are tested. Or the entire problem may need to be redefined. Complex real-world problems are often solved by breaking them down into smaller, more manageable problems. Engineers should be prepared to treat what seems like a failure as an opportunity to learn more about the problem and better refine its solution.

When testing possible solutions, engineers often build test models called prototypes. They may rely on computer simulations to help envision how a solution will work. In situations when the solution will be a large-scale process, such as manufacturing a drug, engineers will often test the process on a smaller scale before "scaling up." As engineers repeat these iterative steps, an optimal solution is developed.

SEP **Construct an Explanation** *How are the practices of science and engineering similar? How are they different? For example, how might a scientist iterate to improve and optimize an experiment's design?*

1.3 REVIEW

1. **Classify** The practices of science and engineering are similar. Label each statement as an example of scientific practices, engineering practices, both, or neither.

   • Solutions are refined in iterative steps.

   • Failures can be used as learning opportunities.

   • Limits involve quantifiable criteria and specific constraints.

   • Goals are broken down into smaller, more manageable goals.

   • The answers to questions are obtained in a systematic process.

   • Restrictions involve defining system boundaries and appropriate data collection plans.

2. **Justify** Explain why quantifiable criteria are important for success in engineering projects. Include the concept of trade-offs in your answer.

3. **Describe** What are the benefits of an effective brainstorming process? Select all correct answers.

   A. Many solution ideas are generated.

   B. The problem will have an obvious solution.

   C. All proposed solutions are represented in the final solution.

   D. Multiple criteria and constraints are defined in the best solution.

   E. Solutions that may not be possible can point toward better solutions.

MASS DISTRIBUTION OF MAMMALS

SEP **Use Mathematics** To make it easier to compare numerical data, scientists have developed a standardized system of measurements known as the International System of units, or SI, from the French *Système Internationale*. The SI unit of mass is the kilogram, abbreviated kg. The masses of blue whales, the largest marine mammals, can be up to 180,000 kg, while the African elephant, the largest terrestrial mammal, can have a mass of more than 6000 kg. In comparison, the largest aerial mammals, such as a large flying fox bat, may have a mass of about 1 kg. **Table 1** shows an estimated mass distribution of terrestrial, marine, and aerial mammal species.

TABLE 1. Mass Distribution in Representative Terrestrial, Marine, and Aerial Mammals

Average estimated mass (kg)	Number of terrestrial mammal species	Number of marine mammal species	Number of aerial mammal species
0.001	140	0	360
0.01	1200	0	480
0.1	700	0	90
1	450	0	1
10	230	4	0
100	80	13	0
1000	5	27	0
10,000	0	9	0
100,000	0	3	0

Sources: Centre for Population Biology, Imperial College at Silwood Park

To compare the masses of mammal species, it is helpful to write and compare values in scientific notation. For example, to compare the mass of the smallest marine mammal to the mass of the smallest aerial mammal, we first write the ratio of the two masses to be compared as a fraction. Then, we convert the values to scientific notation and complete the calculation as shown:

$$\frac{10 \text{ kg}}{0.001 \text{ kg}} = \frac{1 \times 10^1 \text{ kg}}{1 \times 10^{-3} \text{ kg}} = 1 \times 10^{(1-(-3))} \text{ kg} = 1 \times 10^{(4)} \text{ kg} = 10,000$$

The calculated value of 10,000 is one way to represent the ratio of the two masses. However, it can be easier to compare large and small values if we convert this ratio to an order of magnitude. To do this, we calculate the $\log_{10}$ of the value

$$\log_{10}(10,000) = 4$$

This means the average mass of the smallest marine mammals is four orders of magnitude larger than that of the smallest aerial mammals.

FIGURE 1 ▽
The variety in size and shape among mammals is demonstrated by this manatee (a), red fox (b), giraffe (c), and fruit bat (d).

1. **Calculate** Convert the average masses in **Table 1** into scientific notation. Then determine the $\log_{10}$ of each value.

2. **Organize Data** Create a bar graph that shows the number of species in each mammal category using $\log_{10}$ average mass on the horizontal axis. The peak mass is the mass value that includes the most species. Record the peak mass of each distribution.

3. **Compare** Determine the differences in order of magnitude between the three mass distribution peaks.

4. **Interpret Data** What might explain the differences in the mass distributions of terrestrial, marine, and aerial mammals?

5. **Calculate** The SI unit for length is the meter (m). One meter is 100 centimeters (cm), and 1000 meters is 1 kilometer (km). Convert the estimated lengths of the mammals given in the following table to cm and km. Which unit would be most convenient for measuring and reporting the size of each mammal?

Mammal	Length (m)
manatee	3.0
red fox	1.0
giraffe	4.7
fruit bat	0.07

6. **Explain** What relationship, if any, would you expect to exist between an animal's length and its environment?

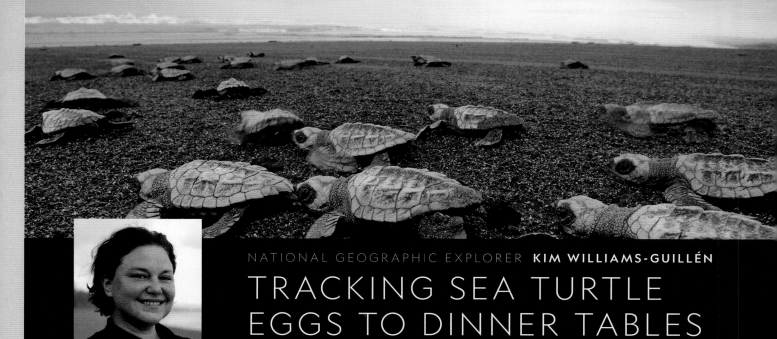

TRACKING SEA TURTLE EGGS TO DINNER TABLES

Dr. Kim Williams-Guillén designed a decoy turtle egg with the aim of tracking poachers.

Conservationist Dr. Kim Williams-Guillén pondered how to track the locations of illegally harvested eggs of endangered and threatened sea turtles in Costa Rica. High in protein and said to taste richer than a chicken egg, sea turtle eggs are a delicacy served in some restaurants and bars. Each egg brings a poacher around one dollar, and a sea turtle lays about 100 leathery-shelled eggs in each nest.

The rainy season is especially busy for poachers around Ostional, Costa Rica. It begins in May and lasts through November. The olive ridley sea turtles' *arribadas*, Spanish for "arrival," begins in June. Once or twice a month, many thousands of them come ashore all at once, awkwardly clambering across the sand to dig nests about one meter deep in the sand. Olive ridleys lead a solitary life, migrating hundreds to thousands of kilometers in the open ocean. Every few years, each female returns to the same area where she hatched. The olives and their close relative, the Kemp's ridleys, synchronize those arrivals. The individuals of other species come ashore a few times during those months. The regular timing of sea turtle nesting opens the door for predators, both the natural and human kind.

The eggs can be collected in a box or bag without breaking. Williams-Guillén noted their resemblance to table tennis balls. Inspired by tracking devices seen on television shows, she concluded that a decoy egg could be made to mimic the texture, feel, size, and most importantly, the weight of a real egg. It would need to be fitted with electronics that could emit a strong signal for several days. The decoy would need to stay in the mix of the real ones and not drift to the top or sink to the bottom. And the fakes would have to look enough like the real thing to escape the notice of an experienced poacher.

Williams-Guillén's design solution was a 3D-printed decoy turtle egg embedded with a GPS–GSM transmitter. Her team placed a decoy in 101 sea turtle nests on four different beaches in Costa Rica. Twenty-five percent were later poached. Six decoys were discovered on the beach, likely identified and discarded by the collectors. The team also estimated a 32 percent failure rate based on their follow-up examination. Yet, the decoys allowed the team to track five of the illegally harvested nests, revealing one trail 137 kilometers long—nearly the entire length of the trade chain from beach collection to dinner table. The decoys were deemed a success for tracing the route of eggs—a positive step in curbing the illegal wildlife trade.

THINKING CRITICALLY

Define a Problem *What problem was Williams-Guillén trying to solve? What were her criteria and constraints? How could she determine whether her design solution was successful?*

TYING IT ALL TOGETHER
PROJECT CETI: DECODING WHALE CODAS WITH ARTIFICIAL INTELLIGENCE

HOW DO WE STUDY THE NATURAL WORLD?

Translating an animal language into human language, as the Case Study describes, would have been impossible only a few years ago. Even today, it is a daunting goal that requires the cooperation of research scientists and engineers in multiple fields.

For Project CETI to be successful in deciphering whale codas, machine learning will require extremely large quantities of data—far more than the thousands of sperm whale recordings that have been collected during the past few decades. The Project CETI team must collect millions, and possibly tens of millions, of audio samples that include data about which whale was speaking, what other whales were present, and what they were doing at the time. Gathering this much detailed data requires an arsenal of acoustical sensors, underwater drones, and video cameras that can record whale sounds and document their activities wherever they go.

In this activity, you will analyze how the practices of science and engineering are involved in the Project CETI investigation. Work individually or in a group to complete these steps.

Ask Questions
1. Write a question that a scientist studying how whales communicate might ask.

2. Write a question that an engineer studying how whales communicate might ask.

Construct an Explanation
3. Describe how CETI scientists might use three of the science practices introduced in this chapter to study whale communication.

4. Describe the design process CETI engineers might use to measure whale sounds.

FIGURE 1-12 ▼
A specialized device that records and tracks sperm whales uses suction cups to stick to a whale's back.

REVIEW KEY CONCEPTS

1. Relate Which of the central practices of scientific inquiry is essential before scientists can plan and carry out investigations?

   A. asking questions

   B. constructing explanations

   C. developing and using models

   D. analyzing and interpreting data

2. Identify How could small physical differences between two individuals of the same species be explained? Select all correct answers.

   A. The individuals have very dissimilar genomes.

   B. The individuals do not belong to the same genus.

   C. The individuals' parent(s) had slightly different DNA.

   D. The individuals have nearly identical DNA with slight variations.

   E. The individuals' DNA has been adapting and evolving throughout their lifetimes.

3. Identify A scientist is studying grasshoppers in local fields. Which statements describe ways the scientist could use models as part of the scientific process? Select all correct answers.

   A. identifying the species of plants found in the local fields

   B. observing the number of grasshoppers on different types of plants

   C. creating a map to show predicted patterns of grasshopper distribution

   D. graphing the number of grasshoppers observed at different times of day

   E. developing data visualizations of the relationship between grasshopper density and rainfall

4. Classify Determine whether each question is an engineering question or a scientific question.

   • How are bacteria affected by temperature changes?

   • What types of bacteria are most likely to grow on human skin?

   • Are beneficial intestinal bacteria harmed when people take antibiotics?

   • Can penicillin be modified in new ways to kill bacteria that are resistant to standard penicillin?

   • How can bacteria containing human insulin genes be modified to increase insulin production?

5. Classify Label each example as a specific practice of science: asking questions, planning and carrying out investigations, analyzing and interpreting data, developing and using models.

   • observing bees visiting various flowers and wondering what factors affect their behavior

   • calculating the average number of flowers of each color visited by bees over several days

   • setting up patches of blue and yellow flowers that are otherwise identical and positioning cameras to record visits by bees

   • devising an algorithm to predict the frequency of random bee visits versus visits influenced by color, odor, amount of nectar, and other factors

6. Sequence The common house cat (*Felis catus*) is classified in the family Felidae, the order Carnivora, the kingdom Animalia, the species *catus*, the class Mammalia, the genus *Felis*, and the phylum Chordata. Place these levels of classification in order.

7. Relate A bioengineer has been hired by a drug company to design an over-the-counter oral antibiotic to treat a specific type of bacterial infection. Effective antibiotics for this disease already exist, but they can only be administered by injection in a hospital setting. Determine which statements represent *criteria* for an acceptable solution.

   A. The drug must be delivered orally.

   B. The drug must be effective in treating the disease.

   C. The drug must be affordable for all socioeconomic groups.

   D. The cost of developing the drug must be within the company's budget.

   E. The drug must be more effective than existing drugs for the same disease.

8. Evaluate Which questions represent global challenges facing humanity that can be addressed by engineering? Select all correct answers.

   A. How can we explain why species evolve over time?

   B. How can we track the migration of a pink lady butterfly?

   C. What can we do to improve the effectiveness of life-saving vaccines?

   D. How can we increase agricultural production while limiting pollution?

   E. How can we remove toxins and pollutants from sources of drinking water?

CRITICAL THINKING

9. **Explain** A genetic mutation causes an individual salamander to be a lighter shade of brown than other salamanders of the same species. This unique characteristic makes the light brown salamander harder for predators to spot. Explain how this mutation may or may not affect future generations of salamanders.

10. **NOS** **Scientific Knowledge** Scientists once hypothesized that proteins were responsible for inherited characteristics in organisms because proteins are very complex molecules. However, scientists later discovered evidence that DNA carries the genetic information organisms pass on to their offspring. How does this example illustrate the concept that science is a human endeavor?

11. **Synthesize** An ecologist has been hired to study how a proposed housing development may affect native wildlife and their habitats. How could the ecologist model the effects of different building plans on the area's biodiversity? In your response, address how the ecologist might define the system in order to study its inputs and outputs.

12. **Predict** Among eastern red-backed salamanders, some individuals have a stripe along their back and others do not. Researchers have found that in cooler climates, a higher percentage of salamanders are striped than in warmer climates. Earth's average temperature is currently increasing. What are three questions a scientist might ask in order to construct an explanation for this phenomenon?

MATH AND ENGLISH LANGUAGE ARTS CONNECTIONS

1. **Write Explanatory Text** Cacti, which are native to arid environments, have needles instead of conventional leaves to help them conserve water and defend themselves from herbivores. Explain how this adaptation is related to the genome of the cactus, how it is passed from one generation of cacti to the next, and what might cause this trait to change in future generations.

2. **Write Explanatory Text** A major highway is being built through an area where many animals are known to migrate regularly. Conservation groups are concerned that the highway will lead to large amounts of roadkill, habitat loss, and reduced biodiversity. Explain how a bioengineer might use the practices of engineering to develop a solution.

Use the information on painted lady butterfly migration on pages 9 to 11 to assist in answering the question.

3. **Reason Abstractly and Quantitatively** Based on information in the passage, estimate how many kilometers per day a painted lady butterfly would have to fly, on average, in order to complete the migration from Europe to the African savanna within its lifetime. What factors related to the butterfly's life cycle might affect this estimate?

4. **Write Explanatory Text** People who suffer from diabetes have trouble producing enough insulin, a hormone that helps regulate blood sugar levels. In 1982, genetic engineers modified the genome of a bacterium, essentially reprogramming bacterial cells to produce insulin for the treatment of patients with diabetes. Explain what makes this an example of bioengineering, and discuss how the practices of science and engineering likely contributed to this solution.

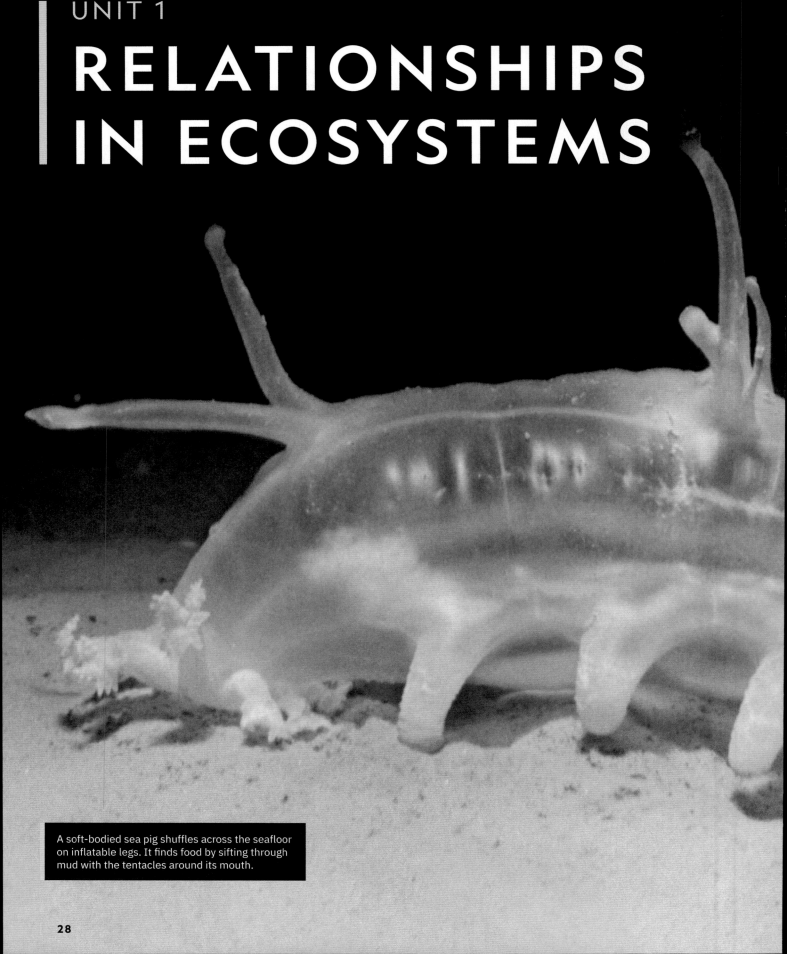

RELATIONSHIPS IN ECOSYSTEMS

A soft-bodied sea pig shuffles across the seafloor on inflatable legs. It finds food by sifting through mud with the tentacles around its mouth.

From a human point of view, life on the ocean floor seems tough. Thousands of meters beneath the surface, organisms contend with some of the most extreme conditions that exist on Earth. Sunlight does not travel to these depths, so it is very dark and cold. Pressures in the deep ocean are hundreds of times greater than on land. Most of the ocean floor is a vast plain of mud and rock. Despite these apparent challenges, a variety of animals, bacteria, and other organisms thrive in this environment.

The sea pig is one of the most common residents on the ocean floor. However, because their habitat is so difficult for humans to reach, much about sea pigs remains unknown.

▼

HOW DO SEA PIGS SURVIVE IN THE DEEP OCEAN?

In this unit you will explore systems and interactions that enable organisms to survive within their ecosystems.

CHAPTER 2
ENERGY AND MATTER IN ECOSYSTEMS

CHAPTER 3
BIODIVERSITY AND ECOSYSTEM STABILITY

CHAPTER 4
POPULATION MEASUREMENT AND GROWTH

▶ **UNIT VIDEO 1** Go online to watch sea pigs in action on the sea floor.

UNDER THE SEA
ILLUMINATING UNIQUE ECOSYSTEMS IN THE DEEP OCEAN

The deep ocean, the part of the ocean below 200 meters where sunlight fades rapidly, is one of the planet's last untouched wildernesses. This environment supports human life by absorbing carbon dioxide from the atmosphere and cycling nutrients into fisheries. Although less than 20 percent of the ocean floor has been mapped, it is estimated to contain vast deposits of natural resources, and countries and corporations are now exploring ways to extract them. To understand the effects of human activities and climate change on deep-ocean ecosystems, marine biologist and National Geographic Explorer Dr. Diva Amon seeks to answer the question, "What lives here?"

OTHERWORLDLY AND WEIRD Diva Amon has led scientific expeditions to explore the wide variety of largely unknown ecosystems in the Gulf of Mexico and the Marianas Trench Marine National Monument. These expeditions focused on characterizing deep-sea coral and sponge communities, bottom-fish habitats, and chemosynthetic environments. Chemosynthetic bacteria make food from chemicals seeping out of the seafloor. In the Gulf of Mexico, these bacteria colonize cold seeps, mud volcanoes, asphalt seeps, and brine pools. In the Marianas, Amon was among the first humans to observe recently formed hydrothermal vents that release plumes of chemical-filled underground water. These vents are hotbeds of chemosynthetic activity. Organisms such as tube worms and mussels that obtain food from the bacteria in these environments create habitats for many other species, which in turn become food for predators.

Of the hundreds of different species of organisms scientists observed on these research missions, most had not been seen before in these regions. Others were seen alive for the first time, and many were potentially undescribed species. For example, a slit shell snail observed in the Marianas in July 2016 was likely an undiscovered species. Scientists estimate that the deep ocean is home to one million species, two-thirds of which have not yet been discovered.

DEEP DIVE WITHOUT DEEP POCKETS Exploring the deep ocean is expensive. Remotely operated vehicles (ROVs) outfitted with machinery for collecting samples,

high-resolution cameras, and other sensors are the workhorses of deep-sea research. These vehicles make measurements and take images that provide data about the types, populations, and behavior of organisms in their natural environment. They are deployed from ships that spend months at sea. During Amon's missions aboard the NOAA ship *Okeanos Explorer* and other ships, she described the rare and unique animals and ecosystems captured by the ROV *Deep Discoverer*. The video footage was live-streamed to the public over the internet. The same technology makes real-time data gathered by the ship's equipment available to collaborating scientists on shore.

This scale of investment in exploration is typically not accessible for developing countries, even though many manage deep-sea environments within their maritime zones. In her home country of Trinidad and Tobago, Amon's nonprofit organization, SpeSeas, has helped pilot first-time explorations using deep-sea cameras developed by National Geographic's Exploration Technology team and lower-cost ROVs that require minimal resources and expertise. The goal of this pilot project was to empower nations to develop and sustain the capacity to investigate their deep-sea backyards.

THINKING CRITICALLY

Analyze *Describe how a human activity such as seabed mining might affect organisms that live in a deep-ocean ecosystem.*

Top: Dr. Diva Amon displays samples collected from the Marianas region of the Pacific Ocean. **Bottom left:** A submersible surveys a hydrothermal chimney. **Bottom right:** Amon regularly encounters unusual animals like this dumbo octopus, named for its large, earlike fins. The octopus pulls its fins and arms inward to swim.

(▶) **UNIT VIDEO 2** Go online to watch our interview with Amon and learn more about her career and research.

CHAPTER 2
ENERGY AND MATTER IN ECOSYSTEMS

Hemlock, spruce, and cedar trees on Admiralty Island, Alaska, provide habitat and food for chicken mushrooms, lichens, and mosses.

2.1 ECOLOGICAL SYSTEMS

2.2 MODELING THE TRANSFER OF ENERGY AND MATTER

2.3 MODELING ENERGY AND MATTER DISTRIBUTION

2.4 CYCLING OF MATTER

Chapter 2 supports the NGSS Performance Expectations **HS-LS2-3**, **HS-LS2-4**, and **HS-LS2-5**.

The Tongass National Forest, which covers nearly 17 million acres in Southeast Alaska, is part of the largest temperate rainforest in the world. The forest has remained largely intact since glaciers retreated thousands of years ago. Fossil evidence shows that some animal species found in the forest today, such as bears and deer, also lived in the area at that time.

CASE STUDY
SOMETHING FISHY IN THE FOREST

HOW DO ENERGY AND MATTER MOVE THROUGH AN ECOSYSTEM?

Biologists have identified several large populations of brown bears living in the temperate rainforest along the Pacific Ocean in Southeast Alaska. About 4300 brown bears inhabit Admiralty, Chichagof, and Baranof Islands in the Tongass National Forest. The bear population density on Admiralty Island is among the highest in the world, at one bear per square mile.

Bears are famous for their enormous appetites. They eat a variety of vegetation including berries, roots, and grasses. Bears also hunt large animals such as moose, deer, and caribou as well as smaller mammals. To obtain their primary source of protein, Alaskan coastal brown bears fish for salmon in the rivers that extend from the forest to the ocean (**Figure 2-1**). These species of salmon are born in freshwater streams and migrate to the ocean where they spend much of their lives. When it's time to reproduce, the salmon return to the same freshwater streams where they were born.

Typically, a bear eats only the most energy-rich parts of the fish, such as the brain and the eggs of female salmon that have not yet spawned. Brown bears gain just over one kilogram of fat per day to store energy to survive through the winter months, during which they lose 20 to 40 percent of their body mass. In particular, pregnant bears must build up ample fat reserves to gestate and feed cubs. Bears carry their meals away from the watershed, where they leave fish carcasses to decay or be scavenged by other animals.

Temperate rainforest soils naturally contain low levels of nitrogen, an element that is abundant in salmon and essential for plant growth. In a river ecosystem, plants and trees enhance conditions for the reproduction and growth of new fish. Thriving vegetation provides shade, stabilizes riverbank soil, filters sediment, and serves as a nutritious food source for other animals and microbes.

The relationship between bears and salmon affects many other organisms and is key to maintaining healthy coastal forest ecosystems. In turn, the forests provide suitable habitats for sustainable populations of bears and salmon. These relationships are characterized by the movement of both energy and matter throughout the ecosystem.

Ask Questions *As you read this chapter, generate questions about the ways in which matter cycles and energy flows between organisms and their environment.*

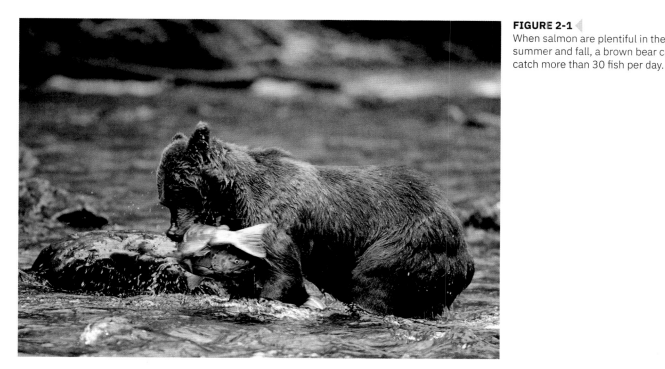

FIGURE 2-1
When salmon are plentiful in the late summer and fall, a brown bear can catch more than 30 fish per day.

ECOLOGICAL SYSTEMS

Walking along a rocky beach at low tide, you discover a shallow depression about the size of a bathtub. It is filled knee-deep with seawater. As you look closer, you notice clusters of seashells clinging to its upper edges. Lining the bottom of the pool are colonies of barnacles and purple mussels. Patches of algae sway among brightly colored sea anemones and sea stars.

You have stumbled upon a tide pool and a community of organisms specialized to survive there. It is like a strange world all its own. Soon, the next high tide will cover the beach and its tide pool communities, hiding them from view once more.

Predict *Consider the relationship between the organisms in a tide pool and the daily cycle of high and low tides. How might an overall increase in sea level affect tide pool organisms?*

 VIDEO

VIDEO 2-1 Go online to learn more about Earth systems.

FIGURE 2-2 ▼
Earth can be organized into four interacting systems.

Earth Systems

You can think of a tide pool as a system that includes interacting living and nonliving things. Like all systems, it has inputs, such as nutrients from the ocean, and outputs, such as waste materials. It is just one example of the many interacting systems that make up the much larger Earth system. The Earth system is made up of four interconnected systems, or spheres: the atmosphere, hydrosphere, geosphere, and biosphere. These four systems are described in **Figure 2-2**.

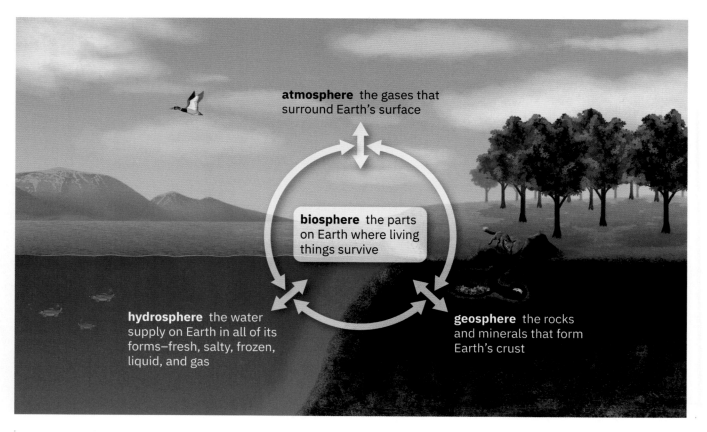

atmosphere the gases that surround Earth's surface

biosphere the parts on Earth where living things survive

hydrosphere the water supply on Earth in all of its forms—fresh, salty, frozen, liquid, and gas

geosphere the rocks and minerals that form Earth's crust

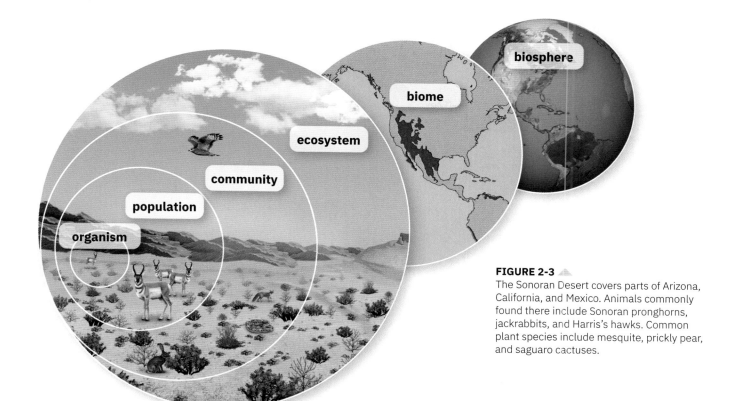

FIGURE 2-3
The Sonoran Desert covers parts of Arizona, California, and Mexico. Animals commonly found there include Sonoran pronghorns, jackrabbits, and Harris's hawks. Common plant species include mesquite, prickly pear, and saguaro cactuses.

Life in the Biosphere

The **biosphere** includes all the parts on Earth where life exists. It extends from the deep ocean to high mountaintops. Whether you are observing a tide pool, forest, desert, or other environment within the biosphere, you will find organisms suited to that environment interacting with one another.

Levels of Organization Ecologists organize organisms and their environments into a series of levels from smallest to largest.

- At the smallest scale is the individual organism, such as a single Sonoran pronghorn shown in **Figure 2-3**.

- A group of individual organisms of the same species forms a **population**. All of the pronghorns in this desert form a population.

- The pronghorn population is part of a larger **community** that includes the other organisms that pronghorns interact with, either directly or indirectly. This community includes the plants the pronghorns eat, as well as the other animals pronghorns compete with for access to resources. It also includes the predators that prey on pronghorns.

- A community exists within an ecosystem. An **ecosystem** includes all the living organisms in the community plus the nonliving environment in which the community exists. The nonliving environment includes things such as water, soil, and climate. The interactions between *biotic factors* (living parts) and *abiotic factors* (nonliving parts) allows for the transfer of matter and energy throughout the system.

- Ecosystems on land fit within larger **biomes**, which are regions characterized by similar plant communities and climate conditions. The ecosystem shown here is part of the desert biome.

- All of Earth's aquatic and land ecosystems make up the biosphere.

> ⚗ **CHAPTER INVESTIGATION**
>
> **Salinity and Brine Shrimp Survival**
> *How does salt concentration affect the hatching of brine shrimp eggs?*
> Go online to explore this chapter's hands-on investigation about factors that affect survival.

FIGURE 2-4
This Cannon Beach tide pool can be studied as its own miniature ecosystem or as a small community within the larger Oregon coastal marine ecosystem.

Ecological Boundaries Like all systems, a community or an ecosystem has boundaries, but how ecologists define those boundaries depends on the relationships they are studying. For example, ecologists studying the organisms in a single tide pool may treat that tide pool as a single ecosystem, or they may consider the tide pool's organisms as just one community within a larger marine ecosystem that includes other communities (**Figure 2-4**). Regardless of their size, all communities depend on the transfer of matter and energy for their survival.

Matter and Energy in Ecosystems

Living things need the input of matter and energy to survive, grow, and reproduce. The movement of matter and energy supports life in Earth's ecosystems. Matter is cycled within ecosystems as the same atoms are used over and over again. Energy—typically from the sun—flows through ecosystems as organisms exchange matter.

Atoms, Molecules, and Compounds Every living and nonliving thing is made of matter. The smallest unit of matter is the **atom**. An element is a substance made from only one type of atom. Six elements essential for life are carbon (C), hydrogen (H), nitrogen (N), oxygen (O), phosphorus (P), and sulfur (S). These elements make up important biological molecules such as carbohydrates, amino acids, and DNA.

Chemical Bonds Atoms exert forces on each other. Forces between two or more atoms can connect them to form a **molecule**. The forces that hold the atoms in a molecule together are called chemical bonds. These bonds connect atoms to form molecules. For example, when two oxygen atoms bond together, they form a molecule of oxygen, or O_2. A compound is a substance made up of two or more different elements bonded together. Carbon dioxide (CO_2), water (H_2O), and glucose ($C_6H_{12}O_6$) are examples of common compounds used by living things.

FIGURE 2-5
Sunlight is the ultimate source of energy in most ecosystems. In the process of photosynthesis, energy from sunlight is used to make glucose and oxygen from carbon dioxide and water.

Chemical Reactions In a chemical reaction, the atoms in one or more substances are rearranged into new substances with different chemical properties. Rearranging a system of atoms requires breaking chemical bonds and forming new chemical bonds. Though no new matter is created or destroyed during a chemical reaction, there is always an energy change: energy is either released or absorbed by the system. Chemical reactions are happening all the time in ecosystems. The majority of energy and matter transformations in living things occur in two chemical processes: photosynthesis and cellular respiration.

- **Photosynthesis** In this process, energy from the sun is transformed into chemical energy by rearranging the atoms in carbon dioxide and water into oxygen and sugar molecules (**Figure 2-5**). Photosynthetic organisms, such as plants, algae, and some bacteria, are the main source of chemical energy in most ecosystems.

- **Cellular Respiration** In this process, chemical energy is released by reactions that break down sugars and other carbon-based molecules. This energy is used to fuel cellular activities. Cellular respiration that occurs in the presence of oxygen is called aerobic respiration. Most organisms use aerobic respiration and need oxygen to live. In aerobic respiration, energy is released when sugar and oxygen are broken down to form carbon dioxide and water. Some organisms can live in low- or no-oxygen environments. These organisms rely on anaerobic respiration, which occurs without oxygen.

CCC **Systems and System Models** *What is the relationship between the inputs and outputs of photosynthesis and aerobic respiration?*

2.1 REVIEW

1. **Distinguish** Explain how a community is distinct from an ecosystem.

2. **Classify** Label each ecosystem component as a biotic or abiotic factor.
   - flowering plants
   - school of fish
   - willow tree
   - soil
   - pond water
   - air

3. **Sequence** Construct a model of the hierarchy of ecological organization. Your completed model should have six levels.

4. **Synthesize** Describe how chemical reactions are important to the movement of energy and matter in an ecosystem.

consumer
decomposer
food web
producer
trophic level

MODELING THE TRANSFER OF ENERGY AND MATTER

When you are feeling sluggish, a quick snack such as an apple will often give you the energy you need to get back to feeling "normal" in a short time. Like a cell phone, your body requires periodic "recharging" in order to function.

Explain *Where do you think the energy you get from eating an apple originally came from? Think about how an apple tree gets energy.*

▼
SEA PIG SURVIVAL

Gather Evidence *Sea pigs digest organic matter from the ocean floor. Identify which ecological role sea pigs occupy in their community. Explain your answer.*

Ecological Roles in Ecosystems

Organisms are categorized by the way in which they get energy. The three major categories are producers, consumers, and decomposers.

Producers Organisms that make their own food are **producers**. They are also called *autotrophs*. (The prefix *auto-* means "self," and the suffix *-troph* means "nourishment.") Most producers, such as plants and algae, use photosynthesis to transform energy from the sun into sugars. Some bacteria and archaea obtain energy in the absence of sunlight. Many of these organisms live near deep-sea vents that spew superheated water full of energy-rich chemical compounds. These organisms use a process called *chemosynthesis* to convert the substances in the water into sugars.

Consumers Organisms that get their energy from eating other organisms are **consumers**. They are also called *heterotrophs.* (The prefix *hetero-* means "different.") Consumers can be classified by what they eat.

- Herbivores, such as grasshoppers, are organisms that eat producers.
- Carnivores, such as frogs, are organisms that eat other consumers.
- Omnivores, such as bears and foxes, are organisms that eat both producers and consumers.
- Detritivores, such as ravens and earthworms, are organisms that eat dead organic matter, which is called *detritus*.

Decomposers Organisms that break down decaying organic matter into simpler compounds that other organisms can use are **decomposers**. Most decomposers are bacteria, archaea, and fungi (**Figure 2-6**).

FIGURE 2-6 ▶
Wood bonnet mushrooms are commonly found growing on decaying logs and branches on the forest floor.

Communities are made up of a variety of producers, consumers, and decomposers. Producers and decomposers have indispensable roles in ecosystems. Producers provide both food and oxygen for all life. Consumers begin the process of breaking down the complex molecules that producers make, and the process is finished by decomposers so the materials can be recycled.

The Transfer of Energy and Matter in Ecosystems

Energy enters most ecosystems as sunlight, which is converted into chemical energy through organisms that carry out photosynthesis. This energy is used by animals and other consumers to fuel life processes. Thus, most organisms require a continuous source of sunlight to survive.

Food Chains The movement of energy and matter within an ecosystem can be modeled using a food chain. Producers are the first link in the chain. Consumers eat the producers and are themselves eaten by other higher-level consumers.

A **trophic level** is the group of organisms in an ecosystem that occupy the same level in a food chain. There are five main trophic levels:

- Producers are at the base of every food chain.
- Primary consumers are herbivores that eat producers.
- Secondary consumers are carnivores and omnivores that eat herbivores.
- Tertiary consumers are carnivores and omnivores that eat secondary consumers.
- *Apex consumers* are the consumers at the top trophic level—those that eat other consumers but are not typically eaten by others.

For example, in the ocean, a food chain can be made up of microscopic floating algae at the producer level, which are eaten by krill at the primary consumer level. Penguins that eat the krill are secondary consumers. These organisms are then eaten by tertiary consumers, such as seals, and so on. A food chain can vary in length depending on the ecosystem it is modeling. In the case of this marine ecosystem, the food chain could grow very long, but will likely end with an apex predator such as a killer whale. A portion of a marine ecosystem food chain is illustrated in **Figure 2-7**.

As organisms are eaten along each link of a food chain, some of the energy they contain is used by the consumer at the next level. In this way, energy is transferred upward through each trophic level in the food chain.

FIGURE 2-7
A portion of a marine food chain includes phytoplankton at the producer level, krill at the primary consumer level, and penguins at the secondary consumer level.

| producer | primary consumer | secondary consumer |

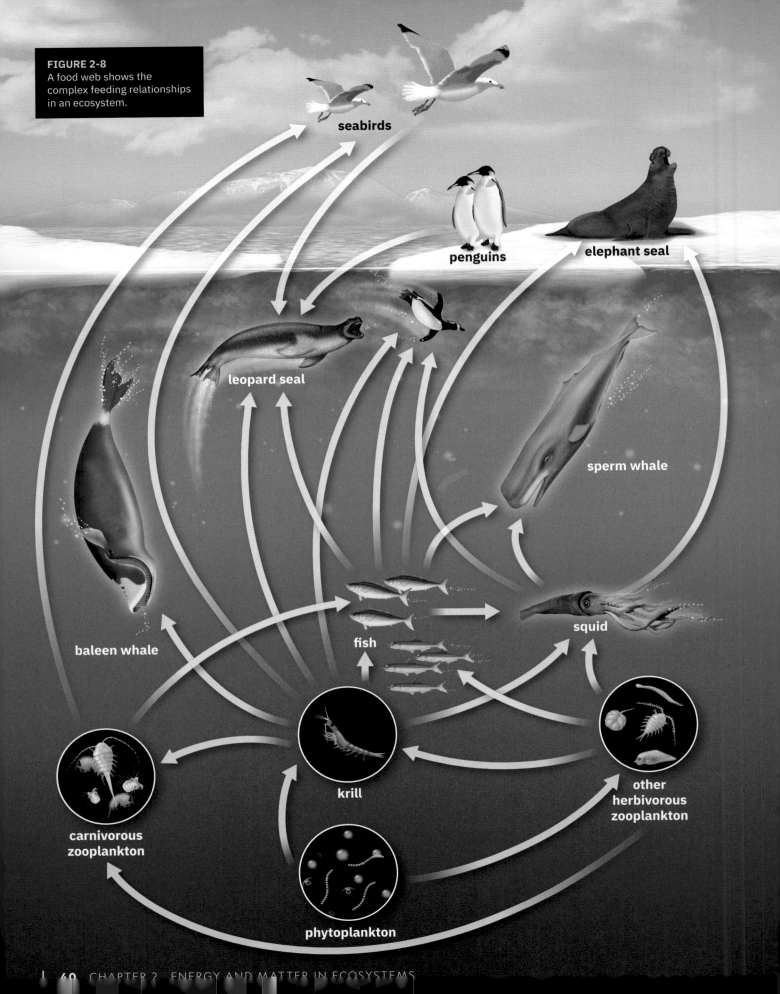

FIGURE 2-8
A food web shows the complex feeding relationships in an ecosystem.

seabirds

penguins

elephant seal

leopard seal

sperm whale

baleen whale

fish

squid

carnivorous zooplankton

krill

other herbivorous zooplankton

phytoplankton

Food Webs The flow of energy through an ecosystem is usually more complex than can be modeled using a simple food chain. Consider how different consumers can feed on many other types of organisms within a marine ecosystem. For example, a secondary-level fish feeds on primary-level krill. A leopard seal might eat the fish or the krill. When it eats the fish, the seal is a tertiary consumer, but when it eats the krill, it is a secondary consumer. Because many different organisms can eat and be eaten by other types of organisms within an ecosystem, food chains combine to form a complex system of feeding relationships known as a **food web**. The complex connections between organisms in an Antarctic food web are shown in **Figure 2-8**.

> **SEP** **Use a Model** *Identify organisms at each trophic level in this Antarctic food web. Why is a food web a more realistic model than a food chain?*

Food Web Stability

This Antarctic food web shows only a small number of the species in the ecosystem it represents. The stability of an ecosystem depends in part on the variety of species in the ecosystem. If a species in the food web is lost, other species may fill its role and maintain the food web's overall stability.

Disruptions to Energy and Matter Transfer A disruption in a food web due to changes in the environment or the loss of a species can have devastating consequences. As the impact of a change in the availability of energy on a lower level of a food web travels up the chain, consumers at higher levels are also affected. The loss of one link in a food chain can affect organisms at levels both above and below it.

The complexity of a food web system often makes it difficult to predict how disruptions will affect other members of the community. For example, the human overfishing of krill, a small crustacean often used to produce nutritional supplements and animal feed, has significantly reduced the Antarctic krill population. This has led to concerns about the sustainability of other wildlife that feed on krill, such as fish, penguins, seals, and whales. As a result, the Scientific Committee on Antarctic Research (SCAR) has implemented the Krill Action Group to develop guidelines and regulations to manage the krill fishing industry.

Go Online **INTERACTIVE FIGURE**

FIGURE 2-8 Go online to see how changes in an ocean community affect feeding relationships in an **Antarctic Food Web**.

 VIDEO

VIDEO 2-2 Go online to learn more about the importance of krill to Antarctic food webs.

2.2 REVIEW

1. **Analyze** Order the roles of producer, primary consumer, and secondary consumer from highest to lowest trophic level.

2. **Explain** Why are decomposers essential to the movement of matter in an ecosystem?

3. **Apply** Use **Figure 2-8** to support or refute the claim that an organism can feed at more than one trophic level.

4. **Identify** Which trophic level, if removed from a food web, would likely cause the most change in the ecosystem?

   A. producer

   B. primary consumer

   C. secondary consumer

   D. tertiary consumer

NATIONAL GEOGRAPHIC EXPLORER **RAE WYNN-GRANT**

USING DATA TO PREVENT HUMAN–BEAR CONFLICT

Dr. Rae Wynn-Grant studies spatial patterns in bear activity to reduce conflict between bears and humans.

▶ **VIDEO 2-3** Go online to see how Wynn-Grant collects and analyzes bear data.

By the early 20th century, humans drove grizzly and black bears out of most of their range in the United States. Today's bear populations are recovering thanks to decades of conservation efforts. But the growing overlap of human and bear habitats has made interactions between the two species more frequent. Carnivore ecologist Dr. Rae Wynn-Grant uses statistical models to identify patterns in bear activity to minimize the frequency and severity of human–bear conflict.

Vehicle collisions and illegal hunting pose serious risks to bears. In addition, as the climate changes, snow and seasonal temperature patterns that cue bears to hibernate no longer occur with the same regularity. Thus, some bears stay active later into the year when food is scarce, making them more likely to seek food sources associated with humans.

Wynn-Grant's statistical models map suitable bear habitats and predict areas of potential conflict with humans. This research involves boots-on-the-ground fieldwork to collect data on bears' health, whereabouts, and behaviors. As part of her research, she tagged black bears to locate their dens and track their survival rates in Nevada's Western Great Basin. By monitoring known "conflict bears," Wynn-Grant found "bear hotspots" correlated with behaviors such as raiding garbage cans and breaking into houses in search of food.

"My work might seem pretty specific to one animal and one place," Wynn-Grant says. "But it gives me an ability to make recommendations for any type of conservation, anywhere. Most conservation is being done in places where there are people, people who need to build towns and cities and highways and roads. So getting it right here means we can probably get it right somewhere else."

Bears can also eat slow-moving livestock and crops that provide them with high-calorie food for relatively little effort. This threat to ranchers' and farmers' livelihoods complicates habitat restoration efforts in the Great Plains of eastern Montana, where Wynn-Grant works to incentivize people to gather camera trap and field observation data. Ideally, the community's scientific engagement will help conserve safe ecological corridors for bears and other animals returning to prairie habitats. █

THINKING CRITICALLY

Predict *The prairie is home to many species of birds, fish, snakes, and small mammals, as well as larger animals including bison, elk, bobcats, and coyotes. How might the return of grizzly bears affect food webs in prairie communities?*

MODELING ENERGY AND MATTER DISTRIBUTION

2.3

KEY TERMS

biomass
biomass pyramid
ecological pyramid
energy pyramid
pyramid of numbers

Less than 30 percent of the energy stored in gasoline is used by a gas-powered vehicle to move it down the road. Instead, most of the energy from the fuel is lost from the engine as heat to the environment. The transfer of energy between trophic levels is even more inefficient.

Explain *Why isn't all of the energy in one organism transferred to the organism that eats it?*

Ecological Pyramids

Food chains and food webs are a way to model the movement of energy and matter in an ecosystem. Each link shows a transfer of energy and matter from one trophic level to another. An **ecological pyramid** is a model used to compare an ecosystem's trophic levels in different ways.

Each tier of an ecological pyramid is one trophic level. Producers form the first level at the bottom of the pyramid. The trophic levels above the producer level are made up of consumers (primary consumers, then secondary consumers, and so on). Each consumer level obtains its energy from the level immediately below it. At every trophic level, some energy is used for metabolic processes and some is lost to the environment as heat. Also, many organisms die and decompose before they can be eaten. The small amount of remaining energy is passed up to the next trophic level. This results in the model's pyramid shape.

The number of trophic levels, and the number of organisms within each level, is limited by the amount of energy available to the ecosystem. Ecologists use three types of pyramid models: energy pyramids, biomass pyramids, and pyramids of numbers.

FIGURE 2-9 ▽
A kestrel, which is a type of falcon, commonly gets the energy it needs by eating primary consumers such as insects and mice.

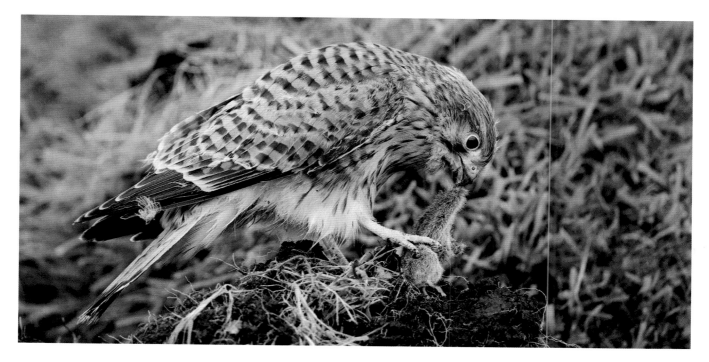

Energy Pyramids

An **energy pyramid** models the distribution of energy across trophic levels in an ecosystem (**Figure 2-10**). It shows an ecosystem's productivity, or the efficiency with which energy is transferred up a food chain or food web. Energy is usually measured in joules (J) or kilocalories (kcal). Energy use in an ecosystem is inefficient because most of the energy produced is unable to be used by organisms.

Because producers absorb certain wavelengths of light, they convert only about one percent of the solar energy that reaches Earth into a usable form they can store in their cells. Yet they produce 100 percent of the energy available to primary consumers. As energy flows from one trophic level to the next, the amount of energy available at each level is only about 10 percent of the energy available at the previous trophic level.

For example, the producers in one community might produce 10,000 J per year of available energy. By feeding on the producers, the primary consumers would use 10 percent of that amount, or 1000 J. The secondary consumers would use 100 J per year, and the tertiary consumers would use 10 J per year, which is just 0.1 percent of the available energy at the base of the pyramid.

Although energy cannot be created or destroyed, clearly much of the energy available to each trophic level is not used. When a consumer such as a grasshopper eats part of a plant, some of the plant tissue cannot be digested and is excreted as waste. The grasshopper converts most of the remaining plant matter into energy that its own body can use for maintenance and movement. In doing so, some of the energy is lost to the environment as heat. On average, only about 10 percent of the energy from the grasshopper's food is stored as chemical energy in the cells of the grasshopper's body. This small amount is the chemical energy that is transferred to any predator that preys on the grasshopper.

SEP **Use Mathematics** *A population of top predators consumes 7 kcal/m²per year. If the ecosystem has four trophic levels, how much energy is available to the primary consumers?*

FIGURE 2-10 ▶
An energy pyramid shows the distribution of energy across trophic levels in an ecosystem. Only 10 percent of the available energy is transferred from one tier to the next. Most energy is lost to the environment as heat.

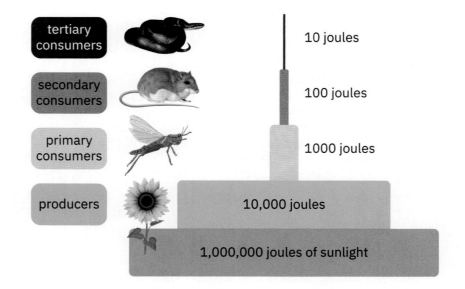

tertiary consumers — 10 joules

secondary consumers — 100 joules

primary consumers — 1000 joules

producers — 10,000 joules

1,000,000 joules of sunlight

tertiary consumers	1.5 g/m²
secondary consumers	11 g/m²
primary consumers	37 g/m²
producers	809 g/m²

FIGURE 2-11
A biomass pyramid shows the distribution of biomass at each trophic level in an ecosystem.

Biomass Pyramids

In contrast to an energy pyramid, a **biomass pyramid** models the total amount of biomass stored in living organisms at each trophic level in an ecosystem (**Figure 2-11**). **Biomass** is commonly defined as the total dry mass of all the organisms within a given area at a specific time. It is usually measured in grams of total biomass per unit area, such as g/m². The dry mass of an organism refers to its mass after all of the water has been removed. Biomass is also sometimes defined in terms of a single element, such as carbon. Like an energy pyramid, the largest tier in a biomass pyramid is typically the producer level. The shape of a biomass pyramid also indicates that at each trophic level, biomass decreases by approximately 90 percent. This corresponds to the 90 percent loss of energy between each level.

CONNECTIONS

EATING LOWER ON THE FOOD CHAIN People sometimes promote a vegetarian diet by touting the ecological benefits of "eating lower on the food chain." They are referring to energy that is lost in transfers between plants, livestock, and humans. When people eat plants, they get a larger proportion of the energy that the plant captured than they would if the plant was used to feed livestock. When plants are used to feed livestock, only a very small percentage of the energy that was stored in the plant body ends up in the meat a person can eat.

In 2019, the average American ate 100.8 kg (222 lb.) of meat. This amounts to about 0.3 kg (or 0.6 lb.) of meat per day. The majority of meat consumed in the United States is chicken at 50.1 kg per capita, followed by beef at 26.3 kg per capita, and then pork at 24 kg per capita.

As some Americans aim to decrease their overall meat consumption, several companies have introduced plant-based meat substitutes to the market. Plants such as grains and legumes are commonly used as protein sources for these plant-based meat substitutes.

Plant-based meals are typically more energy efficient than meat-based meals.

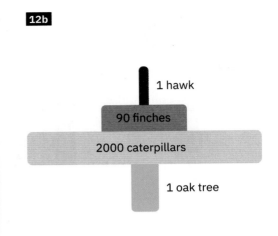

FIGURE 2-12 ▲
A pyramid of numbers shows the actual number of individual organisms at each trophic level in an ecosystem.

Pyramids of Numbers

A **pyramid of numbers** compares the relative number of individual organisms at each trophic level. For most communities, a pyramid of numbers will show that the number of producers required to support the other trophic levels is vastly greater in size (**Figure 2-12a**). The quantity of producers needed to support a community generally outnumbers all the consumer levels combined.

In some communities, however, a pyramid of numbers takes on a diamond shape (**Figure 2-12b**). A classic example of this is a pyramid in which the producers are individual trees that support a community of insects, birds, and possibly other predators. The number of trees is relatively small compared to the number of insects. For every tree, there may be thousands of insects that feed on it, and hundreds of predatory insects that feed on the primary consumers. A group of trees may support enough secondary consumers to support a few birds at the upper trophic levels.

CCC **Stability and Change** *Deciduous trees lose all their leaves each autumn. How might a pyramid of numbers for a deciduous forest ecosystem change across different seasons?*

2.3 REVIEW

1. **Sequence** List the types of organisms in order from the top to the bottom of an ecological pyramid.

   - tertiary consumer
   - producer
   - primary consumer
   - secondary consumer

2. **Explain** Why is less energy available to organisms higher in an energy pyramid than is available to organisms at the base of an energy pyramid?

3. **Predict** How might a fire affect the shape of a forest ecosystem's biomass pyramid?

4. **Represent Data** Build an energy pyramid using the data in the table.

Species	Energy (joules)
A	4,982,000
B	5200
C	500,738
D	47,033

5. **Identify** In your model, label each species with its ecological role in the ecosystem.

MODEL A BIOMASS PYRAMID

SEP **Develop and Use a Model** How can you model the distribution of biomass in an ecosystem?

The freshwater springs of Florida are among the most studied aquatic ecosystems on Earth. In this activity, you will build a model of organisms found in one of these springs to see how biomass is distributed among trophic levels in the ecosystem.

Freshwater springs in Florida can support a large amount of biomass.

Materials

- poster board or large sheet of paper
- marker
- pinto beans, 200 g
- calculator

Scientists sampled various regions of a freshwater spring in Florida to estimate the populations and biomasses of some species found in the spring. The table shows their results.

TABLE 1. Organism Biomass in a Florida Ecosystem

Organism	Trophic level	Population (per 100 m²)	Biomass (g/100 m²)
narrow-leaved arrowhead	producer	16,800	60,480
algae	producer	N/A *	20,160
turtles	primary consumer	80	2000
shrimp	primary consumer	380	2470
insects	primary consumer	450	2025
anemones	secondary consumer	23	322
small fish	secondary consumer	30	330
bass (larger fish)	tertiary consumer	1	74

*The algae are tiny organisms that grow on the narrow-leaved arrowhead plants. There would be too many to count.

Procedure

1. Draw a large triangle on the paper. This will be your biomass pyramid. Divide the pyramid into four rows and label the trophic levels.

2. For your model, assume that one pinto bean represents 270 g of biomass per 100 m². Calculate how many beans would represent the biomass of each species shown in **Table 1**. Round fractions to the nearest whole number.

3. As a group, count out the appropriate number of beans for each species that you calculated in Step 2. Arrange the beans representing each species on the pyramid. Divide rows into multiple parts if there is more than one species at that level. Record the names of the species near the bean piles that represent them.

4. Return all of your beans to the container.

Results and Analysis

1. **Organize Data** Draw a bar graph that shows the biomass at each level.

2. **Calculate** Determine how much biomass is transferred from
   - producers to primary consumers
   - primary consumers to secondary consumers
   - secondary consumers to tertiary consumers

   Use this formula:

$$\text{percent biomass transferred} = 100 \times \frac{\text{total biomass of higher level}}{\text{total biomass of the lower level}}$$

3. **Interpret Data** Can this ecosystem support a higher-level consumer than the bass? Use your graph and pyramid to support your answer.

4. **Evaluate** What happens to the biomass that does not move on to the next trophic level?

CYCLING OF MATTER

Nutrition labels are a familiar part of most food packaging. The information shown in these labels helps consumers make healthful dietary decisions. These choices are often based on how energy efficient a food source is, as the body obtains energy from different types of compounds, such as carbohydrates or proteins, in different ways. Because your body is made up of elements obtained from the food you eat, another key to a wholesome diet is making sure to get these essential nutrients from a large variety of foods. But where does this matter come from? How does matter move through an ecosystem?

Predict *Where does the matter that makes up an organism's body come from?*

Matter Cycles Through Earth's Systems

Earlier in this chapter you learned that energy from the sun provides the primary source of energy for producers at the base of a food chain. This energy flows through food webs as it moves from one trophic level to the next. Because the energy comes from an outside source (the sun), Earth is considered an open system in terms of energy. However, only a tiny amount of matter is lost from Earth at its atmospheric boundary with space. For this reason scientists model Earth as a closed system in terms of matter. Like energy, matter cannot be created or destroyed, so all of the substances that make up all living and nonliving objects on Earth come from already existing matter.

Because the amount of matter on Earth is limited, the cycling of life-sustaining elements is essential for the survival of living things on Earth. A **biogeochemical cycle** is the movement of matter through the biological and geological, or living and nonliving, parts of an ecosystem. Biogeochemical cycles include the water cycle, carbon cycle, nitrogen cycle, and phosphorus cycle. All of these cycles are driven by energy from the sun and Earth's core. They include a variety of interconnected processes:

- **Physical and Chemical Processes** These are the processes by which matter changes physical form or substances are transformed by chemical reactions.

- **Geological Processes** These are the processes that take place in the geosphere, such as the formation of rock or the movement of matter on and below Earth's surface.

- **Biological Processes** These are the processes performed by living organisms, such as photosynthesis and respiration.

All of the matter available to organisms on Earth is subject to these processes. Although matter used by organisms cannot be lost from the Earth system, matter can become unavailable or unusable for organisms in the biosphere.

SEP **Construct an Explanation** *Water is a substance essential to life on Earth. How might water or other substances be made unavailable to organisms in Earth's biosphere?*

The Water Cycle

The hydrologic cycle, or water cycle, circulates water through the environment (**Figure 2-13**). It begins as water evaporates from the surface of the ocean and other bodies of water and condenses to form clouds. Approximately 396,000 cubic kilometers of water evaporates each year, with about 78 percent of it condensing back to liquid form and falling on the ocean as precipitation.

On land, water enters streams and rivers as runoff within an area called a watershed. Some of the water seeps into the soil to become groundwater. The rest flows downhill through rivers and then enters the ocean via a coastal estuary, an area where salt and fresh water mix.

Water is also taken up by plants through their root systems and evaporates from their leaves through a process called *transpiration*. Approximately 90 percent of the water in the atmosphere is the product of evaporation from bodies of water, while the remaining 10 percent comes from plant-based transpiration.

FIGURE 2-13 ▼
The water cycle circulates water on Earth.

CCC **Stability and Change** *How might a disruption to this cycle, such as a drought, affect living organisms?*

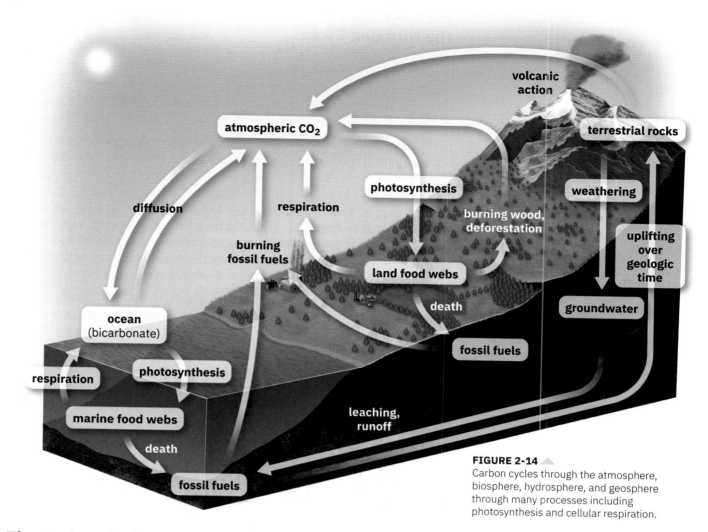

FIGURE 2-14 ◢
Carbon cycles through the atmosphere, biosphere, hydrosphere, and geosphere through many processes including photosynthesis and cellular respiration.

The Carbon Cycle

Carbon cycles through all of Earth's systems (**Figure 2-14**). Carbon enters land food webs when plants take up carbon dioxide from the air for use in photosynthesis. Carbon returns to the atmosphere as carbon dioxide when plants and other land organisms carry out aerobic respiration.

Carbon diffuses between the atmosphere and the ocean. Bicarbonate forms when carbon dioxide dissolves in seawater. Marine producers take up bicarbonate for use in photosynthesis, and marine organisms release carbon dioxide from aerobic respiration.

Earth's rocks and sediments are its single greatest reservoir of carbon. Marine organisms incorporate carbon into their shells. After they die, these shells become part of the sediments. Over time, the sediments become carbon-rich rocks such as limestone and chalk in Earth's crust. These rocks can be uplifted onto land by geological forces. However, producers take up carbon from the air rather than from rocks, so carbon in these reservoirs has little effect on ecosystems.

Fossil fuels such as coal, oil, and natural gas formed over hundreds of millions of years from the anaerobic decomposition of carbon-rich remains of ancient organisms. The burning of fossil fuels derived from these ancient remains puts additional carbon dioxide into the atmosphere.

SEP **Develop a Model** *Draw a model that shows the role of photosynthesis and cellular respiration in the cycling of carbon through Earth's systems.*

The Nitrogen Cycle

Nitrogen gas (N_2) makes up 78 percent of Earth's atmosphere and is so stable that it does not readily combine with any other elements. That means living things cannot directly extract nitrogen from the atmosphere. Nitrogen must be broken down by the nitrogen cycle (**Figure 2-15**) before living things can use it to build molecules such as proteins and DNA.

In the process of nitrogen fixation, some nitrogen-fixing bacteria that live underground in the root nodules of legumes and a few other plants change gaseous N_2 to ammonia, NH_3. This ammonia is converted to ammonium (NH_4^+) during the process of ammonification. Nitrifying soil bacteria, archaea, and fungi convert ammonium to nitrates (NO_3^-) and nitrites (NO_2^-) in the process of nitrification. The bacteria gain energy from this process. Plant roots absorb nitrates and incorporate the nitrogen they contain into plant proteins and nucleic acids. Animals that eat the plants rearrange the chemicals into their own useful proteins and nucleic acids.

Waste products from the consumption of plant proteins are decomposed by ammonifying bacteria. The ammonia they release is ready to enter the nitrogen cycle again for nitrification. Finally, denitrifying bacteria and some fungi reduce nitrates back to their original gaseous N_2 form to complete the cycle.

Some nitrogen also enters the soil as a result of atmospheric nitrogen fixation by lightning. The energy of lightning causes nitrogen gas to react with oxygen in the air to form nitrogen oxides. When dissolved in rainwater, nitrates are formed, which are absorbed by the soil.

FIGURE 2-15 ▼
The nitrogen cycle is the movement of nitrogen through Earth's air, water, and soil.

CCC **Energy and Matter** *How might a decrease in nitrogen-fixing bacteria affect the trophic levels in an ecosystem?*

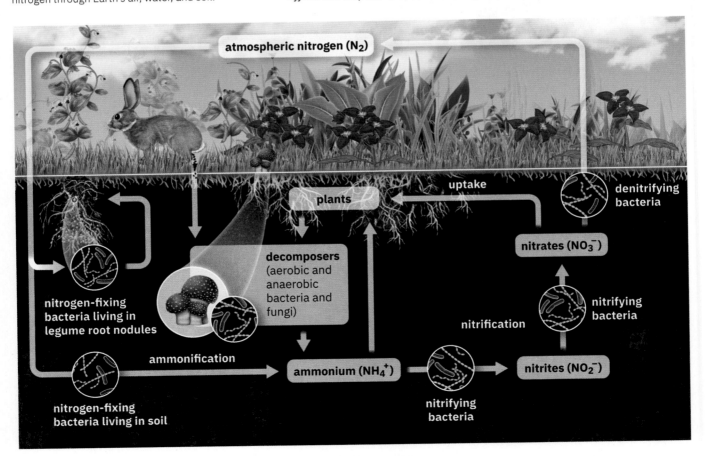

The Phosphorus Cycle

Phosphorus is part of several important biological molecules, including ATP, a compound that provides energy for life processes. Phosphorus is also an essential component in DNA and RNA. Unlike other matter cycles, phosphorus does not exist in the atmosphere in a gas phase. It is mainly cycled through the geosphere, hydrosphere, and biosphere. Most of Earth's phosphorus is bonded to oxygen as phosphate (PO_4^{3-}), which occurs in rocks and sediments. In the phosphorus cycle, phosphorus passes quickly through food webs as it moves from land to ocean sediments, then moves slowly back to land (**Figure 2-16**).

In the geochemical portion of the phosphorus cycle, weathering and erosion move phosphates from rocks into soil, lakes, and rivers. Leaching and runoff carry dissolved phosphate to the ocean. Here, most dissolved phosphorus comes out of solution and settles as rocky deposits. Movements of Earth's crust can uplift these deposits onto land, where weathering releases phosphates from rocks once again.

The biological portion of the phosphorus cycle begins when producers take up phosphate. Land plants take up dissolved phosphate from soil water. Animals on land get phosphates by eating the plants or one another. Phosphorus returns to the soil in the wastes and remains of organisms. In the seas, phosphorus enters food webs when producers take up phosphate dissolved in seawater. As on land, wastes and remains continually replenish the phosphorus supply.

FIGURE 2-16 ▽
Much of the phosphorus cycle takes place in the geosphere.

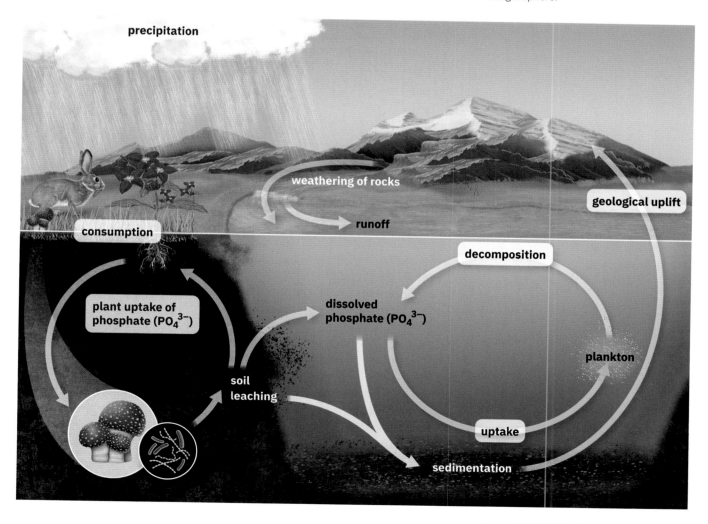

Human Impact on Biogeochemical Cycles

In the absence of humans, carbon, nitrogen, and phosphorus would cycle through the Earth system at a relatively constant rate and amount. However, human activities, such as the burning of fossil fuels and the introduction of synthetic fertilizers, have greatly influenced how matter cycles on Earth.

Climate Change Earth's climates are affected by gases in the lower atmosphere. As energy flows from the sun to the surface of Earth, some energy is reflected back into the atmosphere. Molecules of certain gases in the atmosphere, including water vapor (H_2O), carbon dioxide (CO_2), methane (CH_4), and nitrous oxide (N_2O), absorb some of this solar energy and release a portion of it as infrared radiation, which warms the lower atmosphere and Earth's surface. These gases that warm the lower atmosphere are called *greenhouse gases*. The natural warming of the lower atmosphere by greenhouse gases is called the **greenhouse effect**. Greenhouse gases have a role in determining the average temperatures of the lower atmosphere, and, therefore, the climates on Earth. Our planet would be a cold and mostly lifeless place without this natural warming effect.

FIGURE 2-17 ▼
The amount of carbon dioxide in the atmosphere (red line) has increased along with human emissions (blue line) since the start of the Industrial Revolution in 1750.

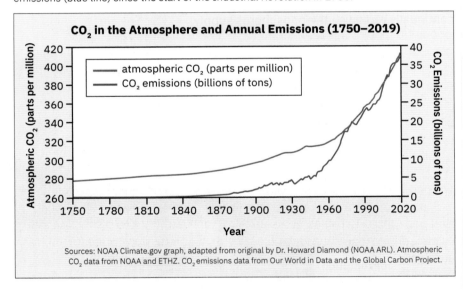

Sources: NOAA Climate.gov graph, adapted from original by Dr. Howard Diamond (NOAA ARL). Atmospheric CO_2 data from NOAA and ETHZ. CO_2 emissions data from Our World in Data and the Global Carbon Project.

When burned in combustion, fossil fuels release carbon into the atmosphere. This excess carbon is a primary contributor to global climate change (**Figure 2-17**). As humans continue to extract and burn fossil fuels, the increased carbon dioxide level in the atmosphere has enhanced the greenhouse effect and caused temperatures on the planet to rise, altering ecosystems drastically. The melting of polar ice caps causes a rise in sea level that will put many coastal areas mostly underwater. The warmer temperatures are also causing increases in extreme weather events, alterations in animal migration patterns, and decreases in agricultural production. Many species are facing extinction as their habitats disappear.

CCC **Cause and Effect** *How do changes in atmospheric carbon influence changes in the hydrosphere?*

Nutrient Pollution In the early 1900s, scientists invented a method of fixing atmospheric nitrogen and producing ammonia on an industrial scale. This process allowed production of synthetic nitrogen fertilizers that have boosted crop yields.

The use of these fertilizers has helped feed a rapidly increasing human population, but it has also added large amounts of nitrogen-based compounds to our air and water. Nitrates from synthetic fertilizers can run off from agricultural fields and contaminate aquatic ecosystems, where it can encourage algal blooms (**Figure 2-18**).

Like nitrogen, phosphorus aids plant growth, so most fertilizers contain phosphorus as well as nitrogen. Phosphate-rich rocks are mined for use in the industrial production of fertilizer. Guano, which is phosphate-rich droppings from seabird or bat colonies, is also mined and used as fertilizer. Phosphates from fertilizers often run off from the site where they are applied and enter aquatic habitats. Other sources of aquatic phosphate pollution include animal waste from farms, sewage released from cities, and phosphate-rich detergents used to wash laundry and dishes. An influx of phosphorus can encourage the growth of aquatic producers, resulting in an algal bloom.

FIGURE 2-18 ◢
Large algal blooms (bright green) in Lake Erie result from agricultural and industrial runoff.

⚗ **CHAPTER INVESTIGATION**

Exploring Brine Shrimp Survival
What is the effect of an abiotic factor other than salinity on egg hatching and survival of brine shrimp?
Go online to explore this chapter's hands-on investigation and design your own investigation about abiotic factors.

2.4 REVIEW

1. **Identify** Which cycle most relies on the processes of photosynthesis and cellular respiration?

   A. carbon cycle   **C.** nitrogen cycle

   B. phosphorus cycle   **D.** water cycle

2. **Identify** Which of these processes are carried out by anaerobic bacteria? Select all correct answers.

   A. decomposition   **C.** denitrification

   B. transpiration   **D.** nitrification

3. **Analyze** Consider the cycles modeled in **Figures 2-13, 2-14, 2-15,** and **2-16** that show what happens to a water molecule, a carbon atom, a nitrogen atom, and a phosphorus atom, respectively. Describe two ways the water cycle is different from the other cycles.

4. **Design** Use **Figure 2-13** to make a simple model that follows an oxygen atom as it cycles through any two of these spheres: atmosphere, biosphere, hydrosphere.

BIOMAGNIFICATION OF MERCURY

SEP **Analyze and Interpret Data** Seven of the most popular fish found on seafood menus are now considered unsafe to eat.

The Environmental Protection Agency (EPA) monitors mercury contamination in commercially fished species and their prey along the west coast of the United States. The data is used to provide seafood consumption warnings for the public.

Table 1 gives the average mercury concentration (in micrograms/gram) for four marine species monitored by the EPA. Herring and shrimp are two common food sources for halibut, while swordfish prey on halibut.

These spot shrimp were harvested in Prince William Sound, Alaska.

TABLE 1. Mercury Concentration in Marine Species

Species	Average mercury concentration (µg/g)	Species average mass (kg)	Average length (cm)
halibut	0.25	140	240
herring	0.078	0.2	25
shrimp	0.009	0.4	18
swordfish	0.99	350	300

Sources: EPA, NOAA

1. **Represent Data** Construct a partial marine food web that includes halibut, herring, shrimp, and swordfish.

2. **Infer** Based on the partial food web, which population do you expect to be the largest in any given community?

   A. halibut and herring

   B. herring and shrimp

   C. shrimp

   D. swordfish

3. **Infer** Based on the partial food web, which population do you expect to be the smallest in any given community?

   A. halibut and herring

   B. herring and shrimp

   C. shrimp

   D. swordfish

4. **Analyze Data** Rank the fish species by mercury concentration. List the species from highest to lowest.

5. **Identify Patterns** How does the ranking of species by population size compare to the ranking of species by mercury concentration levels?

6. **Formulate** State a claim about what happens to the concentration of mercury as it moves through trophic levels. Support your claim with evidence and propose an explanation.

7. **Apply** Halibut is popular on seafood menus. The Food and Drug Administration (FDA) reports that the maximum safe mercury consumption is at or below 0.46 µg/g per week. Based on this recommendation, how many servings per week of wild halibut would be safe?

8. **Design** Using only the data provided, propose one way that farming halibut could make it safer for human consumption.

TYING IT ALL TOGETHER
SOMETHING FISHY IN THE FOREST

HOW DO ENERGY AND MATTER MOVE THROUGH AN ECOSYSTEM?

In this chapter, you learned about the transfer of energy and matter in an ecosystem. The Case Study described relationships among organisms in a Southeast Alaska coastal community (**Figure 2-19**). The rivers and streams in this ecosystem support five species of salmon, which spend up to seven years in the ocean where they gain more than 90 percent of their biomass. Largely due to this abundance of food, Alaskan coastal brown bears are some of the heaviest in the world. A male bear can weigh up to 680 kg after having feasted on salmon for a season.

Biologists studying the vegetation on Chichagof Island in the Tongass National Forest have found that plants that grow as far as 100 meters from rivers where salmon spawn contain higher levels of ocean-derived nitrogen than the same plant species at sites with no salmon (**Figure 2-20**). They estimated that 24 percent of the nitrogen in the needles of spruce trees near salmon streams comes from the ocean. The scientists also determined that trees near salmon habitats grow faster and larger than those farther away.

In this activity, you will develop models to analyze nutrient pathways from marine to terrestrial organisms. Work individually or in a group to complete these steps.

Gather Evidence
1. Research the types and populations of organisms in the Tongass National Forest ecosystem. Focus on defining the boundaries of an ecosystem with a community that includes brown bears, salmon, and trees.

Develop and Use a Model
2. Construct one or more models that represent both

    a. the flow of energy between organisms within the community

    b. the cycling of matter between these organisms and their environment

Your model(s) should identify all trophic levels present in the ecosystem you have defined and show the relative distribution of energy and biomass in the ecosystem.

Construct an Explanation
3. Use your models to explain how marine nitrogen travels from the ocean to the leaves of forest trees.

FIGURE 2-19 ▽
Sitka spruce trees grow three times faster on the banks of salmon streams than those that grow elsewhere.

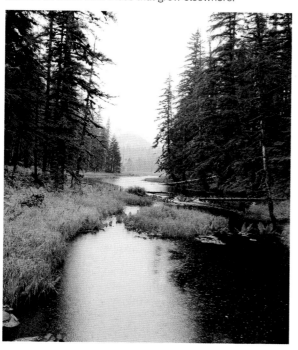

FIGURE 2-20 ▽
Scientists measured the growth rings of spruce trees and the amount of marine nitrogen in their leaves to compare trees near salmon spawning streams to trees at reference sites with no salmon spawning.

Source: Adapted from Helfield, James and Robert J. Naiman, 2001.

REVIEW KEY CONCEPTS

1. **Relate** Which claims are true for all the organisms within a community? Select all correct answers.

   A. They interact with each other.

   B. They are part of the same population.

   C. They are found within the same biome.

   D. They have important roles in the same ecosystem.

   E. They depend on the same biotic and abiotic factors.

2. **Compare** Why are food chains less effective than food webs for modeling ecosystem stability? Select all correct answers.

   A. Energy flow can be shown in a food web but not in a food chain.

   B. Unlike in food webs, all organisms in a food chain are connected.

   C. A food chain shows a concise picture of how energy flows through a stable ecosystem.

   D. Many complex organism interactions in a stable ecosystem are excluded in a food chain.

   E. A disruption to a food chain may not impact the transfer of energy in other food chains within the same stable ecosystem.

3. **Compare** Which claims are most likely supported by the ecological pyramids for the two ecosystems described below? Select all correct answers.

   Consider two unrelated stable ecosystems. Ecosystem A has roughly 10,000 kcal/m² per year available for its primary consumers. Ecosystem B has only 5000 kcal/m² per year available for its primary consumers but contains the same number of trophic levels as Ecosystem A.

   A. Ecosystem A has a greater variety of species than Ecosystem B.

   B. In Ecosystem A, the populations of predators will be double the population of prey.

   C. The trophic levels in Ecosystem A each contain half as many species as those in Ecosystem B.

   D. Secondary consumers are not as well-supported in Ecosystem A as secondary consumers in Ecosystem B.

   E. The amount of energy flowing from primary consumers to secondary consumers in Ecosystem A will be double that of Ecosystem B.

4. **Classify** Sort the organisms based on the given descriptions into four categories: *carnivores*, *detritivores*, *herbivores*, and *omnivores*.

   - Zebras feed on grass and small plants.
   - Sea turtles feed on corals, seaweed, and fish.
   - Wasps feed on insects and plants.
   - Penguins feed on fish.
   - Worms feed on decaying roots and leaves.

5. **Contrast** Select the best model to use to support or refute each of these claims. Choose from three models: *biomass pyramid*, *energy pyramid*, *pyramid of numbers*.

   - An ecosystem is not a closed system.
   - Ecosystems support fewer complex organisms than simple organisms.
   - Consumers obtain the energy they need from the trophic level immediately below them.
   - The populations of producers are larger than the populations of secondary consumers.
   - The amount of matter in living organisms at lower trophic levels is greater than at higher trophic levels.

6. **Identify** What happens to the matter that makes up an organism when it dies?

   A. The matter is destroyed as the body decays.

   B. The matter becomes trapped in the nonliving body.

   C. The matter is converted into new types of matter by producers.

   D. The matter is cycled back to the nonliving and living parts of the ecosystem.

7. **Analyze** A community of plants produces 50,000 kcal/m² per year of energy. The top predators in this ecosystem have only 5 kcal/m² per year available for consumption. How many trophic levels does this ecosystem have?

8. **Explain** Why are photosynthesis and cellular respiration important to the transfer of energy and matter on Earth? Explain your answer.

9. **Summarize** Justify the claim that all living organisms could be sorted into just three major categories: *producer*, *consumer*, and *decomposer*.

CRITICAL THINKING

10. Predict Describe how the use of fossil fuels by humans might affect the carbon cycle and the relative amount of carbon in the atmosphere, hydrosphere, geosphere, and biosphere.

11. Synthesize Gazelles are herbivores that live on the grassy plains of Africa. How would a drought affect the food chain, energy pyramid, and carbon cycle within the ecosystem in which the gazelles live?

12. Evaluate Use **Figures 2-10** and **2-11** to evaluate the claim that Earth can be considered an open system and a closed system in terms of energy and matter.

13. NOS Scientific Knowledge Prior to the discovery of deep-sea thermal vent ecosystems, scientists thought all primary food sources in the deep ocean fell from the ocean surface. How did evidence of chemosynthetic organisms in these deep-sea ecosystems cause scientists to revise their understanding of how energy is produced in living systems?

MATH AND ENGLISH LANGUAGE ARTS CONNECTIONS

1. Use Units to Understand Problems When calculating biomass, biologists assume that about half of an organism's mass constitutes its biomass. In a 100-square-meter area, scientists count n plants. The average mass of a plant is m grams. Write an expression to estimate the mass of the plants in kilograms per square meter. Simplify your answer.

2. Reason Abstractly and Quantitatively Complete the table to show the amounts of energy that flow into and out of each trophic level in an ecosystem.

Trophic level	Energy available (J)	Energy lost (J)
producers		
primary consumers	10,000	
secondary consumers		

Read the following passage. Use evidence from the passage to answer the question.

Established in 1974, the Cabo Rojo National Wildlife Refuge serves as home to more than 300 different plant and bird species. Both native and migratory birds use the refuge, including two famous endemic species, the Puerto Rican emerald and the yellow-shouldered blackbird. Among the most populous plant species are the tamarind, an exotic species introduced to the island, the silk-cotton tree, and the guayacan, the official tree of the city of Cabo Rojo.

3. Cite Textual Evidence Does the passage describe a population, a community, or an ecosystem? Explain your answer.

4. Write Explanatory Text Choose two of the matter cycles and identify a place where parts of both cycles occur. Describe how the cycles are related in that location at the atomic or molecular level.

▶ REVISIT SEA PIG SURVIVAL

Gather Evidence In this chapter, you have seen many examples of organisms and learned about their roles in the cycling of matter and flow of energy through their respective ecosystems. In Section 2, you learned that sea pigs scavenge organic matter from the ocean floor. They are part of a larger community of organisms that together cycle matter and transfer energy throughout the abyssal plain ecosystem.

1. As the sea pigs digest organic matter from the ocean floor, they play an important role in the cycling of matter. How does the sea pig's ecological role help cycle carbon and other matter in its ecosystem?

2. What other questions do you have about sea pigs? What else would you need to know to model the transfer of energy and matter throughout the sea pig's deep-ocean ecosystem?

CHAPTER 3

BIODIVERSITY AND ECOSYSTEM STABILITY

A disturbance, such as a wildfire in Yellowstone National Park, can actually help to maintain biodiversity in an ecosystem.

3.1 ECOLOGICAL RELATIONSHIPS

3.2 BIODIVERSITY

3.3 ECOSYSTEM STABILITY AND CHANGE

The mission of the U.S. National Park Service is to "preserve unimpaired the natural and cultural resources and values of the National Park System for the enjoyment, education, and inspiration for this and future generations." Parks are natural systems too, so the park service also endeavors to maintain each park's ecological processes, which can include major changes to the landscape, such as those caused by fire.

Chapter 3 supports the NGSS Performance Expectations **HS-LS2-6** and **HS-LS2-7**.

CASE STUDY
WHERE THERE'S SMOKE THERE'S FIRE

HOW DO ECOSYSTEMS CHANGE?

Yellowstone National Park, which extends across parts of Wyoming, Montana, and Idaho, is well known for its geysers, hot springs, and abundant wildlife. In the summer of 1988, the park made headlines around the country when wildfires raged unchecked across the region's unique landscape.

That summer, Yellowstone National Park and the Greater Yellowstone Ecosystem that surrounds it were in the midst of a severe drought. Dry conditions made the region ripe for a megafire. A lightning strike in late June sparked the first blaze. At the time, U.S. Park Service and Forest Service fire management policy was to allow natural fires to burn out on their own. However, by late July, fires were spreading at an alarming rate—as much as 6400 acres a day went up in smoke. Wind gusts would send hot cinders soaring more than a kilometer away from the main fire, where they seeded new fires that merged and grew. It was then decided to fight all fires. On August 20, strong winds caused the main fire to race across 150,000 acres, in what became known as "Black Saturday."

In the end, 1.4 million acres of the Greater Yellowstone Ecosystem had burned, including more than one-third of Yellowstone National Park's total area. In the summer of 1988 there were 51 fires within the park, nine of which were human-caused. The rest were started by lightning strikes. Although a snowfall in early September helped get the fires under control, the last fire was not extinguished until November.

People around the country worried that the national park had been destroyed by fire, and many were shocked that the nation's first national park had been allowed to burn for so long without any human intervention. However, fire has always been a force of change in the Greater Yellowstone Ecosystem. Tree ring studies indicate that major fire events have occurred there every 300 years or so. Prior to 1988, the last megafire was in the 1700s.

In fact, many ecosystems, including the Greater Yellowstone Ecosystem, need fire to function properly. The cones of lodgepole pine trees require the intense heat of a fire to open and disperse their seeds. Fire clears undergrowth from the forest, helps to spread seeds for new growth, and adds nutrients to the soil. In the year following the devastating fires, the blackened landscape was once again full of life, blanketed by wildflowers and signs of new tree growth.

Ask Questions *As you read the chapter, generate questions about the ways in which ecological disturbances affect an ecosystem's community of organisms.*

FIGURE 3-1 ▽
These satellite images show how the Greater Yellowstone Ecosystem has changed over time. The yellow zones indicate fire scars from the 1988 fire. Green indicates plant growth. Note that the 2018 image also shows damage from fires that occurred after 1988.

▶ **VIDEO 3-1** Go online to watch a time-lapse video of ecosystem recovery in Yellowstone National Park.

ECOLOGICAL RELATIONSHIPS

A spider lies in wait at the edge of its intricately spun web. A moth flies nearby, unaware of the dangerous obstacle in its path. Just as the moth's wings are about to hit the sticky web, a bird swoops by and snatches the moth from the air. The spider will have to wait a bit longer for its next meal.

Describe *How might the removal of moths from this community affect the ecosystem as a whole?*

Habitat and Niche

Understanding a few basic ecology concepts can help us more fully describe the relationships among the spider, moth, and bird. For example, a *habitat* is the place where an organism lives. Shelter, water, food, and space are the four major components of a habitat. An *ecological niche* refers to the role an organism plays in its community. Similar to a habitat, a niche is made up of all the physical and environmental conditions that an organism needs to survive and reproduce. In contrast to an organism's habitat, a niche also includes all the interactions the organism has with other species. Each species fits into a unique niche that has the species' exact requirements. When two species occupy the same niche, one will be better at obtaining resources, which will result in the exclusion of the other species from that niche.

SEP **Construct an Explanation** *What are two interactions that might make up a spider's niche?*

Predation and Competition

The two primary interactions between organisms within a habitat are predation and competition. **Predation** occurs when one organism, the predator, eats another, the prey (**Figure 3-2**). Carnivores are not the only organisms that are considered to be predators. Herbivores that eat living plants are also predators. **Competition** occurs when two organisms compete for the same limited resource, such as food, shelter, or access to mates. Competition can occur between members of the same species and between members of different species.

FIGURE 3-2
This wasp spider, easily identified by its distinctive black-and-yellow striping, wraps its prey in silk.

Symbiotic Relationships

A close relationship between two or more species in which one or both of the organisms benefits is called **symbiosis**. There are three types of symbiosis: mutualism, parasitism, and commensalism.

Mutualism In mutualism, both organisms benefit. The relationship between an anemonefish and a sea anemone is an example of mutualism (**Figure 3-3**). The fish benefits by using the anemone's tentacles to hide from predators. The anemonefish also keeps the anemone and the area around it clean by eating dead tentacles. The fish's bright coloration lures other fish to the anemone, which the anemone eats. The anemone also gets nutrients from the anemonefish's waste.

SEA PIG SURVIVAL

Gather Evidence *There are few places to hide on the bottom of the ocean. To avoid predators, some types of crabs hitch rides across the ocean floor by clinging to the bottom of sea pigs. How would you categorize this type of symbiotic relationship? Explain your reasoning.*

FIGURE 3-3
A skunk anemonefish hides within the tentacles of a sea anemone in its Indian Ocean habitat. Its body is covered by a mucus that protects it from the sea anemone's stinging tentacles.

Parasitism In parasitism, one organism benefits and the other is harmed. Typically, parasites depend on their host for survival, so they will not kill it. Instead, parasites take what they need and generally cause sickness or some other harm. For example, tapeworms are parasitic worms that take up residence inside the intestines of pigs, cows, or humans, where they can live there for years. The tapeworms take vital nutrients and cause malnutrition in the host. Plants can also be parasites. Mistletoe is a flowering plant that attaches to the branch of a host tree. Its root-like appendages bore into the bark of the tree, where the mistletoe gets a portion of the water and nutrients it needs to survive (**Figure 3-4**).

FIGURE 3-4
When a mistletoe seed lands on a branch, it sends out "roots" that penetrate through the bark. This allows the mistletoe to absorb some of the tree's water and nutrients.

 VIDEO

VIDEO 3-2 Go online to view the symbiotic relationships shown here.

FIGURE 3-5 ▲
Cattle egrets and African buffalo are common sights in Kenya's Maasai Mara National Reserve.

Commensalism In commensalism, one of the organisms benefits from the relationship, while the other receives no benefit but is also not harmed. One example of commensalism is the relationship between African buffalo and cattle egrets. The cattle egrets eat the insects that are kicked up as the African buffalo grazes (**Figure 3-5**).

SEP **Construct an Explanation** *How might ecosystem stability be affected if one member of a symbiotic relationship was removed from the environment?*

3.1 REVIEW

1. **Distinguish** Use an example organism such as a bird, a fox, or a plant, to demonstrate the differences between an ecosystem, a habitat, and a niche.

2. **Predict** Which of these scenarios will increase competition between organisms in a community? Select all correct answers.

   A. A new apex predator moves into the area.

   B. A disease wipes out half the primary consumers.

   C. Increased precipitation boosts vegetation growth.

   D. Half the area is deforested for human development.

   E. The number of consumers born each year equals the number that die each year.

3. **Classify** Categorize each symbiotic relationship as an example of mutualism, commensalism, or parasitism.

   A. Birds eat disease-carrying pests such as ticks from the backs of rhinoceroses.

   B. Some fish pick up scraps of food left behind as stingrays hunt for food.

   C. Certain orchid species attach themselves harmlessly to the upper limbs of trees to obtain sunlight.

   D. Fleas living off the blood of lions can cause illness in their hosts.

   E. Ants eating peony flower nectar protect the plants from other herbivorous insects.

RESTORING A CRITICALLY ENDANGERED FROG POPULATION

The El Rincon stream frog (*Pleurodema somuncurense*) is found only in the headwaters of a single stream in Argentina. Threats to its already-small population include predation by non-native rainbow trout, damming, and habitat destruction by livestock. Biologist Dr. Federico Kacoliris is working to bring this critically endangered species back from the brink of extinction.

Dr. Federico Kacoliris is working to prevent critically endangered species in the Patagonian region of Argentina from going extinct.

On Patagonia's Somuncura Plateau, temperatures frequently dip below freezing and the wind can whip by at speeds up to 60 km/hr. At first glance, this region does not seem to be ideal habitat for a frog species. The secret to the El Rincon stream frog's survival? It lives in hot springs, where the water temperature never drops below 18 °C (64 °F). However, given the species' precise habitat requirements and threats by outside forces, its range is limited to an area less than 5 km².

While the stream is located within the Somuncura Provincial Reserve, until 2012 the area was not actively managed. In 2013, Kacoliris established the Somuncura Foundation, with the goal of protecting the El Rincon stream frog and its habitat.

As part of the species' recovery plan, Kacoliris and a team of researchers collected 40 adult frogs from the wild and established a captive breeding population at La Plata Museum in Buenos Aires, Argentina. To protect the frogs' habitat, they built enclosures to exclude livestock from the stream and removed a small dam to restore water flow. Efforts were also made to educate the local people about the frog and to encourage them to help protect its habitat. In March 2017, 146 juvenile frogs and 50 tadpoles were released back into their native habitat. The following year, an additional 50 juveniles were released.

"My most rewarding experience was to have the opportunity of helping this species go home," Kacoliris said. "The releasing event was shared with children and teachers from a local school. A time after, we confirmed the frogs became established there. Having achieved a healthy habitat with frogs again, and sharing this action with children from the local school was a magic moment that I will always remember."

THINKING CRITICALLY

Argue From Evidence *Why was habitat restoration an important part of the El Rincon stream frog's species recovery plan?*

3.2

KEY TERMS

biodiversity
keystone species

BIODIVERSITY

A trek through a tropical rainforest engages all of your senses. The lush forest is full of the aromas of fragrant flowers, decaying leaf litter, and wet soil. The air is so thick with humidity you can almost taste it. You hear the loud calls of howler monkeys, alerting one another that trespassers are near. You see a flash of red high above as scarlet macaws soar through the forest canopy. One thing is for sure: the tropical rainforest is full of life.

Explain *Why do you think some ecosystems have a greater variety of species than others?*

VIDEO

VIDEO 3-3 Go online to find out more about biodiversity from National Geographic Explorer Dr. Pablo Garcia Borboroglu.

Defining Biodiversity

Biodiversity refers to the variety and variability of life on Earth. A region's biodiversity is measured at three levels:

- Genetic diversity refers to the variety of genes contained within a species and among different species.
- Species diversity refers to all the differences between and within populations of species.
- Ecosystem diversity refers to all the different habitats, niches, communities, and ecological processes within a given location.

Biodiversity is the result of millions of years of evolution. Over the course of many generations, all the species that exist today evolved unique traits and behaviors that differentiate them from all other species. These species evolved in ways that allow them to inhabit different ecological niches.

Scientists estimate that there are 8.7 million eukaryotic species on Earth. And, if you add in prokaryotes, some scientists estimate the total number of species on Earth could top two billion (**Figure 3-6**).

FIGURE 3-6 ▼
The number of unknown species on Earth greatly outweighs the number of known species. Today, scientists think bacteria are the dominant life-form on Earth.

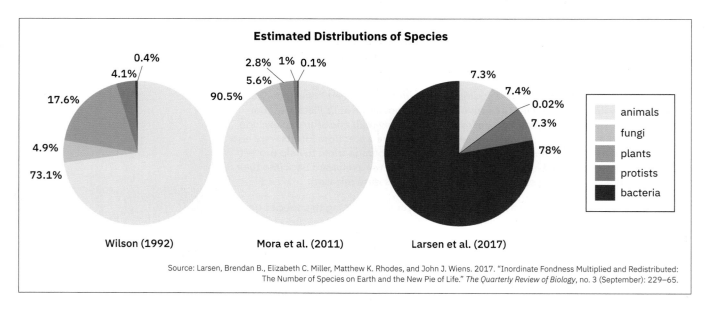

Estimated Distributions of Species

Wilson (1992): 0.4%, 4.1%, 17.6%, 4.9%, 73.1%

Mora et al. (2011): 2.8%, 1%, 0.1%, 5.6%, 90.5%

Larsen et al. (2017): 7.3%, 7.4%, 0.02%, 7.3%, 78%

Legend:
- animals
- fungi
- plants
- protists
- bacteria

Source: Larsen, Brendan B., Elizabeth C. Miller, Matthew K. Rhodes, and John J. Wiens. 2017. "Inordinate Fondness Multiplied and Redistributed: The Number of Species on Earth and the New Pie of Life." *The Quarterly Review of Biology*, no. 3 (September): 229–65.

NOS **Scientific Knowledge** *Use the graphs to explain how scientists' understanding of the diversity of life on Earth has changed over time.*

Measuring Biodiversity

Communities can differ in species diversity even if they are of similar size. There are two components to diversity. The first, *species richness*, refers to the number of different species in a community. The second is *species evenness*, or the relative abundance of each species. For example, a pond that has five fish species in nearly equal numbers has a higher species diversity than a pond with one abundant fish species and four rare ones.

Community structure is dynamic, which means that in any community, the assortment of species and their relative abundances tend to change over time. Communities change over a long time span as they form and then age. For example, over a period of 100 years, changes in environmental conditions may cause an ecosystem to transition from a pond into a meadow. Ecosystems also change over the short term as a result of a sudden environmental change such as a wildfire or flood.

Each species can live only in a specific habitat (**Figure 3-7**). Thus, geography and climate affect community structure. Factors such as soil quality, sunlight intensity, rainfall, and temperature vary with latitude and elevation. Tropical (low latitude) regions receive the most energy from the sun, get ample rainfall, and have the most even temperature throughout the year. For the majority of plant and animal groups, the number of species is greatest near the Equator, and declines as you move toward the Poles. Tropical forest communities have more types of trees than temperate ones. Similarly, tropical reef communities are more diverse than marine communities found farther from the Equator.

CCC **Patterns** *Why do you think regions farthest from the Equator show the least amounts of biodiversity?*

FIGURE 3-7
Red-shanked douc langur monkeys live in the tropical forest canopies of Vietnam and Laos.

CHAPTER INVESTIGATION

Measuring Biodiversity Using Ecological Sampling Methods
How can you measure biodiversity in a plant community?
Go online to explore this chapter's hands-on investigation about ecological sampling methods.

Biodiversity Hotspots

Biologists have identified biodiversity hotspots (**Figure 3-8**) as places rich in endemic species—that is, native species that exist nowhere else—that are threatened by humans. These hotspots, scattered throughout the world, make up about 2.5 percent of Earth's land but contain nearly half of all flowering plant species and more than a third of mammal, bird, reptile, and amphibian species. More than 20 percent of the global human population also lives within these regions. Biodiversity hotspots include

- **California Floristic Province** Located along the Pacific coast of North America, this hotspot is home to both giant sequoia and coastal redwood trees. The critically endangered California condor also lives here.

- **Atlantic Forest** Spread across portions of Brazil, Argentina, and Paraguay, this hotspot is home to 8000 endemic plant species.

- **Mountains of Southwest China** This hotspot is home to 12,000 plant species, 29 percent of which are found nowhere else in the world.

- **Madagascar** This island nation is home to a great diversity of chameleon species as well as hundreds of different lemur species, a unique primate found nowhere else in the world.

Conservation biologists and organizations have developed successful partnerships and educational programs with many countries where biodiversity hotspots exist. Economic solutions include fostering ecotourism and other alternative employment to relieve the human pressure on the native plants and animals found in these regions.

SEP **Evaluate Information** *What is a key characteristic of a biodiversity hotspot?*

FIGURE 3-8 ▼
Scientists have identified 36 biodiversity hotspots, 14 of which are identified here. To be designated as a hotspot, a region must have at least 1500 endemic plant species and have less than 30 percent of the original natural vegetation still intact.

FIGURE 3-9 ▲
A beaver dam transforms a running stream into a calm pool of water in Tierra del Fuego, Argentina.

Keystone Species

A **keystone species** is a species that has a disproportionately large effect on a community relative to its size and abundance. For example, beavers are keystone species in some communities. These large, herbivorous rodents cut down trees by gnawing through their trunks. The beaver then uses the felled trees to build a dam, which forms a deep pool where a shallow stream would otherwise exist (**Figure 3-9**). By altering the physical conditions in a section of the stream, the beaver changes which species of fish and aquatic invertebrates can live there.

SEP **Construct an Explanation** *How is a keystone species different from other species in a community?*

3.2 REVIEW

1. **Identify** What are the characteristics of all biodiversity hotspots? Select all correct answers.

   A. They are dominated by invasive species.

   B. They have the greatest number of extinct species.

   C. They support a rich collection of endemic species.

   D. They exhibit extreme temperatures due to climate change.

   E. They provide habitats for organisms threatened by human activity.

2. **Describe** What is the relationship between biodiversity and ecological niche?

3. **Analyze Data** The table lists the number of different types of trees in three forests.

Type of tree	Forest 1	Forest 2	Forest 3
beech	10	10	14
pine	10	7	14
sycamore	0	3	14

Identify whether each forest has high *species richness*, high *species evenness*, or both.

THE BIODIVERSITY CONSERVATION PARADOX

SEP **Analyze and Interpret Data** The overall biodiversity in New Zealand has increased over time despite an alarming species extinction rate—including the loss of nearly half its endemic bird species—since humans first settled there between 1200 and 1300 CE. Today, there are approximately 598 exotic animal species and 769 exotic plant species in New Zealand. These species were imported or migrated to the island.

The New Zealand Threat Classification System (NZTCS) database maintains a conservation assessment of native species. The classifications include threatened, at risk, not threatened, or data deficient. The data-deficient species have too little information available to determine their status. Some of these data are shown in **Figure 1**.

The endangered kea is a large parrot that lives in the mountains of New Zealand's South Island.

FIGURE 1 ▽
This bar graph shows the breakdown of select native organisms by conservation status.

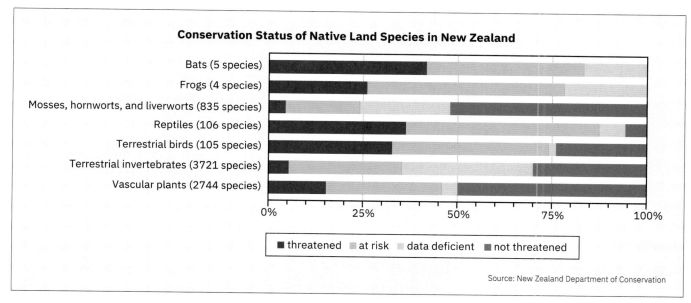

Conservation Status of Native Land Species in New Zealand

- Bats (5 species)
- Frogs (4 species)
- Mosses, hornworts, and liverworts (835 species)
- Reptiles (106 species)
- Terrestrial birds (105 species)
- Terrestrial invertebrates (3721 species)
- Vascular plants (2744 species)

0% 25% 50% 75% 100%

Legend: ■ threatened ▨ at risk ▢ data deficient ■ not threatened

Source: New Zealand Department of Conservation

1. **Calculate** Use the data to estimate the current species richness of the endemic species in the study and exotic plants and animals in New Zealand.

2. **Estimate** The percentage of at-risk and threatened species can be used to estimate the number of species that need conservation efforts. For example, approximately four of five bat species and three of four frog species are threatened or at risk of extinction. Estimate the number of at-risk and threatened endemic species in the remaining categories.

3. **Calculate** Determine the ratio of the total number of at-risk and threatened endemic species studied to the total number of exotic species.

4. **Analyze Data** About 63 species have gone extinct since humans colonized New Zealand. How does the total number of currently at-risk and threatened species compare to the number of extinct species?

5. **Argue From Evidence** Use the data and your calculations to explain why biodiversity does not always reflect an ecosystem's overall health.

ECOSYSTEM STABILITY AND CHANGE

Have you ever noticed how an abandoned parking lot changes over time? At first, tiny plants begin to grow out of cracks in the pavement where new soil has accumulated. Eventually, grasses and small shrubs start growing there too. Plant roots widen existing cracks and form new ones, allowing more soil to build up and more plants to grow. If left alone for long enough, an entirely new community of organisms may become established in the once barren landscape.

Explain *How do you think new plants become established in an abandoned parking lot?*

Ecological Disturbances

An **ecological disturbance** refers to an event of intense environmental stress that occurs over a relatively short time period and causes a large change in the affected ecosystem. These disturbances can be natural or caused by humans. Disturbances can occur at different scales. For example, a tree that falls over in a forest is a relatively minor disturbance. Though smaller in scale than thousands of acres of trees toppled by a windstorm, the lone fallen tree still affects all the organisms that depended on it as a source of food or shelter.

Natural Disturbances A natural disturbance is change or damage to an ecosystem caused by a natural event (**Figure 3-10**). Examples of natural disturbances include

- avalanches and landslides
- fires
- disease epidemics
- insect outbreaks
- extreme weather events such as droughts, floods, hurricanes, tornadoes, and windstorms
- volcanic eruptions

FIGURE 3-10
An earthquake caused this landslide in Ecuador's Tungurahua Province.

Human-Caused Disturbances Humans are part of ecosystems. As such, human activities can also affect ecosystems in many ways, as shown in **Figure 3-11**. One way humans affect ecosystems is the introduction of non-native species. In the United States alone, humans have introduced approximately 50,000 non-native species. Not all non-native species are inherently "bad." In fact, many of the plant species we depend on as food sources are not native. For example, crop plants such as okra, millet, and yams all originated in Africa. Many insects, such as the European honeybee, perform an essential role in ecosystems as pollinators.

However, non-native species that outcompete native species can become a problem. These organisms are called *invasive species*. They wreak havoc in ecosystems by disrupting food webs and damaging habitats. They also cause trillions of dollars in economic damage. For example, invasive mussel species, which clog water intake pipes and distribution systems, are estimated to cause more than $1 billion in damages annually.

Other examples of human-caused ecological disturbances include

- habitat destruction that results from land clearing, such as for agriculture, mining, or urban development

- water, land, and air pollution

- overexploitation of species, such as by overhunting or overfishing vulnerable populations

- climate change

CCC **Cause and Effect** *How might human activities worsen the effects of a natural disturbance such as a hurricane?*

FIGURE 3-11 ▲
Land clearing for human development projects is a major source of human-caused ecological disturbances.

Effects of Disturbance

The magnitude and frequency of disturbances affect communities. A variety of field studies support the *intermediate disturbance hypothesis*, which states that species richness is greatest when physical and biological disturbances are moderate in their intensity or frequency (**Figure 3-12**).

When disturbance is infrequent and of low intensity—meaning it does not remove many individual organisms—the most competitive species will exclude others, so diversity is low. By contrast, when disturbance occurs often or is of high intensity, most of the species present will be colonizers. With a moderate level of disturbance, the community will contain a mix of colonizer and mature species, and so will be most diverse. For example, a windstorm in a forest that knocks down a section of trees will result in a patch of younger plant species within a larger forest of mature trees.

FIGURE 3-12 ▼

According to the intermediate disturbance hypothesis, an ecosystem that experiences disturbances at a moderate frequency or intensity will have the highest biodiversity.

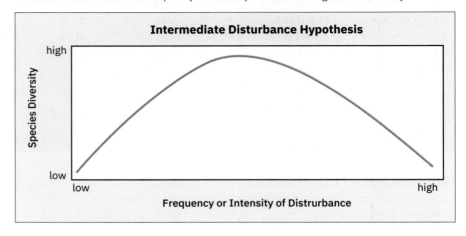

CCC **Patterns** *Why is species diversity greatest when ecological disturbances are moderate in intensity?*

Ecosystem Stability

Ecosystems are constantly changing. Environmental conditions, such as temperature, precipitation, and resource availability vary over time. Ecosystem stability refers to an ecosystem's ability to maintain consistent conditions. A stable ecosystem is able to withstand normal disturbances, maintaining a diverse population of species and supporting ecosystem functions such as the cycling of nutrients and energy. Two components of ecosystem stability are resilience and resistance.

- **Resilience** is the ability of an ecological community to regain its original structure and function following a disturbance. Ecosystems that are resilient show rapid recovery after a disturbance, quickly returning to their original state. Grasslands, which are adapted to frequent fire events, show quick recovery after a fire.

- **Resistance** is the ability of an ecological community to remain unchanged when affected by a disturbance. Ecosystems that are resistant show minimal change following a disturbance. A stable coral reef ecosystem with a high amount of biodiversity and minimal invasive species will likely show resistance after a hurricane, depending on the magnitude of the storm.

Ecological Succession

The species composition of a community will change over time. Often, some species change the habitat in ways that allow others to come in and replace them. This type of change, which takes place over a long interval of time, is called **ecological succession**.

When the concept of ecological succession was first developed in the late 1800s, it was thought to be a predictable and directional process. Which species are present at each stage in succession was thought to be determined primarily by physical factors such as climate, altitude, and soil type. In this view, succession ends in a "climax community," a collection of species that does not change over time and will be rebuilt in the event of a disturbance. Ecologists now know that the species composition of a community changes in unpredictable ways. Communities do not journey along a well-worn path to a predetermined climax state. Random events determine the order in which species arrive in a habitat, and thus affect the course of succession.

Ecological succession begins with the arrival of *pioneer species*, which are species whose traits allow them to colonize new or newly vacated habitats. Pioneer species have an opportunistic life history. This means they grow and mature quickly, and they produce many offspring capable of dispersing. Later, other hardier and slower-growing species replace the pioneers. Then the replacements are replaced, and so on. There are two types of succession: primary succession and secondary succession.

🔬 **CHAPTER INVESTIGATION**

Ecological Succession in an Aquatic Environment
How do biotic and abiotic factors influence succession in a freshwater pond community?

Go online to explore this chapter's hands-on investigation about ecological succession.

CONNECTIONS

PRAIRIE RESTORATION Prior to the arrival of Europeans, the Great Plains and Upper Midwest were covered by immense grasslands. Nearly 445,000 square kilometers of what is now Minnesota, North Dakota, and South Dakota were home to prairie ecosystems. Fire is the key to maintaining grassland ecosystems and preventing succession from taking hold. Historically, these grasslands burned on a regular basis, either caused naturally by lightning strikes or set intentionally by Native Americans to produce fertile land for agricultural purposes and to clear undergrowth to facilitate hunting and travel.

Today, fire is an important part of prairie restoration plans. The goals of prairie restoration are to reconnect isolated patches of prairie, reduce invasive species, and improve habitat for wildlife and grazing animals. Prescribed burns are a method of land management. The resulting nutrient-rich ash acts as a fertilizer and supports new growth of native vegetation. Fire also reduces the accumulation of brush, shrubs, and trees.

Every prescribed burn has a scientific plan that land managers have prepared in advance. It describes the objective of the fire, the fuels that will be used, the size of the fire, the precise environmental conditions under which it will burn, and conditions under which the fire will be suppressed if necessary.

Workers on a fire crew use a drip torch to ignite the prairie into flames as part of a prescribed fire.

FIGURE 3-13 ▲
Small plants have begun to colonize cracks that have formed within hardened lava on the Big Island of Hawaii.

Primary Succession This type of succession takes place in a barren habitat that lacks soil. The earliest pioneers to colonize such environments are often mosses and lichens, which are small, have a brief life cycle, and can tolerate intense sunlight, extreme temperature changes, and little or no soil. Some hardy annual flowering plants with wind-dispersed seeds, such as fireweed, are also frequent pioneers.

Primary succession occurs as land is exposed by the retreat of a glacier, on a newly formed volcanic island, or in a region where volcanic material has buried existing soil. On the Big Island of Hawaii, eruptions by the active volcano Kilauea provide a model example of primary succession. In 2018, volcanic activity added 3.5 km^2 of new land to the Big Island as the lava flowed offshore into the ocean. Additionally, 36 km^2 of existing land was covered by molten lava. Once the lava has cooled and hardened, the stage is set for primary succession to begin (**Figure 3-13**).

Most plant life is dependent on soil, which provides plants with the nutrients they need to grow and survive. Moss and lichen roots help to break apart lava and rock. When they die and decompose, nutrients are added to the soil. Many pioneer species have a symbiotic relationship with nitrogen-fixing bacteria that lets them grow in nitrogen-poor habitats. Seeds of later species can take root inside mats of mosses and lichens. Over time, organic wastes and remains accumulate and, by adding volume and nutrients to soil, help other species take hold. Later successional species often shade and eventually displace earlier ones. Typically, over a long period of time, smaller plants are replaced by shrubs and bushes, which are then replaced by trees and other large plants. As the plant community grows, animals begin to colonize the area, which helps to spread seeds and allows the plant community to continue to grow.

Secondary Succession In this type of succession, a disturbed area within a community recovers. It commonly occurs in abandoned agricultural fields and burned forests (**Figure 3-14**). Because improved soil is present from the start, secondary succession usually occurs faster than primary succession. While primary succession can occur over a period of hundreds or even thousands of years, secondary succession can occur over a period of just 50 years.

FIGURE 3-14
Plants are beginning to regrow as a part of the secondary succession process following a forest fire in Ontario, Canada.

CCC **Stability and Change** *What is the main difference between primary and secondary succession?*

3.3 REVIEW

1. **Classify** Sort the ecological disturbances into natural and human-caused changes.

   • Water is contaminated by toxic chemicals near a hydraulic drilling site.

   • A prairie is converted to agricultural land.

   • A volcanic eruption forces the evacuation of nearby communities.

   • The emergence of cicadas in 15 states leaves exoskeletons on trees.

2. **Compare** How are the two components of ecosystem stability similar and different?

3. **Contrast** Which condition most determines whether succession is primary or secondary?

   A. lack of vegetation
   C. presence of soil
   B. intensity of sunlight
   D. human intervention

4. **Define** Which characteristics are ideal for a pioneer species? Select all correct answers.

   A. are mobile
   D. resistant to toxins
   B. grow slowly
   E. break rock into soil
   C. photosynthetic

OBSERVING BIODIVERSITY IN POND WATER

SEP Engage in Argument From Evidence What microorganisms are found in a pond ecosystem?

Pond water is filled with a diverse set of microscopic organisms, such as bacteria, protozoa, and algae. Pond water may also contain invertebrates, such as worms, crustaceans, and insects. In this activity, you will observe and identify some of the different microorganisms found in a sample of pond water.

Common pond microorganisms include euglena, rotifer, and paramecium species.

Materials

- microscope
- microscope slide with depressed well
- coverslip
- pond water sample
- pipette or dropper
- pencil
- colored pencils (optional)
- computer or tablet with internet access

Safety

Procedure

1. Obtain a sample of pond water from your teacher.

2. Place a drop or two of pond water in the well of the microscope slide. Then cover the slide with a coverslip. **CAUTION:** *Slides and coverslips are fragile, and their edges are sharp. Handle them carefully.*

3. Observe the slide using the low-power (4×) objective lens and scan for organisms. You are looking for tiny living organisms. They may look green, yellow-brown, or clear. Choose one to focus on and center it in your visual field.

4. Change your microscope to the medium (10×) or high power (40×) objective lenses to better view the organism. In your biology notebook, record a description of the organism and the magnification power you are using to view it. Do your best to draw the organism as you see it.

5. Repeat steps 3 and 4 until you have observed two to four different organisms.

6. Using internet resources, try to identify each organism you observed. Record the organism name next to the drawing in your biology notebook. If you cannot identify a specific organism, label it as "unidentified."

7. When you have completed the activity, dispose of the pond water as instructed by your teacher. Be sure to wash your hands with soap and water after you are done.

Results and Analysis

1. **Summarize** Make a summary of your observations and share your findings with the class.

2. **Compare** Compile a list of all the organisms observed by the class. Did you all observe the same organisms? How do you explain any differences?

3. **Analyze Data** Based on the class findings, which organisms were the most abundant? Which were the least abundant?

4. **Explain** What biotic and abiotic factors might influence the diversity of microorganisms found in pond water?

5. **Plan an Investigation** What changes could you make to the investigation to allow you to compare the biodiversity of different ponds?

TYING IT ALL TOGETHER
WHERE THERE'S SMOKE THERE'S FIRE

HOW DO ECOSYSTEMS CHANGE?

In this chapter, you learned about the effects of ecological disturbances on ecosystem stability and change. The Case Study described the role fire plays in the Greater Yellowstone Ecosystem. The 1988 wildfire gave scientists the opportunity to study secondary succession as it has unfolded in real time.

Immediately after the fire, scientists made predictions about how the ecosystem might change over time. Some of these predictions were supported while others were only partially supported or did not occur at all. For example, scientists initially predicted that the abundance of native species would decrease within the burned zones and there would be a greater abundance of non-native species. However, they found that most native plant species reappeared within one to three years after the fire. And while populations of non-native species did increase in some areas, native plants were dominant in the burned zones.

Scientists made some surprising discoveries too. It was initially thought that aspens mainly reproduced from the sprouting roots of a parent tree. However, aspen seedlings were found to have established themselves throughout the burned conifer forests, far away from mature aspen stands. Genetic studies showed that these aspens had indeed grown from seeds and were not genetic clones.

Thirty years after the fire, as expected, lodgepole pines are again thriving in the region (**Figure 3-15**).

Research has shown that fire helps to increase diversity in a forest ecosystem by creating patches of new growth within older established forests (**Figure 3-16**). This dynamic is proving to be the case in Yellowstone National Park today.

In this activity, you will develop an argument to explain how an ecological disturbance such as a wildfire affects ecosystem stability and biodiversity. Work individually or in a group to complete these steps.

Gather Evidence
1. Research how the Greater Yellowstone Ecosystem has changed since the 1988 wildfire. How have its plant and animal communities changed over time? Have other fires impacted the park's ecosystems since 1988?

Scientific Knowledge Is Open to Revision in Light of New Evidence
2. How did a change in scientists' understanding of the role of fire in ecosystem function influence fire management policy in the United States?

Engage in Argument From Evidence
3. Use evidence from your research to evaluate the following claim: "Wildfire is a common ecological disturbance that affects biodiversity in Yellowstone National Park."

Extension Evaluate how climate change is affecting wildfire frequency and intensity. What effect does climate change have on ecosystem stability?

FIGURE 3-15 ▼
Lodgepole pine forest regeneration began soon after the Yellowstone fires of 1988.

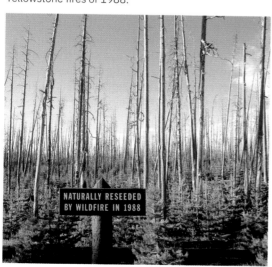

FIGURE 3-16 ▼
Research indicates that biodiversity peaks around 25 years after a wildfire has occurred.

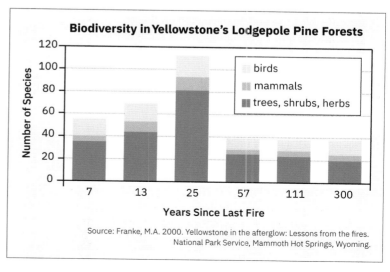

Biodiversity in Yellowstone's Lodgepole Pine Forests

birds
mammals
trees, shrubs, herbs

Number of Species

Years Since Last Fire

Source: Franke, M.A. 2000. Yellowstone in the afterglow: Lessons from the fires. National Park Service, Mammoth Hot Springs, Wyoming.

REVIEW KEY CONCEPTS

1. Contrast Which statement correctly describes how a habitat differs from a niche?

   A. A habitat is the place where an organism lives and a niche is the role filled by that organism along with its interactions within its community.

   B. Habitats are the shelters used by animals for protection against predation and niches are the spaces plants use to put down roots for growth.

   C. A habitat is the environment occupied by an entire ecosystem and niches are the individual environments occupied by organisms in that ecosystem.

   D. Some organisms require large areas in which to live and these are called habitats. Other organisms require small areas and these are called niches.

2. Analyze Which ecological interactions are present in the community described below? Select all correct answers.

Pitcher plants are carnivorous plants that grow in bogs, which are wet areas that have little water flow. Winged insects become trapped in the plants' long tube-like structures where they die and get absorbed by the plant. Bogs also provide habitat for frogs that feed on winged insects, snails, and slugs and grass snakes that feed on frogs, fish, and small mammals.

   A. Pitcher plants are predators.

   B. Frogs compete with pitcher plants.

   C. Grass snakes and frogs are competitors.

   D. Grass snakes have a symbiotic relationship with winged insects.

   E. Winged insects have a symbiotic relationship with pitcher plants.

3. Classify Sort the organisms based on the given descriptions into three categories of symbiotic relationships: mutualism, commensalism, and parasitism.

   • Fleas live in a rat's fur and inject their mouthparts into the rat's skin to feed off the rat's blood.

   • Barnacles attach themselves harmlessly to a humpback whale's body and receive a steady supply of food from the ocean as the whale swims about.

   • Cowbirds lay their eggs in other birds' nests.

   • Algae avoid predators by living inside coral tissues and use photosynthesis to provide food for themselves and the corals.

4. Explain Which claims are true about biodiversity hotspots? Select all correct answers.

   A. Human activities have little impact on biodiversity hotspots.

   B. Biodiversity hotspots cover more than half of Earth's land surface.

   C. Biodiversity hotspots contain species not found anywhere else on Earth.

   D. Large numbers of species are threatened with extinction in biodiversity hotspots.

   E. Educational programs are effective tools in reducing harm to biodiversity hotspots.

5. Predict Which characteristics would most likely be observed in an ecosystem that experiences a moderate level of disturbance? Select all correct answers.

   A. nutrient-poor soil

   B. lack of mature species

   C. mostly colonizer species

   D. relatively high species diversity

   E. mix of colonizer and mature species

6. Describe What do pioneer species provide or make possible in an ecosystem? Select all correct answers.

   A. organic matter

   B. rocks

   C. seeds

   D. shade

   E. soil

7. Relate How would you expect the diversity of species living in a natural area to be related to the number of niches present in that natural area? Explain.

8. Explain Grasslands can burn extensively after a lightning strike but return quickly to a stable state. An ecologist claims that these ecosystems are examples of resilience but not resistance. Explain whether you agree or disagree with this claim and why.

9. Draw Conclusions A plant ecologist observed changes in a field after it was no longer used for farming. Species A covered the field one year after abandonment. Species B replaced much of species A in the second year, and species C became the dominant plant species in the third year. What ecological process was the ecologist most likely observing? Explain your reasoning.

CRITICAL THINKING

10. **Explain** Would it be possible for two different species to occupy the same niche and the same habitat in an ecosystem? Explain your answer.

11. **Synthesize** Why would it be important to track a keystone species in an ecosystem under threat of ecological disturbance?

12. **Argue From Evidence** Use evidence from **Figure 3-12** to support the idea that moderate disturbances actually enhance ecosystem stability.

13. **Explain** Why would it be unhealthy for an ecosystem to never undergo any disturbance of any kind?

14. **NOS** **Making Decisions** When making decisions about managing biodiversity hotspots, why is it important to take social and cultural contexts into consideration?

MATH AND ENGLISH LANGUAGE ARTS CONNECTIONS

Read the following passage. Use evidence from the passage to answer the question.

High biodiversity has been used as an indicator of ecosystem stability. Diversity provides more stability because diseases, invasive species, drought, fire, and other disturbances often harm certain species more than others. Having a diversity of species allows for greater chances of recovery after a disturbance.

1. **Cite Textual Evidence** How would you describe the stability of a forest with several different species but only a few members of each species? Cite information from the text to support your answer.

Read the following passages and examine the data table to answer questions 2 and 3.

An urban green space was divided into three zones of equal area. Species were counted weekly in each zone over a three-month period, then summed and divided by the number of weeks to produce the average values shown in the table.

Organisms	Zone A	Zone B	Zone C
large trees and tall shrubs	13.4	9.4	6
small plants	1.4	1	0.4
insects	8	6	2
birds	3.2	2.3	1
worms	2.2	2	1.3
mammals	1.3	0	0.2

Insect and bird diversity was higher in zones A and B but lower in zone C. This could be attributed to richness in large plant species within zones A and B in contrast to zone C. It has been shown that insects tend to inhabit areas of dense vegetation cover. Thick foliage provides protection from bird and mammalian predators. Birds also require large plant species and dense vegetation for nesting and protection. These results are consistent with large urban trees acting as keystone species that provide crucial habitat resources for many members of a single community.

2. **Evaluate a Science or Technical Text** Do the data support the conclusions presented in the passage regarding differences in biodiversity between zones? Explain your reasoning.

3. **Assess Reasoning and Evidence** Assess the extent to which the reasoning and evidence found in the passage support the claim that large tree species function as keystone species in urban green spaces.

► REVISIT SEA PIG SURVIVAL

Gather Evidence In this chapter, you have seen how organisms interact together in different ecological relationships. In Section 1, you learned that sea pigs have a symbiotic relationship with some types of crabs. You also learned about ecosystem stability and change and the role of biodiversity in maintaining ecosystem stability.

1. How might a change in the stability of a deep-ocean ecosystem affect sea pig survival?

2. What other questions do you have about sea pigs? What else do you need to know to construct an explanation about how ecological disturbances affect their deep-ocean habitat?

CHAPTER 4
POPULATION MEASUREMENT AND GROWTH

The city of Agrigento, Sicily, overlooks the Temple of Olympian Zeus. Rich agricultural soils and sulfur mines have supported the city since it was founded in 580 B.C.E. by Greek colonists.

4.1 MEASURING POPULATIONS

4.2 MODELING POPULATION GROWTH PATTERNS

4.3 FACTORS THAT LIMIT POPULATION GROWTH

A study of human history shows that for many thousands of years, humans have moved across the globe to gain access to the natural, societal, and technological resources that sustain them. Ecologists find that the same is true of any species in an ecosystem. As the availability of resources in a given environment changes, the number of individuals the environment can support changes as well.

Chapter 4 supports the NGSS Performance Expectations **HS-LS2-1** and **HS-LS2-2**.

CASE STUDY
SHARING OUR CITIES

WHAT FACTORS INFLUENCE THE SIZE OF A POPULATION?

The city of Chicago, Illinois, and its surrounding suburbs form one of the most populous metropolitan areas in the United States. Along with more than five million human residents, the region hosts a population of nearly 4000 coyotes. Hundreds of coyotes live within the city of Chicago

NORTH AMERICA
Chicago.

historic range (before 1900)
by 1950
present range

itself, often making dens in public parks and cemeteries. They have also been spotted walking down residential streets and past upscale hotels and shops in the downtown shopping district. Researchers even tracked a mating pair of coyotes to the parking lot of Soldier Field Stadium, where they had built a den in the concrete for their litter of five pups.

Coyotes are native to North American prairies and deserts, which provide open spaces for hunting their preferred prey of rabbits, rodents, and other small animals. While humans have disturbed these natural habitats, human activity has also contributed to

expanding the coyote's range in many ways. Despite having been perceived as a pest species and targeted for eradication over the past century, coyote populations have thrived, spreading eastward to the Atlantic coast and as far south as Panama. Urban development is thought to encourage coyote habitat expansion by clearing forested areas for agricultural use, removing larger predators such as wolves and cougars, and providing resource-rich suburban landscapes.

Chicago is not the only major U.S. city where coyotes live successfully. Thousands of coyote sightings have also been reported in Washington, D.C., and Denver, Colorado, in recent years. To help coyote and human populations coexist peacefully, wildlife ecologists have closely studied coyote behavior in these urban environments. They have found that city and suburban coyotes are larger and live longer than rural coyotes. Near dense human populations, coyotes use wooded habitats and are more active at night in order to avoid contact with people (**Figure 4-1**). For the most part, urban coyotes continue to hunt their natural prey species and do not consume human-sourced food. As top predators, they perform an essential ecological role by controlling rodent, deer, and Canada goose populations in areas inhabited by humans.

Ask Questions *In this chapter, you will learn how various factors influence organism populations. Generate questions about the effects of human activity on populations of native species.*

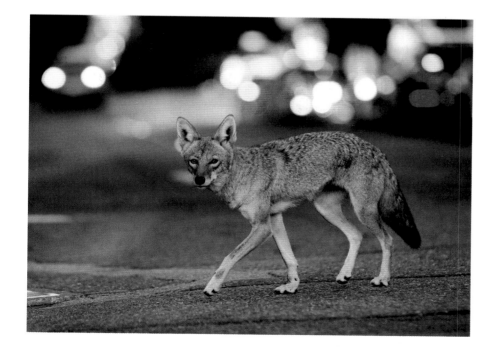

FIGURE 4-1
Shifting its activities to the evening hours helps minimize human interactions for this urban-dwelling coyote.

▶ **VIDEO 4-1** Go online to see the streets of Chicago from a coyote's point of view, as filmed for National Geographic Explorer Dr. Stanley Gehrt's urban wildlife studies.

KEY TERMS

mark–recapture sampling
plot sampling
population density
population distribution
population size
range

MEASURING POPULATIONS

By law, the United States government conducts a census every ten years to measure the population of each community in the nation. To do so, the Census Bureau builds an accurate list of housing unit addresses and asks each household to respond to a short questionnaire about its occupants. This population data is used to determine how to apportion seats in the House of Representatives, draw Congressional districts, and distribute federal funding. According to the 2020 census, there were 331,449,281 residents of the United States in that year.

Compare and Contrast *Suppose you want to count the number of birds in a park. How would this procedure be similar to a census? How would it be different?*

Counting Organisms

A *population* is a group of organisms of the same species that interbreed with one another. Population ecologists are scientists who investigate the factors that affect populations. Data from population ecology studies can be used to make decisions about how to manage a species and to assess the effects of human activities on wild species.

Population size is the total number of individuals in a population. It is often impractical to count all members of a population, so biologists frequently use sampling techniques to estimate population size.

Mark–recapture sampling is used to estimate the population size of mobile animals. With this technique, animals are captured, marked with a unique identifier of some sort, and released (**Figure 4-2**). At a later time, scientists capture another group of individuals from the same population. The proportion of marked animals in the second sample is taken to be representative of the proportion marked in the population as a whole.

FIGURE 4-2
To study the migration of a population of rare Kirtland's warblers, scientists attached tiny radio tags to birds in their winter home in the Bahamas. They then used radio telemetry to detect and track individual birds' movements in their Michigan breeding grounds.

Suppose 100 deer are captured, marked, and released. Later, 50 of these deer are recaptured along with 50 unmarked deer. Marked deer constitute half the recaptured group, so the group previously caught and marked (100 deer) must have been half of the population. Thus, the total population is estimated at 200 deer.

Giving each captured animal a unique mark allows scientists to follow individuals over time. This can reveal information about behavior and environmental factors that influence the individual's likelihood of survival. Tracking devices attached to captured animals can yield information about how a population uses the geographical area, or **range**, in which it lives.

Plot sampling is a method of estimating the total number of individuals in an area based on data from direct counts in some portion of the area. For example, ecologists might estimate the number of grass plants in a grassland or the number of mussels on a beach (**Figure 4-3**) by measuring the number of individuals in each of several one-square-meter plots. To estimate total population size, scientists first determine the average number of individuals per sample plot. Then they multiply that average by the number of plots that would fit in the population's range. Estimates derived from plot sampling are most accurate when species are not very mobile and conditions across their habitat are uniform.

SEP **Use Mathematics** *To estimate the population of mussels on a beach, scientists counted individuals at five different sites. The results of the population survey are shown in **Table 4-1**. What is the average number of mussels they found per site?*

TABLE 4-1. Mussel Plot Survey Data

Site	Number of mussels
A	75
B	96
C	16
D	146
E	87

FIGURE 4-3
Mussel populations are often studied because they spread quickly through connected waterways and can become invasive species if they are transported to new environments.

Population Density

A variety of statistical characteristics can be used to describe a population. In addition to measuring population size, ecologists make detailed observations of organisms' locations in order to determine a population's density and distribution.

Population density is the average number of individuals per unit area or volume. This density is often measured by plot sampling. Examples of population density include the number of dandelions per square meter of lawn, the number of amoebas per milliliter of pond water, or the number of squirrels in a 4000-square-meter city park. The population density of a species that inhabits a large range can be expressed as the average number of individuals per unit area of the population's range.

Population Distribution In a population of organisms, the location of individuals relative to one another is described by the **population distribution**. Members of a population may be clumped together, separated by equal distances, or distributed randomly. The distribution of individuals in a population can also change over time.

FIGURE 4-4 ▽
Differences in resource availability result in patterns exemplified by a clumped distribution of hippopotamuses (a), a near-uniform distribution of nesting seabirds (b), and a random distribution of dandelions (c).

clumped distribution

uniform distribution

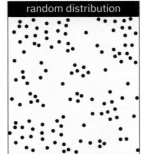
random distribution

- **Clumped Distribution** This is the most common distribution pattern. In a *clumped distribution*, members of a population are closer to one another than would be predicted by chance alone. A patchy distribution of resources encourages clumping. Hippopotamuses clump in muddy river shallows (**Figure 4-4a**). Moisture-loving ferns may cover a damp, north-facing slope and be absent from an adjacent drier and sunnier south-facing slope. A limited ability to disperse also increases the likelihood of a clumped distribution—the acorn really does not fall far from the tree.

- **Near-Uniform Distribution** This distribution type results from intense competition for limited resources. In a *near-uniform distribution*, individuals are more evenly spaced than would be expected by chance alone. Creosote bushes in some parts of the American Southwest grow in this pattern. Competition for limited water among the root systems keeps the bushes from growing close together. Similarly, seabirds in breeding colonies often show a near-uniform distribution. To defend their nesting sites, Australian gannets aggressively lunge and strike at others that come within reach of their beaks (**Figure 4-4b**).

- **Random Distribution** When resources are distributed uniformly through the environment, and proximity to others neither benefits nor harms individuals, a *random distribution* occurs. For example, when the wind-dispersed seeds of dandelions land on the uniform environment of a suburban lawn, the dandelion plants grow in random locations without any particular pattern (**Figure 4-4c**).

The scale of the sampled area and the timing of a study can influence observed population densities and distributions. For example, seabirds are spaced almost uniformly at a nesting site, but the nesting sites are clumped along a shoreline. The birds crowd together during the breeding season but disperse when breeding is over.

CCC **Scale, Proportion, and Quantity** *In the plot sampling method, the area where organisms are counted directly, such as a 1-m² plot of grassland, is called a quadrat. Which type(s) of population distribution would be most effectively surveyed using a quadrat? Explain your answer.*

CHAPTER INVESTIGATION

Designing a Seed Trap
How can you build and test an effective seed trap?
Go online to explore this chapter's hands-on investigation and build your own seed trap prototype.

▶ VIDEO

VIDEO 4-2 Go online to get an aerial view of penguins at their Antarctic breeding grounds.

4.1 REVIEW

1. **Calculate** What is the population density of 10,000 amoebas in a 25-milliliter sample of pond water?

2. **Analyze** A population of acacia trees grows in a savanna at a density of 100 trees per hectare in the east and 200 trees per hectare in the west. What type of distribution does this population have?

   A. clumped   C. near-uniform

   B. dense   D. random

3. **Calculate** Scientists capture a sample of 36 individuals from an estimated population of 180 foxes. Twelve of the captured foxes are red and 24 are gray. Based on this sample, how many foxes in the whole population would they expect to be red?

4. **Justify** Would mark–recapture sampling or plot sampling be a more suitable method for estimating the population of clams in a shallow river? Explain your choice.

MARK–RECAPTURE SAMPLING

SEP **Use Mathematics** How can you estimate a population of organisms that cannot be counted directly?

One of the methods biologists use to estimate population size is the mark–recapture method. This method involves capturing some of the animals in a population, marking them in a way that does not hurt them, and releasing them back into their environment. Later, a random sample of animals from the same population is captured. Biologists can use the proportion of recaptured marked animals in the sample to estimate the size of the population.

This monarch butterfly is marked with a lightweight tag.

Materials

- unknown number of beans in a container
- marker

Procedure

1. The beans in the container represent all of the animals in a population you are studying. Suppose that because their range is very large, it is not feasible to count each individual animal in the population. However, you are able to safely trap and tag some of the animals for later identification. Remove 20 beans from the container. These represent the animals you have trapped during a particular month of your investigation.

2. Make a mark on each bean to tag each animal. Release all of the animals back into their environment by putting the beans back into the container. Shake the container to simulate the animals moving to unknown locations within their range.

3. Again, remove a group of 20 beans from the container at random. Count how many of these animals have tags. In a data table, record the number of animals trapped and the number of tagged animals recaptured. Release the animals by returning the beans to the container.

4. Repeat step 3 several more times. Record your results in the table.

5. For each trial, calculate the percentage of trapped animals that had tags and record your results.

Results and Analysis

1. **Model** Compare the data you obtained for each trial. Do your results vary widely, or are they generally consistent between trials? If these were the results of an actual mark–recapture investigation, what factors in nature could explain the differences in results between trials?

2. **Interpret Data** How do the percentages you calculated in step 5 relate to the number of objects you originally tagged and the total number of objects in the container?

3. **Estimate** Use your data to estimate the total number of beans in the container. Show your calculations.

4. **Calculate** Count all of the beans in the container. How close was your estimate to the actual value? Calculate the percent error in your result.

5. **Evaluate** What changes could you make in your mark–recapture sampling method to improve the accuracy of your estimate?

MODELING POPULATION GROWTH PATTERNS

Populations of organisms, whether they are sunflowers, eagles, or humans, change over time. This change is ultimately because of two factors: the number of births and the number of deaths in the population. For humans, the birth rate is often expressed as the number of live births per 1000 people per year, and the death rate is expressed as the number of deaths per 1000 people per year. **Table 4-2** gives birth and death rates in 2019 for several countries.

TABLE 4-2. World Bank Population Statistics

Country	Birth rate (per 1000 people)	Death rate (per 1000 people)
Czech Republic	10.5	10.5
Japan	7.0	11.1
Kazakhstan	21.73	7.19
Ukraine	8.1	14.7
United States	11.4	8.7

Source: World Bank 2019.

Predict *In which countries would you expect the population to increase in the coming years? Are there any countries where the population is expected to decrease?*

Growth Rates

We can measure births and deaths in terms of rates per individual, or per capita. *Capita* means head, as in a head count. Imagine 1200 mice living in the same field. If 600 mice are born each month, then the birth rate *b* is

> (600 births/1200 mice) = 0.5 births per mouse per month.

Similarly, if 120 mice die each month, then the death rate *d* is

> (120 deaths/1200 mice) = 0.1 deaths per mouse per month.

To calculate the overall **per capita growth rate** *r* for a population, subtract the population's per capita death rate from its per capita birth rate:

$$r = b - d$$

SEP **Use Mathematics** *Find the mouse population's per capita growth rate.*

Immigration and Emigration

Population size is also affected by immigration and emigration. Immigration is the movement of individuals into a population, increasing its size. Emigration is the movement of individuals out of a population, decreasing its size. In many animal species, young of one or both sexes leave the area where they were born to breed in a different place. For example, young freshwater turtles typically emigrate from their parental population and become immigrants at another pond some distance away. By contrast, some species of seabirds breed where they were born.

FIGURE 4-5 ▶
As in many big cat species, a male lion leaves its mother's territory when it is between two and three years old to find a mate from a different pride.

However, some individuals may emigrate and end up at breeding sites more than a thousand kilometers away. In general, the tendency of individuals to emigrate to a new breeding site is related to resource availability, crowding, and avoiding inbreeding (**Figure 4-5**). As crowding increases and resources decline, the likelihood of emigration rises.

CCC **Cause and Effect** *How do immigration and emigration affect the growth rate of a population?*

Biotic Potential and Exponential Growth

A population's per capita growth rate can change over time for many reasons. Food sources or suitable habitats may become more or less available, or a population may be exposed to new predators or disease. However, if shelter, food, and other essential resources were unlimited and there were no external threats, the population would grow indefinitely as long as its birth rate was greater than its death rate.

Under ideal conditions, the population's per capita growth rate would be determined by the reproductive characteristics of its species, including the age at which reproduction typically begins, how long individuals are able to reproduce, and the number of offspring that are produced each time an individual reproduces. This theoretical growth rate is a measure of the population's **biotic potential**. Different species have different biotic potentials. Microbes such as bacteria have some of the highest biotic potentials, whereas large mammals with long lives have some of the lowest.

Imagine a single bacterium in a laboratory flask that provides ideal conditions for survival and growth. After 20 minutes, the bacterial cell divides in two. Those two cells divide, and so on, every 20 minutes. At this growth rate, a population of more than one billion can result from a single bacterium in just 10 hours. The graph of the number of individuals versus time for this bacterial population takes on a J shape. This shape is characteristic of graphs of **exponential growth**, which occurs when a population's per capita growth rate is positive (**Figure 4-6**).

FIGURE 4-6 ▽
If a population's per capita growth rate is positive and resources are unlimited, the number of individuals increases exponentially over time.

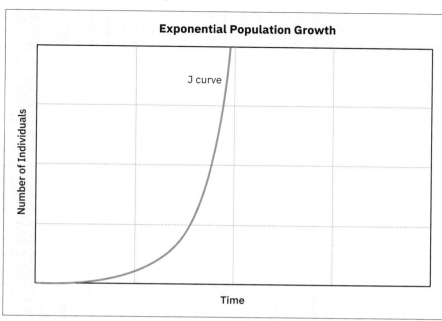

Exponential Population Growth

J curve

Number of Individuals

Time

Go Online SIMULATION

Modeling Population Changes Go online to examine how changes in rates affect the growth of a population.

Regardless of the species, populations seldom reach their biotic potential. A population with a growth rate r greater than zero will increase exponentially, but growth at the maximum potential rate can only occur when conditions are ideal. A bacterial colony might grow to enormous numbers in a laboratory environment, where conditions can be controlled and food supplied indefinitely. But in an outdoor puddle where food is limited and the environment is unstable, such as in **Figure 4-7**, the same bacterial population would grow at a slower rate or even decrease. Although the population can survive in the puddle for some time, the conditions are no longer ideal.

SEP **Construct an Explanation** *Describe the difference between the biotic potential of a population of organisms and the population's growth rate.*

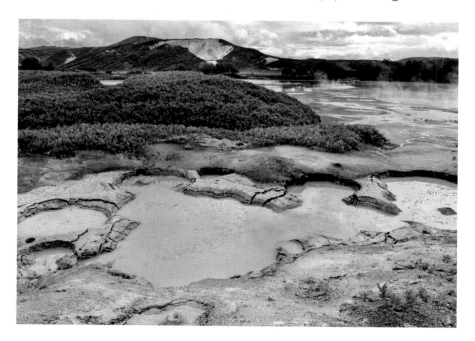

FIGURE 4-7 ◁
Bubbling pots of volcanic mud form in the Uzon Caldera in Kamchatka, Russia. Microbes that are able to survive in this hot, highly acidic environment face little competition with other species as they cluster in mats on the surface of the mud.

Life History and Survivorship

A population's biotic potential is determined in part by how its individual members use resources and energy for growth, survival, and reproduction over the course of their lifetimes. This distribution of resources makes up an organism's *life history*. Patterns in life history vary among species. Ecologists have described two major life history patterns.

Life History Patterns Species that live in unpredictable conditions tend to produce as many offspring as possible, often as quickly as possible. This pattern is called an opportunistic life history. These organisms offer little parental care, instead expending energy to take advantage of a favorable environment that might only be temporary. These organisms are often small in body size and have a short interval of time between generations. For example, weedy plants such as dandelions follow this life history pattern. They mature within weeks, produce many tiny seeds, then die. Coho salmon (**Figure 4-8a**) also live according to this pattern. A female salmon deposits thousands of eggs in a river nest during spawning. Neither she, nor the male salmon that fertilizes the eggs, will survive to see their offspring hatch.

When a species lives in a more stable environment, the ability to successfully compete for resources has a major influence on reproductive success. These conditions favor an equilibrial life history pattern in which parents produce a few high-quality offspring. Compared to species that live in unpredictable conditions, species that live in stable conditions have larger bodies and longer times between generations. The life history pattern of large mammals, which typically take years to reach adulthood and begin reproducing, is representative of these species. For example, a female blue whale reaches maturity between the ages of six and ten years. The whale then produces only one large calf at a time and continues to invest energy and resources in the calf by nursing it after its birth. Similarly, olive trees (**Figure 4-8b**) grow for several years before producing olives. In both whales and olive trees, a mature individual produces young for many years.

Survival Patterns One way to investigate life history traits is to focus on a cohort—a group of individuals born during the same interval— from their time of birth until the last individual dies. Ecologists often divide a natural population into age classes and record the age-specific birth rates and death rates. The resulting data is often summarized in a table.

FIGURE 4-8 ▼
Coho salmon migrate between the ocean and coastal rivers to spawn. A female salmon produces thousands of eggs, but most are eaten by predators before they can hatch (a). Olive trees need sandy soil and a consistent climate with long summers and mild winters to survive. They begin to produce olives at about four to eight years old and can live for hundreds of years (b).

Information about the life history of a species can also be illustrated by a survivorship curve. This plot shows how many individuals born during the same interval remain alive over time. Ecologists describe three types of curves, as shown in **Figure 4-9**.

- **Type I** The death rate remains low until relatively late in life for these organisms, so most individuals survive to reproduce. Humans and other large mammals, such as Dall sheep, that produce and care for one or two offspring at a time have this pattern.

- **Type II** These organisms have a survivorship rate that remains relatively equal across their lifetimes. In birds, small mammals, and some reptiles such as skinks, old individuals are about as likely to die of disease or predation as young ones are.

- **Type III** These organisms have a very high birth rate and a very high death rate soon after birth. Invertebrates, fish, amphibians, and plants such as spider flowers show this type of survivorship.

FIGURE 4-9 ▼
A survivorship curve shows how many individuals in a population survive to a given percentage of the typical maximum life span for that type of organism. In these graphs, the gray lines are theoretical curves, and the blue dots are data from field studies of Dall sheep (a), five-lined skinks (b), and spider flowers (c).

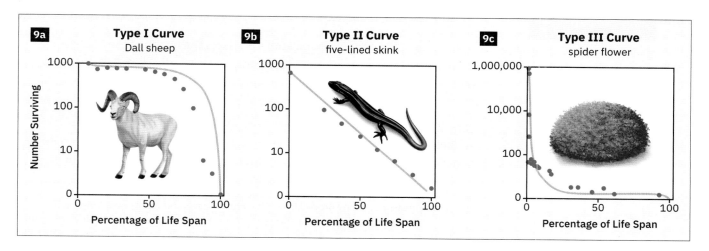

CCC **Patterns** *Which type of survivorship pattern would you expect a species that lives in unpredictable conditions to have? Which type would a species that lives in stable conditions likely have?*

4.2 REVIEW

1. **Compare** Classify each factor as having a positive impact or a negative impact on the growth rate of a population of organisms: birth rate, death rate, rate of immigration, rate of emigration.

2. **Summarize** Describe an ideal scenario where a population of organisms would achieve its biotic potential.

3. **Analyze Data** Based on the death rates listed in the table, what type of survivorship curve do you expect the plant species will have?

4. **Predict** What do you expect will be the survivorship between months 13–15?

The table gives statistics for a cohort of one plant species monitored over a year. Use the data to answer questions 3 and 4.

Age interval (months)	Survivorship (number surviving at start of interval)	Death rate	Birth rate
0–3	996	0.329	0
4–6	295	0.356	0
7–9	176	0.023	0
10–12	154	0.045	3.13

Dr. Heather J. Lynch works to develop mathematical models and apply statistical analyses to conservation biology.

▶ **VIDEO 4-3** Go online to observe a penguin colony that Lynch's group found.

NATIONAL GEOGRAPHIC EXPLORER **HEATHER J. LYNCH**

PENGUIN POPULATIONS PREDICT EFFECTS OF CLIMATE CHANGE

Scientists monitor penguin populations to assess the health of the Southern Ocean ecosystem in one of the most rapidly warming places on Earth. However, visiting penguins in their far-flung, inhospitable habitats is often difficult. Until very recently, many colonies had not been visited for decades and some had never been properly surveyed. To address this problem, quantitative ecologist Dr. Heather J. Lynch has pioneered methods of combining high-resolution satellite imagery with high-performance computing to study polar animal populations.

Lynch is a professor at Stony Brook University whose research focuses on a long-term project to map Antarctica's penguin and seabird populations. Like many seabirds, penguins are highly sensitive to local conditions. Antarctica's five penguin species migrate to specific breeding sites that are suited to their varied nesting and feeding habits. Penguins eat fish and krill, which are small pink crustaceans that feed on phytoplankton under the sea ice. Pink penguin guano stains the areas where penguins nest, and those guano stains are visible by satellite. Using images of penguin colonies and their characteristic guano staining, Lynch and her research group discovered a series of penguin "supercolonies" in the remote Danger Islands. In all, Lynch and her colleagues have discovered over a million penguins through satellite imagery. In addition, they figured out how to use the shade of pink in the guano to analyze the proportion of krill and fish in the penguins' diets. This information is critical to understanding the threats penguins may be facing.

A number of different stakeholders benefit from accurate information on penguin populations. For example, scientists need to understand the effectiveness of Marine Protected Areas, which are designed to conserve and protect marine habitats and the resources within them. Commercial interests, such as krill harvesters and tour operators, also need to know where penguin populations exist to avoid disrupting their food sources and habitats. To address this broad variety of needs, Lynch's group created the Mapping Application for Penguin Populations and Projected Dynamics (MAPPPD). This internet-based tool uses a globally sourced dataset to estimate current Antarctic penguin populations and forecast population trends. ▌

THINKING CRITICALLY

Identify Cause and Effect *Lynch's population models integrated 41 years of data from 70 penguin breeding sites on the Antarctic Peninsula. These studies show that Adélie and chinstrap penguin populations are decreasing, and gentoo penguin populations are increasing. What factors might explain why population trends differ for different penguin species living in the same region?*

FACTORS THAT LIMIT POPULATION GROWTH

4.3

KEY TERMS

carrying capacity
density-dependent factor
density-independent factor
logistic growth

The city of Detroit, Michigan, was settled by French traders in 1701 and incorporated as a city in 1815. Its position on the Detroit River that links Lake Erie and Lake St. Clair made it ideal for transporting goods by ship. The city's population grew exponentially, adding tens of thousands of people per year during the early 20th century. In 1950, Detroit was the fourth largest city in the United States and the epicenter of the automobile industry, with a population of more than 1.8 million people. However, the city's population has significantly declined since that era (**Figure 4-10**).

Predict *What change in resources might have caused Detroit's population decline over the last 70 years? What do you think will happen to the city's population in the future? How might the population of your town or city change in the future?*

FIGURE 4-10 ▽

The city's population increased over its first 150 years, but has been decreasing since 1950.

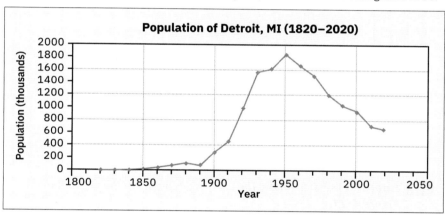

Limiting Factors and Carrying Capacity

Even in a stable environment with favorable conditions, there are limits to how much a population can grow. For a population of humans, some of these limits are imposed by natural boundaries such as the bodies of water that surround Detroit. In addition, humans draw borders and write laws that regulate the number of people that can live in a city, much like coyotes establish territories inhabited only by specific packs.

As in a city, circumstances that curb exponential growth exist in any natural environment. For example, consider a population of water fleas that live in a small pond with plenty of algae and bacteria to eat and no fish or other predators. Even in these conditions, the water flea population could not keep growing exponentially for an extended period of time because they would run out of food and living space. A larger pond, or one with more food, might sustain a larger population of water fleas. However, the population would still not be able to increase indefinitely because the environment's resources are finite.

Population Growth of Duckweed
How and why does the number of duckweed plants in a population change over time?

Go online to explore this chapter's hands-on investigation about factors that affect population growth.

Carrying Capacity When limiting factors affect population size over time, **logistic growth** occurs, yielding an S-shaped curve. The graph shows exponential growth at first. Then, as the growth rate decreases, the population levels off at a constant value (**Figure 4-11**). This **carrying capacity** is the maximum number of individuals that the population's environment can support indefinitely. Carrying capacity is species-specific, environment-specific, and can be affected by changes in the environment.

FIGURE 4-11 ▼
In nature, the increase in a real population may resemble exponential growth at first, but many factors contribute to slowing this growth as time passes.

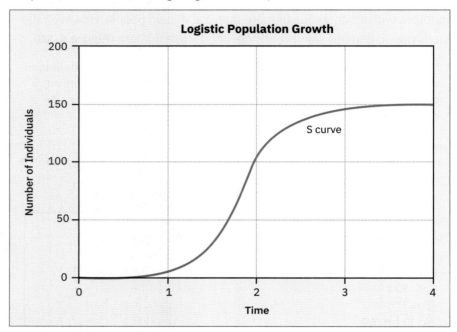

SEP **Interpret Data** *Estimate the carrying capacity of the population in Figure 4-11.*

As time goes on, the growth rate for most organisms stabilizes near zero for many different reasons. Factors that limit the growth of a population can be categorized as density dependent or density independent.

Density-Dependent Factors

A **density-dependent factor** is a limiting factor that is affected by the number of individuals in a given area. The denser the population becomes, the more its growth rate will tend to decrease. Competition, parasitism, disease, and predation are all examples of density-dependent factors that can slow population growth rates and decrease the carrying capacity of an environment.

Competition As population density increases, so does competition for resources such as food and shelter. Eventually, the population reaches the point where there is no longer enough of a resource to sustain it. For example, when small sapling trees in a forest compete for sunlight, many trees are able to grow in a small space (**Figure 4-12**). Eventually, as they grow, the trees crowd each other out, blocking off the sunlight so only a few can survive, and the carrying capacity is reached. Competition has a detrimental effect even on the survivors, because energy they use to compete for resources is not available for reproduction.

CASE STUDY
SHARING OUR CITIES

Ask Questions *Generate questions about how human activity might influence the density-dependent factors that affect an urban coyote population.*

FIGURE 4-12
Plants in the same environment compete for light and space. This competition occurs among plants of the same species or with plants of different species.

Parasites and Pathogens The negative effects of diseases transmitted by parasites or pathogens may increase with population density, which most likely occurs when the disease is transmitted through air and water sources used by the population. In humans, airborne viruses such as severe acute respiratory syndrome (SARS) occur at higher rates in densely populated regions. Chytridiomycosis, a disease that affects hundreds of frog species worldwide, is caused by a fungus that eats the proteins in the frog's skin. This results in infections that may eventually lead to the frog's death by cardiac arrest. The fungus can infect frogs as it floats in the water where the frogs live. It also spreads by contact between individual frogs (**Figure 4-13**). This disease has, to date, no effective control methods in the wild, so it poses a serious threat to biodiversity. Scientists estimate that since the 1990s, more than 200 frog species have declined or become extinct due to chytridiomycosis.

Go Online	SIMULATION

Modeling Population Changes Go online to investigate how density-dependent factors affect the size of a population.

FIGURE 4-13
The American bullfrog (*Lithobates catesbeianus*) tolerates the fungus that causes chytridiomycosis and can carry it to habitats where it infects other frog species.

Predation In any community, the number of predators and the number of prey are connected. Generally, an increase in the size of a predator population results in a decrease in the abundance of its prey. Predator and prey populations sometimes rise and fall in a predictable cyclical fashion. **Figure 4-14** shows historical data for the numbers of Canadian lynx and their main prey, the snowshoe hare. Both populations rise and fall over an approximately ten-year cycle, with the number of predators lagging behind the number of prey. Field studies indicate that lynx population numbers increase or decrease mainly in response to hare population numbers. However, the size of the hare population is affected by the availability of the hare's food as well as the number of lynx. As a result, hare populations continue to rise and fall even when predators are experimentally excluded from areas.

FIGURE 4-14 ▽

Canadian lynx population estimates in the late 19th century are based on counts of lynx pelts that fur trappers sold to the Hudson's Bay Company.

Density-Independent Factors

Sometimes, natural disasters or weather-related events affect population size. A volcanic eruption, hurricane, or flood can greatly diminish the size of a population in an instant, whether it is high or low in density. These events are called **density-independent factors**, because the density of the affected population does not influence the likelihood of the factor's occurrence or the magnitude of its impact. Human-caused events, such as oil spills or clearing land for development or agriculture, can also act as density-independent factors.

In nature, density-dependent and density-independent factors interact to determine a population's size. The occurrence of a density-independent event may intensify the effect of an existing density-dependent factor or introduce new density-dependent factors. For example, in addition to killing some portion of the animals and plants that inhabit a forest, a major forest fire reduces the amount of suitable habitat and food for the remaining populations, and surviving organisms may be less healthy and more vulnerable to predation and disease.

SEP **Construct an Explanation** *Can a density-independent factor lead to an increase in the size of a population? Explain your answer.*

SEA PIG SURVIVAL

Gather Evidence *What density-dependent factors could limit the populations of organisms that live on the ocean floor? What density-independent factors could limit these populations?*

BIOTECHNOLOGY FOCUS

ENVIRONMENTAL DNA Canadian lynx are now very rarely seen and are thus listed as a threatened species according to the Endangered Species Act. Because their tracks are very similar to those of bobcats, it is difficult to accurately determine their populations. Carnivore researchers have collaborated with aquatic scientists to develop a reliable technique for identifying lynx tracks.

An organism's DNA is found in all of its cells, and each species has a unique genome. Animals shed surface cells and waste products as they move through their environments. Cellular DNA can survive in water for a few weeks before degrading. This allows scientists to extract and analyze DNA from a water sample taken from an aquatic environment, giving them information about the species of organisms that exist in the water. The DNA analysis techniques they use are sensitive enough to detect rare species that have not otherwise been observed in the sampled environment.

Animal tracks made in snow become water samples when the snow melts. Using carefully designed methods to avoid contamination, scientists scooped up snow near and underneath fresh tracks they encountered in the northern Rocky Mountains. By applying the same techniques used to analyze environmental DNA for the presence of aquatic species, they were able to identify lynx tracks and differentiate them from tracks made by several carnivore species that share a habitat with the Canadian lynx.

Camera traps occasionally capture lynx in the wild.

4.3 REVIEW

1. **Classify** Label each scenario as a factor that will increase or decrease the carrying capacity for a species.

   A. The most populous predator of the species emigrates.

   B. Favorable environmental conditions boost the birth rate.

   C. All the organisms infected with a contagious disease die off.

   D. A new parasite for the species immigrates into the community.

   The table gives the population sizes in one food chain in a community. Use the data to answer questions 2 and 3.

Organism	Population size (number of organisms)
primary consumers	7×10^5
producers	6×10^6
secondary consumers	3×10^5
tertiary consumers	1×10^1

2. **Analyze Data** A new tertiary consumer predator moves into the community. Sketch the numbers pyramid for the community before and after the arrival of the new predator.

3. **Predict** An infectious disease decimates a population of organisms in a community. For each trophic level, predict what might happen to the numbers pyramid if the disease were to kill species of organisms at that level.

4. If the death rate of a population increases and the birth rate stays the same, in what ways might the graph of population vs. time change? Select all correct answers.

   A. The carrying capacity could decrease if the increase in the death rate is due to a change in a density-dependent factor.

   B. The carrying capacity could increase because there would be room for more organisms than before.

   C. The population would reach the carrying capacity more slowly.

   D. The growth rate of the population could decrease temporarily if the increase in death rate is due to a density-independent factor.

ON ASSIGNMENT The Deadvlei, or "dead marsh," is located in Namibia's Namib-Naukluft National Park. Commonly referred to as "the forest frozen in time," this unique desert ecosystem, which features some of the tallest sand dunes in the world, was once a river marsh. A change in climate over 900 years ago caused the marsh to dry up. Subsequent drought conditions prevented the acacia trees from decomposing. This image was taken by National Geographic photographer Edson Vandeira.

INVASIVE SPECIES POPULATION GROWTH

SEP **Analyze and Interpret Data** In many states, new environmental regulations require recreational boaters to drain boats and liquid containers on land after using public freshwater lakes. Boats moving to a different lake must be fully decontaminated and inspected.

Scientists are concerned about zebra mussels, an invasive species that first appeared in Lake Erie in 1988 and now exists in at least 32 states. The mollusks attach themselves firmly to solid objects and accumulate on the surfaces of docks and boats. They harm native species, compete for food and space, and quickly overwhelm stable aquatic food webs.

A study of an inland lake in Minnesota recorded the zebra mussel population over a period of 10 years. **Figure 1** shows the combined population density of zebra mussels over time.

FIGURE 1 ▼
The density of zebra mussels in one inland lake is reported as a number of organisms per square meter.

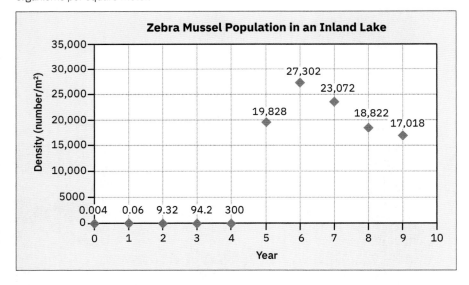

1. **Identify Patterns** During which time period did the population grow at the highest rate, and in which year did it peak?

2. **Predict** What are potential reasons for the population decline in the later years of the study?

3. **Justify** Use the historical population data and details about the role of zebra mussels in the ecosystem to justify the environmental regulations for recreational boaters.

4. **Formulate** A per capita change in a population is the amount of change "per head," or per organism in the initial population. How would you calculate the per capita change in the zebra mussel population density between year 2 and year 3?

5. **Compare** Between which two consecutive years of the study was the per capita increase in zebra mussel population density the largest?

TYING IT ALL TOGETHER
SHARING OUR CITIES

WHAT FACTORS INFLUENCE THE SIZE OF A POPULATION?

In this chapter, you learned about how the characteristics of a species and its environment affect its population. The Case Study described a coyote population living in and around the city of Chicago. Human populations anywhere on Earth cohabit with populations of other native species. We share Los Angeles with mountain lions, Mumbai with leopards (**Figure 4-15**), and Hong Kong and Barcelona with wild boars. Endangered salamanders swim in spring-fed pools with the citizens of Austin, and penguins flock to the beaches of Cape Town.

When developing urban areas, humans make substantial changes to the environment that influence whether and how other species can survive there. Urbanization alters local conditions such as temperature, air and water quality, and light and noise levels. The placement of infrastructure such as roads and dams can lead to habitat fragmentation, cutting off organisms' access to vital resources. In turn, the presence of native species in urban areas can affect human life to varying degrees. While some species may be dangerous to humans, others only act as a nuisance or property hazard, and still others go nearly unnoticed.

In this activity, you will research and evaluate solutions for conserving populations of native species within an urban community. Work individually or in a group to complete these steps.

Obtain Information

1. Choose a city and research the effects of urban development or human interactions on the population of a native species that lives and interacts with humans there.

Propose Solutions

2. Describe at least two actions humans have taken, or could potentially take, to conserve the population you researched.

Evaluate Solutions

3. Compare each of the actions you described in terms of meeting constraints such as safety, cost-effectiveness, environmental impact, and social acceptability. Write an argument to support the solution you think would be most effective based on its ability to operate within these constraints.

FIGURE 4-15 ▽

Leopards visit a residential area near Mumbai, India, to prey on dogs that forage for garbage left out by humans.

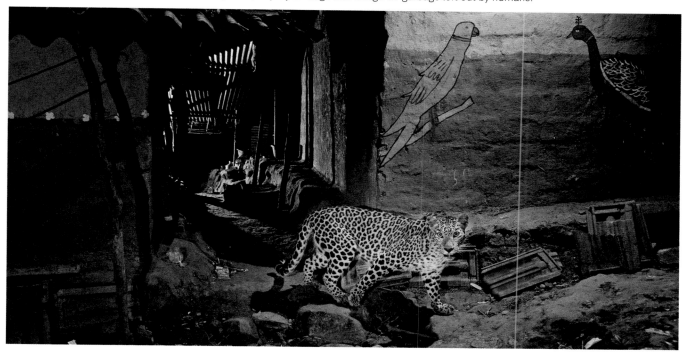

REVIEW KEY CONCEPTS

1. **Calculate** In a meadow, 10 rabbits are captured, marked, and released. The next day, 10 rabbits are captured. Of the recaptured rabbits, 2 have been marked. What is a reasonable estimate for the size of the rabbit population?

   A. between 2 and 10

   B. 10

   C. 50

   D. 100

2. **Interpret** In the sample described in question 1, half of the rabbits had dark gray fur and the rest had brown fur. What can be assumed about the coloration of the population of rabbits?

   A. About half will have dark gray fur.

   B. Gray is the most common fur color.

   C. Gray fur increases the likelihood of being captured.

   D. There are likely many other colors of rabbits in the meadow.

3. **Predict** Which factor would likely result in a clumped population distribution?

   A. flat topography

   B. competition for space

   C. long-distance dispersal of seeds

   D. unequal distribution of resources

4. **Define** How do density-dependent factors affect a population?

   A. They cause a sudden decline in the population.

   B. They cause exponential growth of the population.

   C. They cause the carrying capacity to increase as the population grows.

   D. They slow exponential growth until the population levels out at carrying capacity.

5. **Classify** Categorize the following examples as density-dependent or density-independent factors.

   - lava flow covering a forest
   - flooding after a heavy rain
   - pine bark beetles eating pine trees
   - lack of food resources due to drought

6. **Relate** Construct a mathematical expression that relates birth rate b and death rate d when a population with no migration is shrinking.

7. **Explain** How can a population be described as having a uniform and a clumped distribution at the same time?

8. **Identify Cause and Effect** A population of organisms lives in ideal environmental conditions. However, the population is not growing rapidly. What life history factors might cause this?

9. **Classify** Which reason(s) would justify the use of a plot sampling method to estimate the size of a population? Select all correct answers.

   A. The organism being sampled has limited mobility.

   B. The distribution of resources within the area is unknown.

   C. There are large differences in population density within the area.

   D. You are able to distinguish organisms that have previously been counted.

   E. Rapid and extreme changes in conditions are occurring throughout the area.

10. **Classify** A species of plants produces toxic chemicals that prevent any seeds from germinating in the soil nearby. What word best describes the population distribution that will likely result?

11. **Analyze** How does the ability to attach tracking devices to animals help a scientist study the population to which they belong? Select all correct answers.

    A. It increases the animal's ability to find a mate.

    B. It increases the likelihood of the animals surviving.

    C. It allows the scientist to change the way the animals behave.

    D. It allows the scientist to learn about the range of the population.

    E. It allows the scientist to mark the animals for estimating population size.

12. **Identify** What kinds of changes can lead to an increase in carrying capacity?

    A. More organisms immigrate into the area.

    B. More resources become available in the area.

    C. More waste by-products accumulate in the area.

    D. Carrying capacity is fixed and cannot be changed.

CRITICAL THINKING

13. Justify What method would you use to estimate the population of maple trees in a forest? Explain your reasoning.

14. Evaluate What factors could make a population estimate from a mark–recapture project inaccurate?

15. Analyze In a pond, a species of frogs lives at a high population density. A fungus that causes chytridiomycosis is then introduced into the pond. Describe how a population vs. time graph would look for

a. the frogs, before and after the introduction of the fungus.

b. the fungus.

What circumstances cause the two graphs to look different?

16. Contrast What environmental circumstances result in a J-shaped population curve? What circumstances result in an S-shaped curve?

17. Analyze Why are stable environmental conditions necessary for the survival of organisms that have a type I survivorship curve?

18. Ask Questions Evaluate the following claim: *Hamsters can have large litters of young, sometimes more than 20, and this means hamsters have a type III survivorship curve.* What kinds of questions should you ask about the life history of the hamster that might help you support or refute this claim?

19. NOS Scientific Knowledge Critter cams, radio tags, and environmental DNA help scientists track organisms in the wild. How can evidence from new technologies help confirm or change our scientific knowledge about organism populations?

MATH AND ENGLISH LANGUAGE ARTS CONNECTIONS

1. Write an Argument Use your knowledge of population growth factors to explain why introducing a few individuals of a new species into a new location could be problematic. Use your understanding of biodiversity to frame your argument.

2. Write a Function Develop a formula to calculate the size of a population based on mark–recapture data. Use *P* for the estimated population size, *c* for the number of organisms captured the first time, *r* for the number of organisms captured the second time, and *m* for the number of marked organisms that were captured the second time.

3. Reason Quantitatively A population of organisms grows so that its population vs. time graph forms an S-shaped curve. Describe the slope of a line that is parallel to the curve

a. at the bottom part

b. in the middle part

c. at the top part.

4. Graph Functions Graph the organism data given in the table. Describe the graph and classify the survivorship curve of this organism.

Number surviving	Percent of life span
100	5
91	75
82	93
45	96
10	99

5. Write Informative Text Choose an organism. Describe its life history and determine the type of survivorship curve it likely has.

6. Model with Mathematics The expression $r = b - d$ describes the per capita growth rate *r* of a population with birth rate *b* and death rate *d*. How could emigration (*e*) and immigration (*i*) be included in the expression for *r*?

► REVIST SEA PIG SURVIVAL

Gather Evidence In this chapter, you have learned about factors that affect population size. Many useful mineral resources exist on the ocean floor, so several nations and companies have been exploring the potential of seabed mining.

1. Would human attempts to explore and obtain minerals from the seafloor act as a density-dependent or a density-independent factor? Explain your answer.

2. How might mining the ocean floor affect the carrying capacity for a sea pig population?

RELATIONSHIPS IN ECOSYSTEMS

CHAPTER 2
ENERGY AND MATTER IN ECOSYSTEMS

How do energy and matter move through an ecosystem?

- Living things need the input of matter and energy to survive, grow, and reproduce. The interaction between biotic and abiotic components of an ecosystem allows for the transfer of matter and energy throughout the system.

- Both matter and energy are conserved in Earth's ecosystems.

- Energy and matter transformations occur through chemical reactions. Two important chemical reactions in ecosystems are photosynthesis and cellular respiration.

- The movement of matter and energy through an ecosystem can be modeled using food webs, ecological pyramids, and matter cycles.

CHAPTER 3
BIODIVERSITY AND ECOSYSTEM STABILITY

How is biodiversity related to ecosystem stability?

- Ecosystems that have more biodiversity are more stable than ecosystems with little biodiversity.

- Biodiversity can be measured in terms of species richness and species evenness.

- Natural and human-caused disturbances affect ecosystem stability.

- Resistant ecosystems experience minimal change after a disturbance. Resilient ecosystems recover rapidly after a disturbance and quickly return to their original state.

- Ecosystem recovery after a disturbance occurs in predictable ways.

CHAPTER 4
POPULATION MEASUREMENT AND GROWTH

What factors affect the size of a population?

- A population with a constant growth rate greater than zero and access to unlimited resources will increase exponentially.

- The carrying capacity of an environment is the maximum number of individuals of a species than an environment can support indefinitely.

- Density-dependent factors, such as competition and parasitism, are limiting factors that are affected by the number of individuals in an area.

- Density-independent factors, such as natural disasters and human activity, are limiting factors that affect a population regardless of its size.

Go Online **VIRTUAL INVESTIGATION**

Sea Pigs on the Abyssal Plain
How do sea pigs survive in the deep ocean?
Take control of a remotely operated vehicle (ROV) to observe organisms on the ocean floor.

HOW DO SEA PIGS SURVIVE IN THE DEEP OCEAN?

Argue From Evidence In this unit, you learned that the energy for life processes originates from the sun. Nevertheless, diverse ecosystems thrive on the ocean floor at sunless depths between 3 and 6 kilometers, in generally flat regions called abyssal plains. These plains make up approximately 70 percent of the global seabed.

The Monterey Bay Aquarium Research Institute (MBARI) has monitored an abyssal ecosystem off the central coast of California for 30 years. Their ROV takes frequent high-resolution images of the seafloor and its inhabitants and has measured carbon and oxygen levels to determine what the animals and bacteria there eat and produce. Sea pigs are abundant in this ecosystem. Their main food source is fresh "marine snow," the dead organic matter and waste that sinks from shallow waters to the ocean floor.

Although they share their habitat with many other species of sea cucumbers, octopuses, marine worms, mollusks, crabs, fish, and coral, sea pigs are not usually a food source for other organisms.

MBARI's data indicate that a typical slow and steady supply of marine snow would not provide enough food to support the number of consumers they find in the abyss, but occasional large bursts of matter falling from events at or near the ocean surface can sustain populations deep below for long periods of time.

C **Claim** Make a claim about the role of sea pigs in an abyssal plain ecosystem.

E **Evidence** Use the evidence that you gathered throughout the unit to support your claim.

R **Reasoning** To help illustrate your reasoning, you can develop a model that explains how abyssal plain organisms obtain the energy and matter they need to survive.

In 2019, MBARI located the remains of a baleen whale on the ocean floor. A fallen whale attracts a changing assortment of organisms: larger scavengers feed on the whale's soft parts, smaller organisms look for decomposing tissue in the surrounding sediment, and bacteria and other microbes access the fat trapped inside the whale's bones.

UNIT 2
CELL
SYSTEMS

Escherichia coli, seen here isolated on a sterile surface, is the most common species of bacteria in human intestines.

Bacteria are single-celled organisms that live practically everywhere on Earth. In addition to habitats on land, they are found in the atmosphere, in the ocean, and even in the deepest layer of Earth's crust. Many types of bacteria live on and within plants and animals.

In the human body, bacterial cells vastly outnumber human cells. Bacteria can cause negative effects, such as acne, dental cavities, food poisoning, or infectious diseases. They also have a number of functions in maintaining human health. Beneficial bacteria on your skin and in your nose and mouth stimulate your immune system and protect your body from invasion by pathogens. Hundreds of bacterial species live in the human gastrointestinal tract, where they play a vital role.

WHAT DO BACTERIA DO IN YOUR INTESTINES?

In this unit you will analyze models to understand the structures and functions of cells and how cells grow.

CHAPTER 5
MOLECULES IN LIVING SYSTEMS

CHAPTER 6
CELL STRUCTURE AND FUNCTION

CHAPTER 7
CELL GROWTH

UNIT VIDEO 1 Go online to learn more about how your gut microbiome, an ecosystem of bacteria, works in your intestines.

SOMETHING GOOD IN YOUR GUT

CONNECTING GUT MICROBIOMES TO HUMAN HEALTH

The 30–40 square meters of surface area in your gut interacts with the outside environment every time you take a bite of food. Your gut is home to as many microorganisms as cells that make up your body. The collection of gut microbes forms a symbiotic relationship with you. The microbes thrive in your gut's environment while your body benefits from their metabolic activities. Biological anthropologist and National Geographic Explorer Dr. Katie Amato first started taking a close look at this relationship in howler monkeys in 2010, and she is now trying to answer questions related to the gut microbiome's impact on human nutrition and brain growth.

A WORLD UNIQUELY YOUR OWN By about age three, the composition and function of the human gut's microbiome look much like those of an adult. They stay that way into an individual's 40s, when they begin to naturally shift due to changes associated with aging. That is, unless the microbiome is disrupted by illness, antibiotic use, or other disturbances. Surprisingly, because of these environmental impacts, each person's gut microbiome is unique, like a fingerprint, even though similarities exist among healthy individuals.

Amato focuses her research on the microbe community in the large intestine. She's very interested in humans and the role of the gut's microbiota when food is scarce or when nutritional needs increase, such as during pregnancy. Carrying out research in humans can be difficult, so she uses other primates as models. By collecting data from fecal samples of primates in different environments, she can determine how microbes interact with host nutrition and health.

USING SCIENCE TO EFFECT SOCIAL CHANGE
Amato's research on howler monkeys indicates that the gut microbiome can help protect hosts against periods of food shortage by digesting fiber to produce more energy. Amato also gained insights by comparing gut microbiota data of nonhuman primates with data from humans. These data showed that the human gut microbiome is more similar to that of baboons than

to that of other apes. These patterns likely reflect similarities between the diets and habitats of baboons and human ancestors. The baboons' gut microbiomes, however, showed less variation among individuals than humans did. The greater variation in human gut microbiomes suggests to Amato that humans may be more influenced by environmental changes in location or diet than other primates.

In her research, Amato observes the influence of environmental factors on the gut microbiome, including diet, antibiotics, social interactions, and outdoor exposure. She also sees a relationship between these factors and human health. If she can link certain gut microbes to certain traits and determine how the environment impacts the growth of those microbes, then she can identify which environmental factors are most likely to affect health. By doing so, Amato can help people survive short-term food shortages and better understand the impact of long-term food insecurity on the gut microbiome as well as conditions such as malnutrition, growth stunting, obesity, and diabetes.

THINKING CRITICALLY

Model *Why could baboon gut microbiomes be a good model for studying human gut microbiomes?*

Top: For her Ph.D. dissertation, Dr. Katie Amato spent a year doing field research on wild howler monkeys in Mexico. **Bottom left:** In the wild, baboons eat a variety of plant parts and sometimes meat. Their diet is more like that of humans than that of the more closely related chimpanzees, which primarily eat fruit. **Bottom right:** Amato analyzes fecal samples in her lab at Northwestern University.

▶ **UNIT VIDEO 2** Go online to watch our interview with Amato and learn more about her career and research.

CHAPTER 5

MOLECULES IN LIVING SYSTEMS

Flamingos are born with a white or gray color. As they obtain carotenoids from their diet of shrimp and algae, their colors change.

5.1 ELEMENTS AND COMPOUNDS

5.2 WATER

5.3 CARBON-BASED MOLECULES

5.4 CHEMICAL REACTIONS

Flamingos get their characteristic color from pigment molecules called carotenoids. These molecules give some animals and most plants their red, orange, and yellow colors. The structures of different carotenoid molecules determine which wavelengths of light they absorb. The types of molecules that make up living things share important structural characteristics. Scientists use these patterns to predict how a group of similar molecules functions within an organism or biochemical process.

Chapter 5 supports the NGSS Performance Expectation **HS-LS1-6**.

CASE STUDY
TURNING MOLECULES INTO MEDICINE

HOW ARE THE MOLECULES OF LIFE ASSEMBLED?

In many ways, Earth's living species are its most valuable resources. For example, many of the drugs used in a hospital or available in a pharmacy are derived from plants. Substances such as morphine and other pain relievers come from poppy plants. Colchicine from the meadow saffron treats a common form of arthritis called gout, and quinine from a tropical tree bark treats malaria. Madagascar periwinkle is used to treat cancers such as leukemia and Hodgkin disease.

The Pacific yew (*Taxus brevifolia*), shown in **Figure 5-1**, is a slow-growing tree native to the Pacific Northwest and the northern Rocky Mountains. The logging industry once considered it a "weed" tree with no commercial value. However, Native American people and specialty artisans have long used the Pacific yew's strong, decay-resistant wood for tools and decorative objects.

In the 1960s, scientists at the National Cancer Institute discovered that the thin bark of the Pacific yew contains a compound that inhibits the growth of tumors. They named this compound *paclitaxel* (**Figure 5-2**).

Clinical trials showed paclitaxel to be very effective against ovarian cancer compared with earlier forms of treatment. Unfortunately, the bark of a single yew contains only a tiny amount of paclitaxel, and removing the bark to extract the compound kills the tree. Hundreds of thousands of trees would need to be harvested to obtain enough paclitaxel to treat cancer patients. This fact sparked the search for other ways to synthesize the complex compound. Scientists have tried extracting compounds from yew needles and identifying species of fungi that can produce paclitaxel. They have also genetically engineered bacteria to make taxadiene, an intermediate compound needed to build a paclitaxel molecule. Paclitaxel can now be made in a laboratory, but significant challenges remain in making the process more sustainable and less expensive. Nevertheless, this naturally derived compound has been one of the most effective and versatile tools for cancer treatment to date.

Ask Questions *In this chapter, you will learn about patterns that occur in biological matter at the molecular level. As you read, generate questions you might need to ask if you were a biochemist who wanted to make naturally occurring compounds in a lab.*

FIGURE 5-1 ▼
Removing the thin purple bark from the Pacific yew tree is time-consuming and delicate work.

FIGURE 5-2 ▼
In this model of the paclitaxel molecule, the spheres represent atoms, and the sticks that connect them represent chemical bonds.

chemical bond
covalent bond
element
hydrogen bond
ion
ionic bond
isotope
nonpolar
polar

ELEMENTS AND COMPOUNDS

An Olympic gold medal is required to contain at least 6 grams of pure gold—slightly more than the mass of a U.S. quarter. Imagine 6 grams of gold being divided into smaller and smaller pieces. The smallest possible particle that acts like and appears as gold is a gold atom. Atoms are almost unimaginably tiny. They are much smaller than the smallest particle we can see under a light microscope. The gold in an Olympic medal would consist of about 1.8×10^{22}, or 18,000,000,000,000,000,000,000, gold atoms.

Predict *Gold and oxygen are very different substances. What are some ways in which a gold atom and an oxygen atom might differ?*

The Parts of an Atom

Though an atom is extremely small, it is composed of even smaller components called subatomic particles. The three main types of subatomic particles are *protons, neutrons*, and *electrons*. As shown in **Figure 5-3**, an atom is arranged with protons and neutrons in a central nucleus that is surrounded by a cloud of much smaller electrons.

FIGURE 5-3 ▶
Protons and neutrons make up the nucleus in the center of an atom. Electrons move rapidly around the nucleus. The positions of the electrons are represented by a "cloud" that is darker where the electrons are more likely to be found and lighter where they are less likely to be found.

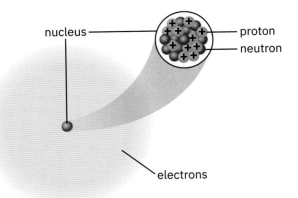

nucleus — proton — neutron

electrons

Protons and Elements The number of protons in an atom's nucleus is called its atomic number, and the atomic number of an atom determines its element. An **element** is a pure substance that consists only of atoms with the same characteristic number of protons. For example, the atomic number of carbon is 6. All atoms with six protons are carbon atoms, no matter how many electrons or neutrons they have. Elemental carbon (the substance) consists only of carbon atoms, and all of those atoms have six protons.

Carbon is a major component of all living things, including humans. When estimating the amount of biomass contained in a trophic level, ecologists assume that, on average, half of the mass of an organism (not including water) is carbon. Even beyond Earth, carbon is considered to likely be important for life. Scientists searching for life across the universe look for evidence of carbon-containing molecules such as carbon dioxide (CO_2) and methane (CH_4). **Table 5-1** lists six elements that have significant roles in biological, physical, and geological systems that support life on Earth.

TABLE 5-1. Six Elements Essential for Life

Element		Symbol	Atomic number	Occurrences in nature
carbon	●	C	6	all organisms and fossil fuels, carbon dioxide gas, Earth's crust, the ocean
hydrogen	○	H	1	all organisms, water
oxygen	●	O	8	in water, Earth's atmosphere (as oxygen and in carbon dioxide), Earth's crust
nitrogen	●	N	7	Earth's atmosphere (as nitrogen gas), soil, plants, proteins
phosphorus	◐	P	15	all organisms, minerals, animal waste
sulfur	○	S	16	minerals, geothermal emissions

Isotopes Different forms of the same element that have the same number of protons but a different number of neutrons are called **isotopes**. For example, one carbon atom may have six neutrons, and another may have seven. An isotope is named using the total number of protons and neutrons in its nucleus. The carbon isotope with six neutrons is carbon-12 (abbreviated ^{12}C). The one with seven neutrons is carbon-13 (^{13}C). Isotopes of the same element are interchangeable in a biological system.

Some isotopes, such as ^{14}C, are radioactive—their nuclei break up spontaneously over time to form other elements. The time it takes for half of a radioactive isotope to decay is called its half-life. Radioactive isotopes exist in tiny amounts in any material. For example, a very small percentage (about 0.012 percent) of the potassium in your body is radioactive ^{40}K.

BIOTECHNOLOGY FOCUS

STABLE ISOTOPE ANALYSIS Not all isotopes are radioactive. Some of the natural isotopes of carbon, hydrogen, oxygen, and nitrogen do not decay. Some of these stable isotopes occur in animal tissues that grow quickly, such as hair and feathers. The isotope ratios of hydrogen and oxygen in these materials reflect the water and atmospheric conditions the animal has experienced, so isotope analysis can give clues as to where the animal has been over a period of time. Scientists use this information to track migratory birds.

In ecology, stable isotope analysis follows the principle that "you are what you eat." Isotopes of some elements make their way through food webs in a consistent pattern as matter is eaten by consumers and incorporated into their bodies. For example, ^{13}C can be used to identify the producer level in a food web. Nitrogen-15 is typically biomagnified, so higher ^{15}N ratios appear in higher trophic levels. When direct observation of food web interactions is not feasible, stable isotope analysis can help ecologists infer an organism's niche within its ecosystem.

The relative amounts (ratios) in which stable isotopes are present in any geographic location comprise that location's isotopic "signature." The ratio of ^2H increases from north to south across North America.

^2H isotope ratio

less ^2H

more ^2H

Charge The property of electric *charge* distinguishes protons, neutrons, and electrons from each other. Protons carry one unit of positive electric charge (+1). Electrons carry one unit of negative electric charge (−1). Neutrons have no charge. The negative charge of an electron is the same magnitude as the positive charge of a proton, so these two charges cancel one another. Thus, an atom with exactly the same number of electrons as protons is *neutral*—it carries no charge (**Figure 5-4**).

FIGURE 5-4 ▶
A neutral carbon atom has six protons, six neutrons, and six electrons.

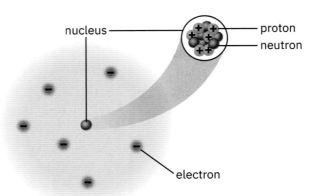

The strength of the force between charged particles depends on the size of the charges and the distance between them. The direction of the forces is determined by the signs of the charges. Charged particles of the same sign repel each other, and charged particles of opposite signs attract each other. An atom's negatively charged electrons are drawn to its positively charged nucleus by these attractive forces, but the electrons also repel each other as they move in a cloud around the nucleus.

An **ion** is an atom that has a different number of electrons than protons. Ions play an important role in cellular functions. For example, the body uses potassium ions to regulate the concentrations of fluids inside cells. All potassium atoms have 19 protons, so a potassium atom that has 19 electrons has no charge (**Figure 5-5a**). However, a potassium atom that has only 18 electrons is an ion with a charge of +1. The 18 +1 charges on 18 of the protons are canceled out by the 18 −1 charges on all 18 electrons, leaving one proton with a charge of +1. The overall effect is an ion with a +1 charge (**Figure 5-5b**).

FIGURE 5-5 ▼
A neutral potassium atom (a) and a potassium ion (b) both have 19 protons, but the potassium ion has one less electron, giving it a charge of +1.

SEP **Use Mathematics** *What is the charge of a nitrogen atom that has 10 electrons?*

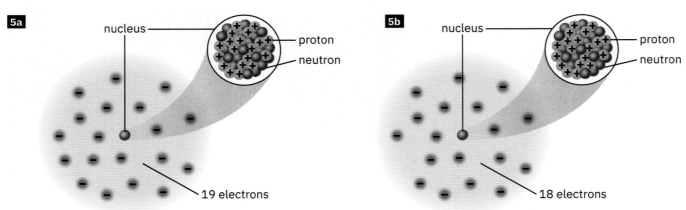

TABLE 5-2. Important Ions in the Human Body

Ion	Function
Ca^{2+}	formation of bones and teeth; muscle contraction; blood clotting
Cl^-	component of gastric juices; regulation of body fluids
Fe^{2+}	component of hemoglobin; role in oxygen transfer
H^+	blood pH control; formation of ATP
K^+	nerve impulses
Mg^{2+}	component of bones and teeth; muscle and nerve function
Na^+	water balance; nerve impulses
Zn^{2+}	role in cell division; growth; healing

Ions have a major role in living systems. **Table 5-2** lists some of the important ions in the human body and provides a short summary of their functions.

Bonds Between Atoms

In Chapter 2, you learned that atoms bond to form molecules such as water and carbon dioxide, and that **chemical bonds** are formed or broken in chemical reactions. The bonding properties of an atom arise from the behavior of its charged particles in the presence of other atoms.

The electrons moving around the nucleus of an atom have energy. The amount of energy an electron has depends on how far it is from the nucleus. When atoms are close to each other, the outermost electrons participate in forming chemical bonds.

Covalent Bonding Two atoms form a **covalent bond** by sharing electrons. In this type of bond, an outermost electron spends some time in the cloud around its nucleus and some time in the cloud around the other nucleus. The two atoms in hydrogen gas (H_2), nitrogen gas (N_2), or oxygen gas (O_2) are bound together covalently to form molecules, as shown with hydrogen in **Figure 5-6**.

6a

H atom   **H atom**

6b

H₂ molecule

FIGURE 5-6
In individual hydrogen atoms, each atom's electron stays close to its nucleus (a). When two hydrogen atoms are close to one another, the attractive forces between each positively charged nucleus and the other atom's negatively charged electron become strong enough to bind the atoms together (b). As they move around, the two electrons spend most of their time in the space between the two nuclei, forming a covalent bond.

Atoms of different elements have different tendencies to attract electrons to themselves, so the electron will spend more time around the nucleus of the atom that is more attractive. **Figure 5-7** shows how atoms of two different elements share electrons.

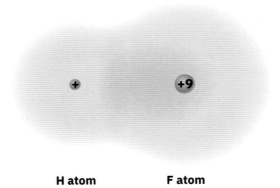

H atom   **F atom**

Elements also differ in the number of outermost electrons they have available to form bonds. **Table 5-3** shows the number of covalent bonds the most biologically important atoms can form with other atoms in a molecule.

TABLE 5-3. Number of Bonds Formed by Essential Elements

Atom		Symbol	Number of bonds
carbon	●	C	4
hydrogen	○	H	1
oxygen	●	O	2
nitrogen	●	N	3

SEP **Develop a Model** *According to **Table 5-3**, a carbon atom forms four bonds and a hydrogen atom forms one bond. How many of each of these atoms could form a neutral molecule? Sketch the molecule.*

Ionic Bonding If two atoms differ very greatly in their tendency to attract electrons, one or more of the outermost electrons in the less attractive atom's cloud can transfer entirely to the more attractive atom's cloud. This results in two ions: the atom that lost electrons now has a positive charge, and the atom that gained electrons has a negative charge. The force of attraction between these oppositely charged ions forms an **ionic bond**. For example, the compound NaCl, or table salt, is held together by ionic bonds between a positive sodium ion (Na^+) and a negative chloride ion (Cl^-).

An ionic bond can also form between an atom and a group of atoms, or between two groups of atoms. Some common ions formed by groups of atoms are ammonium (NH_4^+) and phosphate (PO_4^{3-}).

Chemical Bonds and Energy When the electrons in two atoms move to form a chemical bond, energy is released. Conversely, energy is required to break a chemical bond. The amount of energy needed to break a bond depends on the type of bond and which elements form the bond.

Attractions Between Molecules

Molecules can be attracted to each other as well. Attractive forces between molecules vary in strength. You have seen changes in these forces when you observe water melting or freezing. At low temperatures, water molecules are held close together in a repeating structure to form ice. As the temperature increases, the forces between the molecules become weaker, allowing them to move around as a liquid. Increasing the temperature even more makes the molecules move faster and farther apart until the forces between them are insignificant. The water thus takes the form of a gas.

Polarity Electronegativity is a measure of an atom's attraction for the electrons in covalent bonds. When the atoms in a molecule have similar electronegativity, the electrons are shared equally and the molecule is referred to as **nonpolar**. The electrons are shared equally in the covalent bonds of the hydrogen gas H_2 and oxygen gas O_2, for example, so both molecules are completely nonpolar.

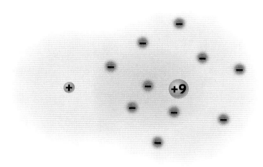

FIGURE 5-8
The hydrogen end of a hydrogen fluoride molecule has a net positive charge due to the relative lack of electrons around the positively charged H nucleus. Likewise, the fluorine end of the molecule has a net negative charge.

Many other atoms form similar bonds. However, they share unequally, with one atom having a greater "pull" than the other and thus an unequal pull on shared electrons. When two different elements, such as hydrogen and fluorine, have different electronegativity values, they do not share electrons equally, as shown in **Figure 5-8**. The part of the molecule that is more attractive to electrons will act as a center of negative charge, and the part that is less attractive to electrons will act as a center of positive charge. Such a molecule is referred to as being **polar**.

Water molecules are polar due to their shape. **Figure 5-9** shows the bent shape of a water molecule (H_2O), in which the two hydrogen atoms are closer together on one side of the oxygen atom. The oxygen atom attracts the hydrogen electrons toward itself so that, effectively, the hydrogen ends of the molecule are slightly positively charged and the oxygen end is slightly negatively charged.

FIGURE 5-9
The bent shape of a water molecule results in a center of positive charge toward the hydrogen atoms and a center of negative charge toward the oxygen atom.

Hydrogen Bonding The elements fluorine, oxygen, and nitrogen are the most highly attractive to electrons. When a polar molecule includes hydrogen bonded to one of these atoms, the F, O, or N atom also attracts the H electrons in nearby molecules to hold the substance together. The force of attraction between a hydrogen atom in one molecule and a highly attractive atom in another molecule is called a **hydrogen bond**. Because hydrogen atoms are very small compared to other elements, the hydrogen end of a molecule can come very close to the positively charged side of the other molecule to which its electron is attracted. The small distance between atoms makes the forces between their molecules stronger (**Figure 5-10**).

SEP Construct an Explanation *Would you expect water molecules to form hydrogen bonds? Explain your answer.*

FIGURE 5-10 ▶
Hydrogen bonds form between atoms of different polar molecules.

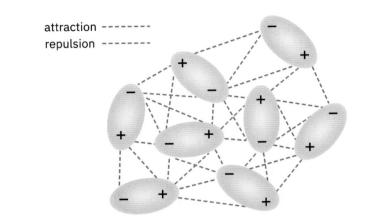

attraction - - - - - - - -
repulsion - - - - - - - -

5.1 REVIEW

1. **Calculate** An oxygen atom has 8 protons, 8 electrons, and 8 neutrons. What is the charge of an oxygen atom? What charge does the nucleus have?

2. **Compare** In the nitrogen cycle, bacteria in plant roots convert atmospheric nitrogen (N_2) into ammonia (NH_3), which is then converted into ammonium (NH_4^+) by bacteria living in the soil. Which statement explains a difference between ammonia and ammonium?

   A. Ammonia has fewer protons than ammonium.

   B. Ammonia has more electrons than ammonium.

   C. Ammonia has fewer neutrons than ammonium.

   D. Ammonia has more bonds than ammonium.

3. **Relate** What specific role does the energy from sunlight play in rearranging atoms during photosynthesis?

4. **Model** A molecule of pentane is made up of 5 carbon atoms and 12 hydrogen atoms. Use the information in **Table 5-3** to sketch a model of a pentane molecule.

WATER

Scientists looking for life on planets, asteroids, and moons often search for signs of water. For example, they have found frozen water and evidence of past water flow on Mars. They study these sites in hopes of finding additional evidence that organisms lived there in the past or exist there now.

Infer *Why do you think finding water on other worlds would be an important sign of potential life?*

KEY TERMS

acid
base
pH
solution

Properties of Water

The unique properties of water make life on Earth possible. Scientific theories of how the first cells formed all involve water, which is present in all living organisms and is thus a fundamental resource in any ecosystem. The hydrogen bonds between its molecules give water many characteristics that are crucial to sustaining life.

FIGURE 5-11
A seal pup pokes its head into the water below a layer of ice.

States of Water Water is the only substance that is present in solid, liquid, and gas states under the temperatures and pressures typically found on Earth. Due to strong hydrogen bonds, the temperature of water changes much more slowly than almost all other common substances when heated. You see this on a lake in the summer. The air temperature will be hot, but the lake will remain cool, and vice-versa in the winter. Water's ability to resist rapid changes in temperature maintains stable conditions in aquatic ecosystems and within the cells of organisms. A lot of energy is needed to break the hydrogen bonds between molecules as water changes in state from liquid to gas.

ice

liquid water

water vapor

FIGURE 5-12
The molecules in ice are farther apart than they are in liquid water. In water vapor, the gaseous form of water, the water molecules are very much farther apart than they are in liquid water.

Density Unlike almost all other substances, liquid water decreases in density as the temperature drops. In the liquid state, the small size of the hydrogen atoms allows water molecules to be close together, as shown in **Figure 5-12**, but the molecules move without any particular pattern. At 0 °C, the molecules settle into a crystal structure in which the hydrogen bonds hold them farther apart. Thus, the solid form of water is less dense than the liquid form, which is why ice floats on water.

SEP **Construct an Explanation** *Why would the facts that water changes temperature slowly and that ice floats in water be essential to the survival of aquatic organisms?*

Cohesion and Adhesion When it rains on a leaf, the water tends to bead up and stick together (**Figure 5-13**). Molecules of some substances resist separating from one another, a property called *cohesion*. Water has cohesion because hydrogen bonds collectively exert a continuous pull on its individual molecules. You can observe cohesion as surface tension, where the surface of liquid water behaves a bit like an elastic sheet.

Similarly, water molecules are attracted to molecules of other substances. This property is called *adhesion*. Cohesion and adhesion drive many processes that sustain multicellular bodies. Inside a plant, water molecules pull on each other and adhere to the walls of narrow pipelines of tissue, enabling columns of water to rise from the roots to the leaves. In some trees, these pipelines extend more than 50 meters above the soil.

FIGURE 5-13
Water forms droplets on the surface of a leaf due to cohesion.

Polarity and Solubility The fact that water molecules are highly polar gives rise to another property that is important in life processes. Opposite charges attract, so if another substance made of polar molecules is placed in water, the positively charged (H) ends of the water molecules attract the negatively charged ends of the other polar molecules. Likewise, the negatively charged (O) ends of the water molecules attract the positively charged ends of the other polar molecules. In water, this attraction is often strong enough to pull those other polar molecules apart, dissolving the substance. A *solvent* is a substance in which another substance, called the *solute*, is dissolved. The mixture of the two substances is called a **solution**. Water is called the "universal solvent" because it dissolves so many other substances (**Figure 5-14**).

Nonpolar molecules, however, do not have different charge distributions at the ends, so they cannot be easily pulled apart by water molecules. To remember this, we say that "like dissolves like." Polar substances can dissolve other polar substances, but a polar substance cannot dissolve a nonpolar substance. For example, oil separates in a layer on top of water.

FIGURE 5-14 ▽
A butterfly perches on a black caiman's eyelid to drink its tears, which contain nutrients dissolved in their water.

Acids and Bases

Recall that when a hydrogen atom is covalently bonded to another atom that strongly attracts electrons, the hydrogen's electron is pulled slightly away from its proton. Hydrogen bonding in water can pull that proton right off the molecule. The detached proton is called a hydrogen ion (H^+). The electron stays with the rest of the molecule, making it a negatively charged ion. For example, a water molecule that loses a proton becomes a hydroxide ion (OH^-). The loss is more or less temporary, because these two ions easily get back together to form a water molecule.

An **acid** is a substance that gives up hydrogen ions in water. By contrast, a **base** is a substance that accepts hydrogen ions in water. Many organisms and biological processes are sensitive to how acidic or basic the surrounding solution is.

We use a value called **pH** as a measure of the relative amounts of H⁺ and OH⁻ ions present in a water-based solution. If a solution has an equal number of H⁺ and OH⁻ ions, its pH is 7 (or neutral). Pure water is neutral. A solution that has more H⁺ ions than OH⁻ ions is acidic, and its pH is less than 7. Conversely, a solution with fewer H⁺ ions than OH⁻ ions is basic, with a pH greater than 7. The pH values of several common substances are shown in **Figure 5-15**.

Acids can be strong or weak. Strong acids ionize completely in water to give up all of their H⁺ ions. Hydrochloric acid (HCl) is an example. When HCl dissolves in water, all of the molecules give up H⁺ ions, leaving Cl⁻ ions behind. The H⁺ released from HCl makes gastric fluid in your stomach very acidic (pH 1–2). By contrast, weak acids do not ionize completely in water. Carbonic acid (H_2CO_3) is an example. It forms when carbon dioxide gas dissolves in plasma, the fluid portion of human blood. Carbonic acid is a weak acid, so only some of its molecules give up a hydrogen ion in water. When carbonic acid loses a hydrogen ion, it becomes an ionic molecule called bicarbonate.

Together, carbonic acid and bicarbonate form a buffer. A buffer is a set of chemicals that can keep the pH of a solution stable by alternately donating and accepting ions that contribute to pH. The addition of too much acid or base can overwhelm a buffer's capacity to stabilize pH. This outcome is catastrophic in a cell or body because most biological molecules function properly only within a narrow range of pH. A slight deviation from that range can halt cellular processes.

FIGURE 5-15 ▽
As shown on this pH scale, acidic substances have pH values less than 7, and basic substances have pH values greater than 7.

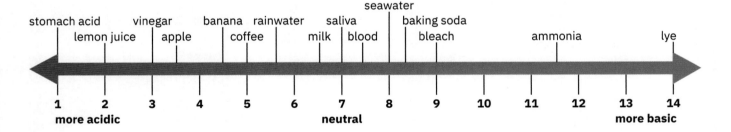

5.2 REVIEW

1. **Sequence** List the three states of water in order from least dense to most dense.

2. **Infer** Sugar dissolves easily in water. What property does this fact demonstrate?

   A. Sugar is acidic.

   B. Sugar has ionic bonds.

   C. Sugar molecules are polar.

   D. Sugar is more dense than water.

3. **Explain** Use the properties of water to explain why when it rains on a road, a layer of gasoline from the road's surface will float on top of a puddle of rainwater.

4. **Infer** Which property of water allows it to be sucked up from a glass into a straw?

   A. It has cohesion.

   B. Its pH is slightly basic.

   C. It resists rapid changes in temperature.

   D. It is less dense as a gas than as a liquid.

POLAR VS. NONPOLAR MOLECULES

SEP **Plan and Conduct an Investigation** How can you determine if a substance is polar or nonpolar?

Water is often called the "universal solvent." In this activity, you will conduct an experiment that uses this property of water to determine whether the molecules of other common substances are polar or nonpolar. You will determine each substance's polarity by mixing it with water and observing the result.

Materials

- **test tubes with rubber stoppers or caps (5)**
- **test tube rack**
- **labels (5)**
- **marker**
- **distilled water, 50 mL**
- **10-mL graduated cylinder**
- **substances to test for polarity (5)**
- **pipet or dropper for each liquid substance**
- **spoon spatula for each solid substance**
- **timer**

Safety

Procedure

1. Obtain the distilled water and the substances to test from your teacher. Label each test tube with the name of each substance.

2. Determine how you will be able to tell whether each substance is polar or nonpolar. Record your criteria.

3. Predict whether each substance is polar or nonpolar. Record your predictions.

4. Use the graduated cylinder to measure and pour 10 mL of water into each test tube.

5. To test a liquid substance, add 10 drops of the substance to the water in one of the test tubes. Place the stopper on the test tube. Mix the contents by shaking or swirling the tube for 20 seconds. Observe the results. Return the test tube to the rack.

6. To test a solid substance, use a spatula to add a pea-sized sample to the water in one of the test tubes. Place the stopper on the test tube. Mix the contents by shaking or swirling the tube. Observe the results. Place the test tube back in the holder.

7. When you have tested all five substances, dispose of the mixtures as instructed by your teacher. Be sure to wash your hands with soap and water after you are done.

Results and Analysis

1. **Interpret Data** How do the results of your tests indicate whether a substance is polar or nonpolar? Did your results match your predictions? Justify your answer.

2. **Explain** Use what you know about the structure of water molecules to explain why water is useful for testing the polarity of other substances.

3. **Apply** Which of your substances are nonpolar? How would you confirm this result using a different solvent?

4. **Draw Conclusions** Some substances only partially dissolve in water. For example, when whole milk is mixed with water, it appears diluted and lighter in color. What might this tell you about this substance?

5.3

KEY TERMS

amino acid lipid
ATP monomer
carbohydrate nucleotide
cellulose nucleic acid
DNA polymer
glucose protein
glycogen starch

CARBON-BASED MOLECULES

The tastes and textures of food that you eat depend largely on the presence of certain molecules. Fruit tastes sweet because it contains sugar molecules, and cellulose molecules make raw vegetables crunchy. The molecular makeup of a substance also determines whether or not an animal can digest it. Cows and goats can digest grass, but humans cannot. Many animals try to eat plastic, but their digestive systems cannot break it down.

Infer *Both sugar and plastic consist mainly of carbon, hydrogen, and oxygen atoms. Why do you think sugar and plastic have very different properties even though they are made of the same elements?*

Elements of Life

Organisms exchange matter and energy with the environment as they grow, maintain themselves, and reproduce. All organisms take up carbon compounds from the environment and use them to build the molecules of life. These molecules are eventually broken down, and their parts are cycled back to the environment in by-products, wastes, and remains. Biological molecules are made of carbon, hydrogen, nitrogen, and other elements, with the key element being carbon. Its ability to form four bonds makes carbon an ideal building block for a vast assortment of molecules. In many ways, the chemistry of carbon is the chemistry of life itself.

Compounds that consist mainly of carbon and hydrogen are called *organic compounds*. Except for water, virtually all of the important compounds in the body of any organism are organic compounds.

FIGURE 5-16 ▽
Open-air landfills in the Iberian Peninsula attract migrating white storks during winter. Although these dump sites provide ample food, some storks also ingest plastic,. Although made mainly of carbon, plastic supplies little to no energy and can damage their internal organs.

Building Blocks of Organic Molecules

The molecules of life are assembled from simpler organic subunits called **monomers**. These building blocks combine to form sugars, fatty acids, amino acids, and nucleotides. A molecule that consists of repeated monomers is a **polymer**.

Many biological molecules, such as carbohydrates, lipids, proteins, and nucleic acids, are very large polymers consisting of thousands of subunits. The structure and function of a biological molecule arises from (and depends on) the order, orientation, and interactions of its subunits.

Hydrocarbons Some of the most common organic polymers are *hydrocarbons*, substances made entirely of carbon and hydrogen. Because a carbon atom can form four covalent bonds, it can join atoms into long chains of repeating structures that feature single, double, or triple covalent bonds. Petroleum, a fossil fuel, is made of hydrocarbons. Gasoline is made from petroleum. Octane, shown in **Figure 5-17**, is one of the compounds in gasoline.

hydrocarbon chain

carbon atom

hydrogen atom

FIGURE 5-17
An octane molecule consists of eight carbon atoms linked in a chain, with 18 hydrogen atoms completing the remaining available bonds.

By themselves, hydrocarbon chains are not very reactive, but they can be made into much more reactive substances by adding functional groups. A *functional group* is a group of atoms that, when added to a hydrocarbon, gives the compound a particular property. Most of the functional groups found in biological molecules contain oxygen or nitrogen, which makes them polar. For example, adding a hydroxyl (—OH) group to the end of a hydrocarbon chain turns it into an alcohol. Carboxyl (—COOH) groups make a molecule into an acid (**Figure 5-18**).

hydroxyl group

carboxyl group

ethanol

acetic acid (vinegar)

FIGURE 5-18
Replacing a hydrogen atom at the end of a short hydrocarbon chain with an oxygen and hydrogen (hydroxyl) group gives the two ends of the molecule different structures. The resulting alcohol molecule is polar. A carboxyl group attached to a hydrocarbon chain makes it polar and acidic.

SEP **Construct an Explanation** *Would you expect a hydrocarbon such as octane to dissolve in water? Why or why not?*

Carbohydrates

Carbohydrates are organic compounds that consist of carbon, hydrogen, and oxygen. Cells use various types of carbohydrates as structural materials and for storing energy. These compounds are oxidized (burned) in the process of cellular metabolism, which releases the energy that organisms need to survive. Think of carbohydrates as fuels that, like gasoline for a car, keep an organism going. Carbohydrates also make up the backbone of **DNA**, the hereditary material in every cell.

Simple Sugars **Glucose** and fructose molecules are the building blocks of the most common carbohydrates. Monomers such as these two molecules are *monosaccharides*. Monosaccharides are often called simple sugars because they are the simplest carbohydrate, and many of them have a sweet taste. Simple sugars have a backbone of five or six carbon atoms and include two or more hydroxyl (—OH) groups.

The —OH functional groups make sugar molecules polar, so they can dissolve and move easily through the water-based internal environments of all organisms. In water, simple sugar molecules form ring-shaped structures such as the ones in **Figure 5-19**.

FIGURE 5-19
Sugar monomers have rings of six atoms, like glucose (a), or five atoms, like fructose (b). When a sugar monomer is incorporated into the structure of a larger molecule, it is often represented using a hexagon or a pentagon.

glucose

fructose

Simple sugars have extremely important biological roles. Bonds in glucose molecules are broken during chemical processes that cells use to release energy. That energy is then used to power other reactions. Simple sugars are also remodeled into other molecules or used as structural materials to build organic polymers.

SEP **Construct an Explanation** *Why are simple sugars a good source of quick energy?*

Complex Carbohydrates Complex carbohydrates are chains of hundreds to thousands of sugar monomers. The most common *polysaccharides*—cellulose, starch, and glycogen—all consist only of glucose monomers, but as substances their properties are very different because of differences in the bonding patterns that link their monomers.

Cellulose is the most abundant organic molecule on Earth. It is the major structural material of plants (Chapter 9), forming tough fibers that act like reinforcing rods inside stems and other plant parts (**Figure 5-20**). Cellulose does not dissolve in water, and it is not easily broken down. Some bacteria and fungi can break it apart into its component sugars, but humans and other mammals cannot. Dietary fiber, or "roughage," usually refers to the indigestible cellulose in our vegetable foods.

BACTERIA IN YOUR GUT

Gather Evidence *Why might the relationship between bacteria and humans be described as symbiotic?*

FIGURE 5-20
Cellulose is a polymer made of long straight chains of glucose monomers. The chains are joined parallel to each other by hydrogen bonds.

In **starch**, different bonding patterns between glucose monomers can make a chain that coils up into a spiral (**Figure 5-21**) or form a branched pattern of chains. Starch does not dissolve readily in water, but it is easier to break down than cellulose. These properties make starch ideal for storing sugars in the watery interiors of plant cells.

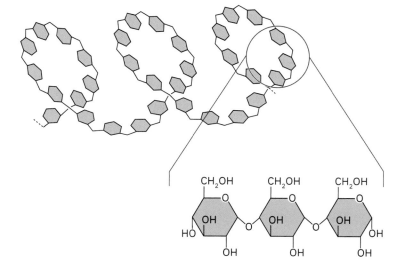

FIGURE 5-21
Amylose, a type of polymer in starch, forms tightly packed spirals that resist being broken down.

CHAPTER INVESTIGATION

Converting Carbohydrates
How does salivary amylase affect the carbohydrates in our food?

Go online to explore this chapter's hands-on investigation about simple sugars and starches.

Animals store sugars in the form of **glycogen**, a polysaccharide that consists of highly branched chains of glucose monomers (**Figure 5-22**). Muscle and liver cells contain most of the body's glycogen.

FIGURE 5-22
Chains of glucose form branches in a glycogen structure. Although it is commonly called "animal starch," glycogen is also found in bacteria and fungi.

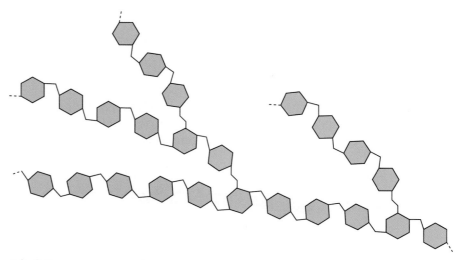

Lipids

Lipids are a group of fatty, oily, or waxy organic compounds that are similar to carbohydrates in many ways. Like carbohydrates, lipids are composed mainly of carbon, hydrogen, and oxygen atoms. Energy storage is one of their primary functions. Lipid molecules vary in structure, but all are partly or completely nonpolar. They are typically made up of one or more hydrocarbon chains that attach to a single, small functional group that includes oxygen.

Fatty Acids Many lipids incorporate *fatty acids*—organic molecules with a carboxyl (—COOH) functional group "head" and a long hydrocarbon "tail" that varies in length (**Figure 5-23**). The tail is nonpolar (fatty), and the head is polar (acid). This gives the two ends of a fatty acid molecule different properties. You are already familiar with these properties, because these molecules are the main component of soap. The nonpolar tails attract oily dirt, and the polar heads attract the dirt to water.

FIGURE 5-23
Stearic acid is a fatty acid that is commonly found in animal fats.

polar functional group
(carboxyl group)   long hydrocarbon chain

Phospholipids One class of biologically essential lipid molecules is the phospholipid, which is characterized by two fatty acid tails joined by a polar head that includes a functional group called a *phosphate group*. The phosphate group consists of a phosphorus atom bonded to four oxygen atoms. Some of the oxygen atoms are not bonded to anything else, making this end of the phospholipid molecule polar and negatively charged. Phosphate groups are found in several types of biological molecules.

In water, phospholipids tend to arrange themselves in layers in which the fatty acid ends face toward each other and the heads face away from each other. This configuration, shown in **Figure 5-24**, is called a phospholipid bilayer. Phospholipid bilayers play an important role in cell structures.

SEP **Construct an Explanation** *Why do you think phospholipid molecules form a phospholipid bilayer in water?*

Nucleotides and Nucleic Acids

You have learned that deoxyribonucleic acid (DNA) molecules carry the genetic instructions for life. The building blocks of these molecules are monomers called nucleotides.

Nucleotide Structure A **nucleotide** consists of a monosaccharide (simple sugar) ring bonded to a nitrogen-containing base and one, two, or three phosphate groups. Nucleotides can act as individual molecules or as monomers that link to form **nucleic acids**.

FIGURE 5-25
In a nucleotide, the phosphate groups are bonded to one of the carbon atoms in the sugar. The base, a group of atoms that form one or two flat rings, is bonded to another of the sugar's carbon atoms.

The **ATP** (adenosine triphosphate) nucleotide, shown in **Figure 5-25**, has a simple sugar component of ribose, three phosphate groups, and a base called adenine. This important molecule carries energy during cellular processes by transferring a phosphate group to another molecule. Removing one of the three phosphate groups from an ATP nucleotide turns it into an ADP (adenosine diphosphate) nucleotide.

Nucleic Acids The molecules that contain the genetic information that determines the makeup of the proteins in all of an organism's cells are polymers of nucleotides. In an individual DNA (deoxyribonucleic acid) nucleotide, the sugar component is deoxyribose, and there are three phosphate groups. The nitrogenous base can be one of four types

- adenine (A)
- cytosine (C)
- thymine (T)
- guanine (G)

FIGURE 5-26
Two complementary strands of nucleotide monomers are held together by hydrogen bonds between the nucleotides' bases to form a DNA molecule.

DNA structure

nucleotide

sugar-phosphate backbone

hydrogen bonds

nitrogenous base

base pairs

sugar-phosphate backbone

sugar

covalent bonds

phosphate group

DNA strands

Go Online	SIMULATION

Building Complex Molecules Go online to use atoms to assemble polymers such as DNA.

In a DNA molecule, adenine pairs with thymine, and cytosine pairs with guanine. Millions of DNA nucleotides linked together comprise a strand of DNA. The backbone of the strand is made of the sugars and phosphate groups in the nucleotides, as shown in **Figure 5-26**. Two such strands coiled in a shape called a double helix form a DNA molecule. The information coded in a DNA molecule lies in the sequence of the four nucleotide bases.

RNA (ribonucleic acid) is the nucleic acid that translates the DNA code into amino acids (and ultimately proteins). It is similar to DNA but it has a different sugar, ribose, rather than deoxyribose, and it uses the nitrogenous base uracil (U) instead of thymine. In an RNA molecule, adenine pairs with uracil, and cytosine pairs with guanine.

CCC **Structure and Function** *How are a complex carbohydrate molecule and a DNA molecule similar? How are they different?*

Amino Acids and Proteins

Proteins perform thousands of different functions in living things. Some proteins are enzymes, molecules that drive all chemical reactions that take place inside a cell. Structural proteins support cell parts and multicellular bodies. Muscle tissue, for example, is made almost entirely of protein. Proteins transport substances, help cells communicate, and defend the body. They also regulate genes. Every cell in your body contains exactly the same genes, but only a subset of genes are active in certain cell types at specific points in time. Proteins turn these genes on and off to control the processes and behaviors that a cell exhibits.

Amino Acids An **amino acid** is a small organic compound with an amine group ($-NH_2$), a carboxyl group ($-COOH$, the acid), and a side chain called an R group. A few amino acids also include a sulfhydryl group ($-SH$). In most amino acids, all three groups are attached to the same carbon atom (**Figure 5-27**). Cells make the thousands of different proteins they need from only 20 types of amino acid monomers. Each type of amino acid has a different R group.

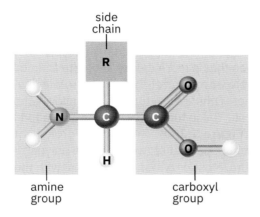

FIGURE 5-27 Amino acids vary by the side chain they contain, but all amino acids have an amine group and a carboxyl group.

Protein Structure A **protein** is made up of a chain of amino acids. Proteins are built brick by brick, amino acid by amino acid. The covalent bond that links amino acids in a protein is called a peptide bond. The order of the amino acids is called the protein's primary structure (**Figure 5-28**). Each type of protein has a unique primary structure.

> **CCC** **Patterns** *A gene is a DNA sequence that carries instructions for making a protein. What characteristic do DNA and protein structures have in common that could explain this relationship?*

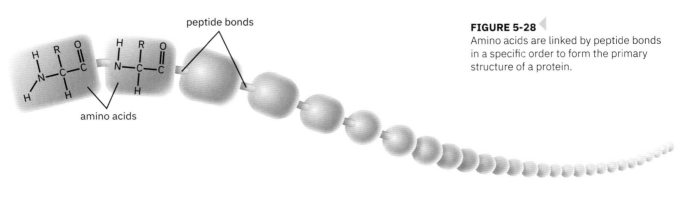

FIGURE 5-28 Amino acids are linked by peptide bonds in a specific order to form the primary structure of a protein.

A long chain of amino acids joined by peptide bonds is known as a polypeptide chain. As amino acids are added to a polypeptide chain, the chain curls up, bending and twisting as hydrogen bonds form between the amino acids. The hydrogen bonds pull sections of the polypeptide chain into characteristic patterns such as coils, as shown in **Figure 5-29,** or sheets connected by flexible loops and tight turns. These patterns are the protein's secondary structure. Almost all proteins have similar patterns in their secondary structures.

FIGURE 5-29 ▶
Hydrogen bonds occur between parts of a growing polypeptide chain to form its secondary structure.

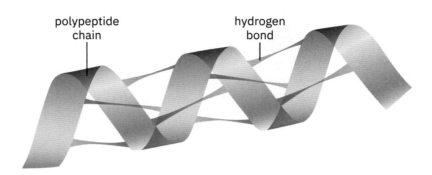

polypeptide chain

hydrogen bond

Hydrogen bonding and other interactions between coils and sheets can make them fold up into compact shapes. Each of these shapes has a particular function that is more or less separate from the rest of the protein. For example, some barrel-like shapes rotate like motors in small molecular machines. Others form tunnels that allow substances to move into and out of a cell. These functional shapes are called the protein's tertiary structure (**Figure 5-30a**). They make a protein into a working molecule. Proteins that consist of two ore more polypeptide chains have a quaternary structure. Most enzymes are like this, with multiple polypeptide chains that collectively form a roughly spherical shape (**Figure 5-30b**).

FIGURE 5-30 ▶
Proteins with compact tertiary structures have shapes that perform specific functions (a). Proteins made from two or more polypeptide chains have a quaternary structure (b).

30a

30b

chain 2   chain 1

5.3 REVIEW

1. **Distinguish** Give an example of an organic molecule that is not a hydrocarbon.

2. **Classify** Label the molecules as simple sugars or complex carbohydrates: cellulose, fructose, glucose, sucrose.

3. **Explain** Why are carbohydrates soluble in water while lipids are not?

4. **Model** Draw one amino acid using the given components. Not all components need to be used.

- CH
- CH_2OH
- CH_3
- COOH
- NH_2

NATIONAL GEOGRAPHIC EXPLORER **ROSA VÁSQUEZ ESPINOZA**

SURVIVAL MECHANISMS AND NEW MEDICINES

Dr. Rosa Vásquez Espinoza explores microorganisms in the Peruvian Amazon. She is studying their survival mechanisms to determine how those processes can be engineered to develop new natural medicinal products.

▶ **VIDEO 5-1** Go online to watch Vásquez Espinoza and a team of researchers gather sample organisms in the Boiling River ecosystem.

Inspired by her grandmother's knowledge of traditional medicines made from plants, herbs, and soils, chemical biologist Dr. Rosa Vásquez Espinoza grew up wondering how nature produces these powerful compounds. Her scientific search has led her to the Boiling River in the Peruvian Amazon. She steps carefully along the steamy banks of the river—one slip into its 99.1 °C waters could render third-degree burns.

Vásquez Espinoza stoops to scrape lichens off the side of a rocky ledge into a jar. Next, she dips a heat resistant test tube into the scalding water to gather cyanobacteria. She then moves upriver, where the water is a bit cooler, to harvest a sample of a microbial mat from the river bottom. She also takes samples of sediments that contain large populations of bacteria. After dinner, the team will set up a microscope and begin analyzing the samples. If one looks especially interesting, they will return to that area the next day to collect more samples.

Vásquez Espinoza thinks the bacteria produce unique molecules that protect them from the high temperatures of their habitats. She hypothesizes that because they enable microorganisms to survive under stressful conditions, these molecules may be engineered into medicines to fight bacterial, fungal, or viral infections, and even cancers. In the laboratory, Vásquez Espinoza also looks at enzymes, molecules that regulate chemical reactions in the organisms, to try to pinpoint substances that have therapeutic properties. Understanding how microorganisms produce these substances may allow scientists to develop sustainable processes for manufacturing and refining them for use as pharmaceutical drugs. In addition, these enzymes' ability to withstand a wide range of temperatures could make them useful for reducing negative environmental impacts of industrial processes that generate toxic waste and pollution.

"If this is possible now, what can we achieve in the next 10 to 20 years?" asks Vásquez Espinoza. "How many more bacteria can we find in our planet that can help make our lives better and also help us protect nature itself? How is it possible that we can go to the moon and don't know fully yet what's at the microbial level in our planet?"

THINKING CRITICALLY

Relate *Enzymes are made of amino acids. How does this information support the hypothesis that enzymes found in the Boiling River microbes could also work in medicines for humans or animals?*

CHEMICAL REACTIONS

Humans have discovered that when we cook food, its flavor and texture change in ways that make it tastier and easier to digest. Many fruits and vegetables can be eaten raw, but some foods should not be eaten without cooking them. For example, plants such as green potatoes, lima and red kidney beans, and cassava naturally contain toxic compounds that are broken down by heat.

Explain *How do you think cooking a food source changes it into a different substance?*

Chemical Reactions in Biological Systems

All biological systems and processes involve changes in matter and energy. At a molecular level, these changes occur during chemical reactions. A **chemical reaction** is a process in which substances change into different substances through the breaking and forming of chemical bonds. Depending on the specific substances involved, this whole process absorbs or releases energy.

Reactants and Products **Reactants** are substances that are the inputs of a chemical reaction. The outputs of the reaction are its **products**. Chemical bonds in the reactants are broken and new bonds form as the atoms are rearranged to make the products. For example, as shown in **Figure 5-31**, by breaking the bonds between carbon and oxygen atoms, the atoms from glucose and fructose molecules can be reassembled to produce sucrose and water.

 VIDEO

VIDEO 5-2 Go online to see how bonds in glucose and fructose molecules are broken to recombine atoms in a chemical reaction.

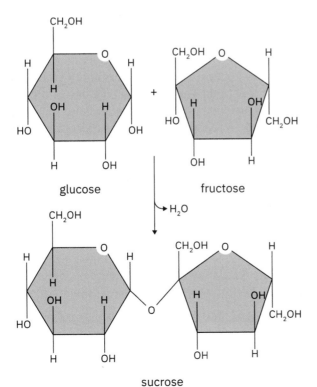

glucose   fructose

H₂O

sucrose

FIGURE 5-31
The simple sugars glucose and fructose react to form a sucrose molecule and a water molecule. Sucrose is found in the roots, fruits, and nectar of plants. It is also known as table sugar.

VIDEO

VIDEO 5-3 Go online to see how methane and oxygen react to form carbon dioxide and water.

Conservation of Matter By now, you have seen the chemical formulas for several compounds, such as water (H_2O), carbon dioxide (CO_2), and oxygen gas (O_2). The letters in these chemical formulas indicate the elements that make up a compound, and the subscript numbers to the right of each element are the number of atoms of that element in the compound. (If there is no number after an element, there is only one atom of that element.) Not only do chemical formulas describe exactly what constitutes a specific compound, but these formulas also provide a useful way to keep track of what happens to matter that undergoes a chemical reaction.

In a chemical reaction, matter is conserved. Although the products are different compounds from the reactants, no new matter is created, and no matter is destroyed. The total number of atoms of each element in the products is the same as the total number of atoms of each element in the reactant. This fact enables us to predict what the products of a reaction between specific reactants might be.

When a substance such as wood or coal is burned, a chemical reaction occurs between the oxygen in the air and one or more of the compounds in the substance, releasing energy in the form of light and heat. Methane (CH_4) is a hydrocarbon compound found in natural gas. When a compound that consists of only carbon and hydrogen is burned in oxygen (O_2), the products must be made of only carbon, hydrogen, and oxygen atoms. As shown in **Figure 5-32**, these products are water (H_2O) and carbon dioxide (CO_2).

FIGURE 5-32
One methane molecule reacts with two oxygen molecules to form one carbon dioxide molecule and two water molecules. An arrow pointing from the reactants to the products is used to indicate that a chemical reaction changes the reactants to the products.

$$CH_4 \qquad 2\,O_2 \qquad CO_2 \qquad 2\,H_2O$$

For matter to be conserved, each individual atom of the reactants must become part of the products, and the products cannot include atoms that were not part of the reactants. During a reaction, one or more reactants become one or more products. Intermediate molecules may form between reactants and products. A reaction is shown as an equation in which an arrow points from reactants to products:

$$CH_4 + 2O_2 \rightarrow CO_2 + 2H_2O$$

A number before a chemical formula in such equations indicates the number of molecules. (If there is only one of a given molecule, the 1 is not shown.) A subscript indicates the number of atoms of that element per molecule. For example, in one molecule of CH_4, there is one carbon atom and four hydrogen atoms. Note that atoms shuffle around in a reaction, but they never disappear. A balanced chemical equation shows that the same number of atoms that enter a reaction remain at the reaction's end.

CCC **Scale, Proportion, and Quantity** *The chemical formula for glucose is $C_6H_{12}O_6$. If a glucose molecule reacts with six oxygen (O_2) molecules, how many carbon dioxide molecules and how many water molecules are produced?*

Energy in Chemical Processes

Cells store energy by building large organic molecules such as polysaccharides, lipids, and proteins from smaller components. The energy of these molecules is released in chemical reactions and used to power life processes such as cell division and growth.

Activation Energy All chemical reactions need an input of energy to break bonds in the reactants. The amount of energy required to start a chemical reaction is called its **activation energy**. For example, in the process of photosynthesis, sunlight provides the activation energy to begin a series of reactions that convert reactants, including carbon dioxide and water, into the products, sugar and oxygen. Similarly, to burn a fuel such as wood, you first need to add energy in the form of heat to ignite the wood.

FIGURE 5-33 ▼
Whether they release or absorb energy, all chemical reactions require an input of activation energy to proceed.

33a **Endergonic Reaction**

Energy

activation energy

energy of products

energy absorbed

energy of reactants

Progress of Reaction

33b **Exergonic Reaction**

Energy

activation energy

energy of reactants

energy released

energy of products

Progress of Reaction

Endergonic and Exergonic Reactions An *endergonic* reaction or process is one in which energy is absorbed. In an endergonic chemical reaction, the total energy of the products is greater than the total energy of the reactants, as illustrated by the graph in **Figure 5-33a**. Photosynthesis is an endergonic process in which the leaves of a plant absorb solar energy to build sugar molecules (Section 6.3). Similarly, when you bake a cake, you add energy in the form of heat, which is absorbed by the reactants (the ingredients) to form a delicious new substance.

In an *exergonic* reaction or process, energy is released. The total energy of the products of an exergonic reaction is less than the total energy of the reactants, as illustrated by the graph in **Figure 5-33b**. Exergonic reactions occur spontaneously once their activation energy is reached. Burning wood is an exergonic process that releases energy in the form of heat and light. Cells use exergonic reactions to release the energy stored in molecules in the process of cellular respiration (Section 6.3).

CCC **Energy and Matter** *The chemical reaction in which glucose and fructose molecules combine to form sucrose is an example of a condensation reaction. Condensation reactions occur when a cell assembles a polysaccharide, such as cellulose, from glucose monomers. Would you expect the process of building a polysaccharide to be endergonic or exergonic? Explain.*

Conservation of Energy

Conservation of Energy Energy is neither created nor destroyed during a chemical reaction. The difference between the energy of the products and the energy of the reactants is equal to the amount of energy absorbed from some source outside the reaction system or released into the surroundings. During a reaction, energy can be transferred from one place to another or converted from one form to another. For example, some of the solar energy absorbed in a photosynthesis reaction is converted into chemical energy that is stored in glucose molecules.

Equilibrium

A mixture of two substances consists of many of both types of molecules randomly moving around near each other in the same space. For a chemical reaction to occur between the substances, the molecules must collide with each other with enough energy to break the chemical bonds that hold the atoms together. Then the atoms must come close enough to each other to form new chemical bonds. The rate of a chemical reaction is a measure of how frequently such collisions occur.

When there is a small energy difference between the products and the reactants, the reaction is reversible, meaning it can proceed in either direction. Under some conditions, more product molecules form. This is called a forward reaction. Under other conditions, more reactant molecules form. This is called a reverse reaction. When the random collisions between molecules produce the forward reaction and the reverse reaction at the same rates, the system is at **equilibrium**.

Rates of Biochemical Reactions

Most biological reactions need help to occur. For example, sucrose seems highly stable. It will sit in a box for years without breaking down spontaneously into glucose and fructose in an exergonic reaction. Cells store energy in organic molecules that are even larger than sucrose, but an organism does not have the time for the spontaneous breakdown of an organic molecule to occur when it needs this energy.

Catalysts A chemical reaction can be sped up by raising the temperature dramatically or changing the pH. However, these conditions are often unsafe or toxic to the organism or cells in which they would need to occur. Instead, cells use **catalysts**, molecules that increase the rate of a chemical reaction without being used up in the process. Catalysts do so by lowering the activation energy needed in the reaction (**Figure 5-34**).

CASE STUDY
TURNING MOLECULES INTO MEDICINE

Ask Questions *Generate a question about how equilibrium affects the process of making a naturally occurring compound in a laboratory.*

FIGURE 5-34 ▼
A catalyst speeds up a chemical reaction by lowering the amount of energy needed to activate the reaction. Catalyst molecules are not reactants. Once they have participated in a reaction between molecules, they can be used again for another reaction.

Enzymes and Substrates Biological catalysts are called **enzymes**. Some enzymes are nucleic acids, but most are proteins. The structure of an enzyme molecule enables its function.

Enzymes lower the activation energy of a reaction by providing pathways for molecules to interact more easily than they would have otherwise. An enzyme has one or more *active sites* on its surface that change their shape so that they can only bind to molecules that have a specific shape, size, polarity, and charge. A molecule that fits an enzyme's active site is called its **substrate**. Together, an enzyme and its substrate(s) form an *enzyme-substrate complex*.

enzyme

substrates

active sites position
the substrates

enzyme-substrate
complex forms

enzyme returns to original shape
and new products are released

In a solution containing randomly-moving molecules, the flexible shape of the enzyme-substrate complex can lower the energy required for substrates to react by bringing them closer to each other and orienting them in positions that favor the reaction, as shown in **Figure 5-35**. The active sites can also work to deform substrates in a way that breaks the bonds between their atoms. Enzymes can also control the rate or direction of a reaction by removing product or reactant molecules, specific substrates, or other molecules present in the solution, that may interfere with the reaction. Once an enzyme's active site releases its substrate, it returns to its original shape so that it can bind to another substrate.

FIGURE 5-35 ▲
An enzyme catalyzes the reaction between two substrates by positioning the substrates when they bind to its active sites, moving them together so that they can react, and releasing the product.

Most enzymes are highly specific and catalyze only a few closely related chemical reactions or, in many cases, only one particular reaction. For example, the enzyme sucrase catalyzes only the breakdown of sucrose. It will not break down similar sugars. Enzymes are often named by changing a suffix *-ose* to *-ase*. Thus, the enzyme maltase breaks down the sugar maltose; the enzyme lactase breaks down the sugar lactose. **Table 5-4** lists a few other important enzymes and their functions.

TABLE 5-4. Enzymes and Their Functions

Enzyme	Function
ATP synthase	synthesizes ATP from ADP and phosphate
nitrogenase	converts atmospheric nitrogen to ammonia
pepsin	breaks down proteins during digestion in the stomach
polymerase	makes RNA and DNA strands in transcription and translation
rubisco	catalyzes the first major step in carbon fixation
trypsin	breaks down proteins during digestion in the small intestine

CCC **Structure and Function** *Use the structural characteristics of proteins and the function of enzymes to explain why it makes sense that many enzymes are proteins.*

CHAPTER INVESTIGATION

Crime Scene Cleaners
Which type of detergent is most effective at breaking down protein-based substances?

Go online to explore this chapter's hands-on investigation about digestive enzymes.

Factors That Influence Enzymes Environmental factors such as temperature, salt concentration, and pH influence an enzyme's shape, which in turn influences its function. Each enzyme works best in a particular range of conditions. With some exceptions, an organism's enzymes work best under its typical physiological conditions: a pH of about 7, normal body temperature, and a salt concentration that matches that of a typical cell.

In general, enzymes increase in efficiency as the temperature rises, but only up to a point. When the temperature rises too much, enzymes begin to shut down. Human body temperatures above 42 °C (107.6 °F) adversely affect the function of many of our enzymes, which is why severe fevers are dangerous.

The activity of enzymes is also influenced by the amount of salt in the surrounding fluid. If there is too little salt, the polar parts of the enzyme attract one another so strongly that the enzyme's shape changes. Too much salt interferes with the hydrogen bonds that hold the enzyme in its characteristic shape, and the enzyme *denatures* (unfolds) and can no longer form a complex with its substrates.

Extreme changes in pH change the proportion of hydrogen ions in an enzyme's environment. The presence of an unusual amount of charged particles affects hydrogen bonds and ionic bonds, and can break the bonds that shape the enzyme and its active site. Almost all biological processes involve chemical reactions that use enzymes. Thus, in order to survive, cells must maintain the optimal conditions that enzymes need to operate.

FIGURE 5-36 ▶
The long rod-like organisms in this electron microscope image are *Clostridium difficile*, a species of bacteria that lives in the human gastrointestinal tract. An excess of *C. difficile* can lead to life-threatening inflammation of the colon or intestines.

SEP **Construct an Explanation** Clostridium difficile, *shown in* **Figure 5-36**, *makes an enzyme called HypD that helps break down hydroxy-L-proline, a molecule that forms the structure of collagen. The bacteria then use the proline (an amino acid) from this molecule for their own growth. Humans do not produce HypD. How might the HypD enzyme be targeted to fight a* C. difficile *infection?*

BIOTECHNOLOGY FOCUS

BIOREMEDIATION OF PLASTIC WASTE Plastics are human-made organic polymers. Plastic molecules are engineered to produce materials with numerous useful properties, one of which is high durability under a wide variety of conditions. This characteristic, combined with the low cost of manufacturing plastic goods, results in a vast global accumulation of plastic waste. One method that scientists are exploring to solve this problem involves identifying and studying organisms that are able to metabolize tough polymers that occur in nature. The chemical mechanisms these organisms use to turn natural polymers into biomass, carbon dioxide, and water may also be applicable to speeding up the degradation of molecularly similar plastics.

Lignin, the polymer that gives wood and bark cells their strength, does not degrade easily. However, many mushrooms, often seen attached to the trunks of trees, can break down lignin. These species are part of a group known as white-rot fungi. Scientists have found that nylon, a strong synthetic material, is also susceptible to degradation by enzymes extracted from white-rot fungi.

Cutin is a fatty acid polymer that makes the surfaces of plants waterproof. Scientists have isolated specific cutinases, or enzymes that break down cutin, in species of bacteria that decompose plants. These enzymes have been shown to be effective at degrading polyethylene terephthalate (PET), a transparent plastic commonly used in food and beverage packaging. Some bacteria have evolved to thrive in plastic-rich environments such as recycling plants and plastic waste deposits by using a cutinase-like enzyme called PETase to digest PET.

Waxworms, the larvae of wax moths, are parasitic caterpillars that eat honey and beeswax from the beehives in which they live. They can also rapidly digest polyethylene, a plastic that is highly resistant to degradation. Polyethylene has strong molecular bonds similar to bonds in beeswax compounds. Scientists are now studying the enzymes and pathways that enable waxworms to break down this ubiquitous plastic.

Darkling beetle larvae, also called mealworms, eat polystyrene foam. Because of its low density, this type of plastic is costly to melt down for transport to recycling facilities.

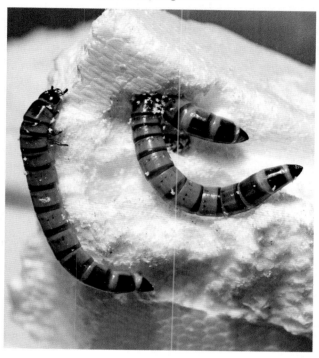

5.4 REVIEW

1. **Classify** The energy of the products in a chemical reaction is 6 kJ. The energy of the reactants is 12 kJ. Is this reaction exergonic or endergonic?

2. **Justify** Is energy considered a reactant in a chemical reaction?

   A. No. All reactants are matter.

   B. No. In an exergonic reaction, energy is a product.

   C. Yes. In an endergonic reaction, energy is a required reactant.

   D. Yes. Activation energy is needed for a chemical reaction to occur.

3. **Analyze** In which chemical equation is matter conserved?

   A. $2 H + 2 O \rightarrow H_2O$

   B. $HCO_3^- + 2 H^+ \rightarrow H_2CO_3$

   C. $6 CO_2 + 6 H_2O \rightarrow C_6H_{12}O_6 + 6 O_2$

   D. $6 C_6H_{12}O_6 + 6 O_2 \rightarrow 6 CO_2 + 6 H_2O$

4. **Classify** Tryptophan is an amino acid found in many foods. In the small intestine, a chymotrypsin molecule attaches to tryptophan to help break down the amino acid. Identify the substrate and the enzyme in this example.

DIGESTIVE ENZYMES AND pH

SEP **Use Mathematics** Scientists estimate that over two-thirds of the world's population is lactose intolerant. People with this condition commonly develop digestive difficulties in early adulthood. Lactose is a disaccharide found in dairy and milk-based products. It is broken down by an enzyme called lactase.

Lactase is one of several enzymes responsible for digestion. Enzymes accelerate the chemical reactions that break down complex biological molecules in food to release energy and smaller molecules. **Table 1** lists the digestive breakdown processes for four digestive enzymes. An enzyme's activity depends on its concentration and environmental conditions such as pH. **Figure 1** shows the dependency of enzyme activity on pH for the four digestive enzymes.

The organs in the human digestive system provide environments with different acidity. For example, the mouth and colon typically have a pH of 7, while the stomach's pH range is 1–3 and the small intestine's pH range is 6–8.

TABLE 1. Digestive Enzyme Roles

Digestive enzymes	Digestive breakdown process
amylase	polysaccharides ↓ disaccharides
lactase	disaccharides ↓ monosaccharides
pepsin	proteins ↓ peptides, amino acids
trypsin	peptides ↓ amino acids

FIGURE 1 ▼
A graph shows the relative enzyme activity over a range of pH.

1. **Organize Data** At what pH is each digestive enzyme the most active?

2. **Interpret Data** Match the digestive enzymes with the human organ in which they are most active.

3. **Relate** Identify the two organs in which proteins and carbohydrates begin the digestive process.

4. **Identify** Which organ is most responsible for lactose intolerance?

5. **Design** Propose a solution or treatment for someone experiencing lactose intolerance.

TYING IT ALL TOGETHER
TURNING MOLECULES INTO MEDICINE

HOW ARE THE MOLECULES OF LIFE ASSEMBLED?

Molecular substances in nature vary widely in complexity. By understanding patterns in the chemical structures of these substances, scientists can predict their functions within biological systems and organisms. The paclitaxel molecule introduced in the Case Study belongs to a category of organic molecules called alkaloids. Alkaloid molecules have at least one nitrogen atom that is typically part of a structure with multiple rings. Most alkaloids are found in plants, and scientists estimate that about 20 percent of plant species contain alkaloids. There are several hypotheses about the roles these compounds play: alkaloids may regulate plant growth, or protect plants from predators, or they may be waste products of plant metabolism.

Alkaloid names usually end in -ine. Many alkaloids, such as caffeine and nicotine, are known to have specific physiological effects on humans. Traditional medicines and healing practices are often derived from the therapeutic effects of alkaloids, some of which include pain relief, inflammation reduction, and antibacterial properties. As advances in biotechnology have allowed for detailed investigation of chemical compounds at the molecular level, scientists are increasingly motivated to study the structures and biological functions of alkaloids for their potential use as drugs to treat cancer and other conditions or diseases such as hypertension, diabetes, and asthma.

In this activity, you will investigate how a plant-derived alkaloid molecule is developed into a medical treatment. Work individually or in a group to complete these steps.

Gather Evidence

1. Research a specific plant alkaloid that is used in modern medicine. In your research, you should identify
   - the plant in which the alkaloid is found, and how the alkaloid is extracted from the plant
   - how the alkaloid affects the human body, and how these effects were discovered
   - the disease or condition the alkaloid is used to treat
   - the name of the medicine that is made from the alkaloid, and how it is made

Communicate Information

2. Construct a visual representation, such as a time line or flowchart, that describes the process by which the alkaloid you chose was developed into a medicine.

Argue From Evidence

3. Tens of thousands of plant alkaloids have been identified, but only a small percentage of these have been approved for pharmaceutical use. Use evidence from your research to support or refute the following claim: *Plant alkaloid research is an effective way to find new medical treatments.*

FIGURE 5-37 ▽
The Madagascar periwinkle (*Catharanthus roseus*) plant is a source of vincristine and vinblastine, alkaloids that are used to treat cancer and Hodgkin disease.

FIGURE 5-38 ▽
Claviceps purpurea, a fungus that infects rye, produces many medicinal alkaloids.

REVIEW KEY CONCEPTS

1. **Contrast** Based on **Figures 5-19** and **5-25**, which functional groups are found in nucleic acids but not in carbohydrates? Select all correct answers.

   A. amine ($-NH_2$)

   B. carboxyl ($-COOH$)

   C. hydroxyl ($-OH$)

   D. phosphate ($-PO_4^{3-}$)

   E. sulfhydryl ($-SH$)

2. **Classify** Which substances are polymers? Select all correct answers.

   A. amino acids

   B. nucleotides

   C. phospholipids

   D. polysaccharides

   E. proteins

3. **Identify** A chemist purifies a single substance from an organism and finds that it contains phosphate groups. In which category could this biological molecule belong?

   A. carbohydrate

   B. fatty acid

   C. hydrocarbon

   D. nucleic acid

4. **Explain** How do covalent bonds and ionic bonds differ?

5. **Classify** Match each description with acids or bases.

   • gives up H^+ ions in water

   • accepts free H^+ ions in water

   • produces a solution with excess free H^+ ions

   • produces a solution with excess free OH^- ions

   • lowers pH to less than 7 when dissolved in water

   • raises pH to greater than 7 when dissolved in water

6. **Identify** A scientist determines that a certain substance has no net charge. Which of these statements must be true?

   A. The number of neutrons and protons in the substance must be equal.

   B. The number of protons and electrons in the substance must be equal.

   C. The number of electrons and neutrons in the substance must be equal.

   D. The number of protons, neutrons, and electrons in the substance must be equal.

7. **Calculate** How many molecules of oxygen (O_2) are required to react with one molecule of propane (C_3H_8) to produce four molecules of water (H_2O) and three molecules of carbon dioxide (CO_2)?

8. **Compare** Do atoms of carbon-12 and carbon-14 have the same charge? Explain why or why not.

9. **Explain** A large carbohydrate molecule can react with water to break it down into smaller sugar molecules. For example, sucrose and water react to form the simple sugars glucose and fructose, releasing energy. If energy must be absorbed to break a chemical bond, how can a reaction that breaks a larger molecule down into smaller molecules be exergonic?

10. **Identify** When glucose is oxidized to release energy, glucose reacts with oxygen to produce carbon dioxide and water. What are the reactants and what are the products in this reaction?

11. **Predict** The exergonic breakdown of starch into glucose is catalyzed by an enzyme called amylase. Which statements are true about this reaction? Select all correct answers.

    A. Some bonds in starch are broken during the reaction.

    B. A starch molecule can bind to the active site of amylase.

    C. Glucose is released from the active site after the reaction.

    D. The bonds of glucose have more energy than the bonds of starch.

    E. The activation energy of the reaction is lower with amylase than without amylase.

CRITICAL THINKING

12. **Draw Conclusions** The long hydrocarbon chains that make up lipid molecules are nonpolar. Nonpolar molecules are usually *hydrophobic*, meaning they repel water. How would this property of lipids be useful in an organism?

13. **Explain** Carbon dioxide has the chemical formula CO_2. It is a linear molecule with a carbon atom in the center that is double-bonded to an oxygen atom on either side. Oxygen tends to attract electrons more strongly than carbon. Would you expect carbon dioxide to be polar or nonpolar? Explain your answer.

14. **Explain** Many organisms use glucose as a source of matter to build other molecules they need for cell metabolism and growth. Based on **Figures 5-19** and **5-25**, what elements can glucose contribute to the synthesis of nucleic acids? What elements would need to be obtained from another source? Explain.

15. **Justify** Corn starch can often sit in a pantry for years without breaking down. Yet, when ingested, corn starch can be digested very quickly by the body. How can these two observations be reconciled?

MATH AND ENGLISH LANGUAGE ARTS CONNECTIONS

1. **Reason Quantitatively** A baker mixes 3 g of yeast with 1000 g of flour and 500 g of water. After allowing the dough to rise, the dough weighs 1450 g. Quantify the change in mass. What can best explain the change in mass of the dough?

2. **Write Informative Text** Enzymes are sometimes included in detergents to help clean stains from clothing. What types of enzymes are used in such applications? How do the enzymes contribute to stain removal? In your answer, include the terms *activation energy* and *catalyst*.

3. **Model with Mathematics** The chemical reaction that links amino acids together to make a protein requires a net consumption of energy. Which of the two models in **Figure 5-33** best represents the energy changes taking place during this reaction, and how does the law of conservation of energy apply to this case? Explain your reasoning.

4. **NOS** **Explaining Natural Phenomena** When molecules react inside cells, the laws of conservation of energy and conservation of matter hold true. These laws also hold true at the level of whole ecosystems. What evidence supports these laws at the molecular level and the ecosystem level? Explain.

► BACTERIA IN YOUR GUT

Gather Evidence In this chapter, you learned about how bacteria can break down certain compounds that humans cannot, such as cellulose. Some bacteria in the gut have also been shown to destroy toxins and mutagens. In addition, bacteria also supply essential nutrients that humans cannot make themselves, such as vitamin K.

1. The variety of bacteria in the human gut have many different mechanisms to synthesize or break down chemical compounds. How do human hosts benefit from having a healthy and diverse bacteria population in their digestive systems?

2. What other questions do you have about the role of the gut bacteria in promoting human health?

CELL STRUCTURE AND FUNCTION

Acetabularia caliculus, also known as umbrella algae, have stalk and radial cap structures that consist of single cells. These algae grow in mudflats, coral reefs, and mangroves.

6.1 CELL STRUCTURES

6.2 CELL MEMBRANES

6.3 PHOTOSYNTHESIS AND CELLULAR RESPIRATION

All living things are made of one or more cells. While most cells are microscopic, some individual cells are visible to the unaided eye, such as this algae. At any size, every cell is a system that performs specific functions in an organism. Understanding how cells work is helping scientists to develop new technologies.

Chapter 6 supports the NGSS Performance Expectations **HS-LS1-5**, **HS-LS1-7**, **HS-LS2-3**, and **HS-LS2-5**.

CASE STUDY
ARTIFICIAL CELL TECHNOLOGY

HOW DO STRUCTURES WORK TOGETHER IN CELL SYSTEMS?

Cells make up all living things, from the smallest single-celled bacteria to the largest multicellular organisms. Scientists around the world have been trying a variety of approaches to build functioning artificial cells (**Figure 6-1**). Artificial cells that can grow and divide on their own could lead to a better understanding of life and have many useful technological applications.

The quest to develop artificial cells began in the late 1950s. Scientists used synthetic and natural materials to mimic cell membranes that could selectively let certain materials in and out. In the following decades, scientists were able to encapsulate proteins and other small molecules into artificial cell-like capsules. Artificial cell membranes have been constructed of lipids, polymers, and proteins, in a variety of combinations.

Some medical applications for this technology involve using cell-inspired lipid membrane capsules to deliver medicinal molecules to patients. Although these lipid capsule structures used for medicine delivery are not exactly artificial cells, they are an important step in the progress of this field of research. These capsules can be designed to target specific cells within the body. The molecules within are delivered when the capsule is absorbed by the patient's cells. In 2020, some of the vaccines to protect against COVID-19 were successfully developed for delivery using a lipid capsule technology.

While some scientists have used synthetic materials to construct artificial cells, others have used a combination of synthetic materials and parts harvested from other cells. Some projects have approached the development of artificial cells by making them from scratch, whereas others have attempted to strip away parts of existing cells to discover the minimal viable parts needed for a functional cell. The variety of approaches reflects the diversity of goals for applications of artificial cell technology.

In recent years scientists have attempted to generate cells that can replicate themselves and communicate with each other. In 2010, scientists built a cell with a synthetic genome by replacing an existing cell's genome with synthetic DNA. Several years later, a self-replicating cell with a minimum genome of fewer than 500 genes was developed (a relatively simple *Escherichia coli* bacterium contains about 4000 genes). As the research continues to progress, scientists' goals are to make these cells more stable and identify critical roles of each gene.

Ask Questions *As you read, generate questions about components and processes of cells that you think could be important and useful in the application of artificial cell technologies.*

FIGURE 6-1
Scientists at Argonne National Laboratory developed these artificial "protocells" that can harvest solar energy.

CELL STRUCTURES

KEY TERMS

cell membrane
chloroplast
cytoskeleton
endosymbiont theory
eukaryote
mitochondria
nucleus
prokaryote

Look at your surroundings. Do you see a friend, a pet, a tree, or perhaps wooden furniture? You see them as a whole person or object, possibly with legs or leaves or other parts. Now imagine looking at their finger, or paw, or a leaf through a microscope, not knowing what you will see. For most of human history, we did not have microscopes. Scientists could only guess at what made up the living objects around them.

Describe *Imagine you are the first scientist to see a living object through a microscope, and you are astounded to see that each item is made up of countless tiny pieces. How would you describe the small pieces you see to other scientists?*

Components of Cells

A cell is the smallest unit of life. All cells share certain organizational and functional features such as a cell membrane, cytoplasm, and DNA (**Figure 6-2**). The **cell membrane** (sometimes called a plasma membrane) is a lipid bilayer that separates the cell from the external environment and controls exchanges between the cell and its environment. The cell membrane encloses *cytoplasm*, a jellylike mixture of water, sugars, ions, and proteins. A cell's internal components, including organelles, are suspended in the cytoplasm. *Organelles* are structures that carry out special functions inside a cell. Organelle membranes separate certain substances and activities.

Nearly every cell contains a DNA genome. In nearly all prokaryotes, that DNA is suspended in the cytoplasm. By contrast, the DNA of a eukaryotic cell is contained in a **nucleus** (plural *nuclei*), an organelle with a double membrane. Some eukaryotes are independent, free-living cells; others consist of many cells working together in multicellular organisms.

Cell systems have traditionally been classified as either prokaryote or eukaryote. Prokaryotes (bacteria and archaea) have simpler cell structures than eukaryotes (protists, fungi, plants, and animals). Appendix E and Unit 3 describe more about the diversity of bacteria, archaea, and eukaryote systems. In this section we will focus on model cell systems of bacteria, animal, and plant cells.

FIGURE 6-2 ▽

Cells include a cell membrane, cytoplasm, and DNA. The bacterial cell (a) is a model of a prokaryotic cell, and the plant (b) and animal (c) cells are models of eukaryotic cells.

cell membrane
DNA
cytoplasm

2a **bacterial cell**

cell membrane
cytoplasm
DNA in nucleus

2b **plant cell**

cytoplasm
DNA in nucleus
cell membrane

2c **animal cell**

DISCOVERY OF CELLS AND CELL THEORY Before microscopes were invented, no one knew that cells existed because nearly all cells are invisible to the unaided eye. Italian astronomer Galileo Galilei designed the first compound microscope using a concave lens and convex lens in the early 1600s. The design was improved by English physicist Robert Hooke 65 years later. Using a three-lens microscope, Hooke observed tiny hairs on a plant stem and the intricate pores in a piece of cork. He coined the term "cells" to describe the smallest components he observed.

A decade later, the first living cells were seen by Dutch scientist Antoni van Leeuwenhoek using a single-lens simple microscope he developed. He noted tiny organisms in rainwater, insects, fabric, sperm, feces, and other samples. In scrapings of tartar from his teeth, Leeuwenhoek saw what he described as "many very small animalcules, the motions of which were very pleasing to behold." He (incorrectly) assumed that movement defined life, and (correctly) concluded that the moving "beasties" he saw were alive. Leeuwenhoek might have been less pleased to behold his animalcules if he had grasped the implications of what he saw: Our world, and our bodies, teem with microbial life.

As described in this chapter, today we know that a cell carries out metabolism, maintains homeostasis, and reproduces either on its own or as part of a larger organism. By this definition, each cell is alive even if it is part of a multicellular body, and all living organisms consist of one or more cells. We also know that cells reproduce by dividing, so it follows that all existing cells must have arisen by division of other cells. As a cell divides, it passes its hereditary material—DNA—to offspring. Taken together, these generalizations constitute the cell theory, which is one of the foundations of modern biology.

Cell Theory

1. Each organism consists of one or more cells.

2. The cell is the structural and functional unit of all organisms. A cell is the smallest unit of life, individually alive even as part of a multicellular organism.

3. All living cells arise by division of preexisting cells.

4. Cells contain hereditary material (DNA), which they pass to their offspring when they divide.

Prokaryotic Cells

All bacteria and archaea are single-celled organisms (**Figure 6-3**), but individual cells of many species cluster together. Outwardly, cells of the two groups appear to be so similar that archaea were once presumed to be a type of bacteria. Both were classified as **prokaryotes**, a word that means "before the nucleus." By 1977, it had become clear that archaea are more closely related to eukaryotes than to bacteria, so they were classified as their own separate domain. The term "prokaryote" is now only an informal designation.

FIGURE 6-3
A scanning electron microscope image shows bacteria from the surface of a mobile phone. Bacteria come in a variety of shapes and sizes.

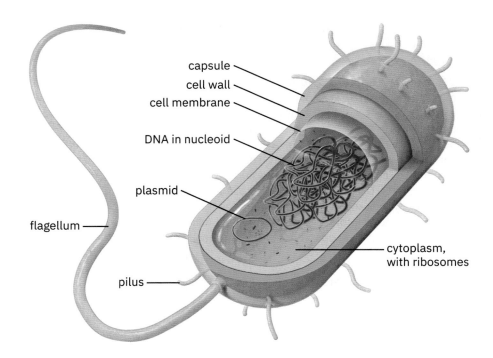

FIGURE 6-4
Some common features of bacterial cells are shown. Different bacteria and archaea have a variety of other shapes and structures.

capsule

cell wall

cell membrane

DNA in nucleoid

plasmid

flagellum

cytoplasm, with ribosomes

pilus

Components of Prokaryotes Prokaryotic cells perform many of the same functions as eukaryotic cells, but with fewer intracellular structures and a less complicated internal framework. Protein filaments under the cell membrane reinforce the cell's shape and provide a scaffolding for internal components (**Figure 6-4**):

- **Cytoplasm** The cytoplasm is a jellylike mixture of water, sugars, ions, and proteins that fills a cell. Ribosomes and DNA plasmids are suspended there. Most metabolism occurs in cytoplasm.

- **Ribosomes** Ribosomes are complex structures made of many protein and RNA molecules. Ribosomes build proteins.

- **Plasmid** Plasmids are small circular molecules of DNA that carry a few genes. Plasmid genes can provide advantages such as resistance to antibiotics. Transfer of plasmids between bacterial cells is an important mechanism of genetic exchange.

- **Nucleoid** Irregularly shaped regions of cytoplasm that contain the cell's essential genetic information are called nucleoids.

- **Cell Membrane** Cell membranes are lipid bilayers with integrated proteins that control the exchange of molecules with the surrounding environment. The structures and functions of cell membranes are described in detail in Section 6.2.

- **Cell Wall** Crystalline material makes up the cell wall that encloses the cell membrane in most prokaryotes. A cell wall protects the cell and supports its shape.

- **Capsule** Many species of bacteria have a capsule, which is a thick, gelatinous enclosure and/or a loosely attached layer of slime. These sticky structures help the cells adhere to each other as well as to many types of surfaces, and they also offer protection against predators and toxins.

BACTERIA IN YOUR GUT

Gather Evidence *Many bacteria in your intestines include a capsule structure. Why would a capsule be a useful feature for bacteria living inside the intestines?*

- **Pilus** A protein filament that projects from the surface of some prokaryotes is called a pilus (plural *pili*). Pili help cells move across or cling to surfaces. A "sex" pilus attaches to another cell and then shortens itself. The attached cell is reeled in, and DNA is transferred from one cell to the other through the pilus.

- **Flagellum** A flagellum (plural *flagella*) is a long, slender structure used for movement. Many prokaryotes have one or more flagella projecting from their surface. A prokaryotic flagellum rotates like a propeller that drives the cell through fluids.

CCC **Structure and Function** *Pick two of the prokaryotic cell components described, and explain how the structure of the component helps it perform its intended function.*

Eukaryotic Cells

Every cell in a **eukaryote** contains a nucleus and typically many additional organelles. Organelles enclosed by lipid bilayer membranes, including endoplasmic reticulum, Golgi bodies, chloroplasts, and mitochondria, are characteristic of eukaryotes. An enclosing membrane allows these structures to regulate the types and amounts of substances that enter and exit an organelle. Through this type of control, an organelle can maintain a specialized environment that allows it to carry out a particular function or store molecules that need to be isolated from the rest of the cell. Ribosomes are found in the cytoplasm of both prokaryotic and eukaryotic cells, and ribosomes are also attached to some parts of the endoplasmic reticulum in eukaryotes.

The Nucleus The cell nucleus (**Figure 6-5**) serves two important functions. First, the nucleus keeps the cell's genetic material isolated and safe from metabolic processes that might damage it. The DNA is suspended in nucleoplasm, a viscous fluid similar to cytoplasm. Second, the nucleus controls the movement of molecules through the nuclear envelope, a specialized membrane composed of two lipid bilayers. Embedded in the two lipid bilayers are nuclear pore complexes, tiny portals that regulate the passage of molecules between the cytoplasm and nucleoplasm. Proteins making up nuclear pores are anchored by a dense mesh of fibrous proteins that supports the inner surface of the membrane. The nucleus also contains one or more nucleoli (singular *nucleolus*), the structure where ribosomes are synthesized.

Go Online **VIRTUAL INVESTIGATION**

Bacteria in the Digestive System
What do bacteria do in your intestines?

Put on your lab coat to grow some bacteria and study how they live and interact.

5a

5b

nuclear envelope
nucleoplasm
DNA
nucleolus
nuclear pore

FIGURE 6-5
A model of an animal cell nucleus (a) is shown alongside a transmission electron microscope image of the nucleus in a pancreas cell from a rat (b).

FIGURE 6-6 ▽
These models represent many common structures of plant (a) and animal (b) cells.

The Cytoskeleton Between the nucleus and cell membrane of all eukaryotic cells is a system of interconnected protein filaments called the **cytoskeleton**. Elements of the cytoskeleton reinforce, organize, and move cell structures (including the nucleus), and sometimes even whole cells. Some are permanent. Others form only at certain times. Motor proteins that associate with cytoskeletal elements move cell parts. The cytoskeleton is made up of three different kinds of filaments. These include microtubules, microfilaments, and intermediate filaments. All are built of many individual subunits that can be lengthened or shortened by adding or subtracting subunits (**Figure 6-7**). Each type of filament has a different structure specific to its function and relative stability.

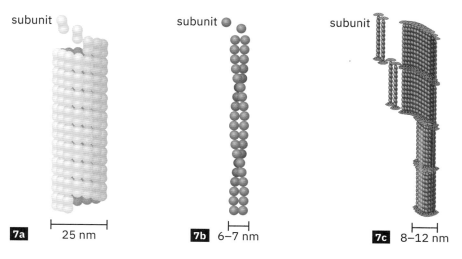

subunit   subunit   subunit

7a 25 nm   **7b** 6–7 nm   **7c** 8–12 nm

FIGURE 6-7
Microtubules (a) are involved in moving cell parts or moving the whole cell. The ability to add or remove microtubule subunits to lengthen or shorten microtubules is important in mitosis (Section 7.2). Microfilaments (b) reinforce cell membranes and function in muscle contractions. Intermediate filaments (c) structurally support cell membranes and tissues and are the most stable of these three parts of the cytoskeleton. A fluorescence microscopy image (d) of epithelial cells isolated from a kangaroo rat kidney shows microtubules in green and microfilaments in red. DNA appears in blue.

7d

Other Membrane-Enclosed Organelles in the Cytoplasm

A variety of membrane-enclosed organelles do jobs in the cytoplasm of cells. Some of them bud from other membranes and others are networked to each other and the nuclear membrane.

- **Vesicles** These structures bud from the cell membrane or from membrane-enclosed organelles. Many types of vesicles carry substances between or within an organelle, or to and from the cell membrane. Small organelles called *peroxisomes* are vesicles containing enzymes that break down molecules such as amino acids and fatty acids (for metabolism) or hydrogen peroxide and ammonia (because they are toxic). Enzymes in vesicles called *lysosomes* break down and recycle macromolecules and cellular debris, repair the cell membrane, and process foreign particles such as bacteria and viruses.

VIDEO

VIDEO 6-1 Go online to observe how organelles move within a cell.

- **Vacuoles** Large, fluid-filled vesicles called *vacuoles* store or break down waste, debris, toxins, or food. In plants, lysosome-like vesicles fuse to form a very large central vacuole that makes up most of the volume of the cell. Fluid pressure in a central vacuole keeps plant cells plump, so stems, leaves, and other plant parts stay firm. The central vacuole has additional functions in some cells.

- **Endoplasmic Reticulum** The system of sacs and tubes that make up *endoplasmic reticulum* (ER) extends out from the outer lipid bilayer of the nuclear envelope. Two kinds of ER, rough and smooth, are named for their appearance in electron microscope images. Smooth ER is involved in the synthesis and storage of lipid molecules. The membrane of rough ER is typically folded into flattened sacs and has thousands of attached ribosomes that give it a "rough" appearance. These ribosomes make protein molecules that thread into the ER's interior as they are assembled. Proteins that are incorporated into the cell membrane or exported from the cell are constructed here.

- **Golgi Body** A *Golgi body* (also called a Golgi apparatus) has a folded membrane that often looks like a stack of pancakes. Enzymes inside Golgi bodies put finishing touches on proteins and lipids that have been delivered from ER. The finished products—membrane proteins and lipids, proteins for secretion, and enzymes—are sorted and packaged in new vesicles. Some of the new vesicles deliver their cargo to the cell membrane; others become lysosomes. In plant cells, Golgi bodies have an additional, major function: They make complex, branched polysaccharides that are a part of the cell wall.

FIGURE 6-8 ▽

Some of the membrane-enclosed structures in a white blood cell from a guinea pig (a) and in a cell from a root of a thale cress plant (b) are shown.

endoplasmic reticulum   nucleus   mitochondrion   Golgi body   vacuole

Mitochondria The structure of a **mitochondrion** (plural *mitochondria*) is specialized for carrying out reactions of aerobic cellular respiration, which generates the ATP used by cells as an energy source (**Figure 6-9**). The inner membrane has many folds that increase the surface area where some reactions of cellular respiration occur. Mitochondria have their own DNA and ribosomes within the matrix. Nearly all eukaryotic cells (including plant cells) have mitochondria, but the number of mitochondria varies by the type of cell and by the organism. For example, single-celled eukaryotes such as yeast often have only one mitochondrion, but human skeletal muscle cells have a thousand or more. In general, cells that have the highest demand for energy tend to have the most mitochondria. Typical mitochondria are between 1 and 4 micrometers in length.

9a

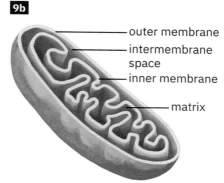
9b
- outer membrane
- intermembrane space
- inner membrane
- matrix

FIGURE 6-9
A microscope image of a mitochondrion in a cell from a bat pancreas (a). Each mitochondrion has two membranes, one highly folded inside the other. The inner compartment formed by these membranes is called the matrix (b). The outer compartment is called the intermembrane space.

Chloroplasts Photosynthesis in plants and in photosynthetic protists takes place in **chloroplasts** (**Figure 6-10**). Plant chloroplasts are oval or disk-shaped. Each has two outer membranes enclosing a fluid interior, the *stroma*, that contains enzymes as well as the chloroplast's own DNA and ribosomes. In the stroma, a third, highly folded membrane forms a single, continuous compartment that appears as stacks of discs. Each disc is called a *thylakoid*. Photosynthesis occurs at the thylakoids, which incorporate many pigments, including chlorophyll (the substance that makes most plants green). During photosynthesis, these pigments capture energy from sunlight to generate other molecules that can be stored and used to drive reactions in cells. In general, specialized cells within plant leaves have the most chloroplasts, because plant leaves receive more sunlight than other parts of plants.

10a

10b
- thylakoid
- stroma
- membranes

FIGURE 6-10
The transmission electron microscope image shows a chloroplast from a leaf of corn (a). Each chloroplast has two outer membranes (b). Photosynthesis occurs in the thylakoids, which are formed within a third, highly folded inner membrane that is called the thylakoid membrane.

Endosymbiont Theory

According to the **endosymbiont theory** for the origin of mitochondria and chloroplasts, these organelles descended from bacteria that entered a host cell and lived inside it. Organisms that live inside another organism are called *endosymbionts*. The term is usually reserved for cells that help their host, or at least do not harm it.

Mitochondria have their own DNA, which is circular and otherwise similar to bacterial DNA. They also divide independently of the cell and have their own ribosomes. Mitochondria are thought to have arisen when an anaerobic host cell engulfed heterotrophic bacteria capable of aerobic cellular respiration. The endosymbionts lived inside their host, where they continued to carry out aerobic cellular respiration and to reproduce. When the host cell divided, it passed on "guest" cells and the ability to carry out this efficient energy-releasing pathway.

As the two species lived together over many generations, the endosymbiont lost some genes that duplicated the function of host genes and donated other genes to the chromosome of the host cell. At the same time, the host became dependent on the ATP produced by its endosymbiont. Eventually, the host and endosymbiont became incapable of living independently. The endosymbiont had evolved into the organelle we call a mitochondrion. The high degree of similarity among the genomes of all mitochondria indicates that these organelles descended from one species of bacteria.

The first chloroplasts evolved after cyanobacteria were engulfed and became endosymbionts for an early eukaryote. Like mitochondria, chloroplasts have many similarities with their ancestral bacteria, including their own circular DNA and their own ribosomes. Genetic similarities between cyanobacteria and chloroplasts have confirmed their close evolutionary relationship, and both perform photosynthesis using the oxygen-producing pathway that evolved in cyanobacteria.

SEP **Construct an Explanation** *As described in this section, eukaryotic cells (**Figure 6-6**) have many more complicated internal components than prokaryotic cells (**Figure 6-4**). Why do you think multicellular organisms are made up of eukaryotic cells?*

6.1 REVIEW

1. **Describe** What is the cytoskeleton and how does it help cell components?

2. **Classify** Label each cell component as a part of a prokaryotic cell, eukaryotic cell, or both.

   - capsule
   - cytoplasm
   - cytoskeleton
   - ER
   - nucleus
   - ribosomes

3. **Identify** Which cell component is responsible for protecting genetic material from chemical processes that occur in the cell?

   A. DNA

   B. Golgi body

   C. nucleus

   D. vesicle

4. **Summarize** Describe three observations that support the hypothesis that mitochondria descended from bacteria that became incorporated into the cytoplasm of eukaryotic cells.

MICROBIOTA OF THE HUMAN BODY

SEP **Use Mathematics** Bacteria have been observed in nearly every organ of the human body.

The largest organ of the human body is the skin, which covers a surface area of about 2 square meters for the average adult. The number of bacteria, also known as the bacterial cell count, is estimated to be about 2×10^{11} on the skin surface of healthy adults. Other body parts and bodily fluids contain measurable amounts of bacteria. **Table 1** lists the typical volumes of organs and fluids in an adult human body and representative estimates of the concentration of bacterial cells.

Staphylococcus epidermis is a type of bacterium that lives on human skin.

TABLE 1. Bacteria in Human Organs and Fluids

Organ or fluid	Estimated volume (cm³)	Estimated concentration of bacteria (cells/cm³)
large intestine	400	3×10^{10}
lower small intestine	400	1×10^{8}
saliva	100	1×10^{9}
stomach	250	1×10^{3}
upper small intestine	400	1×10^{3}

Source: U.S. National Library of Medicine

On average, human cells are larger and less dense than bacterial cells. The largest mammalian cells have a volume of 10,000 µm³ with density comparable to that of water, 1 g/cm³. In comparison, typical bacterial cells have a volume of 0.7 µm³ with a density of about 1.1 g/cm³.

1. **Compare** Use the data to determine the bacterial cell count in human organs and fluids. Rank the organs and fluids from highest to lowest bacterial cell count.

2. **Estimate** Based on your calculations and assuming the rest of the human body has negligible bacterial counts, roughly how many bacterial cells in total are found in an average adult human body?

3. **Calculate** Determine an estimate for the mass of a single human cell in kilograms. Then determine the human cell count in an average 10^{2}-kg adult.

4. **Interpret** Based on the data provided about where bacteria are found in the human body, what is at least one important role bacteria play in the normal function of the human body?

ON ASSIGNMENT This close up of a venomous eyelash pit viper, *Bothriechis schlegelii,* was taken by National Geographic photographer Charlie Hamilton James while in Costa Rica's Osa Peninsula. Special pigment-bearing cells known as chromatophores are a part of the skin and are responsible for the distinctive colors and patterns of each snake.

KEY TERMS

endocytosis
exocytosis
facilitated diffusion
fluid mosaic model
homeostasis
osmosis
selective permeability

CELL MEMBRANES

Opening a window on a nice day may seem like a good idea. An open window lets in fresh air, but you might also end up with a room full of houseflies and other insects. A window screen can let in the air and sounds while keeping out the things you would rather stay outside.

Analyze *Like a room with a window and window screen, what are some reasons a cell might need to control what materials can enter and exit?*

Cell Membrane Structure

Cell systems need to maintain optimal conditions while also communicating and exchanging material with nearby cells and the surrounding environment. A cell membrane regulates what materials can enter or exit the cell, allowing the cell to maintain homeostasis within its environment and communicate with surrounding cells. Cellular **homeostasis** is the maintenance of optimal chemical and physical conditions within a cell, even if the external environment changes.

Fluid Mosaic Model The foundation of all cell membranes is a lipid bilayer that consists mainly of phospholipids. As described in Section 5.3, a phospholipid has a phosphate-containing head and two fatty acid tails. The head is polar and hydrophilic (water-loving), so it interacts with water molecules. The two long hydrocarbon tails are nonpolar and hydrophobic (water-fearing), so they do not interact with water molecules. As a result of these opposing properties, phospholipids mixed with water will spontaneously organize themselves into two phospholipid sheets (bilayer), with hydrophobic tails facing each other and hydrophilic heads facing the aqueous extracellular and intracellular environments (**Figure 6-11**).

FIGURE 6-11 ▶
Phospholipids are organized in cell membranes with the hydrophobic tails facing each other and the hydrophilic heads facing the environments inside and outside the cell.

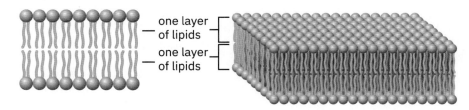

one layer of lipids
one layer of lipids

Proteins and other molecules are embedded in or attached to the lipid bilayer of a cell membrane. Many of these molecules move around the membrane more or less freely. The **fluid mosaic model** describes a membrane as a two-dimensional liquid made up of different substances. The "mosaic" part of the name comes from the many different types of molecules in the membrane.

Membrane fluidity occurs because phospholipids in the bilayer are not chemically bonded to one another. They stay organized as a result of collective hydrophobic and hydrophilic attractions. Individual phospholipids in the bilayer drift sideways and spin around their long axis, and their tails wiggle.

Proteins in the Cell Membrane Many types of proteins are associated with a cell membrane (**Figure 6-12**). Some are temporarily or permanently attached to one of the lipid bilayer's surfaces. Others have a hydrophobic part that anchors the protein permanently in the bilayer. Filaments inside the cell fasten some membrane proteins in place. Each type of protein in a membrane gives a specific function to it. Different cell membranes can carry out different tasks depending on which proteins they include. A cell membrane contains certain proteins that no internal membrane has, so it has functions that no other membrane does.

CASE STUDY
ARTIFICIAL CELL TECHNOLOGY

Ask Questions *Generate questions about possible similarities and differences between cell membranes and proteins in artificial cells and natural cells.*

- **Adhesion Proteins** Cells stay organized in animal tissues because adhesion proteins in their cell membranes fasten them together and hold them in place. Adhesion proteins also provide a cell with information about its position relative to other cells or structures.

- **Receptor Proteins** Cell membranes and some internal membranes incorporate receptor proteins, which trigger a change in the cell's activities in response to a stimulus or signaling molecule. Each type of receptor protein receives a particular stimulus such as a hormone binding to it. The response triggered by a receptor may involve metabolism, movement, division, or even cell death.

- **Enzymes** All cell membranes incorporate *enzymes*, which are proteins that help catalyze chemical reactions in cells (Section 5.4). Some of these enzymes act on proteins or lipids that are part of the membrane. Others work in series and use the membrane as a scaffold. Enzymes associated with the membranes of both mitochondria and chloroplasts, such as ATP synthase, are important parts of cellular respiration and photosynthesis.

- **Transport Proteins** All membranes also have transport proteins, which move specific substances across the bilayer. Transport proteins are important because lipid bilayers are impermeable to most substances, including the ions and polar molecules that cells must take in and expel on a regular basis.

SEP **Construct an Explanation** *Explain why lipid molecules come together to form a double membrane. Why is this structure important for the integration of proteins that function in cell membranes?*

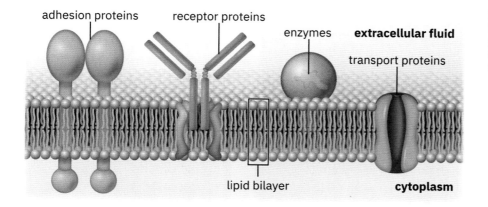

adhesion proteins   receptor proteins   enzymes   **extracellular fluid**
transport proteins
lipid bilayer   **cytoplasm**

FIGURE 6-12
Proteins embedded in the cell membrane perform a variety of functions. Enzymes are enclosed within a membrane that connects to the lipid bilayer.

Movement of Material Across Cell Membranes

Lipid bilayers have **selective permeability**, which means that some substances can move across them and others cannot. Permeability is determined by the physical size and charge of molecules. Hydrophobic molecules, gases, and small, uncharged polar molecules can easily move through the hydrophobic core of the lipid bilayer. However, ions and large polar molecules cannot.

Diffusion Molecules are constantly moving into, throughout, and out of cells. An important part of this movement is *diffusion*, the spreading of atoms or molecules through a fluid or gas. The constant jiggling of particles within a fluid or gas causes particles to randomly bounce off each other or nearby structures. Molecules diffuse from areas of high concentration to areas of low concentration.

The concentration of molecules in a solution is known as the solute concentration. A solution with more concentrated solute is referred to as *hypertonic*, relative to a *hypotonic* solution with a lower concentration of solute.

Osmosis When a lipid bilayer separates two fluids with differing solute concentrations, water will diffuse across it. **Osmosis** is the diffusion of water across membranes, and it is driven by differences in the total solute concentration on opposite sides of the membrane. Water diffuses from a hypotonic fluid into a hypertonic one to balance the solute concentration across the lipid bilayer. This continues until the two fluids are *isotonic*, which means they have the same overall solute concentration. Another way to consider this is that hypotonic solutions have a high concentration of free water molecules, that is, molecules that are not bound to solutes. Those water molecules move to a hypertonic solution that has a lower concentration of free water molecules.

Osmosis can be demonstrated with red blood cells (**Figure 6-13**). If a cell's cytoplasm becomes hypertonic with respect to the fluid outside of its cell membrane, water will diffuse into the cell. If the cytoplasm becomes hypotonic, water will diffuse out. In either case, the solute concentration of the cytoplasm will change. If it changes significantly, the cell's enzymes will stop working, with lethal results. Most cells have mechanisms that compensate for osmosis when the solute concentration of cytoplasm differs from extracellular fluid. In cells with no such mechanism, the volume and solute concentration of cytoplasm changes when water diffuses into or out of the cell.

FIGURE 6-13 ▼
Red blood cells in an isotonic solution (such as the fluid portion of blood) have an indented disc shape (a). Red blood cells in a hypertonic solution shrivel up because water diffuses out of them (b). Red blood cells in a hypotonic solution swell up because water diffuses into them (c).

FIGURE 6-14
Cell membrane proteins, including transport proteins, form dense clusters on the cell membrane. Atomic force microscopy allows scientists to scan a membrane surface and detect proteins sticking up just a few micrometers from the surface. Each peak is a protein in this cell membrane.

Transport Proteins Substances that do not diffuse directly through lipid bilayers can cross a cell membrane only through transport proteins embedded in the membrane (**Figure 6-14**). Each type of transport protein allows a specific substance to cross. For example, calcium pumps pump only calcium ions, and glucose transporters transport only glucose. The ability to move only specific molecules across the cell membrane is an important part of homeostasis. The cell has to regulate what can move into and out of the cytoplasm to maintain its composition.

Some transport proteins form pores, which are open channels through a membrane. Gated transport proteins open and close in response to a stimulus such as a shift in electric charge or binding to a signaling molecule. Other types of transport proteins change shape upon binding and releasing their specific molecule on the other side of the membrane.

Passive Transport Osmosis and diffusion of solutes through the membrane are examples of passive transport. *Passive transport* does not require any energy because the movement of the solute and the direction of its movement are driven entirely by the solute's concentration gradient. **Facilitated diffusion** is the passive transport of solutes through the cell membrane with the help of a transport protein. **Figure 6-15** demonstrates one example of facilitated diffusion, in which glucose is transported with the help of a glucose transport protein.

FIGURE 6-15
A glucose molecule in extracellular fluid binds to a glucose transporter embedded in the cell membrane (a). Binding causes the transport protein to change shape (b). The transport protein releases the glucose in the cytoplasm and returns to its original shape (c).

15a

extracellular fluid

cytoplasm

15b

15c

Active Transport Many cellular processes require transporting solutes across a membrane into a hypertonic solution. Moving a solute against its concentration gradient requires energy. In *active transport*, a transport protein uses energy to pump a solute against its gradient across a cell membrane (**Figure 6-16**). Typically, energy from ATP (Section 6.3) is used to change the shape of the protein. The shape change causes the protein to release a bound solute to the other side of the membrane. Each solute moved by active transport has a specific transport protein. One example of active transport occurs with calcium ions, which act as messengers that trigger various processes inside cells. The concentration of these ions in cytoplasm must be kept thousands of times lower than in extracellular fluid. This gradient is maintained by calcium pumps, which export calcium ions from a cell by active transport.

FIGURE 6-16 ▼
Two calcium ions bind to the specific transport protein (a). Energy from ATP helps the protein to change shape so that the calcium ions are ejected to the opposite side of the membrane (b). After the calcium ions are released, the transport protein resumes its original shape (c).

16a

16b

16c

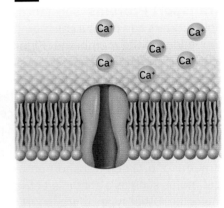

SEP **Use a Model** *Using the figures and examples in this section, describe why it is important to have different, specific proteins for transporting different materials across the cell membrane.*

Go Online **SIMULATION**

Crossing Membranes Go online to transport different substances into and out of a cell.

Vesicle Movement When a membrane is disrupted, the fatty acid tails of the phospholipids in the bilayer become exposed to their watery surroundings. Recall that in water, hydrophobic phospholipids spontaneously rearrange themselves so that their nonpolar tails stay together. Because of this, a membrane tends to seal itself after a disruption. Vesicles form the same way. When a patch of membrane bulges into the cytoplasm, the hydrophobic tails of the lipids in the bilayer are repelled by the watery fluid on both sides. The fluid "pushes" the phospholipid tails together, which helps round off the bud as a vesicle and seals the rupture in the membrane.

Vesicles are constantly carrying materials to and from the cell membrane. This movement requires energy because it involves motor proteins that drag the vesicles along cytoskeletal elements. During **exocytosis**, substances are released out of a cell. In this process, a vesicle in the cytoplasm moves to the cell's surface and fuses with the cell membrane. As the fusion occurs, the contents of the vesicle are released to the surrounding fluid outside the cell (**Figure 6-17a**). During **endocytosis**, large molecules or liquids are taken into a cell by an inward folding of the cell membrane. There are multiple pathways of endocytosis, but all take up substances near the cell's surface in bulk, as opposed to one molecule or ion at a time via transport proteins.

Cells can bring in fluids and molecules from outside the cell in a nonspecific way, or they can ingest molecules that bond to specific receptors that trigger endocytosis. For endocytosis that is triggered by specific molecules, as shown in **Figure 6-17b**, receptor proteins in the cell membrane bind to a substance such as a hormone, or a particle such as a bacterium. The binding triggers a shallow pit to form in the membrane, just under the receptors. The pit sinks into the cytoplasm and traps the targeted molecules in a vesicle as it closes back on itself.

FIGURE 6-17 ▼
In exocytosis (a), a vesicle in the cytoplasm fuses with the cell membrane. Lipids and proteins of the vesicle's membrane become part of the plasma membrane as its contents are expelled. In endocytosis (b), shown here with receptors that match specific molecules, a pit forms in the cell membrane. The target molecules are trapped in a vesicle as the pit deepens and sinks into the cell's cytoplasm.

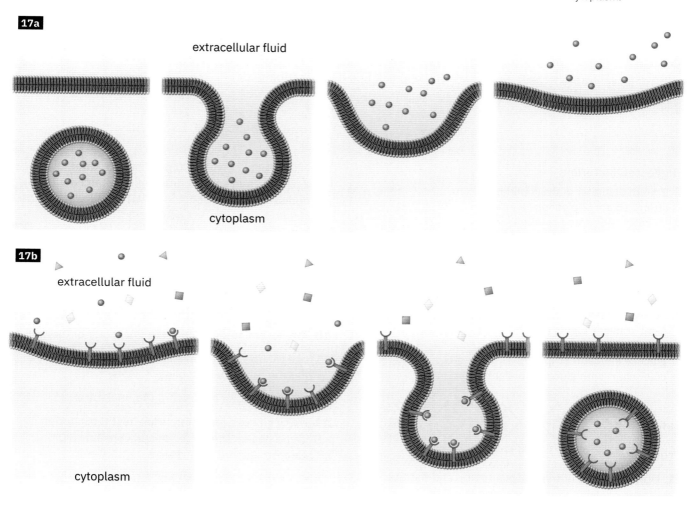

17a

extracellular fluid

cytoplasm

17b

extracellular fluid

cytoplasm

6.2 REVIEW

1. **Relate** In each scenario described, identify whether water must move into or out of the cell to reach equilibrium.

   • The solute concentration outside the cell is higher than inside the cell.

   • The concentration of water molecules outside the cell exceeds the number inside the cell.

   • There is a higher concentration of solute particles inside the cell than outside the cell.

2. **Define** What is the difference between diffusion and osmosis?

3. **Identify** Which of the following types of transport require no energy input? Select all correct answers.

   A. vesicle exocytosis

   B. pumping of calcium

   C. facilitated diffusion of glucose

   D. osmosis of water into a red blood cell

SELECTIVELY PERMEABLE MEMBRANES

SEP **Develop and Use a Model** How do molecules move through the cell membrane?

Cell membranes allow passage of some molecules while blocking passage of others. This selective permeability is important for helping cells maintain homeostasis. In this activity you will use dialysis tubing to model some of the functions of the cell membrane.

Suggested Materials

- 2.5-cm diameter dialysis tubing, 20 cm
- string, 15 cm (2 pieces)
- glucose-and-starch solution
- scissors
- paper towels
- electronic scale
- forceps
- distilled water, 200 mL
- 250-mL beaker
- 5-mL transfer pipets (2)
- potassium iodide solution
- glucose indicator strips (2)
- color chart with glucose concentration

Safety

Procedure

1. Obtain a piece of the dialysis tubing and the two pieces of string that are soaking in water.

2. Open the tubing to a cylinder shape. Use one piece of string to tie one end of the tube to make a bag.

3. Pour the glucose-and-starch solution until the bag is about half full.

4. Tie off the open end of the tubing with the other piece of string. Cut off any extra string material from both ends.

5. Wash the outside of the tubing gently but thoroughly under running water. Then pat it dry with a paper towel.

6. Weigh the tube and record its initial mass.

7. Fill the beaker with 200 mL distilled water, then use a pipet to add several drops of the starch indicator, potassium iodide solution. **CAUTION:** *Iodine stains clothing and skin.*

8. Use the glucose indicator strips to test the solution in the beaker for presence of glucose. Record your initial results.

9. Place the tubing in the water. Record your initial observations about the color of the water.

10. After 15 minutes, record the final color of the water.

11. Use the forceps to take the tube out of the water. Pat the tube dry with paper towels.

12. Weigh the tube and record the final mass.

13. Using glucose indicator strips, test the solution in the beaker for presence and concentration of glucose. Record your results.

14. Once you have all the data you need, move to the cleanup stage.

Results and Analysis

1. **Analyze** Consider the flow of glucose through the membrane. Would the rate of this flow be faster at the start or at the end of the experiment?

2. **Predict** Consider how the glucose concentration changed in the beaker. Describe a setup where the glucose would move in the opposite direction.

3. **Explain** How does this model demonstrate selective permeability? Use your results, including any changes in the mass of the tube and in glucose and starch concentrations, to support your answer.

4. **Argue From Evidence** Most animal cells will swell and burst if they are placed in pure water. Explain why this would happen.

PHOTOSYNTHESIS AND CELLULAR RESPIRATION

KEY TERMS

cellular respiration
electron transport chain
fermentation
photosynthesis

Think about how energy and matter move through ecosystems. For example, when one organism in a food web eats another, it acquires energy and carbon for its own life processes. It uses that energy to carry out cell functions, and the carbon atoms become part of molecules important for each individual cell.

Explain *Think of the cell structures and processes you've learned about in this chapter. Describe how one of those structures or processes uses carbon and energy.*

Energy in Cells

All life is sustained by inputs of energy, but not all forms of energy can sustain life. Sunlight, for example, is abundant here on Earth, but it cannot directly power protein synthesis or other energy-requiring reactions that all organisms need to perform to stay alive. To do so, sunlight must first be converted to chemical bond energy. Unlike light, chemical energy can power the reactions of life, and it can be stored for later use. This section will provide a brief overview of the processes that most often are used to convert energy into a usable chemical form in organisms. Details of the chemical reactions and molecules involved in each step of the processes of photosynthesis and cellular respiration are described in the Appendix.

Photosynthesis and cellular respiration are a critical part of the cycling of matter and flow of energy in ecosystems (Section 2.4). **Figure 6-18** illustrates that the process of photosynthesis converts carbon dioxide, water, and energy from the sun into stored energy in the form of glucose. Aerobic respiration then converts sugar and oxygen into usable energy in the form of ATP.

FIGURE 6-18 ▼
Photosynthesis produces sugars such as glucose and, in most organisms, it also releases oxygen. The breakdown of glucose in aerobic cellular respiration requires oxygen, and it produces carbon dioxide and water (a). The stable structure of glucose stores energy from the sun until it is converted to usable ATP in cellular respiration (b).

FIGURE 6-19 ▼
A phosphate group is added to ADP to make ATP, which can be used to provide energy in a reaction. After ATP is used as part of a reaction, the ADP can be recycled and used again. P_i represents the free inorganic phosphate group that is added to ADP to make ATP (a). An ATP molecule has three phosphate groups, which reflect the "tri" in the molecule name. ADP only has two phosphate groups (b).

Molecules Involved in Respiration and Photosynthesis

There are many important molecules involved in cellular respiration and photosynthesis. Some may be familiar, such as CO_2, H_2O, and O_2, while others may seem more complex. Use the following list as a reference to help identify the roles of other molecules described in this section:

- **Energy Storage** Sugar molecules, such as the glucose produced by photosynthesis, store energy in stable forms.

- **Energy for Other Reactions** A phosphate group added to ADP (adenosine diphosphate) generates ATP (adenosine triphosphate) in the cycle shown in **Figure 6-19**. ATP provides usable energy for many chemical reactions within the cell, such as the reactions required in active transport.

- **Electron Carriers** NADH, NADPH, and $FADH_2$ carry high-energy electrons from one part of the photosynthesis and cellular respiration processes to another. These molecules have a cyclical pattern similar to ATP, except they gain and lose electrons and hydrogen ions (H^+). For instance, NADPH molecules become $NADP^+$, and vice versa.

- **Electron Acceptors** Electrons and hydrogen ions that are delivered by electron carriers ultimately combine with electron acceptor molecules. For example, O_2 accepts electrons and combines with hydrogen ions to form H_2O in aerobic cellular respiration.

19a

phosphate and energy released

ADP + P_i

phosphate and energy added

ATP

19b

phosphate groups

base

sugar

CCC **Energy and Matter** *Observe the ATP cycle represented in Figure 6-19a. Describe what is happening to the matter and energy in this system throughout the cycle.*

Cellular Respiration

All organisms use energy stored in sugars to power the reactions that sustain life. However, to use the energy stored in sugars, cells must first transfer it to ATP or other molecules that can participate directly in chemical reactions. In addition to generating ATP to power reactions in the cell, the process of cellular respiration also releases energy as heat. Because organisms lose energy to the environment constantly, these reactions are important to maintain ideal temperatures for all organisms.

Cellular respiration is the process that harvests energy from an organic molecule to store it in the usable form of ATP. Cells harvest energy from an organic molecule, such as glucose, by breaking it down one reaction at a time. This releases the energy of the molecule in small amounts that can be captured.

Cellular respiration that requires oxygen is called *aerobic cellular respiration*. With each breath, you take in oxygen for your trillions of cells. You ultimately exhale the products: carbon dioxide and water. Aerobic respiration harvests energy from glucose in a process that can be described in three major stages: glycolysis, the Krebs cycle, and the electron transport chain (**Figure 6-20**). In eukaryotes, glycolysis occurs in the cytoplasm, while the Krebs cycle and electron transport chain take place within the mitochondria.

The overall pathway can be modeled with this chemical equation:

glucose + oxygen → carbon dioxide + water + energy

$$C_6H_{12}O_6 + O_2 \rightarrow CO_2 + H_2O + ATP$$

FIGURE 6-20
Trace the arrows to follow the movement of molecules through the steps of aerobic cellular respiration, noticing what reactants go into each step, and what products are generated.

SEP **Use a Model** *Compare the inputs and outputs of the chemical equation to the model shown in **Figure 6-20**. What are similarities and differences between the two models of aerobic cellular respiration?*

Glycolysis Glycolysis is a series of anaerobic reactions that produce ATP by splitting glucose (a six-carbon molecule) into two three-carbon molecules called *pyruvate*. The term *glycolysis* comes from *glyco*, which means "glucose," and *lysis*, which means "split." The pathway occurs in the cytoplasm of all cells, and it is the first step in both aerobic respiration and fermentation. The energy from this reaction is captured in electrons carried by NADH, and in high-energy phosphate bonds of ATP.

Acetyl-CoA Formation The two pyruvate molecules from glycolysis are not yet prepared for the next major stage. First the two pyruvate molecules move into a mitochondrion, where they are converted to acetyl-CoA, a molecule important in many reactions.

The Krebs Cycle The next stage of aerobic respiration, the *Krebs cycle*, releases energy from the acetyl-CoA molecule in a cyclical series of reactions. Energy released in these reactions is captured in electrons carried by NADH and FADH$_2$, and in high-energy phosphate bonds of ATP. All of the carbon atoms that were once part of glucose end up in CO$_2$ molecules, which diffuse out of the cell.

🧪 **CHAPTER INVESTIGATION**

Factors Affecting Cellular Respiration
What are some factors that affect cellular respiration in yeast?

Go online to explore this chapter's hands-on investigation to measure cellular respiration in yeast and observe how different factors affect that process.

Electron Transport Chain and ATP Synthase The last step of aerobic respiration is the **electron transport chain (Figure 6-21)**. In eukaryotes, this step occurs at the inner membrane of mitochondria. In prokaryotes, it occurs at infoldings of the inner cell membrane. Electrons and hydrogen ions are provided by the NADH and $FADH_2$ molecules generated by glycolysis and the Krebs cycle. Electrons flow through the electron transport chain and set up a hydrogen ion gradient that drives ATP synthesis. As the electrons move through the electron transport chain, they give up energy little by little. Molecules in the chain harness that energy to actively transport the hydrogen ions across the inner membrane, from the matrix to the intermembrane space.

The hydrogen ions pumped across the membrane by the electron transport chain pass back through a membrane channel that is part of the ATP synthase enzyme. As the hydrogen ions pass back along the gradient from high concentration to low concentration, they drive the formation of most of the ATP molecules formed during cellular respiration. Electrons and hydrogen ions in the intermembrane space combine with the electron acceptor molecule (O_2 in aerobic cellular respiration) to form water.

FIGURE 6-21

NADH and $FADH_2$ deliver electrons that provide energy to move hydrogen ions into the intermembrane space. Oxygen accepts the electrons and some hydrogen ions at the end of the chain, forming water. The concentration gradient drives hydrogen ions to pass back into the matrix, through the ATP synthase enzyme, which generates large amounts of ATP for the cell.

Other Energy Conversion Pathways

Fermentation Almost all cells can carry out **fermentation**, which is an anaerobic process similar to respiration that converts glucose to ATP that can be used by the cell. In fermentation, the overall gain in energy comes from glycolysis, and the rest of the process primarily serves to return molecules such as NAD⁺ to glycolysis so more ATP can be generated. Fermentation generates much less ATP than respiration processes. Many cells can switch between aerobic respiration and fermentation as needed. For example, when muscle cells run out of oxygen, they switch to a fermentation pathway that generates lactic acid. As lactic acid accumulates (often during exercise), muscles feel fatigued.

Fermentation pathways vary greatly and are named after their end product. Lactate fermentation performed by beneficial bacteria is used to prepare many foods that involve lactic acid. Yogurt, for example, is made by allowing bacteria such as *Lactobacillus bulgaricus* and *Streptococcus thermophilus* to grow in milk. Alcoholic fermentation converts glucose to ethyl alcohol. A yeast species called *Saccharomyces cerevisiae* (**Figure 6-22**) helps produce bread and other products through alcoholic fermentation.

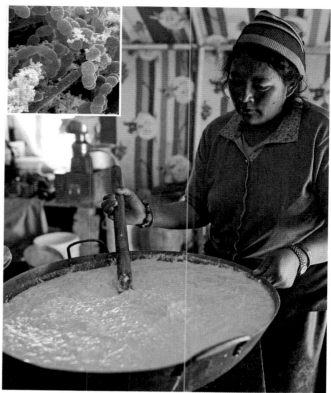

Anaerobic Cellular Respiration Early in the development of life on Earth, prior to photosynthesizing organisms, there was not an abundance of oxygen, and cellular respiration was all anaerobic. Now that Earth is an oxygen-rich environment, most organisms use aerobic respiration, but many bacteria and some other organisms still live in conditions with low or no oxygen. Anaerobic cellular respiration is cellular respiration that uses a molecule other than oxygen at the end of the electron transport chain.

Chemosynthesis In some ecosystems where there is no sunlight (**Figure 6-23**) photosynthetic organisms are not the primary producers of energy (Section 2.2). Chemosynthetic organisms get energy for assembly of their food molecules by removing electrons from inorganic substances such as hydrogen sulfide. Many of these organisms are bacteria and archaea that live in the deep ocean at hydrothermal vents or cold seeps.

FIGURE 6-22

Saccharomyces cerevisiae cells release CO_2 during fermentation, which forms pockets in bread. Yogurt is a product formed through lactate fermentation by *Lactobacillus bulgaricus* in milk. The scanning electron micrographs show these bacteria magnified by more than 2000 times.

 VIDEO

VIDEO 6-2 Go online to observe an example of an ecosystem that relies on chemosynthesis.

FIGURE 6-23

Bubbles of methane gas feed chemosynthetic bacteria at a cold seep at the Pascagoula Dome in the Gulf of Mexico. These chemosynthetic organisms support the growth of these mussels and other organisms, which then attract other animals to this deep-sea habitat.

CHAPTER INVESTIGATION

Designing a Photobioreactor
How can we maximize oxygen and algae production in a photobioreactor?

Go online to explore this chapter's hands-on investigation to design a photobioreactor that can generate energy and oxygen for use during space travel.

▶ **VIDEO**

VIDEO 6-3 Go online to find out more about photosynthesis from National Geographic Explorer Dr. Branwen Williams.

Photosynthesis

Photosynthesis is a pathway that uses the energy of sunlight to drive the synthesis of sugar molecules such as glucose from carbon dioxide and water. The sugars can be stored as polysaccharides for later use, remodeled into other compounds, or broken down to release the energy in their bonds through cellular respiration. Plants and most other autotrophs that harvest energy from the sun by photosynthesis are known as *producers* (Section 2.2).

In plants, photosynthetic protists, and cyanobacteria, the light-dependent reactions are carried out by molecules embedded in a thylakoid membrane. The light-independent reactions run in stroma, the thick, cytoplasm-like fluid that fills the chloroplast. The thylakoid membrane is suspended in the stroma. Similar to the membranes involved in the electron transport chain of cellular respiration, these highly folded membrane structures in the chloroplast are critical for generating ATP.

The structures of chloroplasts mentioned above are described in detail in Section 6.1. Chloroplasts are descendants of ancient cyanobacteria, so it is unsurprising that photosynthesis in eukaryotes is similar to photosynthesis in cyanobacteria. Modern cyanobacteria have thylakoid membranes that carry out the light-dependent reactions, and the light-independent reactions occur in the cytoplasm of these cells.

Photosynthesis is a complex pathway with many reactions. The details of the process are described in the Appendix. Photosynthesis can generally be represented by two major stages: light-dependent reactions and light-independent reactions (**Figure 6-24**).

The overall process of photosynthesis can be modeled by the following equation:

$$\text{carbon dioxide} + \text{water} \xrightarrow{\text{light}} \text{glucose} + \text{oxygen}$$
$$CO_2 + H_2O \xrightarrow{\text{light}} C_6H_{12}O_6 + O_2$$

FIGURE 6-24 ▶
Light drives the production of ATP during the light-dependent reactions in the thylakoid membranes. NADPH and oxygen are also produced. In the light-independent reactions that take place in the stroma, NADPH and ATP from the light-dependent reactions drive sugar production.

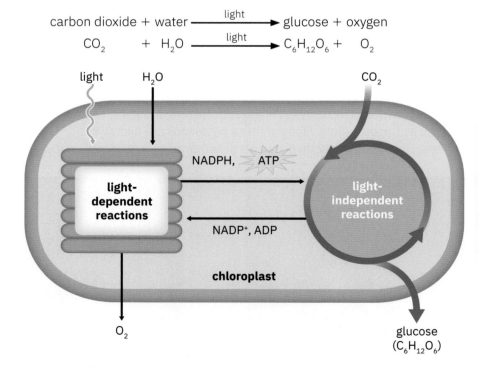

SEP **Use a Model** *Use **Figure 6-24** to describe the inputs and outputs for each of the two major stages of photosynthesis.*

Light-Dependent Reactions The reactions of the first stage of photosynthesis are driven by light and called the *light-dependent reactions*. Visible light is a small part of all the electromagnetic energy radiating from the sun. Visible light powers photosynthesis, which begins when light is absorbed by photosynthetic pigments. Different pigments absorb different colors of light. The main photosynthetic pigment, chlorophyll a, absorbs violet and red light, so it appears green. Most photosynthetic organisms use a combination of pigments to capture more light for photosynthesis.

The light-dependent pathway splits water molecules and releases oxygen. Hydrogen ions and electrons from the water molecules are loaded onto $NADP^+$ to form NADPH. Similar to cellular respiration, the light-dependent reactions of photosynthesis use the harvested energy to move hydrogen ions across a membrane with an electron transport chain. The gradient of hydrogen ions powers the enzyme ATP synthase to make ATP. ATP and NADPH are used to power the light-independent reactions that follow.

Light-Independent Reactions The second stage of photosynthesis builds sugar molecules such as glucose from carbon dioxide and water. They are collectively called the *light-independent reactions* because light energy does not power them. Instead, they run on energy delivered by NADPH and ATP that formed during the first stage. At the end of the second stage, $NADP^+$ and ADP are recycled to work again in the reactions of the first stage. Like many chemical reactions, this process is aided extensively by enzymes, such as rubisco, which helps convert carbon dioxide to glucose. Rubisco is one of the most abundant proteins on Earth.

SEP **Construct an Explanation** *Why are organisms capable of photosynthesis known as "producers" within their ecosystems?*

6.3 REVIEW

1. **Define** Link the processes involving matter and energy to photosynthesis or cellular respiration.

    • Glucose molecules are produced.

    • Glucose molecules are broken down.

    • Light is converted to chemical energy.

    • Stored energy is converted into chemical energy.

2. **Describe** Identify and describe the roles of two important enzymes involved in photosynthesis.

3. **Define** Which processes can proceed in the absence of oxygen? Select all correct answers.

    A. chemosynthesis

    B. alcoholic fermentation

    C. lactic acid fermentation

    D. aerobic cellular respiration

    E. anaerobic cellular respiration

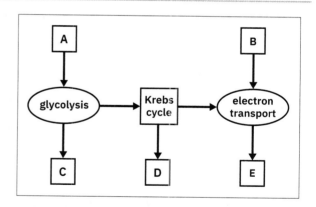

4. **Model** Complete a flowchart model of aerobic cellular respiration by labeling the inputs and outputs to each part of the process. You may use labels ATP, glucose, O_2, and CO_2 more than once.

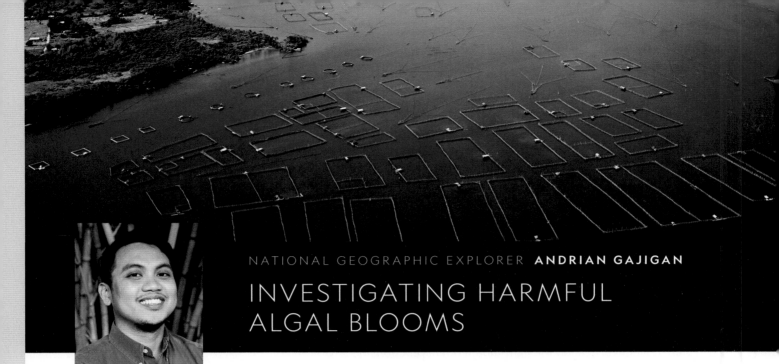

NATIONAL GEOGRAPHIC EXPLORER **ANDRIAN GAJIGAN**

INVESTIGATING HARMFUL ALGAL BLOOMS

In the first half of 2021, the Philippines Bureau of Fisheries and Aquatic Resources issued more than 20 shellfish alerts, recommending people avoid eating shellfish due to red tide toxins. If ingested, these toxins can be debilitating or even fatal for humans and ocean life. How can such red tide events be reduced or stopped? Biochemist Dr. Andrian Gajigan is trying to determine the answer.

Growing up in the Philippines, Gajigan witnessed firsthand the damage caused by harmful algal blooms (HABs), sometimes known as red tides. HABs form when rapid growth, or blooming, of single-celled organisms turns water red. In the Philippines, single-celled dinoflagellates and diatoms are responsible for HABs. Of the 2000 species of known dinoflagellates, roughly one-half are photosynthetic but only about 20 produce toxins.

Algal blooms can be beneficial as the photosynthesizing organisms fuel the ocean food web. When toxic species bloom, however, the toxins move through the food chain causing fish to die and shellfish to become dangerous to eat. The amount of photosynthesis occurring during blooms of toxic and nontoxic algal species does increase oxygen in the water. However, when large quantities of photosynthetic organisms die and decompose, so much oxygen is depleted from the water that many fish and other animals either leave the area or die because not enough oxygen is available to carry out cellular respiration.

Gajigan is investigating the role of viruses in red tides, focusing on those that infect dinoflagellates and other marine algae. Often, viruses keep populations of dinoflagellates in check. But viruses can also form symbiotic relationships with cells and give them a survival advantage. By studying the viruses, Gajigan is trying to figure out what encourages blooming algal growth and how it might be slowed or stopped.

Gajigan sees his research as an intersection of his fascination with science and community activism in his home country. Outside the lab, Gajigan encourages equity and inclusion in STEM fields. He wants to establish a research program in the Philippines to train the next generation of explorers and lead projects across the Asia-Pacific region as a way of staying connected to his roots.

THINKING CRITICALLY

Explain *Why are marine algae important in the ocean food web? Why would finding a way to slow or stop harmful algal blooms be important to society as well as to the environment?*

TYING IT ALL TOGETHER ENGINEERING
ARTIFICIAL CELL TECHNOLOGY

HOW DO STRUCTURES WORK TOGETHER IN CELL SYSTEMS?

In this chapter you learned about parts of cells and how those structures carry out particular functions in both prokaryotic and eukaryotic cells. Many scientists, inspired by the natural process of photosynthesis and its mechanisms in nature, have started to develop different methods of artificial or synthetic photosynthesis.

Photovoltaic cell technology has been used to build solar panels and solar arrays for decades (**Figure 6-25**). Over time, there have been major improvements in efficiency. However, there are still significant costs and material wastes associated with the technology. Researchers think artificial photosynthetic approaches can lead to more efficient and flexible modes of converting sunlight to usable energy by using materials that are readily available as parts of living cells. Although there are other carbon-based molecules that may be made by artificial photosynthesis pathways, the primary goal of many researchers is to use light energy to split water molecules and make hydrogen fuel.

Like other aspects of artificial cell research, studies of artificial photosynthesis include a wide variety of approaches. These approaches include harvesting chloroplasts for use in the construction of artificial cells and building synthetic cells that use photosynthetic pathways not present in nature (**Figure 6-26**).

In this activity you will research artificial photosynthesis and explain how it could be used to improve existing energy technologies.

Analyze the Problem

1. Scientists think artificial photosynthesis could be the key to the next generation of renewable energy technologies. Research how artificial photosynthesis works. Research at least two different approaches used by scientists to develop artificial photosynthesis systems.

Evaluate Solutions

2. Describe some current limitations of artificial photosynthesis. Compare artificial photosynthesis with other current renewable energy technologies, such as photovoltaic cells used in solar arrays. Describe some advantages that might come from further developments in artificial photosynthesis.

Science, Technology, and Society

3. Write an opinion article about why continually developing new and more efficient energy technologies is important for society and the environment.

FIGURE 6-25 ▽
An aerial photograph shows the extensive layout of photovoltaic cells built into rugged terrain in China.

FIGURE 6-26 ▽
Synthetic cells from the U.S. Department of Energy Joint Genome Institute contain tiny chloroplasts.

REVIEW KEY CONCEPTS

1. **Identify** Select the characteristics that describe a typical eukaryotic cell but NOT a typical prokaryotic cell. Select all correct answers.

   A. capable of dividing

   B. contains a nucleus

   C. has a cell membrane

   D. contains DNA in the form of a plasmid

   E. has complex membrane-enclosed organelles

2. **Identify** Name each of the described cellular structures.

   • contains a eukaryotic cell's DNA

   • has two forms: rough and smooth

   • is an organelle where the reactions of photosynthesis take place

   • is made up of microfilaments, intermediate filaments, and microtubules

   • is a membrane-enclosed sac used to transport materials from one organelle to another

3. **Classify** Identify each as prokaryotic or eukaryotic.

   • animals

   • archaea

   • bacteria

   • fungi

   • plants

4. **Draw Conclusions** With the help of transport proteins, many glucose molecules produced in a leaf cell during photosynthesis are moved into other cells of the plant. What type of membrane transport would be used to do this?

   A. endocytosis

   B. exocytosis

   C. facilitated diffusion

   D. osmosis

5. **Predict** Which stage of cellular respiration or photosynthesis would be unable to begin without carbon dioxide?

   A. glycolysis

   B. Krebs cycle

   C. light-dependent reaction

   D. light-independent reaction

6. **Compare** How is the role of NADPH in photosynthesis similar to the role of NADH in cellular respiration?

7. **Predict** What will happen to the phospholipid molecules in a lipid bilayer if they are disrupted and broken apart within an aqueous environment?

8. **Describe** Which stage of cellular respiration takes place in the cytoplasm of the eukaryotic cell?

   A. acetyl-CoA formation

   B. electron transport chain

   C. glycolysis

   D. Krebs cycle

9. **Label** Determine which type of membrane-embedded protein—enzyme, adhesion protein, receptor protein, or transport protein—is described by each phrase below.

   • facilitates chemical reactions

   • attaches a cell to surrounding cells

   • controls entry of substances into the cell

   • senses signals from the extracellular environment

10. **Explain** Why is the term *fluid mosaic* used to describe cellular membranes?

11. **Analyze** In the absence of oxygen, a certain organism is still able to produce ATP from glucose. Which process is the organism likely utilizing?

    A. chemosynthesis

    B. fermentation

    C. Krebs cycle

    D. light-independent reaction

CRITICAL THINKING

12. **Explain** What advantage do eukaryotic cells derive from having membrane-enclosed organelles, which are lacking in prokaryotic cells?

13. **Explain** Both chloroplasts and mitochondria have complex inner membranes with a high number of folds. What is the advantage of having folded, convoluted inner membranes?

14. **NOS** **Scientific Knowledge** Antoni van Leeuwenhoek made incorrect assumptions as he observed microscopic organisms for the first time. How have advancements in microscopy increased our understanding of cells?

15. **Explain** Respiration can refer to gas exchanges that occur when breathing air in and out of the lungs, as well as to the chemical reactions that take place in mitochondria. What similarities are there between these two processes that make the use of the word *respiration* appropriate for both?

16. **Compare** What distinguishes vacuoles from other types of vesicles?

17. **Explain** Describe how carbon cycling in ecosystems relates to the processes of photosynthesis and cellular respiration.

MATH AND ENGLISH LANGUAGE ARTS CONNECTIONS

1. **Synthesize Information** The words *hypotonic* and *hypertonic* are used in this chapter to describe solute concentration. Name some other words that use the prefixes *hypo-* and *hyper-*. How do the definitions of those words relate to the meanings of hypotonic and hypertonic?

2. **Model With Mathematics** Sketch a graph to show how the amount of glucose produced during photosynthesis would change over the course of a year in a tree that loses its leaves in the winter. Describe the shape of the graph.

3. **Reason Quantitatively** The cellular structures described in this chapter are very small and could not be observed until microscopes were invented. Cells vary in size, but many eukaryotic cells are about 10 micrometers (μm) in diameter. The human eye can only see objects as small as about 0.1 millimeter (mm) in size. Assuming that the average size of a eukaryotic cell is 10 μm, how many eukaryotic cells, end to end, could fit onto a 0.1-mm line?

Read the following excerpt from the writings of Antoni van Leeuwenhoek about his early observations of microorganisms. Use evidence from the passage to answer the question.

I then most always saw, with great wonder, that in the said matter there were many very little living animalcules, very prettily a-moving. The biggest sort ... had a very strong and swift motion, and shot through the water ... like a pike does through the water. The second sort ... oft-times spun round like a top ... the other animalcules were in such enormous numbers, that all the water ... seemed to be alive.

4. **Draw Evidence From Texts** What did van Leeuwenhoek find most interesting about his observations? How does the focus of his observations differ from what a microbiologist might focus on today?

▶ REVISIT BACTERIA IN YOUR GUT

Gather Evidence In this chapter, you learned bacterial cells have structures and mechanisms that allow them to survive and obtain energy inside the intestines. However, dietary changes and medications can drastically change the types and amounts of bacteria growing in the human gut and can sometimes lead to illness.

1. Sometimes people taking antibiotics experience an increase in pathogenic bacteria populations in their gut and develop gastrointestinal illness as a result. How do you think antibiotics might cause this?

2. What other questions do you have about how changes in the variety of gut bacteria can negatively affect human health?

CHAPTER 7

CELL GROWTH

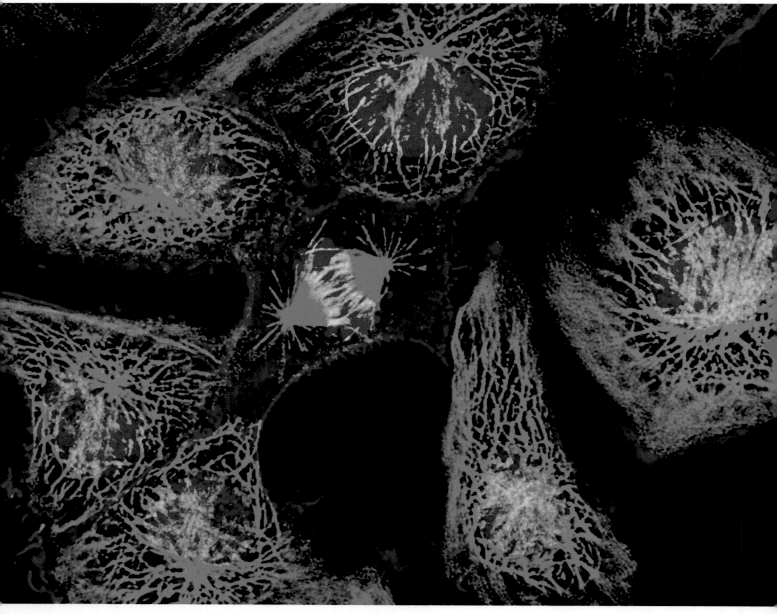

Fluorescent dyes brightly highlight DNA (yellow/orange) and microtubules (green) in cells originally from the kidney of an African clawed frog. The center cell is undergoing mitosis.

For multicellular organisms to grow and survive, their cells must continually replicate and divide. But when this process doesn't occur in an orderly manner, things can quickly go awry.

Chapter 7 supports the NGSS Performance Expectations **HS-LS1-1** and **HS-LS1-4**.

CASE STUDY
IMMORTAL CELLS: THE STORY OF HENRIETTA LACKS

HOW DO CELLS DIVIDE AND GROW?

In February 1951, the onset of puzzling symptoms led 31-year-old Henrietta Lacks to visit a doctor at Johns Hopkins Hospital in Baltimore, Maryland. Lacks was diagnosed with what would turn out to be an aggressive form of cervical cancer. She would be dead within the year, leaving behind her husband and their five children.

Without obtaining Lacks's consent—a common practice at the time—a biopsy of her cervical tissue was given to Dr. George Gey's tissue lab at Johns Hopkins. There, the scientists discovered that, unlike most other cells, the cells from her tissue sample doubled every 20–24 hours. This discovery led to the cultivation of the first line of living human cells. Although Lacks died on October 4, 1951, her immortal cells continue to live on today.

These cells were named "HeLa" cells, using the first two letters of her first and last names, although her true identity was not released to the public until many years later. Many scientists consider this line of cells to be one of the most important biomedical breakthroughs of the 20th century. In addition to an integral role in the development of the polio vaccine, HeLa cells have also

been used to study a variety of viruses and diseases, including human immunodeficiency virus (HIV) and tuberculosis. They have also been used to study the effects of hormones, toxins, and drugs on the growth of cancer cells. The discovery that a certain stain could be used on HeLa cells to make their chromosomes visible led to breakthroughs in genetic medicine. This technique allowed scientists to find genetic links to diseases such as Down syndrome and led to the development of genetic screening tests such as amniocentesis.

Two Nobel Prizes have been awarded to scientists who used HeLa cells in their scientific investigations, including research on human papillomavirus (HPV), a virus that causes cervical cancer. HeLa cells have been used in tens of thousands of published studies. Trillions of HeLa cells are in use as a part of scientific research around the world. HeLa cells have even been sent into space to help determine the effects of low gravity and radiation on cell growth.

Ask Questions *As you read, generate questions about why controlled cell division is important for the growth and maintenance of organisms. Consider what makes HeLa cells different from other cells.*

FIGURE 7-1 ▽
Cells taken from Henrietta Lacks (1920–1951) were used to develop HeLa cell lines.

FIGURE 7-2 ▽
A scientist at the Curie Institute in Paris, France, observes HeLa cells using fluorescent microscopy to visualize the location of a specific protein, shown in red on the computer screen.

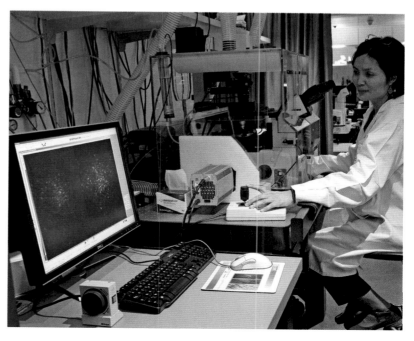

7.1

KEY TERMS

apoptosis
binary fission
cytokinesis
interphase
mitosis
oncogene

CELL CYCLES

The human body grows by dividing its cells to make new ones. Think about the average size of a fifth grade school student and how much taller they will grow in the four years until they start high school. Now think about an adult you know and whether they have grown any taller over a four-year time frame.

Analyze *Consider the types of cells in a human, such as blood cells and skin cells. Do you think cells in your body all grow and divide at the same rate?*

▶ **VIDEO**

VIDEO 7-1 Go online to see how quickly *E. coli* grow and divide.

Life Cycles

In biology, a life cycle is a sequence of distinct stages that occur during an organism's lifetime, from a single cell, through development, until that individual's death. Consider the life cycle of a butterfly, for example: egg, larva (caterpillar), pupa (chrysalis), and adult (butterfly). At each stage, the butterfly looks and acts differently. Individual cells also have a life cycle and a life span.

Prokaryotic Cell Cycle Prokaryotic cell cycles are generally described in three parts that include (1) the time between reproduction events, (2) the replication of DNA, and (3) the completion of cell duplication. Bacteria typically reproduce by **binary fission**, a type of asexual reproduction (**Figure 7-3**). The process begins when the cell replicates its single chromosome. Addition of new membrane and wall material elongates the cell to nearly double its size and moves the two DNA molecules apart. Membrane and cell wall material are deposited across the cell's midsection, yielding two identical descendant cells.

FIGURE 7-3 ▽
The bacterial cell (a) duplicates its chromosome (b), then divides (c) after nearly doubling in size. The new cells (d) can then begin the cycle and duplicate again.

3a → 3b → 3c → 3d

The growth rate of bacteria is affected by the availability of resources. When environmental conditions are optimal and enough resources are available to double their mass and their DNA, bacteria will rapidly proceed to the reproductive part of their cell cycle. If resources are scarce, they will divide more slowly.

Under optimal conditions in a laboratory setting, *Escherichia coli* can divide every 20 minutes and quickly grow exponentially into a huge number of new organisms. The *E. coli* that are widely present in the human digestive system have access to an abundance of carbohydrates and a favorable growth temperature, but they also have to deal with competition from other species and rapid changes in conditions and nutrition provided by their host.

▼ BACTERIA IN YOUR GUT

Gather Evidence *E. coli and other bacterial populations can grow incredibly quickly. What factors help keep the different types of bacteria in the human gut in balance so no one type of bacteria takes over?*

Eukaryotic Cell Cycle Dividing eukaryotic cells pass through a series of intervals and events shown in **Figure 7-4**. A typical cell spends most of its time in interphase. During **interphase**, the cell increases its mass, roughly doubles the number of its cytoplasmic components, and copies its chromosomes in preparation for division. Interphase is typically the longest part of the cycle, and it consists of three stages: G1, S, and G2. G1 and G2 were named "Gap" intervals because outwardly they seem to be periods of inactivity, but they are not. Most cells are building molecules and performing other functions during G1.

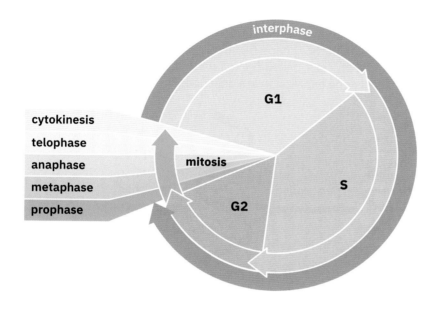

FIGURE 7-4
G1, S, and G2 are part of interphase, and the length of these intervals differs among cells. Mitosis includes several stages that describe how a cell's DNA is divided into two nuclei.

Go Online	**SIMULATION**

Go online to examine how a cell grows and divides during the **Eukaryotic Cell Cycle**.

Cells preparing to divide enter S ("synthesis") phase, when DNA replication occurs (**Figure 7-5**). In G2, cells continue to grow and make proteins.

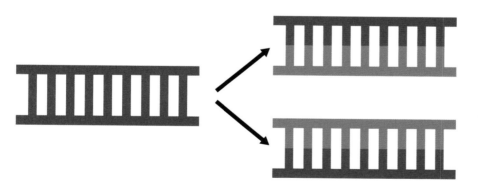

FIGURE 7-5
DNA is replicated in the S phase of the cell cycle. DNA replication is described as *semiconservative* because each strand of the original DNA is paired with a new DNA strand to form two copies. Details of the mechanism of DNA replication are described in Chapter 11.

The remainder of the cell cycle consists of the cell division process. **Mitosis** is a mechanism for cellular division that maintains the correct number of chromosomes. The cytoplasm usually undergoes **cytokinesis** after mitosis, dividing the cytoplasm and pinching the cell membrane to produce two new descendant cells. The steps of mitosis will be described in detail in the next section.

SEP **Construct an Explanation** *How do you think the cell cycles might be different for a fast-growing bacterium, compared with a cell in a fully grown multicellular organism?*

Eukaryotic Cell Cycle Control

Cell division is tightly regulated via changes in gene expression. Like the accelerator of a car enables it to move forward, some changes cause the cell cycle to advance. Other mechanisms are like car brakes, pausing the cell cycle. In the adult human body, brakes on the cell cycle normally keep the vast majority of cells in a resting state known as G0. Most of your nerve cells, skeletal muscle cells, heart muscle cells, and fat-storing cells spend most of your life resting.

Genes are functional units of DNA. When genes are expressed, an RNA copy of the gene is generated and used to build a protein (**Figure 7-6**). The genes expressed and timing of gene expression not only control the cell cycle but also ultimately shape the identity of each cell in a multicellular organism. This process, called *cell differentiation*, is discussed in Section 7.3. Details of gene expression are described in Section 11.3.

FIGURE 7-6 ▶

Genes are functional units of DNA that carry information. That information is typically transcribed into an RNA molecule that is used by ribosomes to instruct the synthesis of proteins. Proteins perform most of the work in the cell, including those functions that regulate the cell cycle.

DNA   transcription   RNA   translation   protein

Built-in checkpoints in the cell cycle ensure that the cell does not progress from one phase to another unless certain criteria are met. For example, adequate nutrients are available to support cell growth, cellular damage is identified and repaired, and the entire genome has been completely and accurately copied. Protein products of "checkpoint genes" interact to carry out this control process. The primary checkpoints represent an opportunity for the cell to pause or terminate cell division—each of these checkpoints is regulated by a different subset of checkpoint genes.

For example, a checkpoint that operates in S phase monitors the cell's chromosomes for damage during DNA replication. Checkpoint proteins that function as sensors recognize damaged DNA and bind to it. Upon binding, they trigger other events that stall the cell cycle, and also enhance expression of genes involved in DNA repair. After the problem has been corrected, the brakes are lifted and the cell cycle proceeds. If the problem remains uncorrected, other checkpoint proteins may initiate a series of events that eventually cause the cell to self-destruct.

SEP **Use a Model** *Using the steps shown in the eukaryotic cell cycle model (**Figure 7-4**), explain when you think checkpoint genes would be expressed. When do you think genes involved in replicating and repairing DNA might be expressed?*

Cancer Disruption of cell cycle checkpoints can have negative consequences. Checkpoint genes (and their protein products) are often involved in mechanisms that cause cancer. Sometimes a random or inherited mutation in a checkpoint gene results in a dysfunctional protein product. In other cases, the expression of a checkpoint gene is wrong, and a cell makes too much or too little of its product. When checkpoint mechanisms fail, a cell loses the ability to repair damage and/or replicate the genome accurately. The problem is compounded when checkpoint malfunctions are passed along to the cell's descendants. Over time, this uncontrolled cell growth can lead to tumor formation.

A gene that has a tumor-causing mutation is called an **oncogene**. An oncogene can transform a normal cell into a tumor cell. Oncogene mutations in reproductive cells can be passed to offspring, which is a reason that some types of tumors run in families. Genes that are involved in cell growth that can mutate to become oncogenes are called *proto-oncogenes*.

One proto-oncogene (*EGFR*) encodes an epidermal growth factor (EGF) receptor that binds EGF molecules. When a normal EGF receptor binds an EGF molecule, it triggers the cell to begin mitosis (**Figure 7-7a**). Mutations in the *EGFR* gene can change the EGF receptor so that it stimulates mitosis even in the absence of EGF molecules (**Figure 7-7b, c**). Many tumors have mutations in the *EGFR* gene.

VIDEO

VIDEO 7-2 Go online to learn more about how cancer begins.

FIGURE 7-7 ▽
Under normal circumstances, an EGF receptor stimulates mitosis only when it binds an EGF molecule (a). However, a mutated EGF receptor can stimulate mitosis constantly, leading to excess cell division and cancer (b). The photo (c) shows human breast tissue labeled with a brown tracer molecule that marks active EGF receptors. These cells are dividing uncontrollably.

7a

normal EGF receptor

EGF

EGF

receptor stimulates mitosis only after EGF binds

7b

mutated EGF receptor

receptor stimulates mitosis constantly

7c

Other genes may cause cancer when mutations ruin the function of their protein products. Tumor suppressor genes code for proteins that are related to DNA repair and other regulatory functions. When these proteins are missing, tumors form. The protein products of checkpoint genes called *BRCA1* and *BRCA2* are tumor suppressors. The *BRCA* gene products help maintain the structure and number of chromosomes during mitosis and repair damaged DNA. They also play a role in regulating growth factors for cells of breast and ovarian tissues. Mutations in these genes lead to tumors in the breast, prostate, ovary, and other tissues.

FIGURE 7-8 ▶

Tadpoles develop back legs and then front legs as they turn into adult frogs. The cells of the tadpole's tail are eliminated through apoptosis during development.

Cell Death and Apoptosis As organisms grow and develop, sometimes cells need to be replaced or removed, ending the cell cycle. One way that cells die is through a controlled process called apoptosis. **Apoptosis**, or programmed cell death, is a process by which a cell self-destructs in a controlled, predictable manner. During apoptosis, enzymes destroy a cell's parts. Some enzymes chop up cytoskeletal proteins and the histones that organize DNA. Others snip apart nucleic acids. As a result of this self-inflicted damage, the cell shrivels up and dies without spewing out its contents. These cells are engulfed by other cells, and many of the remaining parts are broken down and recycled. In a mature organism, apoptosis plays a role in normal cell turnover and in defense against cancer. During development, apoptosis shapes structures by eliminating excess cells, removing those cells that do not contribute to the expected final form. For example, in the development of an adult frog, a tadpole's tail is eliminated through apoptosis (**Figure 7-8**).

7.1 REVIEW

1. **Calculate** Under ideal conditions, how long would it take a colony of 1000 *E. coli* bacteria to reach a population size of 64,000 cells?

2. **Model** Create a simple flow chart for the three stages of interphase as a cell prepares to divide.

3. **Summarize** At the most basic level, what is the difference between a cancer cell and a normal cell? Why do cancer cells result in tumors?

4. **Define** Which processes are affected by checkpoint genes during the cell cycle? Select all correct answers.

   A. cell differentiation

   B. repair of damaged DNA

   C. recognition of DNA replication errors

   D. self-destruction of cells with certain problems

   E. monitoring for favorable conditions for duplication

IDENTIFYING GENE MUTATIONS IN CANCER CELLS

SEP **Analyze and Interpret Data** Gene mutations that cause cancerous tumors can be identified in tissue samples.

Cancerous tumors are often the result of gene mutations that cause some genes to be expressed too much or cause other genes to shut down and not function. One technique called a DNA microarray can detect the expression of genes in tissue samples. In a DNA microarray, the DNA for each gene being tested is attached to individual spots in an array of many wells.

Test samples are generated by making DNA that matches all the genes expressed in the cells of a tissue sample. Healthy cell DNA is marked with one color of fluorescent dye, and the cancer cell DNA is marked with another color of fluorescent dye. The dyes fluoresce or "light up" when the test DNA matches up with the DNA attached to the well. When the samples are added together to the microarray, the resulting color of fluorescent light tells scientists whether the genes are expressed in normal cells, cancer cells, or both. Microarrays in the lab are designed to test the expression of thousands of genes at once.

Figure 1 is a representation of the results of a partial DNA microarray performed on two tissue samples, one with normal cells and one with cancer cells, collected from the same type of tissue. **Table 1** identifies the genes being tested in each well.

DNA Microarray Results

FIGURE 1
Results of a DNA microarray are shown. Each microarray well tests one specific gene. The fluorescence color in each well of the microarray indicates which cells in the samples (normal or cancer) are expressing each gene. The colors have the following meanings:

If the well is red, the gene is expressed at a higher level in cancer cells.

If the well is green, the gene is expressed at a higher level in normal cells.

If the well is yellow, the gene is expressed equally in both types of cells.

TABLE 1. The Roles of the Genes Tested in the DNA Microarray

A	supports cellular structure and shape		F	provides strength to cells in skin, hair, and nails
B	encourages cell growth		G	secretes mucus to line air pathways
C	stops cells from dividing too fast		H	enables lung cells to expand and contract
D	encourages cell growth		I	stops cells from dividing too fast
E	provides strength to cells in skin, hair, and nails			

---

1. **Organize Data** Interpret the results of the DNA microarray to identify how genes are expressed in normal and cancer cells.

2. **Classify** Using the data given in **Figure 1** and **Table 1**, identify the oncogenes and mutated tumor suppressor genes.

3. **Analyze** Based on the results, how do you think the cancerous cells compare with normal cells? Explain your answer.

4. **Infer** Based on the genes being tested, what type of tissue sample was most likely used in this DNA microarray test?

   A. hair   **C.** nail

   B. lung   **D.** skin

MITOSIS

Imagine you are preparing for a classroom crafting project and are responsible for making sure each of your classmates all have the same materials available for the project. Each craft station needs to have the exact same items, such as glue, paper, string, and wire, so every student can complete the task successfully. Similarly, when cells divide, they need to ensure new cells all end up with the correct materials to live.

Infer *Why do you think it would be important for a dividing cell to make sure all of the new cells have the same contents?*

Chromosomes

Most prokaryotes have a single circular chromosome. By contrast, most eukaryotic cells have multiple chromosomes that differ in length and shape. Human cells have 46 chromosomes. Stretched out end to end, the double-stranded DNA in a single human cell would be about 2 m (6.5 ft) long, but all that DNA fits into a nucleus less than 10 micrometers in diameter. Proteins that associate with DNA help keep it organized and can help to pack DNA very tightly when needed. In eukaryotes, a DNA molecule wraps at regular intervals around proteins called *histones*. These DNA-histone spools look like beads on a string in micrographs (**Figure 7-9a**). Interactions among histones coil the DNA into a tight fiber. A typical eukaryotic chromosome consists of one DNA molecule and its many associated proteins.

In preparation for mitosis, a eukaryotic cell will duplicate its chromosomes through DNA replication (Section 11.2). After replication, the two identical DNA molecules are referred to as **sister chromatids**, attached to one another at a constricted region called the *centromere*. The duplicated chromosomes condense fully into their familiar "X" shapes (**Figure 7-9b**) before the cell divides.

FIGURE 7-9 ▶
At regular intervals, the double-stranded DNA molecule is wrapped around a core of histone proteins (a). The DNA and proteins associated with it twist tightly into a fiber. The fiber coils multiple times and at its most condensed, a duplicated eukaryotic chromosome has an X shape (b). This structure consists of two identical DNA molecules (sister chromatids) attached at a centromere.

9a

9b

Mitosis

In the human body, somatic cells are those that are not involved in reproduction. These cells are diploid, which means they contain two copies of each chromosome. One set of chromosomes is contributed by an egg and the other set is contributed by a sperm in the process of fertilization. Except for a pairing of different sex chromosomes (XY) in males, the chromosomes of each pair are homologous, or the same. Females have matching sex chromosomes (XX). **Homologous chromosomes** have the same length, shape, and centromere location, and they carry the same genes. However, they do not have the exact same DNA sequence, unlike the sister chromatids produced by DNA replication.

The two homologous chromosomes of a pair are not identical. They are inherited from the gametes (egg, sperm) of two genetically distinct parents. Cell division by mitosis produces two cellular descendants, each with the same number of chromosomes as the original cell (**Figure 7-10**). In addition to total number, each descendant cell must inherit the full complement of chromosomes, without duplicates or missing chromosomes. A cell cannot function properly without a copy of each chromosome.

CASE STUDY
IMMORTAL CELLS: THE STORY OF HENRIETTA LACKS

Ask Questions *Although Henrietta Lacks's original cells had 46 chromosomes, most HeLa cell lines now have between 70 and 90 chromosomes, among other changes. What other questions do you have about HeLa cells and how they are different from the somatic cells in your body?*

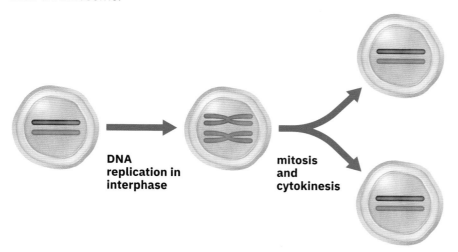

DNA replication in interphase

mitosis and cytokinesis

FIGURE 7-10
Mitosis maintains the correct number of chromosomes. One homologous chromosome is inherited from each parent. DNA replication results in sister chromatids, identical copies of each chromosome. Then, mitosis and cytokinesis separate the sister chromatids into two new cells. Each descendant cell is genetically identical to the parent cell.

Compare **Figure 7-10** with the cell cycle diagram shown in Section 7.1 (**Figure 7-4**). When a cell is in G1, each of its chromosomes is made of one double-stranded DNA molecule. DNA replication occurs during the synthesis, or S phase, so by G2 each chromosome has two double-stranded DNA molecules.

These sister chromatids stay attached to one another until mitosis is almost over, and then they are pulled apart and packaged into two separate nuclei. When sister chromatids are pulled apart, each becomes an individual chromosome that consists of one double-stranded DNA molecule. Thus, each of the two new nuclei that form by mitosis contains the same number and types of chromosomes as the parent cell. During cytokinesis, these nuclei are packaged into separate cells. Each new cell starts its life in G1 of interphase.

SEP **Construct an Explanation** *What are the differences between homologous chromosomes and sister chromatids?*

FIGURE 7-11 ▼

Although mitosis is a continual process, it is often described in stages. Micrographs show plant cells (onion root, *left*) and animal cells (fertilized eggs of a roundworm, *center*) at each stage. The illustrations (*right*) demonstrate mitosis for a diploid cell with two chromosome pairs. The nucleus and chromosomes are enlarged to show each stage.

interphase

early prophase

late prophase

metaphase

anaphase

telophase

Stages of Mitosis and the Cell Cycle

Mitosis can be divided into separate stages (**Figure 7-11**). These stages include:

- **Interphase** Cells prepare for mitosis during this stage of the cell cycle. When a cell is in interphase, its chromosomes are relaxed in many regions to allow gene expression and DNA replication.

- **Early Prophase** Chromosome condensation begins. A tightly condensed structure keeps the chromosomes from getting tangled and breaking during division. As prophase continues, the nuclear envelope breaks up. Fibers form the *mitotic spindle,* a specialized structure of microtubules and other molecules.

- **Late Prophase** This stage is sometimes called prometaphase. As the nuclear envelope completely breaks down and chromosomes fully condense, spindle fibers made of microtubules extend from opposite poles, attaching to chromosomes at the centromere. The individual sister chromatids are each attached to a spindle fiber (one from each pole). The spindle fibers begin moving the chromosomes to the center.

- **Metaphase** During this stage, a fully formed mitotic spindle with sister chromatids all attached to the spindle aligns at the center of the cell.

- **Anaphase** During anaphase, spindle microtubules separate the sister chromatids of each duplicated chromosome and move them toward opposite poles of the cell.

- **Telophase** This stage begins when one set of chromosomes reaches each spindle pole. Each set consists of the same number and kinds of chromosomes that the parent cell nucleus had before replication. The nuclear envelope reassembles around each set of chromosomes as they decondense. At this point, mitosis is finished.

- **Cytokinesis** After mitosis is completed, the cell membrane pinches to form a cleavage furrow to separate the cell into two new cells (in animals) or forms a cell plate for the separation (in plants).

CCC **Structure and Function** *How is the structure of sister chromatids important in ensuring that each resulting nucleus gets one of each chromosome during the stages of mitosis?*

VIDEO

VIDEO 7-3 Go online to watch ovary cells from a hamster undergo mitosis.

△ CHAPTER INVESTIGATION

Plant Growth Through Mitosis
How do rates of cell division relate to plant growth?

Go online to explore this chapter's hands-on investigation about mitosis in plants.

7.2 REVIEW

1. **Model** Describe how you would construct a simple structural model of a single eukaryotic chromosome using large beads, string, and any other materials you might need. Identify the role of each material in the model.

2. **Relate** Human cells have 46 chromosomes. How many of these chromosomes come from the father and how many come from the mother?

3. **Sequence** Describe mitosis by ordering processes that occur during different stages.

   - Nuclear envelope breaks up completely.
   - Nuclear envelope forms around chromosomes.
   - Sister chromatids are aligned in the middle of the cell.
   - Chromosomes in the nucleus begin to condense around centromeres.
   - Sister chromatids are pulled apart toward opposite poles of the cell.

MODELING MITOSIS

SEP **Develop a Model** How can cell growth be modeled?

Cell division allows organisms to make more cells and grow. Before cells can divide from one cell into two descendant cells, the replicated chromosomes in the cell must separate into two new nuclei. In this activity, you will build models showing what happens during each step of mitosis in an animal cell.

This cell is dividing abnormally, with the DNA (yellow) separating into three new cells.

Suggested Materials

- camera, tablet, computer
- craft paper, poster paper
- beans, moldable clay, pasta, yarn
- pipe cleaners, bendable wire
- scissors, glue, transparent tape

Procedure

1. Decide whether you will make a digital or physical model.

2. List the materials you will use to build your model.

3. Discuss with your teacher how you will make and present your model.

4. If building a physical model, determine what materials will represent each of these parts: cell membrane, chromosomes (sister chromatids), nuclear envelope, and spindle fibers.

5. Build and label a model of the cell that has three to four pairs of chromosomes going through mitosis. Your model should represent what happens in the cell during early prophase, late prophase (or prometaphase), metaphase, anaphase, and telophase.

6. Once you are done, clean up and return unused materials to the materials station.

Results and Analysis

1. **Evaluate** Consider the materials you selected to represent various components of the cell during mitosis. Were these materials good choices for representing the structure and function of each cell component? Why or why not?

2. **Compare** How many chromosomes were in the nucleus at the start of prophase compared with the number of chromosomes in each of the two new nuclei at the end of telophase? Explain why there is a difference.

3. **Draw Conclusions** Some herbicides work by preventing the formation of spindle fibers in plant cells. Using your models, explain how these herbicides would affect mitosis.

4. **Explain** In some cases, the mitotic spindles cannot attach properly to some of the chromosomes. As the chromosomes are pulled apart to the poles of the cell, some chromatids cannot be pulled at the same speed and start to lag. Using your models, explain which stage of mitosis would be affected and the likely result of this situation.

CELL DIFFERENTIATION

Think about how different parts of your school are organized to match their function. Classrooms may be full of chairs and desks, while a gym or other large room might have extra space for students to move. A cafeteria might have long tables for eating. The cells in multicellular organisms are in some ways like the different rooms and areas that make up your school.

KEY TERMS

cell differentiation
meristem
stem cell

Explain *Similar to different rooms in your school, multicellular organisms have different cell types. Why do you think organisms need a variety of cells?*

Multicellular Organisms

All cells in sexually reproducing organisms are derived from a single cell, the *zygote*. Consider the anatomy of the organisms in **Figure 7-12**. Each of their very distinct structures is made up of cells, and those cells in each organism all contain the same exact *genome*. How can these different structures develop if the cells all contain the same "instructions"? As the cells divide and the organism develops, different cell types express different subsets of genes. This is called *selective gene expression*. It is the key to **cell differentiation**, the process by which cells become specialized to serve different functions in a multicellular living system (Sections 9.1 and 10.2). Cell differentiation can also be affected by factors in the environment that cause changes in gene expression, such as nutrient availability and temperature.

FIGURE 7-12 ▼
What do an ocean sunfish in the Pacific Ocean, an armadillo in the United States, a South American green mantis, and a dragon blood tree in Yemen have in common? Each of these organisms started from a single cell that led to many differentiated cell types.

Stem Cells

Stem cells are special undifferentiated cells. Their descendants can be either stem cells or they can become different specialized cell types that make up the tissues and organs of a complex organism. The cells shown in **Figure 7-13**, as well as many other cell types, make up the tissues and organs of multicellular organisms (Section 10.2).

Most multicellular organisms replace or repair damaged cells and tissues lost to injury, but some organisms have a unique capacity for regeneration. Some sea stars, for example, can regrow an entire body from a single arm and a bit of the central disk. No vertebrate can grow a body from a limb, but many salamanders and lizards can replace a lost tail.

FIGURE 7-13
Each cell in an organism has the same set of DNA instructions, but different genes are expressed. A small selection of human cell types is shown here.

fat cell

muscle cell

nerve cell

stem cell

immune cell

skin cell

STEM CELL RESEARCH Researchers use stem cells to investigate normal cell differentiation and disease progression, to produce healthy cells to replace damaged or diseased cells that the body cannot replace on its own, and to test the safety and efficacy of drugs.

Stem cells with pluripotency have the most promise in regenerative medicine, because they can give rise to all cell types in the human body. One source of pluripotent human embryonic stem cells is from donated or nonviable human embryos (blastocyst stage). Another source is to use "reprogrammed" cells—cells obtained from adult tissue that have been genetically engineered for pluripotency. These cells, called induced pluripotent stem (iPS) cells, behave like embryonic stem cells. To produce iPS cells, for example, fibroblasts from skin are converted to iPS cells by introducing synthetically modified RNAs. The RNAs are taken up by fibroblasts, then translated into proteins that induce dedifferentiation, which is the opposite of differentiation.

There are many remaining questions and technological hurdles for using stem cells in the treatment of human disease, but some results have been promising. An iPS cell–based therapy for a degenerative form of blindness known as age-related macular degeneration has improved vision in a small number of patients. Stem cell–based treatments for a variety of conditions have also proven effective in animal models. For example, researchers have used embryonic stem cells to cure diabetes in mice.

Axolotls, which are a type of salamander, can regenerate limbs, spinal cord, and parts of the brain and heart. This makes them a popular model for researchers who study regeneration. Mammals cannot regenerate entire structures. However, they do have the ability to regenerate tissues over time, including the skin, blood, intestinal lining, and liver. Stem cells and other similar cells are key to producing new or replacement tissues.

Human embryonic stem cells form soon after fertilization, when mitotic divisions produce a small cluster of cells. Each cell in the cluster is *pluripotent,* meaning it can develop into any of the cell types in a human body. Stem cells become more specialized as development continues. In an adult, for example, blood stem cells located in bone marrow give rise to both red and white blood cell types but not muscle cells or nerve cells.

Skin cells, blood cells, and other cell types that your body replaces on an ongoing basis arise continually from adult stem cells. Skin or blood lost to injury can be replaced. However, organs or tissues such as the heart and brain, for example, do not have a robust adult stem cell population. Thus, some tissues are not replaced if they are damaged or lost. Death of cardiac muscle cells during a heart attack permanently weakens the heart, and spinal cord injuries can result in permanent paralysis.

CCC **Structure and Function** *Observe the different cell types shown in* **Figure 7-13***. Describe how you think two of the cell type structures are likely to support their functions.*

Meristem Cells
A young plant grows mainly by lengthening. An older woody plant grows by lengthening and thickening. During both processes, tissues arise from the activity of meristems. A **meristem** is a region of undifferentiated cells that divides continually during the growing season. Meristem cells in plants are comparable to stem cells in animals. When they divide, some meristem cells differentiate while others remain undifferentiated. In plants, the differentiating cells give rise to specialized tissues as they enlarge and mature.

CHAPTER INVESTIGATION

Cell Differentiation in Plant Leaves
Can leaf structures be identified based on the appearance of differentiated cells?
Go online to explore this chapter's hands-on investigation on how cells in a leaf differentiate.

Figure 7-14 shows some of the cell types found in plants. Plants have two primary organs: roots (typically underground) and shoots (stems and leaves). These organs are made up of three different tissue types, including dermal, vascular, and ground tissue. The dermal tissue system consists of cells that cover and protect the plant's surfaces. The vascular tissue system includes the cells that carry water and nutrients from one part of the plant to another. The ground tissue system is essentially everything that is not part of the dermal or vascular tissue systems. Cells that carry out the most basic processes for survival (growth, photosynthesis, and storage) are part of the ground tissue system. More details of plant tissues, organs, and systems are described in Section 9.1.

FIGURE 7-14 ▼
Primary (apical) meristem growth is shown in a shoot tip of privet (a) and a root tip of corn (b). Meristem tissues differentiate into complex structures demonstrated by the vascular tissue cells in a stem cross section (c) and dermal, vascular, and ground tissue cells in a barley leaf cross section (d).

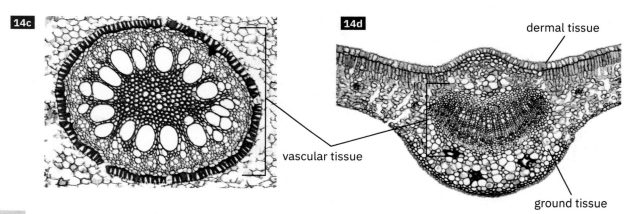

7.3 REVIEW

1. **Define** What causes cells to become specialized as parts of different tissues in a multicellular organism?

   A. Cells in different tissues have unique DNA.

   B. Cells can randomly differentiate during mitosis.

   C. Selective gene expression causes cells to become specialized.

   D. All cells with different functions are inherited from the parents.

2. **Explain** Give one example of why living organisms need to have stem cells, even after they are fully developed.

3. **Relate** Meristem can differentiate into which types of tissues? Select all correct answers.

   A. dermal tissue

   B. ground tissue

   C. muscle tissue

   D. nervous tissue

   E. vascular tissue

ON ASSIGNMENT National Geographic photographer David Liittschwager has photographed the eyes of many organisms across the animal kingdom. This Eurasian eagle owl, a *Bubo bubo*, demonstrates the complex structures that make up and surround the eye. Specialized muscle cells control the structures of the eye, which include millions of cells that perform different functions in the absorption and interpretation of light.

Dr. Camila Espejo's background in wildlife medicine and disease ecology helps to inform her research with Tasmanian devils.

NATIONAL GEOGRAPHIC EXPLORER **CAMILA ESPEJO**

FINDING CLUES TO DIAGNOSE CANCER BEFORE IT SPREADS

Intrigued by a 1996 photograph of large facial tumors on a Tasmanian devil, veterinarian Dr. Camila Espejo set out to learn more about the contagious cancers threatening the devils. Could studying them help diagnose cancer in humans?

Found only in Tasmania, these large marsupials were hunted nearly to extinction in the 1800s. Today, Tasmanian devils face a new threat: two forms of a fatal cancer that causes disfiguring facial tumors. Researchers originally thought the cancers were caused by a virus, because very few transmissible cancers exist. Espejo had another hypothesis. She began taking blood samples to test for extracellular vesicles (EVs). EVs are tiny membrane-enclosed structures that store and transport products between cells. They are thought to be key to the spread of cancer throughout the body.

To capture Tasmanian devils, the research team sets out special traps baited with lamb. At night, the devils go into the traps to eat and fall asleep. The researchers return in the early morning to weigh and microchip the animals. They also take biological samples such as blood. Espejo tests the blood serum for EVs and a common protein biomarker that she first discovered by growing tumor cells in the lab. By testing individual devils' blood, she confirmed that devils show this biomarker in their EVs three to six months before the appearance of tumors. She thinks the protein is the host's response to the spreading cancer cells, and "mark" that cancer is present. The biomarker is the same in all devils that have one of the facial tumor cancers. Humans with cancer also have similar biomarkers. EVs made by tumor cells advance the spread of cancer by communicating with other cells throughout the body. The presence or absence of the biomarker proteins allows the researchers to identify healthy Tasmanian devils to put into wildlife reserves.

"Currently, I am working to develop a more scalable early diagnostic test for devil facial tumor disease," Espejo says. "This will provide hope to this iconic species and boost conservation strategies to preserve devils from their possible extinction. In the long term, I hope to keep helping other species under threat, especially in the development of new diagnostic platforms."

With more conclusive data, the potential exists for using a similar biomarker test in humans to diagnose cancers before they spread.

THINKING CRITICALLY

Infer *Think about the cell cycle and how it is changed by cancer. How could identifying a biomarker related to the spread of cancer cells impact health care?*

TYING IT ALL TOGETHER
IMMORTAL CELLS: THE STORY OF HENRIETTA LACKS

HOW DO CELLS DIVIDE AND GROW?

Unlike normal cells, HeLa cells do not have the mechanism that limits the number of times a cell can divide. In 1989, scientists at Yale University discovered that HeLa cells have high levels of telomerase, an enzyme required for elongation of telomeres. Telomeres are specialized structures at the end of linear chromosomes, and they get shorter with each cell division, leading to aging and eventual cell death. HeLa cells can divide continuously in part because the telomeres are continually elongated.

HeLa cells have become an invaluable resource to biomedical researchers. However, the history of these cells, in light of the historical treatment of African Americans and concerns raised by the Lacks family, poses several complex ethical issues.

In 2013, Henrietta Lacks's genome was published online by a molecular biology lab in Europe, and was subsequently taken down because of privacy concerns. Today, members of the Lacks family sit on the board of a National Institutes of Health (NIH) working group that determines who is allowed to access HeLa genetic sequence information. Although millions of dollars have been made through the commercialization of patented HeLa cells, the family has only recently been compensated. Most of this compensation has gone to the Henrietta Lacks Foundation, which was established in 2010 to raise awareness about ethical issues in health care access and scientific research, with a particular focus on minorities and underserved communities.

In this activity, you will research the biology of HeLa cells and examine ethical issues related to their use. Work individually or in a group to complete these steps.

Gather Evidence

1. Research what makes HeLa cells unique and different from the cells you learned about in this chapter. Describe why those unique qualities have made HeLa cells such a powerful research tool.

Nature of Science

2. Consider and write brief statements about the following ethical issues presented by this case study:

   A. informed consent

   B. anonymity of samples collected from patients

   C. right to privacy regarding genetic information

Present Your Findings

3. Make a digital presentation featuring a variety of media, including images or videos, to present your research and findings to your class.

FIGURE 7-15
This confocal light micrograph of HeLa cells shows the cell nuclei in pink, mitochondria in red, and microfilaments of the cytoskeleton in green.

REVIEW KEY CONCEPTS

1. **Compare** Which activities occur during cellular division in both bacteria and eukaryotes? Select all correct answers.

   A. DNA is replicated.

   B. Chromosomes condense around histones.

   C. Proteins are synthesized as a cell prepares to divide.

   D. New plasma membrane forms as cell division proceeds.

   E. The cell nucleus divides followed by division of the cell cytoplasm.

2. **Relate** Match each statement with one stage of the cell cycle: G1, S, G2, or mitosis.

   • Chromosomes are duplicated.

   • Duplicate chromosomes move apart.

   • The cell prepares to replicate its DNA.

   • Proteins needed for chromosomal movement are synthesized.

3. **Contrast** Which terms are relevant to bacterial cell cycles, and which are relevant to eukaryotic cell cycles?

   • binary fission   • mitosis

   • cancer   • oncogenes

   • cell differentiation

4. **Explain** Which statements are true concerning cell cycle control in eukaryotes? Select all correct answers.

   A. A tumor is a group of cells that has stopped dividing.

   B. Checkpoint genes code for proteins that are involved in regulating the cell cycle.

   C. Most cells in multicellular organisms divide constantly throughout the organism's life.

   D. If newly synthesized DNA is damaged and cannot be repaired, tumor formation may result.

   E. A tumor may develop in a multicellular eukaryotic organism as the result of a mutation in a proto-oncogene.

5. **Classify** Sort each cell type into one of two categories: differentiated cells, undifferentiated cells.

   • embryonic stem cells   • skin cells

   • immune cells   • stem cells

   • meristem cells   • vascular tissue cells

6. **Describe** Which statement describes an event that occurs during mitosis?

   A. DNA unwinds from histones to assume an elongated shape.

   B. Sister chromatids remain paired, moving together as new descendant cells form.

   C. Microtubules attach to the centromere region that connects duplicate chromosomes.

   D. Homologous chromosomes are pulled apart, each descendant cell receiving a different set of chromosomes.

7. **Predict** Suppose a mutation event prevents a cell from producing tubulin subunits that can assemble to form microtubules. Which outcome would most likely occur as this cell undergoes cell division?

   A. The cell membrane will not be able to break down to allow chromosomal movement.

   B. Replication of chromosomes will not occur to produce genetically identical sister chromatids.

   C. Chromosomes will not be able to fully condense and will tangle and break as division proceeds.

   D. Sister chromatids will not be able to separate from each other and move to opposite poles of the dividing cell.

8. **Relate** Which claims are true about differentiated and undifferentiated cells? Select all correct answers.

   A. Once a cell differentiates, it is no longer pluripotent.

   B. Undifferentiated cells can divide to replace injured cells.

   C. As a cell undergoes differentiation, it loses genetic material.

   D. Undifferentiated cells express all genes encoded in their DNA.

   E. Differentiated cells selectively express genes needed for one type of cell.

9. **Identify Cause and Effect** Certain chemical substances have been shown to react with DNA to change its chemical structure. As a result, these substances have been labeled as carcinogens, or substances that cause cancer. Why might chemical changes in DNA lead to cancer?

10. **Explain** Why does DNA have to be accurately duplicated during cell division?

CRITICAL THINKING

11. Infer Certain enzyme levels increase during certain phases of the cell cycle and decrease during others. In which phase of cell division—G1, S, G2, or mitosis—would you expect to see an increase in the level of DNA repair enzymes? Explain your reasoning.

12. Model A student wants to model cell division for a diploid cell having two chromosomes. To represent the two chromosomes, she has cut two short pieces of yarn of equal length and two long pieces of yarn of equal length. What will the student need to do to continue making her model? Explain your reasoning.

13. Relate How are cytokinesis and mitosis related? Why are both necessary for a cell to successfully divide?

14. NOS Science, Technology, and Society In 2006, researchers at Kyoto University in Japan developed a technique for inducing mouse skin cells to "dedifferentiate" back to a pluripotent stem cell state. They did this by changing gene expression in the cells so that the cells reverted to their original undifferentiated form. These cells are called induced pluripotent stem cells, or iPS cells. Since then, researchers have produced human iPS cells from human skin cells. Theoretically, human iPS cells could be used to produce any type of human cell, including sperm and egg cells. What ethical questions does this situation raise? Pose at least two questions.

MATH AND ENGLISH LANGUAGE ARTS CONNECTIONS

1. Reason Abstractly and Quantitatively Complete the table to show the total number of cells resulting after each round of cell division.

Generation	Total number of cells
0	1
1	2
2	
4	

2. Infer From Statistics A section of a root tip was prepared for observation under a microscope. One thousand cells were analyzed to determine the number of cells at each stage of mitosis. The results of this analysis are summarized in the table.

Stage of mitosis	Number of cells
early prophase	26
late prophase	4
metaphase	24
anaphase	19
telophase	14

What can you infer from this information about the amount of time that any given cell spends in mitosis? In interphase? Explain your reasoning.

Read the following passage. Use evidence from the passage to answer the question.

Planarian flatworms are small, soft-bodied invertebrates usually less than 3 cm in length. They have wide, flat bodies and two eyes on the top of their heads. If you slice a planarian flatworm in half, each half will grow back into a healthy flatworm. In fact, if you cut a flatworm into 200 pieces, each piece will regenerate into an entirely new and healthy worm. Most other animals lack planarians' ability to regrow lost body parts, but they can regrow cells to some degree, such as when a wound heals. The processes that allow a wound to heal are similar to those that enable a flatworm to regenerate lost parts of its body.

3. Draw Evidence From Texts Use evidence from the text to contrast stem cell locations and capabilities in planarian flatworms versus humans.

4. Write Explanatory Text A diagram in a textbook depicts an embryo of a frog with an arrow pointing toward a tadpole. Another arrow points from the tadpole to an adult frog. Write text to explain how this series of illustrations involves both cell division and differentiation.

► REVISIT BACTERIA IN YOUR GUT

Gather Evidence In Section 1 of this chapter, you learned about factors affecting the growth of bacteria. In addition, there is an extensive population of viruses, called bacteriophages, that can infect and kill bacteria.

1. How do you think bacteriophages in your gut might affect bacteria populations there?

2. What other questions do you have about the bacteria and viruses that live in your digestive system?

CELL SYSTEMS

CHAPTER 5
MOLECULES IN LIVING SYSTEMS

How are the molecules of life assembled?

- Atoms join by chemical bonds to form molecules and compounds. In a chemical reaction, energy is used to break these bonds and the atoms are recombined into new substances.

- Life depends on the unique properties of water. The solubility, high cohesion, and ability to regulate temperature are related to the fact that water molecules are highly polar and tend to form hydrogen bonds with each other.

- Many organic molecules are assembled from simpler carbon-based subunits. The major groups of organic compounds are carbohydrates, lipids, proteins, and nucleic acids.

- Chemical reactions can absorb or release energy, but they require activation energy to proceed. Enzymes lower the required energy and increase the rate of a reaction.

CHAPTER 6
CELL STRUCTURE AND FUNCTION

How do structures work together in cell systems?

- Eukaryotic cells have more complex structures than prokaryotic cells. These include a nucleus to protect DNA and membrane-enclosed organelles that perform specific functions within cells.

- The lipid bilayer structure of membranes and associated proteins allows cells to control what materials enter and exit cells and organelles.

- Aerobic cellular respiration uses glucose and oxygen to generate ATP that can be used in reactions. Other respiration and fermentation pathways are used to generate ATP in the absence of oxygen.

- Photosynthesis uses light and carbon dioxide to make glucose that cells can use to store energy.

CHAPTER 7
CELL GROWTH

How do cells divide and grow?

- Cells duplicate DNA, grow, and divide through the cell cycle. This cycle is influenced by both genetic and environmental factors.

- Mitosis organizes chromosomes to ensure cells end up with the correct number of chromosomes.

- Mutations in genes that control the cell cycle can lead to the development of cancerous tumors.

- Different cell types in a multicellular organism contain the same DNA, but differences in gene expression allow stem cells and meristems to form different cell types with specific functions.

> **Go Online** **VIRTUAL INVESTIGATION**
>
> **Bacteria in the Digestive System**
> *What do bacteria do in your intestines?*
> Put on your lab coat to grow some bacteria and study how they live and interact.

WHAT DO BACTERIA DO IN YOUR INTESTINES?

Develop a Model In this unit you learned how molecules interact to form cell systems and how cell systems form the tissues that make up complex multicellular organisms. You learned in Unit 1 how many different types of organisms exist together to maintain balanced ecosystems.

Human intestines enclose a complex ecosystem that hosts many species of bacteria, archaea, viruses, and fungi. Together, all these microscopic organisms are known as the gut microbiome. Due to its complexity, and because many of these organisms cannot live outside the intestine, it has been difficult to determine all the types of organisms and their roles. Recently, scientists have been able to use genetic technology to assess the microbiome's diversity of DNA. They have identified hundreds of previously unidentified species of bacteria and viruses that routinely colonize human intestines. These organisms maintain a balanced ecosystem within the intestines, resisting infection and contributing to the health of the human host.

Scientists have developed many new methods to learn more about the symbiotic relationship between hosts and their gut microbiomes and to study the interactions between the colonizing organisms. Some studies attempt to understand differences in human microbiomes, as influenced by factors such as region and diet. Other laboratory studies use "gut-on-a-chip" models to mimic the complexity of the intestinal system by directly studying how bacterial species interact with intestinal cells in very small, controlled quantities. Our understanding of the intestinal microbiome is constantly changing and improving.

 Claim Make a claim about the role of *E. coli* and other bacteria in the intestines of humans.

 Evidence Use the evidence that you gathered throughout the unit to support your claim.

 Reasoning To help illustrate your reasoning, develop a model that describes the structures of the bacteria and how they function within the host intestine, as well as how the diversity of organisms in the intestine affects the bacteria.

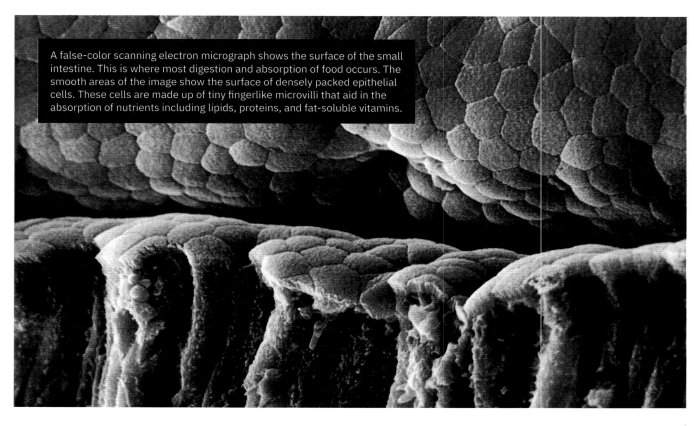

A false-color scanning electron micrograph shows the surface of the small intestine. This is where most digestion and absorption of food occurs. The smooth areas of the image show the surface of densely packed epithelial cells. These cells are made up of tiny fingerlike microvilli that aid in the absorption of nutrients including lipids, proteins, and fat-soluble vitamins.

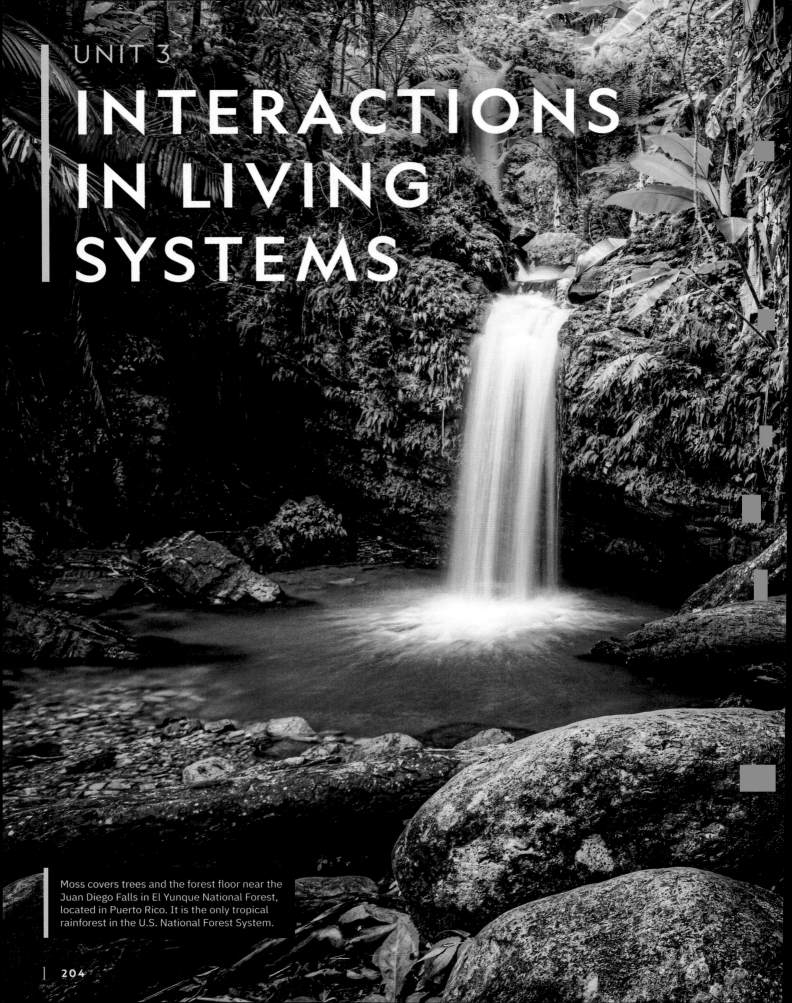

INTERACTIONS IN LIVING SYSTEMS

Moss covers trees and the forest floor near the Juan Diego Falls in El Yunque National Forest, located in Puerto Rico. It is the only tropical rainforest in the U.S. National Forest System.

Tropical rainforests contain the most biodiverse ecosystems on Earth. These forests receive direct sunlight almost all year, resulting in consistently warm temperatures, high humidity, and frequent rainfall. These conditions are essential in maintaining habitats for about two-thirds of all known species of plants. In one hectare (10,000 m²) of tropical rainforest, there may be hundreds of species of trees. In contrast, a temperate deciduous forest may have four to eight tree species in one hectare.

This diversity of plants supports the vast number and variety of animal and microbial species that live in the rainforest. Surviving in such close proximity requires organisms to interact with each other not only in complex food webs but also as communities of species that share resources and information about changes in their environment.

▼

HOW DO RAINFOREST SPECIES COMMUNICATE?

In this unit, you will investigate the systems that allow organisms to survive, grow, reproduce, and respond to their environments.

CHAPTER 8
DIVERSITY OF LIVING SYSTEMS

CHAPTER 9
PLANT SYSTEMS

CHAPTER 10
ANIMAL SYSTEMS

UNIT VIDEO 1 Go online to learn more about rainforest ecosystems and the communities of organisms they support.

UNDER THE CANOPY
MONITORING PLANT REGENERATION IN THE AMAZONIAN LOWLANDS

A herd of 150 or more white-lipped peccaries shove their way through the lowlands of the Amazon rainforest in southeastern Peru. The piglike animals' scents bond them together, and they grunt and clatter their teeth, barking if a threat is nearby. Their foraging behaviors mimic the actions of a bulldozer as they root through the leaf litter, eating anything they come across and mulching the soil. Are such behaviors helpful or harmful to the ecosystem? Ecologist Dr. Varun Swamy considers peccaries beneficial because they keep other dominant species in check, allowing rarer species that are weaker competitors to survive and grow.

IMPACTS ON TREE SPECIES REGENERATION

Swamy's research focuses on the lowland Amazon plant community. His primary concerns are the canopy and subcanopy trees that set the stage for all other life in the ecosystem. His overall goal is a better understanding of the regeneration processes across multiple life stages. These include fruit fall and seed dispersal, seed germination, seedling establishment, sapling growth, and the eventual death of centuries-old canopy trees. Saplings that have a healthy start in the vertical journey to the canopy have the best chance of replacing their parents. Data collected in areas where peccary populations have been eliminated because of the overhunting of wild animals for the bushmeat trade support his conclusions. The peccary herding lifestyle and foraging behavior benefit the regeneration of canopy trees.

The Peruvian black spider monkey is another key organism in Swamy's quest for answers. In Peru, this species is called *maquisapas*, a word that means "long arms." It is one of the largest primate species in South America. Swamy notes that these animals act as "seed-dispersing machines" for fleshy-fruited canopy trees due to their size, agility, activity, and diet. The rapid processing of fruits through their digestive tracts results in a constant "rain" of intact seeds from the forest canopy down to the floor. Swamy has found that in areas where the monkeys have been overhunted, the dispersal of seeds of fleshy-fruited trees has been greatly reduced.

Without the spread of seeds far from parent trees, another factor takes on an important role in regeneration processes. Swamy's research examines the antagonistic interactions between plants and their "natural enemies"—a term that refers to a broad collection of harmful fungi, bacteria, protists, and viruses. These microorganisms have evolved to feed exclusively on the seeds and seedlings of a single or a few closely related tree species. They live in and around large adult trees and destroy the fallen seeds or young seedlings. Future generations of these trees are spatially distant from their parents because they grow only by dispersed seeds that have escaped the reach of these natural enemies.

TECHNOLOGY EXPANDS THE STUDY AREA

Swamy's research now includes the collection of data from much larger areas thanks to the use of mini-copter drones. Bird's-eye views of the rainforest canopy reveals leafing, flowering, and fruiting patterns and allow for identification of species as well. Sharing this aerial footage on online citizen-science platforms also allows nonscientists across the world to contribute to the data collection and analysis, which increases the world's interest in preserving this treasure trove of biodiversity.

THINKING CRITICALLY

Infer *Why might seeds that germinate near the parent trees be less successful than those that are carried long distances by wind or animals?*

Top: Dr. Varun Swamy operates a drone in the field as a colleague looks on. **Bottom left:** White-lipped peccaries steamroll through the rainforest, eating anything they find. These omnivorous mammals live in herds of 20–300 individuals that forage over hundreds of square kilometers of rainforest each year to survive. **Bottom right:** Using a drone, Swamy gets a close-up view of a canopy tree crown that towers over 50 meters above the forest floor and collects data on its health and reproductive status.

▶ **UNIT VIDEO 2** Go online to watch our interview with Swamy and learn more about his career and research.

DIVERSITY OF LIVING SYSTEMS

The hyphae and fruiting structure of the fungus *Aspergillus ustus* is magnified 600 times in this scanning electron micrograph.

8.1 BACTERIA AND ARCHAEA

8.2 PROTISTS

8.3 FUNGI

8.4 VIRUSES

Most organisms are invisible to the unaided eye. Although we can often see large groups of microorganisms when they grow together, most individual microbes can only be observed directly using a microscope. Magnification has revealed that these tiny creatures live in practically every habitat on Earth.

Chapter 8 supports the NGSS Performance Expectation **HS-LS1-2.**

CASE STUDY
SPACE STATION STOWAWAYS

HOW ARE THE CHARACTERISTICS OF AN ORGANISM RELATED TO ITS PLACE IN AN ECOSYSTEM?

The International Space Station (ISS) is a laboratory hovering in low Earth orbit, operated by several multinational space agencies. Scientists investigate numerous phenomena in the microgravity environment. In recent missions, biologists have performed experiments in microbiology, plant growth, and the physiological effects of space travel. They have also used the ISS's satellite imaging capabilities to assess the productivity of Earth ecosystems. To ensure that experiments function properly, everything that enters or is attached to the space station is decontaminated before it is brought on board. Dust and debris from Earth are removed from all cargo and scientific equipment, and even the astronauts are quarantined pre-flight to avoid transporting infectious microbes to the station.

However, all humans host essential and diverse communities of microbes that cannot be removed. Living on the ISS under unusual conditions such as microgravity, high exposure to radiation, and psychological stress can weaken the immune system. All the air and water on the ISS is recycled through closed supply systems that can harbor microbial contaminants. Thus, the ISS crew thoroughly cleans the station every week, and NASA closely monitors the microbiome aboard the station to determine what types of microbes exist there (**Figures 8-1** and **8-2**).

More than 200 species of bacteria and fungi have been identified in air, water, and surface samples collected on the ISS. The most abundant types of microorganisms found are associated with human microbiomes. Scientists have also identified some previously unknown bacterial strains that thrive on the ISS.

Studying how microbes survive in space not only helps scientists understand potential risks to astronauts' health but also uncovers possibilities for using microbe-based biotechnology in space applications. For example, bacteria or fungi that can survive space travel could potentially be useful for producing food and medicine for long-term missions. Scientists are also investigating the ability of some microbial species to make fertile soil by breaking up rock. Other species might form building materials on other planets.

Ask Questions *In this chapter, you will study many diverse organisms, some closely related to those that live on the ISS. As you read, generate questions about how characteristics of these organisms relate to where and how they live.*

FIGURE 8-1 ▼
Dr. Don Pettit prepares biological samples for storage in a freezer on the ISS.

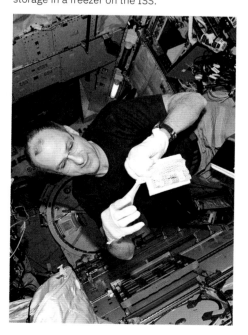

FIGURE 8-2 ▼
A diverse collection of organisms can be isolated from different locations on the ISS. The majority of identified species are bacteria and fungi (eukaryota).

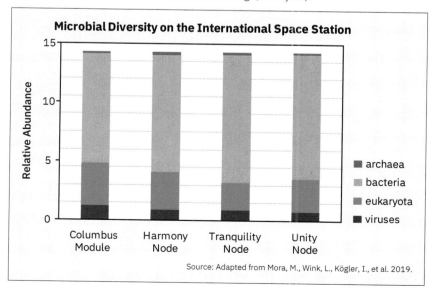

Source: Adapted from Mora, M., Wink, L., Kögler, I., et al. 2019.

BACTERIA AND ARCHAEA

Imagine you are sorting a box full of school supplies into groups based on similar characteristics. You might sort them by size or material, or possibly by how they are used. For years, scientists sorted and classified organisms in similar ways, based on comparing observable characteristics. However, that does not work very well when the organisms are incredibly tiny.

Predict *How do you think scientists might classify different species of bacteria that are tiny and appear to have similar characteristics?*

Classifying Prokaryotes

When the modern system of naming organisms was developed in the 1700s, there were just two kingdoms, Plantae (plants) and Animalia (animals). In the 1860s, a third kingdom was introduced, Protista, which included all microorganisms. Microscopes continued to improve, and scientists continued learning more about cells and microorganisms.

Historically, scientists classified unidentified single-celled organisms by comparing them against a known group based on shape, metabolism, and properties of the cell wall. The more traits the organism shared with the known group, the closer they were thought to be related. The wide variety of single-celled organisms, in particular, were difficult to classify but clearly did not fit into a single kingdom. By the 1950s, scientists suggested there were five kingdoms.

In the 1970s, scientists began studying the sequences of RNA in the ribosomes of organisms. Then, in the 1990s, technology advanced to allow scientists to begin studying entire genomes of organisms. These developments changed the way organisms could be classified and led to the three-domain system. These uses of DNA and RNA sequence comparison are a type of **phylogenetic analysis**, which is a constantly improving group of methods in which genetic sequences are compared to estimate relatedness between organisms. Phylogenetic analysis techniques are described in more detail in Section 14.1 and Appendix E.

Prior to the initial suggestion of the three-domain system in 1977 and its formal proposal in 1990, scientists often grouped bacteria and archaea together as "prokaryotes" because they are both single celled and have similar visible features. However, sequencing of RNA in the ribosomes of different organisms revealed that archaea were a distinct group of organisms. The branching in **Figure 8-3** reflects the hypothesis that archaea and eukaryotes are thought to have a common ancestor that is separate from the bacteria domain.

The three domains are commonly divided further into six kingdoms of organisms, including archaea, bacteria, plants, fungi, animals, and protists. However, these traditional kingdom divisions are not based on modern phylogenetic analyses. Appendix E provides more information on the three-domain model and how scientists classify organisms.

NOS **Scientific Knowledge** *How have advancements in technology and scientific techniques affected how scientists classify microorganisms?*

FIGURE 8-3
Bacteria, Archaea, and Eukarya encompass the three domains of life, all of which descended from a common ancestor. Archaea and Eukarya are thought to have a common ancestor that is separate from the Bacteria domain.
On cladograms such as this one, a longer distance between groups indicates a more distant evolutionary relationship. Shorter distances indicate that groups are more closely related.

Prokaryote Diversity

Scientists' understanding of the diversity and number of bacteria and archaea has also changed dramatically with improvements in DNA sequencing and phylogenetic analyses. Many bacteria and archaea are difficult to isolate or grow outside of their native environments, so they are difficult to study. New techniques allow DNA in samples collected from an environment to be sequenced and analyzed. Many thousands of new species of bacteria and archaea have been identified in environments ranging from hot springs to human intestines.

Prokaryote Structures **Figure 8-4** shows structures that are typical of bacteria. These structures are discussed in detail in Chapter 6. Bacteria are often shaped like rods (bacilli) and spheres (cocci), but others are shaped like commas (vibrios) or spirals (spirilla or spirochetes). In addition to those shapes typically found among bacteria, archaea species with square, triangle, and other irregular shapes have also been discovered.

FIGURE 8-4
Most prokaryotes have similar basic structures. Bacteria and archaea come in many shapes, including bacillus, vibrio, coccus, spirillum, and spirochete.

capsule
cell wall
cell membrane
DNA in nucleoid
plasmid
flagellum
pilus
cytoplasm, with ribosomes

bacillus   vibrio   coccus   spirillum   spirochete

Prokaryote Metabolism

Metabolic diversity—the different ways organisms obtain and use energy and matter—gives certain species of bacteria and archaea the ability to thrive in a variety of environments. Many bacteria are anaerobic, which means they can (or must) live where there is no oxygen. Others are aerobic, which means they require (or at least tolerate) oxygen. There are four possible modes of obtaining energy and nutrients (**Table 8-1**) and, as a group, bacteria and archaea use them all.

- *Photoautotrophs* carry out photosynthesis to build their own food from an inorganic source of carbon such as carbon dioxide. Like plants, they assemble their food using light as an energy source.
- *Chemoautotrophs* fuel the assembly of their food by using energy from inorganic substances such as hydrogen sulfide. These bacteria and archaea are producers in dark places such as the seafloor.
- *Photoheterotrophs* use light energy to fuel the breakdown of organic molecules they obtain from the environment.
- *Chemoheterotrophs* obtain both energy and carbon through the breakdown of organic compounds. Pathogenic bacteria are chemoheterotrophs that extract the organic compounds they need to live from a host. Other bacterial chemoheterotrophs are decomposers.

SEP **Construct an Explanation** *Describe how the metabolism of an organism affects what environments it might be able to live in.*

TABLE 8.1. Modes of Obtaining Energy and Carbon by Different Groups of Organisms

Type of metabolism	Carbon source	Energy source	Organisms
chemoautotrophs	inorganic source such as CO_2	chemicals	archaea, bacteria
chemoheterotrophs	organic source such as glucose	chemicals	animals, archaea, bacteria, fungi, nonphotosynthetic protists
photoautotrophs	inorganic source such as CO_2	light	archaea, bacteria, photosynthetic protists, plants
photoheterotrophs	organic source such as glucose	light	archaea, bacteria

Bacterial Diversity and Ecology

There are thousands of species of bacteria, and new ones are constantly being discovered. In addition to genetic, shape, and metabolic differences, bacteria are often distinguished based on their cell walls, which affects their ecological roles. *Gram-positive* bacteria have cell walls with a thick outer layer of peptidoglycan, which is a molecule made of sugar and amino acids. This layer retains purple stain when a technique called Gram staining is used to prepare samples for viewing under a microscope. In *Gram-negative* bacteria, the cell wall is surrounded by an outer membrane and has a thinner peptidoglycan layer that retains very little dye during Gram staining. Outer membranes in some Gram-negative bacteria generate vesicles to help the bacteria adhere to surfaces or evade immune systems of their hosts.

While there is no clear consensus for the classification of bacteria, it is helpful to look at some traditional informal groups. Cyanobacteria, Gram-positive bacteria, and proteobacteria are a few of the groups that show the diversity and ecological importance of bacteria.

Cyanobacteria Cyanobacteria are a group of Gram-negative bacteria that perform photosynthesis. Photosynthesis evolved in many bacteria, but only cyanobacteria release oxygen as a by-product. Evidence suggests that chloroplasts in plants evolved from ancient cyanobacteria. This is described in the *endosymbiont theory* detailed in Section 6.1. Some cyanobacteria also carry out nitrogen fixation, which means they incorporate nitrogen from the air into ammonia (NH_3). Nitrogen fixation is an important ecological service. Photosynthetic eukaryotes need nitrogen but they cannot use the gaseous form (N_2). Plants and photosynthetic protists can, however, take up ammonia released by nitrogen-fixing bacteria. The nitrogen cycle is described in Section 2.4.

Some cyanobacteria partner symbiotically with fungi to form *lichens*. Others grow on the surface of soil, but most are aquatic. Aquatic cyanobacteria grow as single cells or as long filaments of cells arranged end to end (**Figure 8-5**). When conditions become unfavorable for growth, some filamentous cyanobacteria produce thick-walled resting cells. These cells can be dispersed and remain dormant until conditions improve.

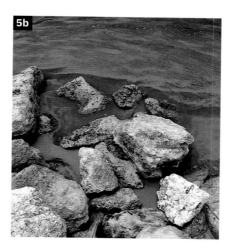

FIGURE 8-5
This micrograph reveals chains of cyanobacteria, including larger, circular resting cells (a). In large quantities, cyanobacteria can form blooms that harm aquatic ecosystems, such as this bloom in Lake Okeechobee, Florida (b).

Gram-Positive Bacteria Most Gram-positive bacteria are chemoheterotrophs, and many are decomposers. Decomposers break down complex organic molecules in the wastes and remains of other organisms, leaving inorganic leftovers that serve as nutrients for plants. Decomposers also break down pesticides and pollutants, improving the environment for other organisms. *Actinomycetes* species are Gram-positive decomposers that grow through soil as long, branching chains of cells. Their presence gives freshly exposed soil its distinctive "earthy" smell. Many antibiotics, including streptomycin and vancomycin, were first isolated from *Actinomycetes* bacteria.

Lactic acid bacteria are another Gram-positive subgroup. These cells break down sugars in milk and produce lactic acid as a by-product of fermentation (Section 6.3). *Lactobacillus* species can spoil milk, but they are also used to produce cheese and yogurt. Lactic acid released by these bacteria produces a sour taste and changes the shape of milk proteins, causing the milk to thicken.

Soil bacteria in the *Clostridium* genus and the *Bacillus* genus are Gram-positive cells that form endospores when conditions are unfavorable. An **endospore** contains the cell's DNA and a bit of cytoplasm in a protective coat (**Figure 8-6**). It is functionally similar to the resting cells cyanobacteria use to survive difficult conditions, but it is much tougher. Unlike active cells, endospores withstand exposure to extreme heat, freezing temperatures, drought conditions, disinfectants, and ultraviolet radiation. Many human pathogens produce endospores.

FIGURE 8-6
Clostridium bacteria take on a drum-stick shape (a) when endospores (b) are forming. Endospores can withstand unfavorable conditions.

Proteobacteria Proteobacteria is the largest bacterial group. This diverse group of Gram-negative bacteria is linked based on similarity in their ribosomes' RNA sequences, but they do not necessarily have similar structural or metabolic characteristics. Most proteobacteria are aerobic. Some are photosynthetic, but they do not produce oxygen. Other proteobacteria are chemoautotrophs or chemoheterotrophs. The chemoautotrophic species *Thiomargarita namibiensis* is among the largest prokaryotes. It can be up to 0.75 mm wide (**Figure 8-7a**).

Many chemoheterotrophic proteobacteria live inside other organisms. Members of the genus *Rhizobium* live in the roots of legumes such as peas and beans. The bacteria receive sugars from the plant and, in turn, provide the plant with ammonia they produced by fixing nitrogen. The most well-studied prokaryote is *Escherichia coli* (**Figure 8-7b**), a bacillus that lives in mammalian intestines and is easily grown in the laboratory. *Rickettsias* are very tiny proteobacteria that live inside cells. The genomes of mitochondria are most similar to those of *Rickettsias*. This indicates that the bacterial ancestors of mitochondria were related to proteobacteria.

CCC **Structure and Function** *Describe the structural differences between Gram-positive and Gram-negative organisms. How do these differences affect the ecological roles of some of these organisms?*

FIGURE 8-7
T. namibiensis cells (a) are large enough for individual cells to be seen with the unaided eye. *E. coli* (b) is the most-studied prokaryote, common in laboratories and important in mammalian digestion.

Bacteria and Human Health

Bacteria and other microorganisms that normally live in or on our body are our normal microbiota (explored in Unit 2). These cells outnumber our own cells, and they are our first defense against pathogens. For example, lactic acid produced by bacteria in the human mouth, gut, and vagina help keep acid-intolerant pathogenic bacteria from taking hold. Some bacteria that live in our gut also benefit us by producing essential vitamins. Our intestines are home to lactic acid bacteria that synthesize some B vitamins that we cannot make, and also to *E. coli* that produce vitamin K.

Toxins and Disease Bacteria cause many common diseases (**Table 8-2**). Most pathogenic bacteria harm us by way of toxins that disrupt our health. The toxin may be a substance that bacteria release into their environment or a molecule that is part of the cell's wall. Botulinum toxin released by *Clostridium botulinum* disables nerve cells, which is why a dangerous paralyzing food poisoning occurs after ingesting the bacteria. Toxins from bacteria may not harm cells directly, but instead elicit an immune response that produces symptoms such as fever and aches.

Whooping cough (pertussis) and tuberculosis are bacterial respiratory diseases spread by coughs or sneezes. *Mycobacterium tuberculosis*, the cause of tuberculosis, infects about a quarter of the human population. In most people, the infection is inactive and does no harm. If the infection becomes active, bacteria grow in the lungs and cause severe lung damage. Each year, more than a million people die as a result of active tuberculosis.

Streptococcus and *Staphylococcus* are Gram-positive cocci that infect the outer layers of the skin, often causing infection when an injury occurs. *Streptococcus* also causes strep throat and scarlet fever. Gonorrhea, syphilis, and chlamydia are bacterial infections transmitted by sexual contact.

TABLE 8-2. Examples of Bacterial Diseases

Disease	Typical bacterial cause	Description
botulism, tetanus	*Clostridium botulinum, Clostridium tetani*	muscle paralysis by bacterial toxin
chlamydia	*Chlamydia trachomatis*	sexually transmitted infection
cholera	*Vibrio cholerae*	diarrheal illness
gonorrhea	*Neisseria gonorrhoeae*	sexually transmitted infection
impetigo, boils	group A *Streptococcus, Staphylococcus aureus*	blisters, sores on skin
Lyme disease	*Borrelia burgdorferi*	rash, flulike symptoms, spread by ticks
Rocky Mountain spotted fever	*Rickettsia rickettsii*	rash, flulike symptoms, spread by ticks
strep throat	*Streptococcus pyogenes*	sore throat, can damage heart
syphilis	*Treponema pallidum*	sexually transmitted infection
tuberculosis	*Mycobacterium tuberculosis*	respiratory disease
whooping cough	*Bordetella pertussis*	childhood respiratory disease

Bacterial pathogens sometimes enter the body in tainted food or water. Most cases of bacterial food poisoning occur after bacteria-rich animal feces contaminate food. In regions where safe drinking water is not readily available, cholera sickens millions of people each year and kills an estimated 100,000 people. Cholera-causing bacteria (*Vibrio cholerae*) produce a toxin that causes intestinal cells to malfunction, and this results in a potentially fatal diarrhea. Tainted water also spreads *Helicobacter pylori*, which causes stomach ulcers. *H. pylori* is the only bacterial species known to cause cancer; a long-term infection increases the risk of stomach cancer.

Lyme disease (**Figure 8-8**) is a bacterial disease that is transmitted by a *vector*, which carries the bacteria between hosts. Ticks move the spirochete bacteria (typically *Borrelia burgdorferi*) that cause the disease between vertebrate hosts. Infection may initially cause a bull's-eye-shaped rash at the site of the tick bite. A long-term infection can harm joints and the nervous system.

SEP **Communicate Information** *Describe at least two ways that bacterial pathogens are transmitted to cause infection in new hosts.*

FIGURE 8-8 ▶
The spirochete bacteria (a) that cause Lyme disease are transmitted to humans by vector insects such as this deer tick (b).

Archaea

Archaea and bacteria often live alongside each other and have many physical similarities, but they have many differences that are not visually obvious. Archaea cell walls include different molecules that help them live in what we would consider extreme environments. Also, their cell membrane contains lipids that are different from bacteria. Like eukaryotes, archaea organize their DNA around histone proteins, which bacteria do not have. The enzymes and signals that archaea use to transcribe RNA and translate proteins are more similar to those of eukaryotes than bacteria.

Archaeal Habitats and Diversity Some archaea species can live in places where few or no other cells survive (**Figure 8-9**). For example, they are the most abundant cells in the ocean's deepest, darkest waters. Archaea were first discovered in hot springs, and many are extreme **thermophiles**, meaning they grow at a very high temperature. Some archaea that live near deep-sea hydrothermal vents grow even at 110 °C (230 °F). Other archaea are extreme **halophiles**, meaning they live in highly salty water. Salt-loving archaea live in the Dead Sea, the Great Salt Lake, and smaller brine-filled lakes. Most are photoheterotrophs that capture light energy using a red pigment.

FIGURE 8-9
Microbial communities around deep-sea hydrothermal vents include both bacteria and archaea, which perform chemosynthesis and serve as producers for other organisms that can flourish in this ecosystem.

Many archaea, including some extreme thermophiles and extreme halophiles, are **methanogens**. While some bacterial species can live in most of the environments where archaea are found, the only known methanogens are species of archaea. Methanogens are chemoautotrophs, and their ATP-producing reactions also produce methane (CH_4), an odorless gas. Methanogenic archaea are strict anaerobes, meaning they cannot live in the presence of oxygen. They abound in sewage, marsh sediments, and the animal gut. Cattle have methanogens in their stomachs and release methane gas by belching. About a third of humans have significant numbers of methanogens in their intestine. So far, no archaea have been found to be human pathogens.

SEP **Construct an Explanation** *Explain generally how the structures of archaea and bacteria compare. How do these structures affect where different species live?*

8.1 REVIEW

1. **Evaluate** Which questions are useful in defining the characteristics of a new species of bacteria? Select all correct answers.

    A. Do the bacteria produce oxygen?

    B. What is the shape of the bacteria?

    C. How do the bacteria obtain energy?

    D. How many cells do the bacteria have?

    E. How thick is the layer of peptidoglycan in the bacterial cell wall?

2. **Define** List some of the ways that different types of bacterial infections can spread.

3. **Distinguish** Sort the characteristics according to which group(s) of bacteria they apply to: cyanobacteria, Gram-positive bacteria, or proteobacteria. Characteristics may be related to more than one group.

    • have an outer cell membrane
    • form endospores
    • perform photosynthesis
    • have a thick cell wall

4. **Describe** In what type of environments have archaea typically been found?

KEY TERMS

colonial organism
phytoplankton
protist
pseudopod
zooplankton

PROTISTS

Do you have a junk drawer or a box where you throw things you are not sure what to do with? For years, scientists classified protists together in their own kingdom because they were organisms that did not quite fit into any other categories. Now, however, scientists have much more evidence about how protists are related to each other and other organisms.

Analyze *How has the kingdom of protists been like a "junk drawer" for scientists?*

Classification of Eukaryotes and Protists

The kingdoms of the eukaryote domain that are likely the most familiar to you are plants, animals, and fungi. However, eukaryotes also include a fourth diverse kingdom of organisms commonly referred to as **protists**. Despite the designation as a kingdom in many classification systems, protists are no longer considered a valid biological group because no single trait unites them. Some protists are more closely related to plants, fungi, or animals than to other protists.

Scientists continue to investigate exactly how all the various eukaryotes are related, and phylogenetic analyses have led to systems that differ from the traditional kingdoms. One widely used organization distributes eukaryotes into six supergroups based on evolutionary relationships, or how closely scientists think they are related. Supergroups are a taxonomic level of organization between domain and kingdom (Appendix E).

Four of the supergroups include protists exclusively. A fifth group includes plants (Chapter 9) and their protist relatives. Animals (Chapter 10), fungi, and their protist relatives are members of the sixth group. **Figure 8-10** shows the five most important supergroups. This section will review characteristics and examples of some protists that are in each of these five eukaryotic supergroups. You will notice that even within each supergroup, the organisms described are incredibly diverse, and there are not necessarily any uniting characteristics to easily describe each supergroup.

NOS **Scientific Knowledge** *How have advances in scientific knowledge helped scientists better understand the relationships between the many different organisms called protists?*

FIGURE 8-10 ▼
Eukaryotes are often divided into supergroups for ease of discussion. However, scientists' understanding of the evolutionary relationships between organisms is constantly changing and improving.

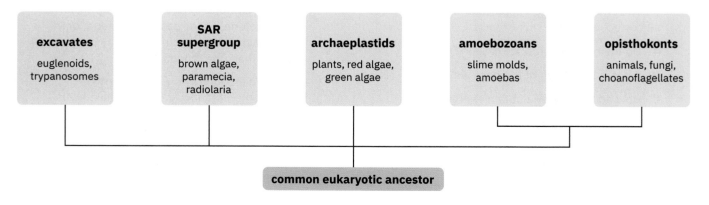

excavates	**SAR supergroup**	**archaeplastids**	**amoebozoans**	**opisthokonts**
euglenoids, trypanosomes	brown algae, paramecia, radiolaria	plants, red algae, green algae	slime molds, amoebas	animals, fungi, choanoflagellates

common eukaryotic ancestor

Protist Characteristics

Most protists live as single cells, but some are colonial or members of multicellular organisms. A **colonial organism** consists of cells that live together but remain self-sufficient. Each cell retains the traits required to survive and reproduce on its own. By contrast, the cells of a multicellular organism have a division of labor and are interdependent.

Given the differences in organization, it is not surprising that protists vary widely in size. The smallest known free-living protist is a single-celled, green alga about 1 micrometer in diameter. The largest protists are giant kelps that regularly grow more than 30 meters in length.

Metabolism Most protists need oxygen to live. However, some are adapted to living in places with little or no oxygen. These anaerobic protists have modified mitochondria that allow them to make ATP without oxygen.

Protists include *autotrophs* and *heterotrophs*. Autotrophs, such as various types of algae, carry out photosynthesis by the same oxygen-producing photosynthetic pathway as cyanobacteria. They produce much of the oxygen we breathe and serve as food for other organisms, including humans. Heterotrophic protists obtain carbon and energy by breaking down organic materials. Some absorb organic molecules directly from their environment. Others capture and ingest smaller organisms such as bacteria. A few are able to change how they obtain energy depending on their environment.

Habitats The overwhelming majority of protists are free-living and aquatic in seawater or freshwater habitats. However, some live in moist soils, and others live on or in other organisms. Protists can benefit their hosts. For example, some photosynthetic protists live in the tissues of corals and supply their animal host with sugars. Other protists are pathogens, including the one that causes malaria.

Common Structures Protists are eukaryotes, so they all have a nucleus. In addition, most have other standard eukaryotic organelles such as an endoplasmic reticulum and Golgi body. All protists have at least one mitochondrion. Some typical organelles are shown in **Figure 8-11**, which illustrates the body systems of two different single-celled, freshwater protists called *Euglena* and *Paramecium*.

FIGURE 8-11 ▽
These diagrams highlight interesting features of euglena and paramecium systems. Euglena and paramecium both have typical features of eukaryotes that are not shown, including endoplasmic reticula, Golgi bodies, and mitochondria.

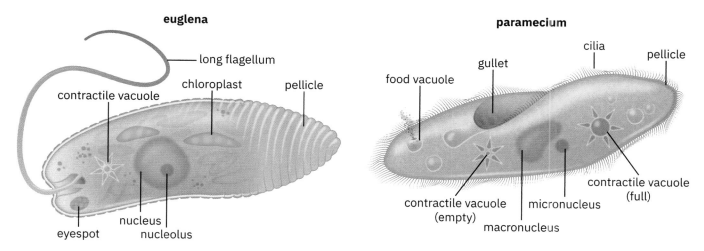

Structures That Vary Protists have a wide variety of characteristics that help them survive in their particular habitats.

- **Outer Coverings** Most single-celled protists have a protective layer at their cell surface. *Radiolaria* and diatoms make a glassy silica shell. *Foraminifera* build a calcium carbonate shell. By contrast, the outer layer of *Euglena* is a *pellicle* that constrains the cell's shape, but flexes enough to allow the organism to bend and squeeze through openings.

- **Movement-Related Structures** Most single-celled protists are able to move from place to place during part or all of their life cycle. Some protists, such as *Euglena*, propel themselves by moving one or more flagella. Others, such as *Paramecium*, move by means of cilia. Others crawl along by extending lobes of cytoplasm.

- **Contractile Vacuoles** The interiors of freshwater protists such as *Euglena* and *Paramecium* are saltier than their freshwater habitat, so water tends to diffuse into the cell. To keep from bursting, these protists operate one or more contractile vacuoles. These are organelles that collect excess water from the cytoplasm and then contract and expel it out of the cell through a pore.

- **Chloroplasts** Many protists have chloroplasts. Chloroplasts work to convert light energy into chemical energy that can be stored and ultimately used for cell processes.

Protist Diversity

As indicated, the term *protists* includes a wide variety of different organisms. The following survey of the five most important supergroups represents only a part of the structural and ecological diversity of protists.

Excavates All excavates are unwalled cells with one or more flagella. The supergroup name refers to an "excavation," a groove that functions in feeding in some members of this group.

- *Giardia intestinalis* is anaerobic and has two nuclei and multiple flagella. It causes giardiasis, a common waterborne disease. A person becomes infected by ingesting cysts that were passed in the feces of a previous host. When a cyst reaches the host's intestine, the cell inside becomes active and attaches itself to the intestinal wall (**Figure 8-12**). The resulting symptoms include cramps, nausea, and diarrhea. Giardia cysts often enter streams and lakes via the feces of wild animals, which is why hikers are advised to treat water from such sources before drinking it. Boiling kills the cysts. Microfilters are also effective.

FIGURE 8-12
The *Giardia lamblia* in this scanning electron micrograph are another species that causes giardiasis. The active, feeding stage is shown, with flagella that help the organism move.

- Trypanosomes are long, tapered cells with a flagellum that emerges from the back of the cell and extends toward the front of the cell (**Figure 8-13**). Movement of the flagellum causes the membrane to wiggle in a wavelike manner that propels the cell. All trypanosomes are parasites. Biting insects transmit those that infect humans. For example, tsetse flies spread *Trypanosoma brucei*, the agent of African sleeping sickness. *T. brucei* lives in blood and other body fluids, where it absorbs nutrients across its body wall. Infected people feel drowsy during daytime and often cannot sleep at night. An untreated infection results in coma and, eventually, death.

FIGURE 8-13
This scanning electron micrograph shows *Trypanosoma brucei* alongside red blood cells from a human host.

- Euglenoids such as *Euglena* (**Figure 8-14**) are free-living, primarily freshwater protists closely related to trypanosomes. Depending on their environment, some are heterotrophs that engulf bacteria and small protists. Others are autotrophs. Euglenoids have chloroplasts that evolved from a green alga. They carry out photosynthesis when there is light but can become heterotrophs in the dark. An eyespot near the base of a long flagellum helps the cells detect light.

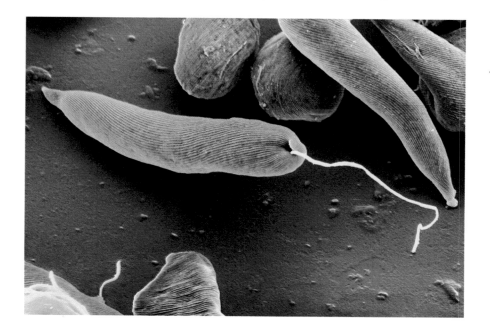

FIGURE 8-14
This color-enhanced scanning electron micrograph shows the outside of *Euglena granulata*, which is covered by a protective pellicle and has a flagellum for movement.

CHAPTER INVESTIGATION

Classification Systems
What classification system should be used to sort different algae?
Go online to explore this chapter's hands-on investigation to design your own classification system for algae.

SAR Supergroup The SAR supergroup is made up exclusively of protists. It is an incredibly diverse grouping of organisms.

- Brown algae are multicellular "seaweeds" of temperate or cool seas. Most grow along rocky seashores. They range in size from microscopic filaments to the largest protists—the giant kelps (**Figure 8-15**). Like trees in a forest, kelps shelter a wide variety of other organisms. Kelps are also the source of algins (or alginates), which are polysaccharides used to thicken foods, drinks, cosmetics, and personal care products.

- Diatoms are single-celled or colonial protists that secrete a transparent silica shell. The shell consists of two parts that fit one inside the other, like a shoe box and its lid. Diatoms are a component of the **phytoplankton**, the community of photosynthetic cells that live in the upper sunlit waters of lakes and seas. Phytoplankton is the base for aquatic food chains and the source of about half of Earth's photosynthetically produced oxygen. When marine diatoms die, their remains fall to the seafloor.

- *Paramecium* is a single-celled organism common in ponds (**Figure 8-16a**). Its covering of cilia allows it to move and helps it feed. The cilia sweep water laden with food particles into an oral groove at the cell surface and then into a gullet where vesicles digest the food.

- Malaria is a potentially deadly infectious disease caused by four species in the genus *Plasmodium* (**Figure 8-16b**). Different species infect different hosts. In 2020, 241 million cases of malaria in humans led to more than 600,000 deaths. A human infection begins after a mosquito carrying an infectious form of the *Plasmodium* bites a person. The organism completes its life cycle inside the human host, and the next mosquito that bites that human can pick up the *Plasmodium* and continue to spread the disease.

FIGURE 8-15 ▽
This kelp forest, located on Cortes Bank in the North Pacific Ocean, is home to many other organisms.

- Radiolaria have a silica shell (**Figure 8-17**) and many gas-filled vacuoles that keep the cell afloat. Radiolaria are part of plankton and are most abundant in nutrient-rich tropical waters.

- Foraminifera have a chalky calcium carbonate shell. Most species live on the seafloor, where they probe the sediments for prey. Others are part of the marine **zooplankton**, a collection of tiny heterotrophs that drift or swim in the sea. Foraminifera and radiolaria have lived in the seas for millions of years, so remains of countless cells have fallen to the seafloor. Over time, geologic processes can transform accumulated foraminifera shells into chalk and limestone, two types of sedimentary rock.

CCC **Structure and Function** *Describe how the structures of some protists in the SAR supergroup are related to how they function in their particular environments.*

FIGURE 8-16
Paramecium and *Plasmodium* species are vastly different, despite being part of the same supergroup. Notice the full contractile vacuole in this freshwater *Paramecium caudatum* (a). These *Plasmodium gallinaceum* are shown invading the midgut of a mosquito (b). This species of *Plasmodium* causes malaria in poultry.

FIGURE 8-17
This light micrograph reveals the variety of silica structure shapes that enclose radiolaria. Living radiolaria push lobes of cytoplasm (pseudopods) through pores in the shells to obtain food.

VIDEO

VIDEO 8-1 Go online to see how slime molds move across a surface.

Amoebozoans Amoebozoans are shape-shifting heterotrophic cells that typically lack a cell wall or pellicle. They move and capture smaller cells by extending thick lobes of cytoplasm called **pseudopods**. There are two groups of amoebozoan protists: amoebas and slime molds.

- Amoebas are single cells (**Figure 8-18a**) that live in marine or freshwater sediments or in damp soil. They are important predators of bacteria. A few amoebas are human pathogens. *Entamoeba* infects the human gut, causing cramps, aches, and bloody diarrhea. Infections are most common in developing nations where amoebic cysts contaminate drinking water. The freshwater species *Naegleria fowleri* can enter the nose and cause a rare but deadly brain infection.

- Slime molds are sometimes described as "social amoebas." They are common on the floor of temperate forests. Cellular slime molds spend most of their existence as individual amoeba-like cells. Each cell ingests bacteria and reproduces by mitosis. If food runs out, thousands of cells stream together to form a cohesive multicellular unit that can move to a suitable area. Plasmodial slime molds spend most of their life cycle as a plasmodium, a mass with many nuclei that forms when a cell undergoes mitosis many times without dividing its cytoplasm. A plasmodium streams along surfaces, feeding on microbes and organic matter (**Figure 8-18b**).

FIGURE 8-18 ▶
A false-color transmission electron micrograph of *Entamoeba histolytica* (a) reveals ingested human red blood cells (green ovals). *Fuligo septica* (b), a plasmodial slime mold, moves along the bark of a dead pine tree.

Archaeplastids The archaeplastid supergroup includes land plants, green algae, and the protists that are most closely related to plants. All archaeplastids have cells with cellulose walls and chloroplasts that evolved from cyanobacteria. Green algae (**Figure 8-19a**) were long considered to be protists but scientists now classify many of them as plants. Green algae share many features with land plants, including the characteristic green chlorophyll pigments.

Red algae are photosynthetic, generally multicellular protists that live in clear, warm seas. Most grow either as thin sheets or in a branching pattern (**Figure 8-19b**). One subgroup, the coralline algae, deposits calcium carbonate in its cells. The rigid material produced by these algae contributes bulk to some tropical reefs. Two gelatinous polysaccharides, agar and carrageenan, are extracted from red algae for use as thickeners or stabilizers in foods, cosmetics, and personal care products. Agar is also important in microbiology. When mixed with appropriate nutrients, it forms a semisolid culture medium that can be used for growing bacteria or fungi. Another red algal product is nori, the sheets of dried seaweed used to wrap sushi. Nori is derived from the red alga *Porphyra*.

Opisthokont

Opisthokont Opisthokonts include fungi, animals, and the protist relatives of both groups. The protist group most closely related to animals is the *choanoflagellates*. Each choanoflagellate cell has a flagellum surrounded by a "collar" of thread-like projections (**Figure 8-20**). Movement of the flagellum sets up a current that draws food-laden water through the collar. Some sponge cells have a similar structure and function.

Most choanoflagellate species live as single cells, but some are colonial. The colonies arise by mitosis, when descendant cells do not separate after division, but rather stick together with the help of adhesion proteins. The adhesion proteins of choanoflagellates are similar to those of animals, and researchers have discovered that even solitary choanoflagellates have these proteins. Researchers continue to study choanoflagellates to learn more about what the earliest animals may have been like.

FIGURE 8-19
Chlamydomonas (a) is one genus of green algae that lives in soil and water and includes approximately 150 species. Light microscopy reveals that these single-celled algae each have two flagella.
Eucheuma (b) is a genus of algae that includes species that are brown, green, and red in color. The multicellular red algae shown is being harvested for food at a seaweed farm in Malaysia.

FIGURE 8-20
This choanoflagellate was isolated from wet soil. Its long flagellum is not visible here.

8.2 REVIEW

1. **Describe** Identify the characteristics common to nearly all protists. Select all correct answers.

   A. have cells that have a nucleus

   B. contain chloroplasts

   C. have mitochondria

   D. live as isolated single cells

   E. populate aquatic habitats

   F. require oxygen to live

2. **Explain** Why are protists often described as a kingdom even though they are not considered a valid biological group?

3. **Identify** Match the organisms to the structure that helps it move: flagella, cilia, or pseudopods.

   - paramecia
   - amoebas
   - trypanosomes

4. **Distinguish** Which supergroups include protists most closely related to animals, and which include those most closely related to plants?

FEATURES OF PARAMECIA AND EUGLENAS

SEP **Construct an Explanation** What features of paramecia or euglenas can you identify?

Observing paramecia or euglenas under a microscope will provide the opportunity to recognize an organism's structures by looking at a real-world example rather than viewing a diagram in a text. This will allow you to see the structural organization within an organism. You will construct an explanation about how paramecium or euglena systems and structures compare with both simpler bacteria and more complex multicellular organism systems.

An amoeba extends a psuedopod to engulf a paramecium.

Materials
- compound microscope
- prepared slides of paramecia or euglenas
- reference diagrams of paramecia or euglenas (**Figure 8-11**) and bacteria (**Figure 8-4**)

Safety

Procedure

1. Place your prepared slide of either paramecia or euglenas on the microscope stage.

2. Use the low-power objective (4× magnification, then 10× magnification) to locate several paramecia or euglenas.

3. With the organisms in focus, use the high-power objective (40× magnification) to make observations.

4. In your biology notebook or a digital device such as a laptop or tablet, create a diagram that reflects the organism you see under the microscope.

5. Label the structures of the organism based on what you know about protists such as paramecia or euglenas. If you know the name of the structure, label it. Also include what you think the structure's function might be, whether you label the structure or not.

6. Compare your observations and diagram to the diagram provided by your teacher or from the textbook. Identify structures in the provided diagrams that match the structures from your observations. Update your diagram with additional labels and functions of those structures and make any corrections.

7. Return your materials to their stations and clean up.

Results and Analysis

1. **Identify** What structures of the organism were you able to identify under the microscope? Were there any structures in the labeled diagram from the textbook or provided by your teacher that you were unable to identify using your microscope?

2. **Compare** How do the structures of protists, such as paramecia or euglenas, compare with the structures of bacteria? What are the similarities and differences?

3. **Infer** How are the structures that make up the living systems of paramecia or euglenas the same as those of more complex multicellular systems, such as humans? How are they different?

FUNGI

An iceberg in the ocean can appear to be enormous, but 90 percent of its ice is below the surface where you cannot easily see it. Some fungi are similar to icebergs. Above ground, you may see a mushroom. But the mushroom is connected to a vast underground network far larger than what you see above the ground.

Infer *For the type of fungus described, what do you think might be the function of the part of a fungus that sticks up above the ground? The part below ground?*

8.3

KEY TERMS

chitin	lichen
endophyte	mycelium
fungus	mycorrhiza
hypha	spore

Characteristics of Fungi

A **fungus** (plural, *fungi*) is a eukaryotic heterotroph that feeds by secreting digestive enzymes onto organic material and then absorbing the resulting breakdown of products. Like plants, fungi have cell walls and a life cycle that involves producing **spores**—small reproductive units that can be dispersed and grow new organisms. **Chitin**, a nitrogen-containing polysaccharide (Section 5.3), is the main component of fungal cell walls. Like animals, to whom they are more closely related than plants, fungi are heterotrophs. Unlike either plants or animals, fungi include both single-celled and multicellular species.

Organization and Structure Single-celled fungi are commonly referred to as yeasts. We use some yeasts to bake bread and make alcoholic beverages. Others cause human yeast infections. Yeasts most often reproduce asexually by budding. During budding a descendant cell with a small amount of cytoplasm pinches off from its parent.

Most fungi are multicellular. Powdery mildews, shelf fungi, and mushrooms are examples. A multicellular fungus consists of a mesh of microscopic thread-like filaments collectively referred to as a **mycelium** (plural, *mycelia*). Each filament in the mycelium is a **hypha** (plural, *hyphae*). Look for these features in the figures throughout this section.

 VIDEO

VIDEO 8-2 Go online to see yeast reproduce by budding.

Metabolism, Nutrition, and Dispersal Most fungi require oxygen, but some species are full-time or part-time anaerobes. For example, yeasts that are used in baking bread and making wine can switch between aerobic respiration and fermentation depending on the availability of oxygen in their environment (Section 6.3).

Most fungi are *decomposers* (Section 2.2). Decomposers are organisms that feed on organic remains by breaking down molecular components into smaller subunits that can be absorbed. A smaller number of fungi live on or inside living organisms and draw nourishment from their host.

Fungi disperse by producing spores. Fungal spores can be single celled or multicellular, but all are microscopic. Many spores cannot move on their own, but some types of fungi produce spores with flagella.

(▶) VIDEO

VIDEO 8-3 Go online to see how some mushrooms form fruiting bodies to disperse spores.

Types of Fungi

As of 2022, scientists have used phylogenetic analyses to identify eight phyla in the Fungi kingdom (Appendix E). The different types of fungi can also be sorted into five major subgroups based on the structure of their spores and how the fungi produce them (**Figure 8-21**).

- There are four phyla of fungi that make spores that have flagella and can move. The most commonly known of these fungi are called *chytrids*. Most chytrids are aquatic decomposers, but some live inside plants or animals. Chytrids usually reproduce asexually, producing spores at the tips of hyphae.

- Two phyla of fungi have traditionally been called *zygote fungi*. Zygote fungi typically produce thick-walled resting spores during sexual reproduction. However, they most often exist as a mold, which is a mass of hyphae that grows rapidly over organic material and produces spores asexually at the tips of specialized hyphae.

- Although they are not always considered a separate phylum, *glomeromycetes* are a group of soil fungi that form a mutually beneficial partnership with plant roots. Their hyphae extend inside the cell wall of plant root cells. Glomeromycetes produce spores asexually at the tips of hyphae that extend out of the host's root.

- *Sac fungi* (one phylum) reproduce sexually by producing spores in sac-shaped cells. In some species such as morels, these cells form on a fruiting body. Sac fungi include yeasts, molds, parasitic species, and species that partner with photosynthetic cells to form lichens.

- *Club fungi* (one phylum) reproduce sexually by producing spores on club-shaped cells. Mushrooms are the fruiting bodies of club fungi. Shelf fungi, puffballs, and stinkhorns are other examples of club fungi. The group also includes plant pathogens such as smuts and rusts.

CCC **Structure and Function** *Describe the structures that help fungi produce and distribute spores.*

FIGURE 8-21 ▶
Different fungi have different spore-bearing structures.

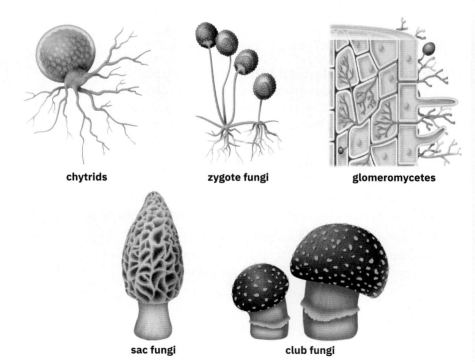

chytrids   zygote fungi   glomeromycetes

sac fungi   club fungi

Ecological Roles of Fungi

Fungi provide an important ecological service by breaking down complex compounds in organic wastes and remains. Some soluble nutrients released by this process enter soil or water. Plants and other producers can then take up the nutrients to meet their own needs. Bacteria also serve as decomposers, but they tend to grow mainly on surfaces. By contrast, fungal hyphae can extend deep into a decaying log or other bulky food source.

Mutualisms Many fungi take part in mutualisms, which are beneficial partnerships between different species (Section 3.1). Some fungi act as **endophytes**, living within different parts of plants, including the roots, stems, and leaves. While not all endophytes are mutualistic, many provide benefits for their plant host and exchange materials with the plant. For the plants they inhabit, endophytes have been shown to improve stress tolerance, promote growth, and help protect against pathogens.

A **mycorrhiza** (plural, *mycorrhizae*) is a type of mutualism in which a soil fungus forms a partnership with the root of a vascular plant. An estimated 80 percent of the vascular plants form mycorrhizae with a glomeromycetes fungus. Hyphae of these fungi enter root cells and branch in the space between the cell wall and the plasma membrane (**Figure 8-22**). Some sac fungi and club fungi form mycorrhizae in which hyphae surround a root and grow between its cells. Most forest mushrooms are fruiting bodies of mycorrhizal club fungi.

Hyphae of all mycorrhizal fungi functionally increase the absorptive surface area of their plant partner. Hyphae are thinner than even the smallest roots and can grow between soil particles. The fungus shares water and nutrients taken up by its hyphae with plant root cells. In return, the plant supplies the fungus with sugars.

FIGURE 8-22 ▼

Observe the detail of mycorrhizal fungi (light gray) interacting with the root of a grass plant (a). Relationships like these extend root networks of plants, an example of which is shown for a different plant in the cross section (b).

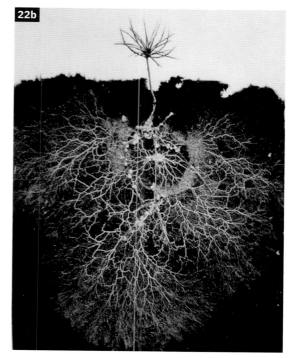

RAINFOREST CONNECTIONS

Gather Evidence *How do mycorrhizal networks connecting trees help maintain the health of the rainforest?*

Mycorrhizal networks transfer water, carbon, nitrogen, and other materials between different plants. Other chemicals that can be transferred between plants serve as signals, effectively letting plants communicate when nutritional conditions change or when there is a threat that is affecting a plant in the network. In response to a defense signal, other plants in the network can increase production of toxins and other compounds that help them resist infestation or other attacks.

A **lichen** is a composite organism that consists of a sac fungus and either cyanobacteria or green algae (**Figure 8-23**). Some types of lichen include more than two species. Fungus makes up the bulk of a lichen's mass, with its hyphae providing structural support to the photosynthetic cells. These cells provide the fungus with sugars and, if the cells are cyanobacteria, with fixed nitrogen. Lichens play an important ecological role by colonizing places too hostile for most organisms, such as exposed rocks. They break down the rock and produce soil by releasing acids and by holding water that freezes and thaws. Once soil forms, plants can move in and take root. Long ago, lichens may have lived on land before plants.

Fungal partners also enhance the nutrition of some animals. Chytrid fungi that live in the stomachs of grazing hoofed mammals such as cattle, deer, and moose aid their hosts by breaking down otherwise indigestible cellulose. Similarly, fungal partners of some ants and termites serve as an external digestive system. Leaf-cutter ants gather bits of leaves to feed a fungus that lives in their nest. The ants cannot digest leaves, but they do eat some of the fungus.

SEP **Construct an Explanation** *Explain how the structures of fungi help them in establishing symbiotic relationships with other species.*

FIGURE 8-23 ▼
Lichen can colonize many inhospitable locations, such as this rock face (a). The cross section of lichen (b) shows algae cells in dark red near the surface of the lichen. The threadlike hyphae of the fungus are stained blue and red.

Parasites and Pathogens Many sac fungi and club fungi are plant parasites. Powdery mildews (sac fungi) and rusts and smuts (club fungi) are parasites that grow in living plants. Their hyphae extend into cells of stems and leaves, where they suck up photosynthetically produced sugars. The resulting loss of nutrients stunts the plant, minimizes seed production, and may eventually kill it. However, the plant usually does not die before the fungus has produced spores on the surface of its infected parts.

Other fungi are pathogens that kill plant tissue with their toxins and then feed on the remains. The club fungus *Armillaria* causes root rot by infecting trees and woody shrubs in forests worldwide. Once an infected tree dies, the fungus decomposes the stumps and logs left behind. In one forest in Oregon, the mycelium of a single honey mushroom (*Armillaria solidipes*) extends across nearly 10 square kilometers. It has been growing for an estimated 2400 years.

Many more fungi infect plants than animals. Among animals, those that do not maintain a high body temperature are most vulnerable to fungal infections. White-nose bat syndrome (caused by *Pseudogymnoascus destructans*) has caused widespread problems in North American bat populations since 2007. Hundreds of fungal species infect insects, and some turn their hosts into zombies that no longer control themselves, forcing the insects to disperse fungal spores (**Figure 8-24**).

Most human fungal infections involve sac fungi on body surfaces. Infected areas are raised, red, and itchy. For example, several species of sac fungi infect skin of the feet, causing "athlete's foot." Sac fungi also cause skin infections misleadingly known as "ringworm." No worm is involved. A ring-shaped lesion forms as fungal hyphae grow out from the initial infection site. Life-threatening fungal infections are rare and most often occur in people whose immune response is weak because of other health issues.

FIGURE 8-24 ▽

An ant infected by a *Cordyceps* fungus stops performing its normal activities as it is taken over by the fungus. After it dies, hyphae burst out of the ant to release spores.

HUNTING FOR TRUFFLES Truffle-producing fungi are highly prized by gourmet food consumers. While prices vary depending on the market, Piedmont white truffles (*Tuber magnatum*) typically cost more than $3300 per kilogram. Burgundy black truffles (*Tuber uncinatum*) average more than $870 per kilogram. Because they cannot be readily cultivated and demand a high price, truffle hunters are very secretive about their favorite hunting areas. Interestingly, the secret to hunting truffles is related to a dispersal strategy that has evolved among this group of fungi.

Truffles are the fruiting bodies of some mycorrhizal fungi that partner with tree roots. Truffles form underground near their host trees and, when mature, produce an odor similar to that of an amorous male wild pig. Female wild pigs detect the scent and root through the soil in search of their seemingly subterranean suitor. When they unearth the truffles, they eat them and then disperse fungal spores in their feces.

Because humans would rather eat the truffles themselves instead of feeding them to pigs, dogs are often used to hunt for truffles. Dogs have a sense of smell thousands of times better than humans, and they can be trained to sniff out only ripe truffles. Truffles take years to develop and ripen.

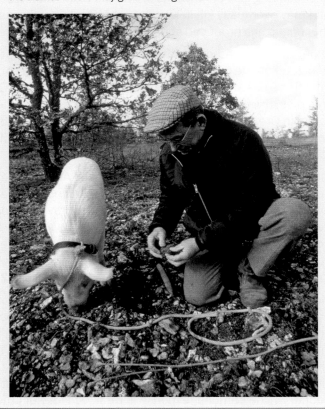

This man in France hunts truffles with his pig. The pig can detect the truffles where they grow underground.

Uses of Fungi

Many fungal fruiting bodies serve as human food. Button, shiitake, and oyster mushrooms decompose organic matter, so these species are easily cultivated. By contrast, other edible mycorrhizal fungi such as chanterelles, porcini mushrooms, morels, and truffles need a living plant partner, so they are typically gathered from the wild. Each year thousands of people become ill after eating poisonous mushrooms they mistook for edible ones (**Figure 8-25**).

Fungal fermentation reactions help us make a variety of products. Fermentation by one mold (*Aspergillus*) helps make soy sauce. Another mold (*Penicillium*) produces the tangy blue veins in cheeses. A packet of baker's yeast holds spores of the sac fungus *Saccharomyces cerevisiae*. When these spores grow in bread dough, they ferment sugar and produce carbon dioxide that causes the dough to rise. Other strains of *S. cerevisiae* are used to make wine and beer, and they are also used in the production of ethanol biofuel.

Geneticists and biotechnologists make use of yeasts for research. For example, checkpoint genes that regulate the eukaryotic cell cycle (Section 7.1) were first discovered in the yeast *S. cerevisiae*. This discovery was the first step toward our current understanding of how mutations in these genes cause human cancers. Genetically engineered *S. cerevisiae* and other yeasts are now used to produce proteins that serve as vaccines and medicines.

Some naturally occurring fungal compounds have medicinal or psychoactive properties. The initial source of the antibiotic penicillin was a soil fungus (*Penicillium chrysogenum*). Another soil fungus gave us cyclosporin, an immune suppressant used to prevent rejection of transplanted organs. Ergotamine, a compound used to relieve migraines, was first isolated from ergot (*Claviceps purpurea*), a club fungus that infects rye plants.

FIGURE 8-25 ▼
Fungal fruiting bodies take many forms. Identifying whether a mushroom is useful, edible, or poisonous is critical. Fly agaric (a) and porcini (b) mushrooms have some visual similarities, but the first is poisonous and the second is edible. Chicken of the woods (c) is edible, while turkey tail mushrooms (d) have medicinal purposes.

8.3 REVIEW

1. **Identify** Which characteristics are common to **ALL** fungi? Select all correct answers.

   A. reproduce asexually

   B. require oxygen to live

   C. digest organic material

   D. have a cell wall made of chitin

   E. form a mesh of filaments

2. **Describe** What is one way that fungi and plants benefit in a mutualistic relationship?

3. **Identify** Which type of spores are involved in the asexual reproduction of fungi?

   A. spores with flagella at tips of hyphae

   B. spores in sac-shaped cells

   C. thick-walled resting spores

   D. spores on club-shaped cells

4. **Describe** Consider one example of a parasitic relationship between a fungus and a plant. What happens to the fungi and plants in this relationship?

THE C-VALUE ENIGMA

SEP **Use Computational Thinking** The genome of an axolotl salamander is ten times larger than the genome of a human and more than 100,000 times larger than the genome of a bacterium.

Genome size, represented by the total amount of DNA in any cell of an organism, is often reported as the *C-value*, measured in base pairs. It is a constant among all organisms of the same species. The small sections of the total DNA that encode for proteins are called genes. The human genome consists of 3.2 billion base pairs with about 25,000 genes. **Table 1** lists the C-value and approximate number of protein-encoding genes for a selection of organisms. **Figure 1** shows the values in the table on a log-log plot.

TABLE 1. C-value and Number of Genes for a Selection of Organisms

Organism	C-Value (10⁹ base pairs)	Approximate number of protein-encoding genes
Ambystoma mexicanum (axolotl)	320.000	23,000
Anopheles gambiae (mosquito)	0.3	13,500
Escherichia coli (bacteria)	0.005	3200
Homo sapiens (human)	3.2	25,000
Neoceratodus forsteri (Australian lungfish)	43	31,120
Oryza sativa (rice)	0.47	51,000
Plasmodium falciparum (malaria parasite)	0.023	5000
Polychaos dubium (amoeba)	670	15,000
Saccharomyces cerevisiae (yeast)	0.012	6000

FIGURE 1
This log-log plot of C-value and number of genes shows a wide range of values.

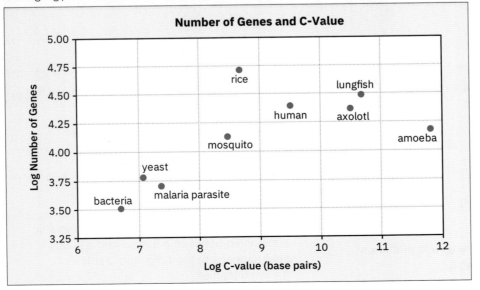

FIGURE 2 ▽

Organisms such as axolotls (a), rice plants (b), yeast (c), and Australian lungfishes (d) do not all necessarily have the number of genes you would expect, relative to their apparent complexity.

1. **Identify Patterns** Describe the general trend between number of genes and C-value.

2. **Justify** Explain why plotting a log-log plot helped identify patterns in the data.

3. **Compare** Based on what you know about them, rank the organisms by their complexity.

4. **Organize Data** Group organisms by relative genome size compared to humans.

5. **Synthesize** Use your analysis of the data to support a claim about C-value and organism complexity.

8.4

KEY TERMS

bacteriophage
capsid
lysogenic pathway
lytic pathway
retrovirus
viral envelope

VIRUSES

Have you ever been performing a lab activity and were missing the lab equipment you needed? Or maybe you could not find the material that was best for building a model of a scientific process, and you had to borrow from another group. Every time a virus infects a host cell, it has to borrow equipment from the host to reproduce its own proteins and genome.

Explain *What kind of "equipment" do you think a virus might need to replicate itself?*

Viruses and Their Classification

A virus is a noncellular infectious particle that can replicate only inside a living cell. By many definitions, viruses are not alive. Unlike cells, viruses do not maintain homeostasis or engage in metabolic processes such as ATP production, and they cannot reproduce on their own. A virus that is not inside a host cell is referred to as a *viral particle*. With rare exceptions, viral particles can only be viewed with an electron microscope.

Viruses outnumber the stars in the universe and exist everywhere on Earth. For every bacterium, there are about 10 virus particles. Viruses infect every kind of known organism, yet each virus is highly specialized. A few viruses, such as the mimivirus, that are large enough to see with a light microscope can themselves become infected by other viruses.

A viral particle always includes a viral genome inside a protein shell called a **capsid**. During infection, some proteins of the capsid must bind to proteins at the surface of a host cell. Because of this binding, each type of virus can only infect specific kinds of cells. Viruses are classified by the structure of their capsid, their genome, and how they replicate.

Virus Genomes The genetic material of a virus particle can be either DNA or RNA. In cells, RNA serves many important functions, including as an intermediate message (a messenger RNA, or mRNA) between the DNA genome and the translation of proteins the cell needs (Chapter 11). DNA replication and transcription of DNA into mRNA occurs in the nucleus. Translation of mRNA to proteins occurs in the cytoplasm. Because viruses rely on these same processes when infecting a host cell, the type of virus genome affects how it behaves and replicates. Virus genomes generally fall into the four following categories:

- **Double-Stranded DNA (dsDNA)** dsDNA viruses have genomes that are most similar to those of living organisms. Many of these viruses replicate in the host cell's nucleus and rely on its cell machinery. Some dsDNA viruses are able to replicate their genome and capsids on their own in the host cell's cytoplasm. Herpesviruses, papillomaviruses, poxviruses, and adenoviruses are examples of dsDNA viruses.

- **Single-Stranded DNA (ssDNA)** ssDNA viruses of eukaryotes mostly replicate in the nucleus. Parvoviruses, which infect cats and dogs and cause fifth disease in humans, are ssDNA viruses.

SEP **Construct an Explanation** *Why do you think most DNA viruses replicate inside the nucleus of their host cells?*

- **Single-Stranded RNA (ssRNA)** Some RNA genomes are very similar to mRNA, and the viral RNA can be directly translated into proteins by a host cell, while others undergo additional steps to replicate. Coronaviruses and influenza viruses are both important groups of viruses with ssRNA genomes. Most ssRNA viruses replicate in the cytoplasm. Among the exceptions are human immunodeficiency virus (HIV), which has a replication phase that occurs in the nucleus.

- **Double-Stranded RNA (dsRNA)** dsRNA viruses evolved from ssRNA viruses. Different members of this group infect a wide variety of hosts, including bacteria, fungi, plants, and animals. The rotaviruses that cause gastroenteritis have dsRNA genomes. RNA virus genomes typically encode their own genome replication enzymes and replicate in the cytoplasm of host cells.

Virus Capsid Structures A virus capsid consists of a few unique protein subunits arranged in a repeating pattern. When viral proteins assemble as a helix around a strand of nucleic acid, the result is a rod shape or a filamentous, fiber-like shape. Many plant viruses, including the tobacco mosaic virus (ssRNA), have this type of structure (**Figure 8-26a**).

Bacteriophages are viruses that infect bacteria, and most have a complex structure. **Figure 8-26b** includes the T4 bacteriophage, a dsDNA virus common in the human gut. The viral genome is enclosed within a polyhedral (many-sided) "head." Other protein components of the T4 viral particle include a hollow helical sheath through which viral DNA is injected into a bacterial cell, and "tail fibers" that attach the virus to that cell.

The tobacco mosaic virus and the T4 bacteriophage are called *nonenveloped viruses* because their outermost layer is the protein capsid. By contrast, the nearly spherical (often icosahedral, or 20-sided) capsid of most animal viruses is covered by a **viral envelope**, a layer of cell membrane derived from the cell in which the virus formed. SARS-CoV-2 (severe acute respiratory syndrome coronavirus 2)—the cause of COVID-19—is an enveloped ssRNA virus (**Figure 8-26c**).

CCC **Structure and Function** *Consider that most virus genomes need to be small. Why do you think virus capsid structures might use many repeating structures instead of a large number of unique proteins?*

FIGURE 8-26 ▽
These are just a few examples of the different shapes and structures that can make up viral particles.

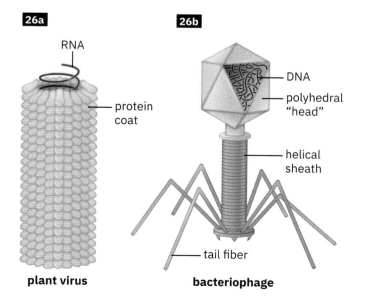

26a

RNA

protein coat

plant virus

26b

DNA

polyhedral "head"

helical sheath

tail fiber

bacteriophage

26c

glycoprotein spike

membrane protein

envelope protein

lipid envelope

RNA and nucleocapsid protein

SARS-CoV-2

Virus Replication

Virus replication is particularly interesting and varied, because each virus depends on the infected hosts in different ways. Typically, when a virus encounters a host cell it can infect, viral capsid proteins bind proteins of a host's cell membrane. Then viral genes enter the cell. Viral genes hijack the cell's internal machinery, causing it to make viral components that self-assemble as viral particles. The particles are then released into the environment. Two life cycle examples are those of bacteriophages and human immunodeficiency virus (HIV).

FIGURE 8-27 ▼
Bacteriophages can undergo lytic or lysogenic pathways inside a host bacterium.

virus injects DNA into host bacteria

lytic pathway

host cell copies viral DNA and makes viral proteins

viral particles assemble

host cell lyses and viral particles are released

bacterial chromosome

lysogenic pathway

viral DNA is incorporated into host cell genome

host cell copies viral DNA each time it replicates

viral DNA is reactivated in descendent cells and the lytic pathway makes more viral particles

Bacteriophage Replication A bacteriophage such as T4 replicates using two pathways (**Figure 8-27**). Both pathways start when the virus attaches to a bacterium and injects DNA (**Figure 8-28**).

In the **lytic pathway**, viral DNA is immediately replicated and transcribed, causing the host cell to produce new viral DNA and proteins. These viral components assemble as virus particles, which escape when the cell breaks open (lyses) and dies.

In the **lysogenic pathway**, viral DNA becomes integrated into the host cell's genome. However, viral genes are not expressed, so the host cell remains healthy. When this cell reproduces, a copy of the viral DNA is passed on with the host's genome. The DNA remains in the genome of the cell's descendants until it is reactivated and starts the lytic pathway.

FIGURE 8-28 ▶
A bacteriophage starts an infection by injecting its DNA genome into a host cell. This colored transmission electron micrograph shows a T4 bacteriophage injecting its DNA into *E. coli.*

infection

assembly

HIV RNA

reverse
transcription

HIV DNA

integration

RNA

transcription

translation

HIV
proteins

HIV Replication

HIV Replication RNA viruses, such as HIV, that use reverse transcriptase to produce viral DNA are called **retroviruses**. This means that HIV's ssRNA genome is "reverse transcribed" into DNA that can be incorporated into the host genome where it can code for viral particles (**Figure 8-29**). Drugs that fight HIV infection interfere with different steps of the replication cycle. HIV replication can be described by the following steps:

- **Infection** During infection, spikes of viral glycoprotein attach to proteins in the cell's plasma membrane. The host cell's plasma membrane and the viral envelope fuse, allowing viral enzymes and RNA to enter the cell.

- **Reverse Transcription and Integration** The viral enzyme reverse transcriptase converts viral RNA into double-stranded DNA. Once viral DNA has been made, it is moved into the nucleus, along with another viral enzyme that integrates the DNA into the host chromosome.

- **Transcription** Viral DNA is transcribed into RNA. Some of that transcribed RNA is the genome of new HIV particles.

- **Translation** Some of the transcribed RNA encodes viral proteins and is translated to make the proteins of the HIV capsid.

- **Assembly** The viral proteins and RNA assemble at the host cell's plasma membrane. New viruses gain a viral envelope when they bud off from the cell (**Figure 8-30**).

FIGURE 8-29
The human immunodeficiency virus brings its own enzymes to a human host cell, which allow it to reverse transcribe its RNA genome into DNA that it integrates into the host genome.

Go Online **INTERACTIVE FIGURE**

FIGURE 8-29 Go online to learn more about virus structure and step through the process of **HIV Replication**.

FIGURE 8-30
A colored transmission electron micrograph shows an HIV particle budding off a cell (a). The key structures of an HIV particle include several structural proteins, enzymes, and an RNA genome (b).

30a

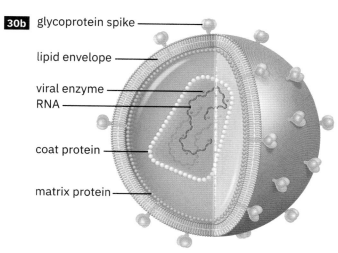

30b

glycoprotein spike

lipid envelope

viral enzyme
RNA

coat protein

matrix protein

Viruses and Human Health

Common Viruses Many viruses live in our body without any ill effects, but others are pathogens, meaning they cause disease. Viral diseases usually produce brief, mild symptoms, such as by causing common colds. Viruses that infect cells in the lining of our gastrointestinal tract may cause vomiting and diarrhea. Infections by some viral pathogens can persist for long periods, or even for life. An initial infection by one of these viruses causes symptoms that subside quickly. However, the virus remains present in a latent (resting) state and can reawaken. For example, herpes simplex virus 1 (HSV-1) can remain dormant in nerve cells for years before becoming activated by stress. When this virus replicates, it causes painful "cold sores" at the edge of the lips. Another herpesvirus causes similar sores on the genitals.

Measles, mumps, rubella (German measles), and chicken pox are potentially deadly viral diseases of childhood that, until recently, were common worldwide. Today, most children in developed countries have been vaccinated against these illnesses. A vaccine primes the body to fight a pathogen.

A few viruses can cause cancer. Infection by certain strains of sexually transmitted human papillomaviruses (HPV) is the main cause of cervical cancer. Similarly, infection by some hepatitis viruses raises the risk of liver cancer. Epstein-Barr virus, the cause of infectious mononucleosis, also raises the risk of lymphoma (a blood cell cancer).

Emerging Viral Diseases An emerging disease is a disease that has only relatively recently been detected in humans, or has recently expanded its range. These examples are considered to be emerging diseases in terms of human history.

- **AIDS** Acquired immunodeficiency syndrome (AIDS) is a viral disease that was first identified in humans in 1981. Since then, it has caused about 39 million deaths. AIDS is a communicable disease, meaning the HIV infection that causes AIDS spreads from one infected person to another. Scientists now know that HIV was circulating in parts of Africa since the beginning of the 20th century before it became a widespread disease in other parts of the world.

- **West Nile** The virus that causes West Nile disease cannot spread directly from person to person. Mosquitoes carry this virus from host to host, so these insects are called vectors. Birds are a "reservoir" for West Nile virus, which means that the virus can replicate in birds, and that birds serve as a source of virus for new human infections. West Nile virus was unknown in North America until 1999, when it emerged in New York. It has since spread across the continent. From 1999 through 2019, there were nearly 52,000 reported human cases of West Nile disease in the United States and 2390 deaths.

- **Zika** The Zika virus is a relative of West Nile virus. It is transmitted by mosquitoes and also by sexual contact. Zika has been known in Africa since 1947, but was recently introduced to South America. Most people have mild symptoms, but some develop a temporary paralysis. An infection during pregnancy raises the risk of miscarriage and of microcephaly (an unusually small brain and head) in the developing child.

VIDEO

VIDEO 8-4 Go online to learn more about the viruses that cause Ebola.

- **Ebola** Ebola is caused by enveloped ssRNA viruses first identified in Africa in 1976. Within three weeks of infection, a person develops flulike symptoms, followed by a rash, vomiting, diarrhea, and bleeding from all body openings. The virus is transmitted by contact with body fluids, so caregivers must wear protective gear (**Figure 8-31**). While most outbreaks are small, an outbreak that began in Guinea killed more than 11,000 people between the end of 2013 and 2016.

- **SARS and COVID-19** SARS (prevalent in 2002–2004) and COVID-19 (starting in 2019) are caused by similar coronaviruses, named for their crown or "corona"-shaped capsid. Both viruses are thought to have jumped from bat species to become infectious in humans and were first detected in China. These coronavirus infections are transmitted through the air and cause respiratory and other symptoms. Through May 2022, more than 522 million cases of COVID-19 were recorded worldwide, with more than 6 million reported deaths.

FIGURE 8-31 ▲
Medical personnel must take extreme caution when treating patients or performing any tasks associated with the highly contagious and deadly Ebola virus (a). A colored transmission electron micrograph shows the unique structure of an Ebola virus particle (b).

Influenza Viruses and Viral Reassortment
Influenza viruses are enveloped ssRNA viruses. Influenza strains are defined by and named for the varying structures of two viral proteins—hemagglutinin (H) and neuraminidase (N)—that extend through the viral envelope (**Figure 8-32**).

FIGURE 8-32 ▼
A colored transmission electron micrograph of an avian influenza virus (a) shows many of the features demonstrated in the influenza virus model (b). The hemagglutinin and neuraminidase proteins are important for infection.

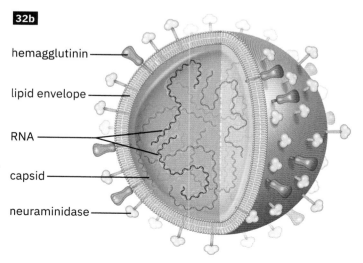

hemagglutinin

lipid envelope

RNA

capsid

neuraminidase

Influenza genomes are made up of eight genome segments that can be swapped between related viruses that infect a host at the same time (**Figure 8-33**). Viral reassortment occurs all the time, and it can be dangerous. For example, the H5N1 strain is a bird flu that has a high mortality rate in humans but is not easily transmitted. H1N1 (the swine flu) is rarely deadly, but it is transmitted easily. If both strains were to infect the same individual at the same time, the result could be a new strain that has a high mortality rate and is also highly transmissible.

To keep up with changes in the prevalence of different H and N proteins in the viral population, scientists develop a new flu vaccine every year. However, determining which flu strains will be around in the future is not an exact science. Even after a flu shot, a person is susceptible to a virus that differs from the strains targeted by the vaccine. New influenza strains arise through mutation and also by viral reassortment.

SEP **Construct an Explanation** *Why do new vaccines have to be developed every year for influenza viruses?*

FIGURE 8-33 ▶
Viral reassortment can cause rapid changes in the influenza virus population. Changes in H and N proteins, in particular, affect how the virus interacts with and infects host cells.

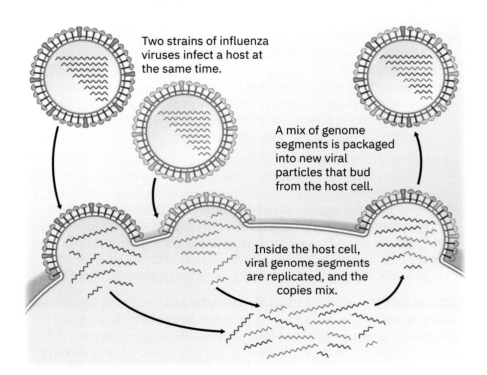

Two strains of influenza viruses infect a host at the same time.

A mix of genome segments is packaged into new viral particles that bud from the host cell.

Inside the host cell, viral genome segments are replicated, and the copies mix.

8.4 REVIEW

1. **Identify** Which characteristics are common to **ALL** virus particles? Select all correct answers.

   A. contain DNA or RNA

   B. have a protein-based capsid

   C. are single-celled with nucleus

   D. replicate within a host cell

   E. have double-stranded genetic material

2. **Describe** What are the four major groups of viral genomes, and where do they typically replicate?

3. **Describe** Which shape describes most of the capsids of viruses that infect animals?

   A. filamentous fiber

   B. nonenveloped helix

   C. enveloped icosahedral

   D. polyhedral head with helix

4. **Contrast** In what ways are bacteriophage and HIV replication similar and different?

ON ASSIGNMENT In late February of 2020 Milan, Italy, was in crisis as the SARS-CoV-2 virus spread rapidly through the population, overwhelming hospitals and killing many residents among Italy's aging population. National Geographic photographer Gabriele Galimberti and his partner undertook to photograph and interview quarantined residents as they struggled with loneliness, fear, and uncertainty in the face of a new pandemic.

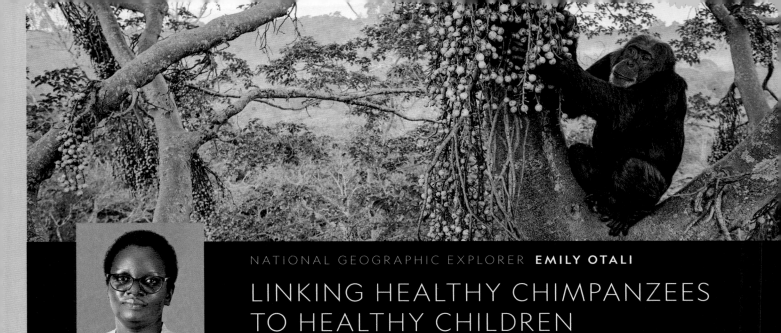

NATIONAL GEOGRAPHIC EXPLORER **EMILY OTALI**

LINKING HEALTHY CHIMPANZEES TO HEALTHY CHILDREN

Dr. Emily Otali works with communities surrounding the Kibale National Park in Uganda to protect the chimpanzees that live there.

The chimpanzees were making strange grunting calls, a signal that a hunt was about to begin. One clung to the base of a tree, beating it with his feet and a stick. Others gathered, focused on another huge tree. The next thing primatologist Dr. Emily Otali saw were monkeys raining down from the tree and racing away in all directions. By the time she reached the tree, the chimpanzees were feasting on five monkeys. The hunt was over.

Otali was exhilarated by this experience of observing her first hunt. She knew at age nine that she wanted to work with animals as an adult. As the Field Director of the Kibale Chimpanzee Project in Uganda, she celebrates the fact that she lives her childhood dream. The 1400 or so chimpanzees in Kibale National Park, divided into about seven different communities of 50–200 members each, comprise one of the largest populations in East Africa. Even though they live in a protected area, and are generally increasing in population, they are not without threats from the humans that surround them.

Of great interest to Otali is the threat of respiratory diseases moving into the chimpanzee population from the humans who work as guides, trail cutters, foresters, and researchers or who visit as tourists. Since 1987, the rate of respiratory infections has increased yearly and has become the leading cause of death in the Kibale chimpanzees, a statistic repeated in other East African populations. In 2013 alone, five chimpanzees from one Kibale community died during a single outbreak attributed to a human rhinovirus-C. This was the first time that this virus was identified in chimpanzees.

The rhinoviruses that cause respiratory problems invade and destroy tissues in the body. After lifelong exposure to such viruses, the human body's immune system can often fight off an infection after a few days. However, the chimpanzees, lacking this long-term exposure, have not developed similar protective responses. Knowing that schools often act as sources of respiratory infections, Otali's project "Healthy Children—Healthy Chimps," focuses on using outbreaks in the area's youth as an early warning system of sorts. She visits forest edge schools to monitor the respiratory health of the students, collect clinical samples for virus identification, and educate children on their role in keeping chimpanzees healthy.

THINKING CRITICALLY

Argue From Evidence *What evidence would you look for to support Otali's claim that the respiratory diseases enter the park through humans going there?*

TYING IT ALL TOGETHER
SPACE STATION STOWAWAYS

HOW ARE THE CHARACTERISTICS OF AN ORGANISM RELATED TO ITS PLACE IN AN ECOSYSTEM?

The Case Study described why microorganisms are found even on the International Space Station (ISS), and how scientists study the effects of space travel on these organisms. In some cases, the presence of bacteria and fungi in space can have unfortunate consequences. In the late 1990s, the Russian space station Mir was inundated with black and green mold growing behind control panels and forming slimy films on numerous surfaces. The mold posed a serious safety risk. It corroded windows, rubber gaskets, electrical components, space suits, and other materials. Even on Earth, indoor mold and mildew are difficult to remove; astronauts on the ISS must combat the same kinds of hardy fungal formations to protect their health, their equipment, and the station itself (**Figure 8-34**).

Aspergillus niger is a species of fungus commonly found on the ISS. Normally harmless to humans, it can cause respiratory disease in people with weakened immune systems. The fungus is also of particular interest to space scientists because it is widely used in the biotechnology industry to produce a variety of acids, proteins, enzymes, and other useful substances. Studies have found that *A. niger* can withstand extreme conditions of the kind that occur in space, including prolonged microgravity, massive doses of radiation, and low temperatures, making it a promising candidate for manufacturing materials needed on long missions (**Figure 8-35**).

In this activity, you will investigate how the characteristics of *Aspergillus niger* enable it to thrive in space. Work individually or in a group to complete these steps.

Obtain and Evaluate Information
1. Research the fungus *Aspergillus niger*. In your research, identify its physical qualities and the systems it uses to grow, form colonies, and reproduce.

Develop a Model
2. Construct a model that illustrates how at least two different characteristics of *Aspergillus niger* would help it survive in space.

Communicate Information
3. Use digital media to make a presentation that explains your model.

FIGURE 8-34 ▼
This door shows one surface where fungal growth occurs regularly on the ISS.

FIGURE 8-35 ▼
Aspergillus niger spores are very resistant to radiation, with significant rates of survival after extremely high doses.

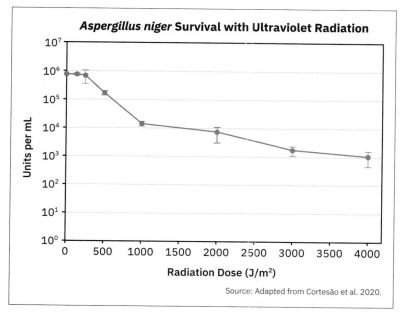

Source: Adapted from Cortesão et al. 2020.

REVIEW KEY CONCEPTS

1. **Identify** Which approach would be most useful in determining whether a newly discovered unicellular organism should be classified as bacteria, archaea, or eukaryotes?

   A. Define its cellular shape.

   B. Test its metabolic requirements.

   C. Analyze the sequence of its genome.

   D. Observe how it responds to Gram staining.

2. **Classify** Use the characteristics of four bacterial species described in the table to identify each species as a photoautotroph, chemoautotroph, photoheterotroph, or chemoheterotroph.

Bacteria species	Energy source	Carbon source
Rhodopseudomonas palustris	sunlight	organic acids
Sterolibacterium denitrificans	sulfur compounds	carbon dioxide
Nitrosomonas eutropha	ammonia	organic animal waste
Chlorbium tepidum	sunlight	carbon dioxide

3. **Predict** Some bacterial pathogens enter the human body via ingested food or water, multiply, and attack the human intestines. Which characteristic(s) would you expect to observe in these species? Select all correct answers.

   A. require oxygen

   B. produce toxins

   C. tolerate acidic conditions

   D. convert sunlight into energy

   E. obtain nutrients from other organisms

4. **Explain** How do mycorrhizae assist plants? Select all correct answers.

   A. by inhibiting plant pathogens from entering plant cells

   B. by breaking down and removing the decaying parts of plants

   C. by increasing a plant's ability to absorb water and nutrients from soil

   D. by increasing the number of photosynthetic cells that produce sugars for the plant

   E. by allowing chemical compounds to move between plants as a form of communication

5. **Contrast** How do colonial single-celled organisms differ from multicellular organisms? Select all correct answers.

   A. Colonial single-celled organisms do not contain mitochondria; cells of multicellular organisms do.

   B. Colonial single-celled organisms can live independently, whereas cells from a multicellular organism cannot.

   C. Colonial single-celled organisms are always much smaller than multicellular organisms, not reaching more than a few centimeters in size.

   D. Colonial single-celled organisms differentiate to perform many different functions, whereas cells in multicellular organisms all express the same genes.

   E. Each cell in a colonial single-celled organism can reproduce to form a new organism; only certain cells in a multicellular organism can reproduce.

6. **Contrast** What components are present in both viruses and cells? Select all correct answers.

   A. cytoplasm

   B. genomes

   C. organelles

   D. proteins

   E. ribosomes

7. **Sequence** Place each step in the correct sequence to describe how a retrovirus such as HIV infects its host cell.

   • Viral DNA is integrated into the host genome.

   • Viral RNA is translated into structural proteins.

   • HIV infects the host cell.

   • New viruses are assembled.

   • Viral DNA is transcribed into RNA.

   • Viral RNA is reverse transcribed into DNA.

8. **Predict** What do you think the genome of an ssRNA virus needs to encode if the virus replicates in a eukaryotic host cell's cytoplasm?

   A. enzymes for DNA replication

   B. enzymes for reverse transcription of RNA to DNA

   C. enzymes for RNA replication

   D. ribosomes

9. **Infer** How is the structure and shape of a mycelium well adapted to the role of decomposition that many fungi have in their ecosystems?

10. **Compare** How do viral lytic and lysogenic pathways compare?

CRITICAL THINKING

11. **NOS** **Scientific Knowledge** What evidence did scientists historically use to classify eukaryotes, and how did new technologies provide evidence that led to the more recent classification of eukaryotes into six supergroups?

12. **Identify Patterns** *Giardia intestinalis* and *Trypanosoma brucei* are both parasitic protists. *G. intestinalis* typically enters a new host in the form of cysts before the cells become active in the host's digestive tract. *T. brucei* does not form cysts before infecting a new host. Explain why *G. intestinalis* takes the form of cysts, whereas *T. brucei* does not.

13. **Justify** An effective antifungal drug can kill fungal pathogens without harming the host's cells. A scientist is developing a new antifungal drug for use in humans. She proposes using a chemical compound known to inhibit chitin synthase, an enzyme that is important in the biosynthesis of chitin. What argument can the scientist use to justify her proposal?

14. **Synthesize Information** The fungus that causes white-nose syndrome in North American bats was likely transported from Europe to China. Given that bats do not migrate between these locations, how do you think the infectious fungus could have been transported?

MATH AND ENGLISH LANGUAGE ARTS CONNECTIONS

1. **Write an Argument** The Outer Space Treaty of 1967 established a set of principles governing space exploration. One principle reads: "States shall avoid harmful contamination of space and celestial bodies." Some scientists worry that microorganisms from Earth could colonize other planets if carried there by human-made spacecraft. Is this a valid concern? Write an argument explaining your reasoning.

2. **Reason Quantitatively** Researchers used light microscopy to observe the pumping action of contractile vacuoles in living cells of the protist *Chlamydomonas*. The researchers measured the time interval between contractions as a function of solute concentration in the external medium surrounding the cells. Describe the relationship between pumping rate and solute concentration. What does this relationship suggest about the role of the contractile vacuole in these freshwater organisms?

External medium	Solute concentration (mole/kg water)	Time between contractions (seconds)
distilled water	0.000	15.8
distilled water: tap water (1:1)	0.032	22.0
tap water	0.065	28.9

Read the following passage. Cite evidence from the passage to answer the question.

By the late 1880s, a variety of pathogenic bacteria, fungi, and protists had been identified using a combination of microscopic observations and controlled infection experiments. However, viruses were completely unknown, mainly because microscopes were not powerful enough to view them. In 1892, scientists discovered that a disease affecting tobacco plants was caused by an agent that passed through pores too small to allow bacteria through. Many scientists thought that the agent must be a very small bacterium. Others thought that chemical compounds excreted by bacteria must cause the disease. It wasn't until virus particles could be viewed using an electron microscope in 1941 that scientists agreed that the tobacco mosaic virus was the agent responsible for the disease.

3. **Cite Textual Evidence** How does this passage illustrate the idea that new technologies advance scientific knowledge? Cite information from the text to support your answer.

▶ REVISIT RAINFOREST CONNECTIONS

Gather Evidence In this chapter, you learned how many tiny organisms, and some viruses that infect them, live in all different environments. The rainforest is an incredibly biodiverse habitat with many interacting organisms.

1. What are some roles that you think bacteria might play in the rainforest ecosystem?

2. What other questions do you have about how microscopic organisms interact in the rainforest?

CHAPTER 9

PLANT SYSTEMS

This grove of aspen trees in Utah is thought to be the largest and most dense living organism on Earth.

This aspen grove, named Pando, a Latin word meaning "I spread," covers 106 acres and consists of more than 40,000 trees. Aspen is a clonal species, which means that genetically identical trees can sprout from its roots. Though current trees are only around 130 years old, scientists think the aspen grove got its start near the end of the last ice age, about 11,700 years ago.

Chapter 9 supports the NGSS Performance Expectations **HS-LS1-2** and **HS-LS1-3**.

CASE STUDY
FLOWER POWER

HOW DO PLANTS RESPOND TO CHANGES IN THE ENVIRONMENT?

Sunflowers (*Helianthus annuus*) are common sights in agricultural fields where they are grown for food and oil production. But farms are not the only places where fields of sunflowers grow. These easily identifiable flowers have also been planted after environmental disasters such as the nuclear accidents at the Chernobyl Nuclear Power Plant in Ukraine in 1986 and at the Fukushima Daichi Nuclear Power Plant in Japan in 2011.

Planting sunflowers in contaminated areas is an example of *phytoremediation*, which is the use of plants to extract chemical contaminants from soil or water. The goal of phytoremediation is to recover polluted soil and help restore soil fertility.

Sunflowers grow quickly and can grow nearly anywhere without much intervention. These popular plants are *hyperaccumulators*, meaning they are able to take up and store high concentrations of metals from the soil or water where they grow. These substances are stored in the plants' tissues, including their roots, stems, and leaves. Sunflowers are particularly adept at absorbing zinc, copper, lead, and radioactive wastes.

Phytoremediation of radioactive materials works because some radioactive isotopes are chemically similar to nutrients that the plants normally absorb. For example, cesium behaves like potassium, a critical nutrient for plant growth and development. Strontium is similar to calcium, which plants require for structural support. As part of a Chernobyl remediation project, sunflowers were grown in rafts floating in a contaminated pond. Within two weeks, the amounts of radioactive cesium and strontium in the water had decreased by 90 percent.

Once the sunflowers absorb the materials, the plants are harvested and safely disposed of. Phytoremediation is a particularly attractive solution for soil contamination (**Figure 9-1**), as it is significantly less expensive to grow and dispose of plants than it would be to remove the soil itself. However, while the use of sunflowers has gained popularity as a remediation technique, several factors can affect its success. For example, not all species of sunflowers are effective hyperaccumulators, so planting the right species is key. The type of soil can also affect how well the plants are able to extract toxic materials. While the sunflowers have been effective at Chernobyl, projects at Fukushima did not have the same results. Researchers continue to study how to make the most effective use of these plants in the reclamation of polluted sites.

Ask Questions *As you read this chapter, generate questions about systems and processes that would enable a plant to transport toxic substances from soil or water into its tissues.*

FIGURE 9-1
Coal-fired electrical power plants produce fly ash that contains heavy metal pollutants. The heavy metals accumulate in the surrounding soil and water. Phytoremediation can be used to remove these substances.

KEY TERMS

cuticle
lignin
nonvascular plant
organ
organ system
phloem
stomata
vascular plant
vascular tissue
xylem

PLANT ORIGINS AND DIVERSITY

What color is Earth? In images of the sunny side of the planet taken from space, white clouds swirl above blue oceans, and land masses appear in shades of brown. Of the many forms of life on Earth, only one can be directly observed at this scale—the patches of green visible on almost all continents are plants. There are about 435,000 unique species of land plants, and plants constitute over 80 percent of all the biomass on Earth.

Explain *Why do you think plants are such a dominant life-form on Earth?*

Plant Evolution

Plants are multicellular eukaryotes that carry out photosynthesis and typically live on land. Fossil evidence indicates that between 500 million and 400 million years ago, land plants evolved from a freshwater green alga that grew at the water's edge. Like their green algal relatives (Section 8.2), plants have cells with walls made of cellulose, they have chloroplasts that contain chlorophyll, and they store sugars as starch.

A green alga absorbs all the water, dissolved nutrients, and gases it needs through its outer surface. Water also keeps the alga afloat, supporting its weight and maximizing its exposure to sunlight for photosynthesis. But to survive on land, plants needed to adapt to very different conditions than their aquatic ancestors faced.

Structural Adaptations Land plants are exposed to air, so the water they need for photosynthesis readily evaporates into their surroundings. To reduce water loss, plants secrete a waxy **cuticle** that seals their outermost tissue layer, the epidermis (**Figure 9-2**). Pores called **stomata** (singular, *stoma*) span the cuticle and epidermis. Stomata can open to allow carbon dioxide into the plant or close to conserve water.

FIGURE 9-2 ▽
A cross section of a leaf shows some plant structures that evolved as adaptations for surviving on land.

- cuticle
- epidermis
- **vascular tissues**
- xylem
- phloem
- stoma

On land, a plant must obtain water and nutrients from soil and transport these materials to wherever they are needed in the plant's body. Some land plants accomplish this by direct absorption, similarly to green algae. In contrast, more than 90 percent of modern plant species have internal pipelines made of **vascular tissue** to perform transport functions. **Xylem** is the vascular tissue that distributes water and mineral ions taken up by roots. **Phloem** is the vascular tissue that distributes sugars made by photosynthetic cells.

A polymer called **lignin** stiffens cell walls in vascular tissue. Lignin-reinforced vascular tissue not only distributes materials. It also helps land plants stand upright and supports their branches. Branches with many leaves increase the amount of the plant's surface area that is available for capturing light and exchanging gases with the atmosphere.

Reproductive Adaptations Like related algae, plants produce two types of reproductive cells. *Spores* are single cells that develop into a new organism by dividing. *Gametes* are sex cells that fuse together and develop into an embryo. Plants reproduce by releasing spores or gametes into their environment.

New plant structures evolved to enable reproductive cells to disperse in dry habitats, such as by wind or land animals. For example, a *pollen grain* is typically a one- or two-celled structure that contains a male gamete. The outer layer of a pollen grain is highly resistant to abrasion, heat, decay, and other environmental dangers it may encounter on the way from one plant to another (**Figure 9-3**).

The development of the *seed* was an enormous advancement for land plants. Seeds are multicellular structures that include a preformed embryonic root, stem, and leaf as well as a food supply to increase the embryo's chance of survival. A protective seed coat allows water and oxygen to reach the growing embryo until it is ready to germinate.

CCC **Structure and Function** *What are two structural advantages that enable plants to survive on land?*

FIGURE 9-3
Pollen grains vary widely in size, ranging in diameter from a few to hundreds of micrometers in land plants. Pollen grains are so indestructible that they commonly appear in the fossil record. The pollen grains in this scanning electron microscope image come from various types of plants. A plant's species can often be identified by the markings and shape of its pollen grains.

Major Plant Groups

Modern plants can be divided into two main groups based on whether they have a system for moving water and nutrients within the plant. The **vascular plants** have transport systems made of vascular tissue. Although some **nonvascular plants** known as bryophytes do not have xylem or phloem, they do have internal conducting vessels. They absorb nutrients through their surface rather than withdrawing them from soil, so they can colonize rocky sites where vascular plants cannot take root. Nonvascular plants are the only plant life in some parts of the Arctic and Antarctic. Evolutionary relationships between the nonvascular and vascular plants remain a matter of investigation.

Vascular plants can be further categorized by their reproductive systems. Seedless vascular plants include the ferns and other similar plants that reproduce by dispersing spores. The seed plants include gymnosperms, which produce unprotected seeds on a cone or stem, and angiosperms (flowering plants), which produce seeds enclosed within a fruit. **Figure 9-4** summarizes the relationships among the major plant groups and the traits of each group.

FIGURE 9-4 ▽
The first land plants to evolve from an ancient alga were nonvascular. Seedless vascular plants emerged later, followed by vascular plants with seeds.

CCC **Structure and Function** *Many tiny individual moss plants clump together to form the blanket of moss shown in **Figure 9-4**. In general, nonvascular plants tend to be very small in size relative to vascular plants. Why do you think this is?*

Nonvascular plants
- no xylem or phloem
- seedless

liverworts   mosses
          hornworts

Seedless vascular plants
- vascular tissue present
- seedless

club mosses,   whisk ferns,
spike mosses   horsetails,
                     ferns

Gymnosperms
- vascular tissue present
- pollen grains
- unprotected seeds

gnetophytes, ginkgos,
conifers, cycads

Angiosperms
- vascular tissue present
- pollen grains
- seeds form in a floral ovary that becomes a fruit

flowering plants

ancestral alga

Plant Tissues

The body of a plant is organized into tissues, organs, and organ systems. *Meristem* tissue is made up of undifferentiated cells that divide and develop into more complex tissues that provide specialized functions. Plants are made up of three general types of complex tissue:

- **Dermal Tissue** The dermal tissue system consists of tissues that cover and protect the plant's exposed surfaces. The epidermis is dermal tissue.

- **Vascular Tissue** The vascular tissue system includes the tissues that carry water and nutrients from one part of the plant body to another (**Figure 9-5**). Xylem tubes have two structures, called vessels and tracheids. Phloem is made up of sieve tubes. Vascular tissue also provides plants with structural support.

- **Ground Tissue** The ground tissue system is essentially everything that is not part of the dermal or vascular tissue systems. Cells that carry out the most basic processes necessary for survival are part of the ground tissue system. Flexible, thin-walled *parenchyma* cells give ground tissue a variety of properties that are essential for growth, photosynthesis, and storage functions.

FIGURE 9-5 ▽
In this cross section of a *Clematis* stem, bundles of vascular tissue are surrounded by ground tissue. The stem's outer surface is made of dermal tissue.

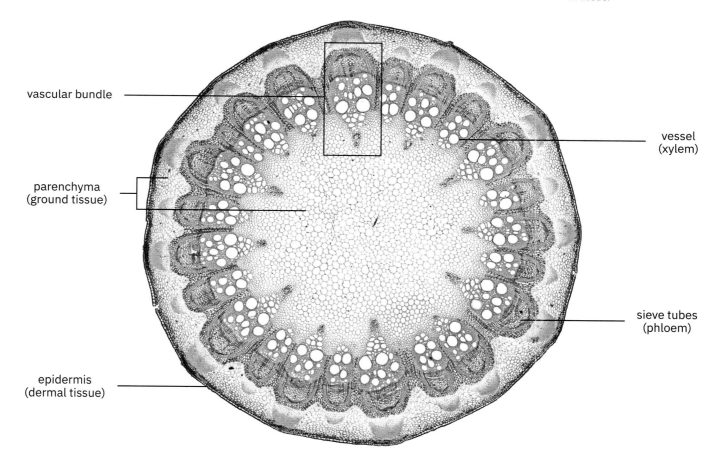

vascular bundle

parenchyma (ground tissue)

epidermis (dermal tissue)

vessel (xylem)

sieve tubes (phloem)

Plant Organs and Organ Systems

An **organ** is a structure made up of different types of tissue that work together to perform a task. Plant organs includes stems, leaves, roots, and reproductive structures. An **organ system** is a set of interacting organs that carry out a particular body function. A vascular plant's body has two organ systems: shoots and roots (**Figure 9-6**). The *shoot system* consists of stems, leaves, and reproductive organs such as flowers. The *root system* absorbs water and dissolved minerals, and it often serves to anchor the plant in soil. Most shoots grow above the ground and most roots grow below it, but there are many exceptions to this general rule.

FIGURE 9-6 ▶
A plant's vascular system contains a hierarchy of systems and organs.

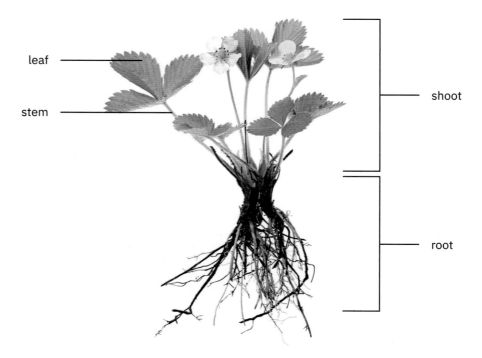

leaf

stem

shoot

root

Stems In addition to water and nutrient transport, the stems of a vascular plant provide structural support and keep leaves positioned for photosynthesis. Stems can grow above or below the soil, and in many species they are specialized for storage or asexual reproduction. They characteristically have nodes, which are regions of the stem where leaves attach. New shoots (and roots) can form at nodes. A young plant grows mainly by lengthening of its stems. Older woody plants grow by stems lengthening and thickening.

Leaves The main organs of photosynthesis in most plant species are leaves. Leaves contain the stomata that allow carbon dioxide to enter the plant and allow water to leave. Leaves are typically thin, with a high ratio of surface area to volume.

Roots The primary function of a plant's roots is to take up water from the soil. As roots grow, they stabilize the plant and provide more surface area to absorb water. The roots of a typical plant are as extensive as its shoots, and often more so. In many species, roots also store nutrients.

CCC **Systems and System Models** *Draw a simple diagram that models the root and shoot systems of a plant that is common in the area where you live. In your drawing, use arrows to show the flow of water and sugar molecules.*

Stem and Root Variations Many types of cacti and succulents have fleshy photosynthetic stems specialized to store water. Flowers, spikes, small leaves, or entire plants may form at nodes. The triangular stems of the cactus in **Figure 9-7a** perform photosynthesis for this plant, which has no leaves.

New roots typically branch from existing roots. However, in some plants, roots can form on stems or leaves. In a few species, such as the banyan tree in **Figure 9-7b**, roots form above ground at nodes on trunks or lower branches and then grow into the ground. In some plants that grow on other plants for support, such as the orchids in **Figure 9-7c**, roots develop from nodes in the stem and hang in the air. These roots absorb moisture from the surrounding air.

FIGURE 9-7
The green stems of *Ariocarpus fissuratus* (a) look like leaves, but they store water and are photosynthetic. The roots of a banyan tree (b) hang down from its branches. Orchids (c) grow in tropical climates where their roots can obtain water from humid air.

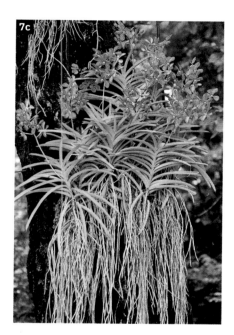

9.1 REVIEW

1. **Describe** Early plants developed an adaptation that allowed them to flourish on land. What are the two key properties of this structure?

2. **Distinguish** Which characteristics occur in seeds but not in spores? Select all correct answers.

   A. multicellular

   B. unprotected

   C. does not require germination

   D. embryonic root, stem, and leaf

   E. easily dispersed in wind and water

3. **Distinguish** Match the terms to describe the functions of these plant tissues: *dermal*, *vascular*, and *ground*.

   • stores nutrients

   • plant growth

   • transports water

   • photosynthesis

   • protects plant surfaces

   • transports nutrients

INVESTIGATING LEAF STOMATA

SEP **Conduct an Investigation** What can the stomata of a plant tell you about its environmental conditions?

Plants have pores on their leaves called stomata (singular, *stoma*). In most plants, each stoma is surrounded by a pair of guard cells that are responsible for opening and closing the pore. Stomata play a critical role in gas exchange through the leaves.

In this activity, you will study the stomata from two different plants. You will count the number of open and closed stomata in each plant and then make inferences about the plants and the environment in which they live.

Leaf stomata respond to changes in the humidity of the surrounding air.

Materials

- **compound microscope**
- **leaf impression slides (2)**
- **leaf samples (2)**

Safety

Procedure

1. Place the first leaf impression slide under the microscope. View the sample using the 4×, 10×, and 40× objective lenses. The stomata are the circular structures seen throughout the leaf. They will appear to be more circular in shape if they are open.

2. Observe a single stoma using the 40× objective lens and sketch it in your biology notebook. Label the stomal opening and guard cells.

3. Switch back to the 10× objective lens. Count the number of open stomata you see in your field of view and record it in your biology notebook. Next, count and record the number of closed stomata you see in your field of view.

4. Repeat Steps 1 through 3 for the second leaf impression slide.

5. Study the leaf samples from both plants whose leaves you viewed under the microscope. Based on your observations of the stomata and your observations of the leaves, write a prediction in your biology notebook about the environment each plant lives in.

6. Return materials to their stations and clean your work area.

Results and Analysis

1. **Describe** What is the hierarchical relationship among the guard cells, stomata, and the leaf?

2. **Infer** Based on the stomata data you collected, which plant is likely to lose less water to the environment? What does this tell you about the environment in which the plant normally lives?

3. **Infer** What characteristics of the succulent leaf enable the plant to retain water and maintain homeostasis in a desert environment?

4. **Predict** If one of the plants were experiencing an extended dry period, how would you expect its stomata to react?

TRANSPORT IN PLANTS

Your heart is a muscular pump that pushes blood through the vessels of your circulatory system to deliver oxygen, nutrients, and specialized cells throughout your body. Similarly, a plant's vascular system transports the substances the plant needs to survive. Unlike your circulatory system, a plant has no "heart" to pump liquids.

Explain *What do you think drives the movement of water through a plant?*

KEY TERMS

feedback mechanism
transpiration

Water Transport in Plants

In vascular plants, water travels inside long, narrow xylem cells called *tracheids*. Lignin strengthens tracheid cell walls, lending structural support to stems and other organs that contain xylem. In addition to tracheids, flowering plants have xylem *vessels*, which are tubes made from shorter, wider cells stacked end to end. Vessel walls are reinforced by rings, spirals, or networks of lignin, as shown in **Figure 9-8**. Water flows lengthwise through tracheids and vessels. Vessels have openings in their walls that allow water to flow laterally from one vessel to another as well.

Like drinking straws, xylem tubes must conduct water upward from the roots of a plant to its leaves. However, tracheids and vessels are made of dead cells that cannot use energy to pump water against gravity. Instead, the upward movement of water in vascular plants occurs as a result of evaporation and cohesion.

xylem (vessels)

phloem

FIGURE 9-8
Xylem cells stack to form vessels in the stem of a castor oil plant. Rings of stiff lignin in the xylem cell walls help hold the stems upright. Tubes of phloem run alongside the xylem tubes.

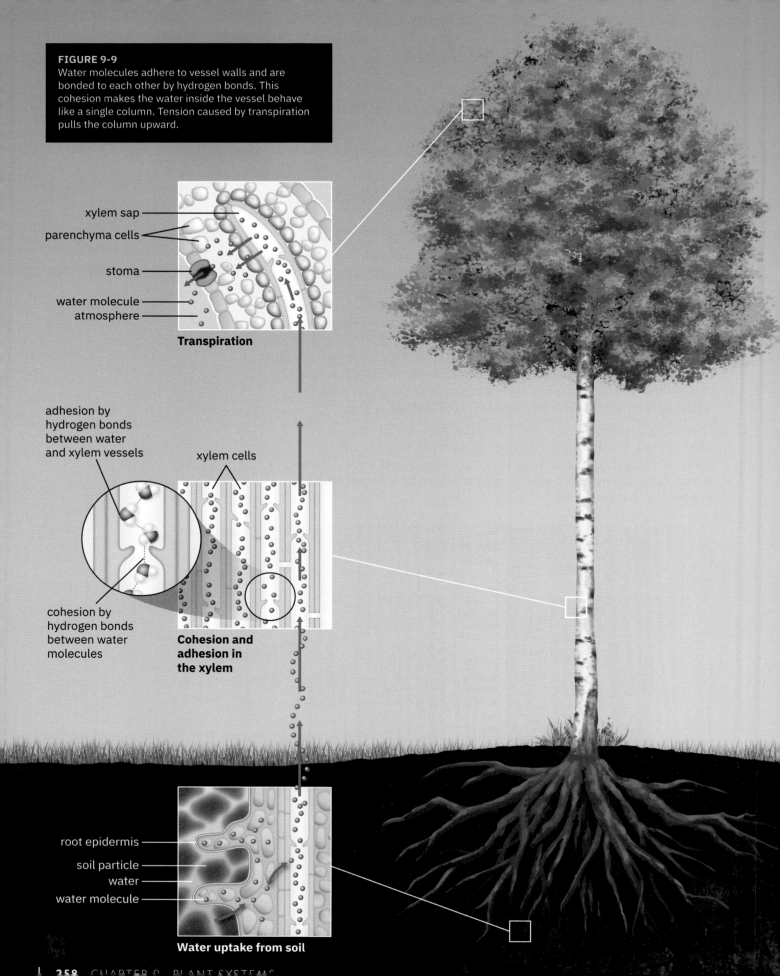

FIGURE 9-9
Water molecules adhere to vessel walls and are bonded to each other by hydrogen bonds. This cohesion makes the water inside the vessel behave like a single column. Tension caused by transpiration pulls the column upward.

xylem sap
parenchyma cells
stoma
water molecule
atmosphere

Transpiration

adhesion by hydrogen bonds between water and xylem vessels

xylem cells

cohesion by hydrogen bonds between water molecules

Cohesion and adhesion in the xylem

root epidermis
soil particle
water
water molecule

Water uptake from soil

Cohesion–Tension Theory

The *cohesion–tension theory* explains that water in xylem is pulled upward as water molecules move out of the plant into the surrounding air. This creates a continuous negative pressure called *tension*. **Figure 9-9** illustrates this mechanism, which begins with water evaporating from leaves and stems. The evaporation of water from a plant's aboveground parts is called **transpiration**.

Transpiration's effect on the water inside a plant is a bit like what happens when you suck a liquid through a straw. Because the water molecules are attracted to each other by hydrogen bonds, a pull on one molecule tugs on the others to which it is attracted (cohesion). As a result, the force (tension) applied by transpiration pulls on entire columns of water that fill xylem tubes. The tension extends all the way from leaves that may be more than 20 meters in the air, down through the branches and stem, and down into the roots where water is being taken up from soil.

Water is pulled upward in continuous columns because xylem tubes are narrow, and water moving through a narrow channel (such as a straw or a xylem tube) resists breaking into droplets. This phenomenon is partly an effect of water's cohesion and partly because water molecules are attracted to hydrophilic materials, such as the cellulose in the walls of xylem tubes (Chapter 5).

SEP **Construct an Explanation** *What is the role of transpiration in the movement of fluids through xylem?*

Mechanisms for Water Conservation

Plants open and close their stomata to regulate transpiration rates. A pair of guard cells borders each stoma. When these two specialized epidermal cells swell with water, they bend slightly so a gap (the stoma) forms between them. When the guard cells lose water, they collapse against one another, closing the stoma. **Figure 9-10** shows open and closed stomata on the surface of a leaf.

Open stomata allow water to leave the plant. Even under conditions of high humidity, the interior of a leaf or stem contains more water than air. Thus, water vapor diffuses out of a stoma whenever it is open. As much as 99 percent of the water a plant takes up from the soil can be lost by transpiration from open stomata.

Go Online **INTERACTIVE FIGURE**

FIGURE 9-9 Go online to trace the **Movement of Water and Nutrients Through a Plant**.

FIGURE 9-10
The guard cells on this lavender leaf are about 14 micrometers long. The stoma on the left is closed, while the one on the right is open.

Connecting Plant Structures With Their Functions
How is plant structure connected to function?

Go online to explore this chapter's hands-on investigation about plant anatomy.

Carbon dioxide also enters a plant through the stomata. A lot more water is lost through open stomata than molecules of carbon dioxide are gained. During the day, each open stoma loses about 400 molecules of water for every molecule of carbon dioxide it takes in. When a plant's stomata are closed, it cannot exchange enough carbon dioxide and oxygen with the surrounding air to support critical metabolic processes.

Recall that homeostasis refers to the maintenance of stable internal conditions (Section 6.2). **Feedback mechanisms** allow a plant to maintain homeostasis by balancing the loss of water to the atmosphere with its need to bring in carbon dioxide for photosynthesis. Stomata open or close based on cues that include humidity, light intensity, the level of carbon dioxide inside the leaf, and hormonal signals from other parts of the plant. For example, the roots of some plants release a hormone when soil moisture is low. This stimulus triggers the guard cells to release water in response. As a result, the guard cells collapse and the stomata close.

CCC **Cause and Effect** *Over evolutionary time, the size of a plant species' stomata may change, or the plant species may develop fewer or more stomata in a given area, in response to environmental changes. How might a sustained increase in air temperature affect the size or number of stomata on a leaf?*

CASE STUDY
FLOWER POWER

Ask Questions *Generate questions about the roles of a plant's water and nutrient transport mechanisms in phytoremediation.*

Nutrient Transport in Plants

Phloem is the vascular tissue that conducts sugars and other organic solutes through the plant. Conducting tubes of phloem are called *sieve tubes*. Each sieve tube is made up of a stack of living cells called *sieve elements*. Unlike in xylem tubes, fluid flows only lengthwise through sieve tubes.

Pressure Flow Theory A plant makes sugar molecules during photosynthesis. Some of these molecules are used by or stored in the cells that make them. The rest of the sugar molecules are moved through sieve tubes to other parts of the plant.

Inside sieve tubes, fluid rich in sugars—mainly sucrose—flows from a source to a sink. A source is a region of plant tissue where sugars are being made or released from storage. Photosynthetic tissues are typical source regions. A sink is a region where sugars are being broken down or put into storage for later use. Tissues of developing roots and fruits are typical sink regions. The *pressure flow theory* explains how fluid pressure pushes sugar-rich fluid inside a sieve tube (**Figure 9-11**).

A pressure gradient between the two regions drives the movement of sugar-rich fluid from a source to a sink. For example, consider mesophyll cells in a leaf, which make far more sugar than they use for their own metabolism. Photosynthesis in mesophyll cells sets up the leaf as a source region. Excess sugar molecules made by these cells diffuse into adjacent companion cells through the cell wall.

Once inside a companion cell, sugar molecules diffuse through the cell wall into associated sieve elements. The sugar increases the solute concentration of the sieve tube's cytoplasm, so it becomes hypertonic with respect to the surrounding cells. Water follows the sugar by osmosis, moving into the sieve tube from surrounding cells.

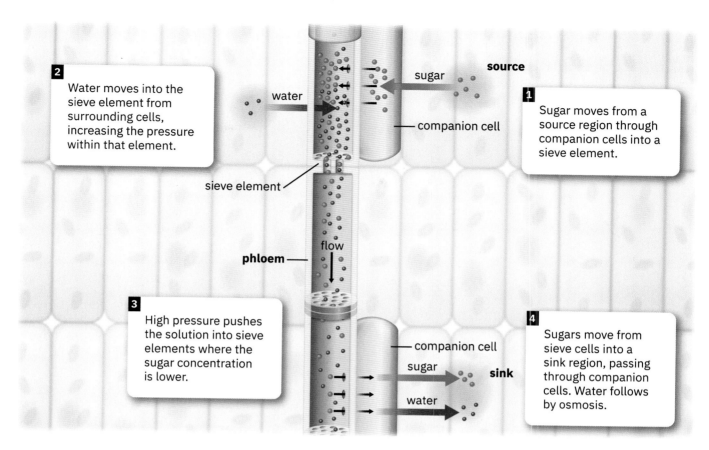

2 Water moves into the sieve element from surrounding cells, increasing the pressure within that element.

water

sugar **source**

1 Sugar moves from a source region through companion cells into a sieve element.

companion cell

sieve element

flow

phloem

3 High pressure pushes the solution into sieve elements where the sugar concentration is lower.

companion cell

sugar **sink**

water

4 Sugars move from sieve cells into a sink region, passing through companion cells. Water follows by osmosis.

The rigid cell walls of mature sieve elements cannot expand very much, so the inflow of water raises the pressure in the tube. Pressure inside a sieve tube can be very high—up to five times higher than that of an automobile tire. High fluid pressure inside the tube pushes sugar-rich cytoplasm from one sieve element to the next, toward a sink region where the fluid pressure is lower. Pressure inside a sieve tube decreases at a sink because sugars leave the tube in this region. Sugar molecules diffuse into companion cells and then move into adjacent sink cells. Water follows, again by osmosis, so the fluid pressure inside the sieve elements decreases in sink regions.

FIGURE 9-11 ▲
The movement of water by osmosis into regions of high concentrations of sugar drives the pressure changes in phloem.

CCC **Structure and Function** *Explain how sieve element structure helps in transporting the products of photosynthesis.*

9.2 REVIEW

1. **Explain** Which condition forms the basis of the pressure flow theory?

   A. Water free of nutrients diffuses easily by osmosis.

   B. The tissues of roots and fruits serve as storage for nutrients.

   C. The cell walls of sieve tubes are flexible and expand with the inflow of fluid.

   D. Nutrient-rich fluid in photosynthetic tissues has higher pressure than fluid elsewhere.

2. **Relate** Which plant structures are necessary for transpiration? Select all correct answers.

   A. flowers   C. leaves   E. phloem

   B. stems   D. xylem

3. **Relate** Explain the vital role stomata play in regulating plant metabolic processes such as photosynthesis.

4. **Contrast** Describe the similarities and differences between xylem and phloem.

PLANT REPRODUCTION

After a walk through a grassy field, you notice both you and your dog are covered in tiny pointed objects, each with a few thin, sharp spikes. These objects, called spikelets, contain grass seeds and can easily poke into the body of a moving host. With your help, some of the spikelets may end up in a favorable location for the seeds to grow, ensuring a future for the next generation of plants.

Infer *A single grass plant releases hundreds of spikelets per year. Why do you think a plant would need to produce such an abundance of seeds?*

Plant Life Cycles

Plants have a clearly defined life cycle in which they alternate between producing spores and producing gametes (**Figure 9-12**). In the *gametophyte generation*, the plant produces gametes, or sex cells, by mitosis. At the end of this generation, two gametes fuse to form a zygote that contains genetic information from both of its parent cells.

During the next stage, called the *sporophyte generation,* the zygote undergoes mitosis to develop into a multicellular plant. To complete this stage, the plant's cells undergo meiosis (Section 12.1) to make *spores,* which are single reproductive cells that have half the genetic information of the parent plant. Spores are capable of developing into a new individual without combining with another reproductive cell. A spore undergoes mitosis to become a gametophyte plant, and the cycle repeats.

Plant cells belonging to each generation exist within specific plant body structures. For example, in a giant sequoia tree, the sporophyte consists of the parts we can see—roots, trunk, branches, leaves, and cones—which all grew from a zygote. The gametophyte takes the form of cells found within pollen grains and in tiny structures deep inside the cones. In all plants, one generation is dominant over the other, and the nondominant generation may rely on the dominant generation for survival.

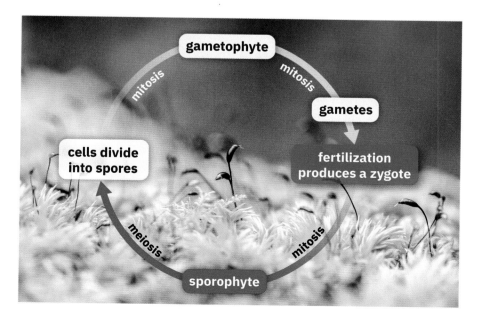

FIGURE 9-12
A gametophyte produces zygotes, and a sporophyte produces spores. Both generations can coexist as parts of the same plant.

FIGURE 9-13
Sporophytes take a variety of forms. The thin stalks of moss sporophytes (a) aid in spore dispersal. Fern sporangia (b) cluster on fronds of the dominant sporophyte. Pine tree cones (c) produce spores.

Sexual Reproduction

Plant sexual reproduction requires fertilization of a female gamete (egg) by a male gamete (sperm). The offspring plant inherits genes from both parent cells. An individual plant may produce gametes of only one type so that another plant is needed for sexual reproduction to occur. A single plant may also produce both male and female gametes. In some species, this type of plant can fertilize itself, but in other species, male and female gametes of the same plant are incompatible with each other.

Nonvascular Plants Nonvascular plants are the only modern plants in which the gametophyte generation is dominant. However, even the gametophytes tend to be small and low growing due to the absence of a vascular system. All nonvascular plants disperse by releasing spores. For example, in **Figure 9-13a**, moss sporophyte capsules rise above the green leaf-like gametophyte generation. The sporophyte's tall, thin shape positions the spores to be easily carried away by wind. After dispersal by the wind, a spore germinates and grows into a filament of cells from which one or more gametophytes develop. Closer to the ground, rain stimulates moss gametophytes to release flagellated sperm. In order to reach and fertilize the plant's eggs, the sperm require a film of water in which to swim. Mosses also reproduce asexually by fragmentation when a bit of gametophyte breaks off and develops into a new plant.

Seedless Vascular Plants The key difference between ferns and other vascular plants is their production of spores rather than seeds. Spore production usually occurs on certain areas of the fronds (leaves), which develop sporangia in clusters called *sori* (**Figure 9-13b**). Inside the sporangia, meiosis occurs to form spores. The spores disperse and grow into tiny, heart-shaped gametophytes. Though ferns are vascular plants, fertilization in ferns is much like that of mosses. Sperm from a male gametophyte must be carried by water to the female plant. The sporophyte generation is dominant in ferns. The sporophyte is larger than the gametophyte and it has roots and large fronds that persist for an extended time. In contrast, the gametophyte dies soon after reproducing.

Gymnosperms Gymnosperms feature two evolutionary advances for plants. First, the sporophyte, rather than the gametophyte generation, is dominant in gymnosperms. Second, gymnosperms carry out fertilization without being surrounded by water. They are the first plants to be completely adapted to a terrestrial lifestyle.

Pine trees have a life cycle typical of gymnosperms. Like most gymnosperms they are wind-pollinated. The pine tree is a sporophyte that produces spores on specialized structures called cones (**Figure 9-13c**). Conifers produce both male and female cones. In most pine species, each tree makes one type of cone: either small, soft pollen (male) cones or large, woody seed (female) cones. Both types of cones have scales arranged around a central axis. Each scale of a pollen cone contains pollen sacs in which pollen grains develop. Pollen cones release these tiny grains to drift with the winds. Fertilization takes place within the female cone. After fertilization, the zygote grows into an embryo within the seed. The surrounding cone provides nutrition for the developing embryo. The seed is released, germinates, then develops into a new sporophyte.

CCC **Structure and Function** *What are the primary differences between moss and fern reproduction and reproduction in other types of plants?*

VIDEO

VIDEO 9-1 Go online to see how a cedar tree disperses pollen.

CONNECTIONS

SAVING SEEDS In the past, food crops were location-specific. People developed and grew plant varieties that did well in their region, and they saved seeds from their crops to plant the following year. Now, many traditional varieties of crop plants are disappearing as a few large companies supply farmers with the same strains of seeds worldwide. Different varieties of plants are resistant to different diseases, so widespread planting of one variety increases the risk that a disease could decimate the global supply of a crop. The more varieties of a crop we plant, the more likely it is that some will resist a particular disease.

Sustaining the wild relatives of crop plants provides a form of insurance because it maintains a reservoir of genetic diversity. Plant breeders can draw upon that diversity to meet future challenges. Storing seeds in seed banks is one way to ensure the survival of potentially useful plants. Today, there are more than 1700 seed banks around the world. The most ambitious, the Svalbard Global Seed Vault, was built in 2008 on a Norwegian island about 1100 kilometers from the North Pole. This so-called doomsday vault serves as a backup for other seed banks. The seeds are stored deep inside a mountain, in a permanently chilled, earthquake-free zone 130 meters above sea level. The location was chosen to keep the seeds high and dry even if global climate change causes the polar ice caps to melt. The vault also has an advanced security system and has been engineered to withstand any nearby explosions.

The Svalbard vault now holds the world's most diverse collection of seeds, with more than one million samples and material from nearly every nation. Under the deep-freeze conditions in Svalbard, the seeds are expected to survive for about 100 years.

The Svalbard Global Seed Vault is capable of storing 4.5 million seed samples.

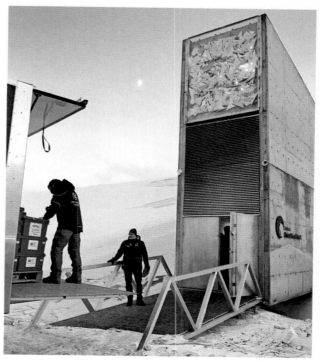

Flowering Plant Reproduction

Flowering plants, with more than 300,000 living species, are the world's most successful plants, having adapted to almost every habitat on Earth. The success of the flowering plants can be attributed to their flowers and fruits. A bright, colorful flower attracts animals such as birds, bats, bees, and other insects that obtain nectar and, in the process, deliver pollen to other flowers. Different animals eat the fruit that develops from a flower, dispersing the seeds far and wide. Both pathways represent major improvements in ensuring genetic diversity and reproductive efficiency for flowering plants over gymnosperms and other groups that rely on more passive forms of reproductive cell distribution.

FIGURE 9-14 ▶
A flowering plant's reproductive system is part of its shoot system and contains groups of reproductive organs that produce gametes, promote their fertilization, and feed and protect the zygote.

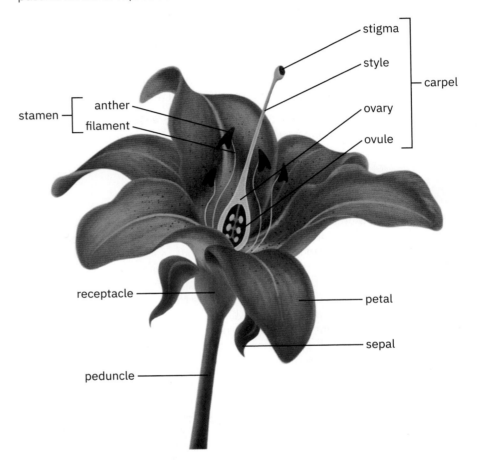

Reproductive Parts Like all vascular plants, the sporophyte is the dominant phase in flowering plants. Gametophytes are produced within the flowers of the sporophyte. A *flower* is a specialized reproductive shoot. Floral structure varies, but most flowers include the parts shown in **Figure 9-14**. *Sepals*, which usually have a green leaf-like appearance, ring the base of a flower and enclose it until it opens. Inside the sepals are *petals*, which are often colored and scented. The petals surround the stamens. **Stamens** are organs that produce pollen. A typical stamen consists of a tall stalk (the filament), topped by an anther that holds four pollen sacs. The innermost part of the flower is the **carpel**, the organ that captures pollen and produces eggs. The carpel consists of a stigma, style, and ovary. The sticky or hairy *stigma*, which is specialized for receiving pollen, tops a stalk called the *style*. At the base of the style is an *ovary*, a chamber that contains one or more ovules. After fertilization, an *ovule* matures into a seed and the ovary becomes a fruit.

Pollination The fertilization process in flowering plants, called double fertilization, is unique in that two sperm are involved. One sperm fertilizes the egg, forming a zygote that develops into the embryo in the seed. The other sperm fuses with two cells in the female gametophyte to form a special nutritive tissue in the seed called endosperm.

Pollination is the act of transferring pollen grains from the male anther of a flower to the female stigma. Some flowering plants are self-pollinators. That is, the pollen produced in one anther of a flower pollinates the stigma of the same flower. Other flowering plants are cross-pollinators. In this process, the pollen from a flower in one plant is used to pollinate a flower of a different plant of the same species.

Pollen is transferred from one flower in a variety of ways, including dispersal by wind, water, or animals. Grasses and other plants pollinated by wind do not benefit by attracting animals, so they do not expend resources making scented, brilliantly colored, or nectar-laden flowers. Wind-pollinated flowers are typically small, nonfragrant, and green, with insignificant petals and large stamens that produce a lot of pollen.

Passive pollination by animals, as shown in **Figure 9-15**, occurs as a pollinator moves from one flower to another to obtain the nectar that is typically stored in the female part of the plant. If it comes into contact with the flower's anther, the pollinator's body picks up pollen that may be transferred to the stigma of the same flower or another flower. The flowers of a given species bloom only during specific and limited times of the year. This limits the pollinator to seeking nectar from one species at a time and helps to ensure that pollen picked up from one flower will be brought to a flower of the same species.

CCC **Structure and Function** *How do flower structures facilitate animal-driven pollination?*

FIGURE 9-15
Crocus flowers bloom in the spring and are visited by bees that carry their pollen from flower to flower.

 VIDEO

VIDEO 9-2 Go online to learn how bees' buzzing helps some plants reproduce.

Asexual Reproduction

Many flowering plants can reproduce asexually. Each new plant is a clone, or genetic replica, of its parent. Entire forests of quaking aspen trees (*Populus tremuloides*) are actually stands of clones that grew from root suckers—shoots that sprout from shallow lateral roots. The quaking aspen grove in Utah that was described at the beginning of this chapter consists of about 47,000 genetically identical shoots. The plant shown in **Figure 9-16**, *Kalanchoë daigremontiana*, is commonly known as "mother of thousands." It reproduces asexually by growing tiny plantlets on its leaves.

FIGURE 9-16

Each tiny plant along the leaf edges of the *Kalanchoë daigremontiana* plant is a clone of the parent plant.

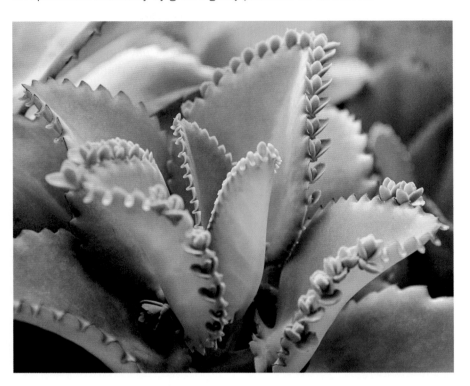

Vegetative Reproduction Vegetative reproduction is a form of asexual reproduction in which a new plant grows from a stem, leaf, or root of a parent plant. In many plant groups, a new plant can regenerate from just a fragment of tissue from its parent. Some plants form specialized structures for vegetative reproduction.

- *Stolons* are stems that branch from the main stem of the plant and grow horizontally on the ground or just under it. They are commonly called runners because in many plants they "run" along the surface of the soil. Stolons have nodes from which roots and shoots can sprout and develop into new plants. Strawberries reproduce using stolons (**Figure 9-17a**).

- *Rhizomes* are fleshy stems that typically grow underground in a horizontal direction. In many plants, the main stem is a rhizome, and it often serves as the primary region for storing food. Shoots that sprout from nodes grow aboveground for photosynthesis and flowering. Irises are examples of rhizomes (**Figure 9-17b**).

- *Tubers* are thick, fleshy storage structures made from the stem of a plant. Tiny buds that grow on a tuber's surface potentially develop into a new plant. Potatoes are examples of tubers (**Figure 9-17c**).

- *Bulbs* consist of a short, flattened stem covered in overlapping layers of thickened modified leaves called scales. The dry, paper-like outer scale of many bulbs serves as a protective covering. The lower portion of a bulb gives rise to roots. The upper portion produces scales and new shoots. Bulb scales contain starch and other substances that a plant holds in reserve during times when conditions in the environment are unfavorable for growth. When favorable conditions return, the plant uses these stored substances to sustain rapid growth. Onions and lilies are examples of bulbs (**Figure 9-17d**).

SEP **Construct an Explanation** *What are two advantages and two disadvantages of asexual reproduction in plants?*

FIGURE 9-17 ▽
Specialized structures for vegetative reproduction include strawberry stolons (a), iris rhizomes (b), potato tubers (c), and onion bulbs (d).

9.3 REVIEW

1. **Distinguish** Match each term to mosses, ferns, or conifers to distinguish the fertilization requirements for each plant group. Each term may be related to one or more plant groups.

   - cones
   - pollen
   - spores
   - water

2. **Explain** What two features have made angiosperms the most successful plants on Earth, and why?

3. **Classify** Match the flower structures to the stamen or carpel. Some flower structures may not have a match.

   - anther
   - filament
   - ovary
   - petals
   - pollen sacs
   - sepals
   - stigma
   - style

4. **Explain** Why is it beneficial for a flowering plant species to bloom only during a specific and limited time of the year?

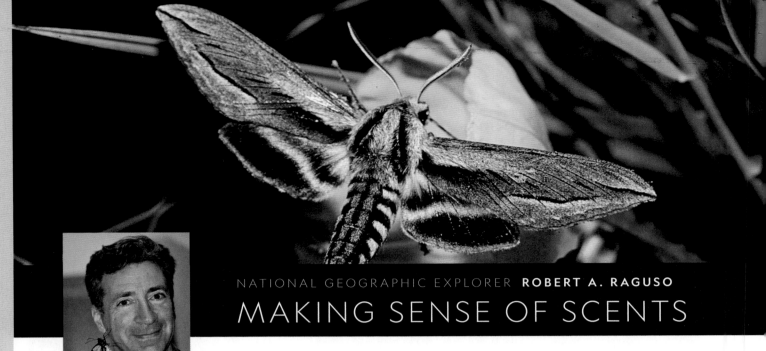

NATIONAL GEOGRAPHIC EXPLORER **ROBERT A. RAGUSO**

MAKING SENSE OF SCENTS

Dr. Robert Raguso is a pioneer in the field of floral scent and the ability of plants to attract insect pollinators.

Flower fragrances are Dr. Robert Raguso's specialty. As a graduate student, he noticed a distinct lack of research into the relationship between flower scents and pollinators. He has been researching that connection ever since.

Many insect species that have a close relationship with plants are nearsighted or colorblind. Often, it is a flower's scent, rather than its color or other characteristics, that helps insect pollinators find just the right flower to use as a food source or a place to lay their eggs.

An important part of the botany courses Raguso teaches, whether in the lab at Cornell University or at a remote field station, is to have students follow their noses.

"We find interesting smells and then use analytical chemistry to connect perceptions—even emotions—to the universal language of chemistry," Raguso says. "One of our rules is 'if you use a simile to describe a scent, you need to include the ideal [version] in your analysis.'"

This wisdom was taught to Raguso by his daughter when she was five years old. He and his daughter had been running through a field of blooming mustard plants when she commented that the flowers smelled like chocolate. Taking the mustard flowers back to the lab, she suggested that they compare the compounds in the mustard plant to those in a real chocolate bar. Analyzing both, Raguso found they shared a common compound called vanillin that gave them their sweet aroma. This sweet scent attracts bees and other insects that pollinate the mustard plant as they crawl around on the flowers slurping nectar and gathering pollen on their bodies.

In addition to perceiving light in the ultraviolet range of the spectrum that humans cannot see, many insects can also perceive scents that we cannot smell. Raguso has learned that flowers that don't seem to have a strong or distinctive odor to humans can have scents that are quite enticing to pollinators. Even within the same geographic area, the exact mixture of scent compounds can differ among populations of the same flower species. This means that the flowers in one population might smell just a tiny bit different from another. As a result, one population may attract more (or different) pollinators than the other.

"Scents can be clues to health, stress, disease, diet, metabolism, even climate," Raguso says. "There's nothing frivolous about fragrances!"

THINKING CRITICALLY

Explain *Why is it useful to compare analytical results to standard reference materials, as Raguso does with aroma compounds?*

PLANT RESPONSES TO THE ENVIRONMENT

When it gets too hot, an animal such as a lizard can scurry underneath a rocky outcrop to beat the heat in the shade. However, while plants don't have the luxury of movement, they do have a number of mechanisms in place that let them respond to changes in their environment and maintain homeostasis.

Analyze *Consider the structures of a plant. What are some ways a plant might cope with hot and dry conditions?*

Plant Responses

Just like animals, plants have mechanisms to maintain the internal conditions required for survival. Additionally, plants have adaptations that allow them to survive in a variety of environments with differing conditions. For example, the shape of a cactus's spines helps to reduce water loss in its arid habitat.

Plant Hormones Most animal development occurs before adulthood. By contrast, plant development continues throughout the plant's lifetime. A plant adjusts to external conditions by changing growth patterns. Changes in form and function are triggered by environmental cues such as temperature, gravity, night length, the availability of water and nutrients, and the presence of pathogens or herbivores. This developmental flexibility requires extensive coordination among plant cells. Cells in different tissues or even different parts of a plant coordinate activities by communicating with one another through hormones. A **hormone** is a chemical substance that is produced in one part of an organism and acts as a messenger to either activate or suppress activity in another part of the organism. For example, plant cells are stimulated to undergo mitosis by the release of hormones that circulate within the plant's tissues.

All cells in a plant have the ability to make and release hormones. Plant hormones can be released far from the tissue they affect. For example, cells in an actively growing root release a hormone that also keeps shoot tips actively growing. **Table 9-1** lists examples of plant hormones and their functions.

TABLE 9-1. Plant Hormones and Their Functions

Hormone	Functions
gibberellins	Gibberellins stimulate cell division and elongation in stems. They also promote germination and stimulate flowering in some plants.
ethylene	Ethylene stimulates fruit ripening. It is also involved in abscission, which is the process by which a plant sheds leaves or other parts.
cytokinins	Cytokinins stimulate differentiation of cells in the growing tip of a plant's roots. They also stimulate cell division in shoots and prevent the formation of lateral roots.
auxins	Auxins are involved in the formation of plant parts, differentiation of vascular tissues, formation of lateral roots, and shaping the plant body in response to environmental stimuli.

VIDEO

VIDEO 9-3 Go online to watch a plant respond to gravity and a light source as it grows.

🧪 **CHAPTER INVESTIGATION**

Homeostasis in Plants

How do the roots of a plant develop in response to moisture?

Go online to explore this chapter's hands-on investigation about feedback mechanisms in plants.

FIGURE 9-18 ▽

The plant hormone auxin, which promotes cell growth along the length of a stem, causes a calla lily (a) to bend toward a sunny window by acting only on cells on the shady side of the stem. Thigmotropism makes a pumpkin vine (b) coil around a rod by continually bending toward it.

Environmental Triggers Environmental cues—such as light, gravity, and contact—can trigger movements in plants. The movement of a plant in response to an environmental stimulus is called a **tropism**.

- **Light** A directional response to light is called a *phototropism*. Many plants can change the orientation of their leaves or other parts in a direction that depends on a light source. For example, an elongating stem curves toward a light source, thus optimizing the amount of light captured by leaves for photosynthesis in low-light environments (**Figure 9-18a**). Leaves or flowers of some plants even change position in response to the changing angle of the sun throughout the day, a phototropic response called *heliotropism*.

- **Contact** A directional response to contact with an object is called *thigmotropism*. A vine's tendrils coiling around an object is an example of this type of tropism (**Figure 9-18b**).

- **Gravity** Even if a seedling is turned upside down just after germination, its primary root and shoot will curve so the root grows down and the shoot grows up. A directional response to Earth's gravitational pull is called *gravitropism*. The hormone auxin is involved in gravitropism. Low levels of auxin stimulate root growth, but high levels of auxin inhibit root growth. In horizontally growing roots, auxin builds up on the bottom side of the root so that the upper side grows faster. As a result, the root tip grows downward in the direction of the force of gravity.

- **Water** The directional growth of plant roots in response to water levels is called *hydrotropism*. Though less understood than other types of tropisms, evidence suggests that plant roots can detect water in their environment and modify the direction of root tip growth.

CCC **Cause and Effect** *Explain how the movement of a plant toward a light source is an example of a feedback mechanism.*

Injury Responses Volatile compounds are chemical compounds that evaporate readily into the air. Plants release volatile chemicals that can be used for communication with other plants and other organisms. The plant's internal conditions and environmental cues determine what compounds are released. For example, when a tomato plant detects the chemical signature of substances that a hornworm secretes from its mouth, the plant releases volatile compounds that attract parasitic wasps that feed on the worms (**Figure 9-19**). Neighboring plants also detect volatile chemicals released in response to herbivory and respond by increasing production of chemicals that make them less palatable.

Daily and Seasonal Responses

Plants respond to cycles of environmental change with daily and seasonal cycles of activity.

Circadian Rhythms A circadian rhythm is a cycle of biological activity that repeats every 24 hours or so. For example, a bean plant holds its leaves horizontally during the day but folds them close to its stem at night. Bean plants exposed to constant light or constant darkness for a few days will continue to move their leaves in and out of the "sleep" position at the normal time of sunset and sunrise. Similar mechanisms cause flowers of some plants to open only at certain times of day. For example, the flowers of plants pollinated mainly by night-flying bats open, secrete nectar, and release fragrance only at night. Periodically closing flowers protects the delicate reproductive parts of the plant at times when the likelihood of pollination is lowest.

> **RAINFOREST CONNECTIONS**
>
> **Gather Evidence** *Unlike animals, plants do not have specialized organ systems for producing and receiving sound. How do plants communicate with other species?*

FIGURE 9-20

In temperate climate regions, temperature falls and the length of night increases in autumn. Trees respond by ceasing food production, and the unused chlorophyll in their leaves breaks down. In the absence of the green pigment of chlorophyll, the red and yellow pigments remaining in the leaf become the most visible.

Seasonal and Climatic Responses Except at the Equator, the amount of daylight varies with the season. Days are longer in summer than in winter, and the difference increases with latitude. These seasonal changes in light availability trigger seasonally appropriate responses in plants. *Photoperiodism* refers to an organism's response to changes in the length of day relative to night.

Flowering is a photoperiodic response in many species. Such species are called long-day or short-day plants depending on the season in which they flower. These names are somewhat misleading, as the main trigger for flowering is actually the length of night, not the length of day. Irises and other long-day plants flower only when the hours of darkness fall below a critical value. Chrysanthemums and other short-day plants flower only when the hours of darkness are greater than a critical value.

Yearly cycles of leaf loss and dormancy are also photoperiodic responses. Plants that drop their leaves before dormancy are typically native to regions too dry or too cold for optimal growth during part of the year (**Figure 9-20**). For example, deciduous trees in the northeastern and midwestern regions of the United States lose their leaves around September or October. The trees remain dormant during the months of harsh weather that would otherwise damage tender leaves and buds. Growth resumes when milder conditions return in spring.

On the opposite side of the world, many tree species native to tropical monsoon forests of South Asia lose their leaves during the dry season. The region receives a lot of rain annually, but almost none falls between October and April. Dormancy helps the trees survive the seasonal drought-like conditions. New growth appears near the beginning of the monsoon season, just in time to be watered by ample rains.

Climate also drives plant responses (**Figure 9-21**). The seeds of desert annuals, plants that live for only one season, avoid drought by sprouting only when the soil is moist. The new plants make seeds quickly before they, too, die. Desert perennials make seeds over several seasons. In deserts where rains fall seasonally, perennials conserve water by making leaves only after a rain and shedding them when dry conditions return.

SEP **Construct an Explanation** *In regions of the world that are hit by tropical cyclones, high winds damage and uproot plants, and coastal plant habitats may be flooded with seawater for extended periods. How might plant structures and systems withstand and respond to periods of high winds and excess water?*

9.4 REVIEW

1. **Label** Match the functions to the plant hormone, *ethylene, gibberellin, cytokinin,* or *auxin,* that triggers them.

   - breaking dormancy
   - cell division
   - differentiation of root cells
   - formation of vascular tissue
   - body responses to stimuli
   - ripening of fruit
   - stem elongation

2. **Classify** In some plants, what type of response is flowering?

   A. gravitropic
   B. phototropic
   C. photoperiodic
   D. thigmotropic

3. **Distinguish** Which scenarios demonstrate plant tropisms? Select all correct answers.

   A. The stamen of a flower bends toward an insect that lands on it.

   B. The continually growing leaves of a plant move in a rhythmic daily pattern.

   C. The roots of plant growing on the edge of a cliff extend straight downward.

   D. The temperature of the flowers of a plant increases when the flowers turn toward the sunlight.

   E. The flowers of a plant open in the early morning, wilt by the afternoon, and fall off the stem within a few days.

BUD BURST AND FLOWERING IN A CHANGING CLIMATE

SEP **Mathematical Thinking** Changing climate conditions affect the biological responses of plants to the beginning of spring. Nature field notes taken by Henry David Thoreau, 19th-century American naturalist and philosopher, are among the earliest records of the unfurling of green leaves and flowering as winter turns into spring. A research site in Concord, Massachusetts, where Thoreau lived, continues to monitor plant and tree responses to both seasonal and long-term climate change. **Figure 1** documents springtime shifts between 1856 and 2012, based on combined data from the late 1800s and a recent study.

As temperatures warm, leaves burst from plant buds and flowers begin to bloom.

FIGURE 1 ▽

Temperature dependence is shown for two types of observable changes in plants as spring begins: first bud burst (emergence of new leaves) and first flowering.

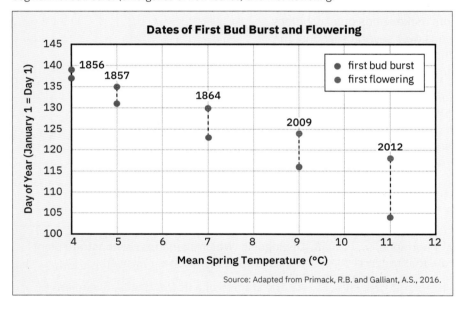

Source: Adapted from Primack, R.B. and Galliant, A.S., 2016.

1. **Analyze Data** What is the change in mean spring temperature between 1856 and 2012?

2. **Model** Use the graph to develop linear functions that model the dependence of first bud burst day and first flowering day on mean spring temperature.

3. **Justify** Use the mathematical models to state a claim that compares the plant responses to changes in temperature.

4. **Calculate** Day 1 corresponds to January 1. Use this to determine the approximate dates of first bud burst and first flowering in 1856 and in 2012. About how many days pass between the plant responses?

5. **Apply** The mean spring temperature in Concord, MA, during 2020, one of the warmest years on record, was about 15°C. Estimate the first bud burst and first flowering dates in 2020. How many days passed between plant responses?

6. **Predict** What will happen to the number of days between first bud burst and first flowering if the trends in global climate change continue?

7. **Predict** How might the observed pattern in the number of days between first bud burst and first flowering affect the reproductive cycle of flowering plants in this region?

TYING IT ALL TOGETHER ENGINEERING
FLOWER POWER

HOW DO PLANTS RESPOND TO CHANGES IN THE ENVIRONMENT?

In this chapter, you learned about plant structures and how they function to help plants grow, survive, reproduce, and respond to changes in their environment. The Case Study described the process of phytoremediation, which takes advantage of a plant's selective intake of water and nutrients to remediate soil and water that has been contaminated with pollutants. Factors including soil type, the amount and type of contamination, and the length of the growing season affect a plant's efficiency at cleaning contaminated sites.

Sunflowers are not the only plant species used in phytoremediation projects. Other plants used to remediate contaminated areas include Indian mustard, willow, poplar, various types of grasses, and legumes such as mung beans and horse gram (**Figure 9-22**). Some remediation projects have specifically incorporated plants for their aesthetic qualities. For example, willow trees were incorporated into the design of Amsterdam's Westergasfabriek Park in the Netherlands (**Figure 9-23**). This former gas facility was repurposed as a large public recreational park.

In this activity, you will develop a model to show how plant systems interact in the removal of harmful substances from contaminated water or soil. Work individually or in a group to complete these steps.

Gather Evidence
1. Research the process of phytoremediation. What plant systems are involved in the removal of harmful materials from the soil or water the plant is grown in? What plant species are the most successful at removing contaminants?

Develop and Use a Model
2. Choose a plant from your research and use digital media to construct and present a model that shows how the plant could be used to remove harmful substances from the soil or water where it grows. Label the plant systems involved and indicate how the substance moves through the plant.

Evaluate Solutions
3. Use your research and model to explain why cultivating certain plants might be an effective solution to remediate contaminated areas. What are some constraints related to using plants in remediation projects?

FIGURE 9-22 ▽
Plant species differ in their effectiveness at removing specific metals from soil.

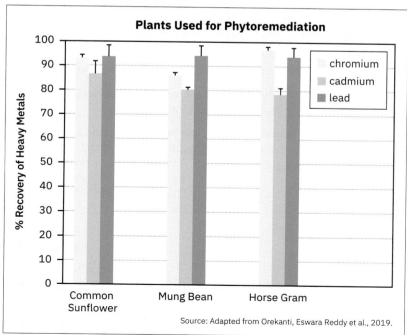

Plants Used for Phytoremediation

% Recovery of Heavy Metals (y-axis, 0 to 100)

Legend: chromium, cadmium, lead

x-axis: Common Sunflower, Mung Bean, Horse Gram

Source: Adapted from Orekanti, Eswara Reddy et al., 2019.

FIGURE 9-23 ▽
Phytoremediating plants are included in attractive parklike landscapes at former coal and gas processing sites.

REVIEW KEY CONCEPTS

1. **Compare** In what ways are plants that grow on land similar to green algae? Select all correct answers.

   A. They produce seeds.

   B. They contain chloroplasts.

   C. They have cellulose in their cell walls.

   D. They store sugars in the form of starch.

   E. They use vascular tissue to transport nutrients and water.

2. **Classify** Which statement describes how flowering plants and vascular plants are related?

   A. All flowering plants are vascular plants.

   B. All vascular plants are flowering plants.

   C. Flowering plants cannot be vascular plants.

   D. Flowering plants can be vascular or nonvascular.

3. **Identify** Which are roles of roots? Select all correct answers.

   A. absorb water from the soil

   B. anchor the plant

   C. initiate sexual reproduction

   D. protect the plant from extreme temperatures

   E. store nutrients

4. **Sequence** After a long drought, the soil around a plant has become dry. Sequence the steps in the process that helps the plant conserve water.

   • Stomata close.

   • Guard cells collapse.

   • Hormone is released.

   • Guard cells release water.

   • Roots detect low soil moisture.

5. **Identify** Which plant group has a dominant gametophyte stage?

   A. conifers

   B. ferns

   C. flowering plants

   D. mosses

6. **Define** In double fertilization, one sperm fertilizes the egg. What structure is formed when the other sperm fuses with two cells in the gametophyte?

7. **List** Which are the typical characteristics of a flower that relies on wind pollination? Select all correct answers.

   A. full of nectar

   B. green

   C. large amounts of pollen

   D. small

   E. strong fragrance

8. **Identify** Name the tropism each stimulus causes.

   • gravity   • light

   • sunlight   • touch

   • water

9. **Identify** Which are examples of photoperiodism? Select all correct answers.

   A. a vine coiling around a branch

   B. a tree losing its leaves in autumn

   C. a flower growing toward the brightest source of light

   D. a plant closing its stomata when conditions are dry

   E. a plant flowering only when the length of darkness is short enough

10. **Predict** Which two labeled parts of the leaf cross section in **Figure 9-2** would contain the most lignin?

11. **Identify** As a tree starts to leaf out in the spring, are the roots acting as a source or sink for the plant?

12. **Identify** What cell division process allows a gametophyte to produce gametes?

13. **Compare** Differentiate between a spore, a seed, and a fruit. Which plant groups produce which?

CRITICAL THINKING

14. Construct an Explanation After being harvested, fresh fruit is often shipped to markets thousands of miles away, a process that can take days or weeks. To prevent fruit from overripening during transport, shipping companies use ventilation to limit the buildup of gases emitted by the fruit. Explain how this technique can help slow ripening.

15. Analyze Explain how the development of stomata allowed early plants to adapt to life on land.

16. NOS Scientific Investigations A student wants to examine how a disruption in homeostasis affects plant growth. Identify a hypothesis and describe a possible experimental setup the student could use to test that hypothesis.

17. Contrast How do xylem and phloem differ? Include their functions and structures in your description.

18. Explain What are some typical adaptations of flowering plants that increase the chances that the pollen from one flower reaches another flower of the same species?

MATH AND ENGLISH LANGUAGE ARTS CONNECTIONS

1. Reason Quantitatively Transporting water from the roots to the top of a tall tree requires a large difference in pressure. Compare the pressure at the top of the tree to the pressure at the bottom of the tree. Explain why this difference occurs and how it enables water to travel upward.

2. Write Explanatory Text Why do the asexual reproductive structures of plants often make good sources of food for humans? Give an example.

3. Synthesize Information The Irish Potato Famine in the 1840s was due, in part, to the planting of a single variety of potato. This variety was very susceptible to potato late blight, a disease that was introduced into Ireland in the 1840s and quickly decimated the entire potato crop. How could planting multiple varieties of potatoes have helped prevent the famine?

Consider the following paragraph on how to propagate strawberries. Use evidence from the passage to answer the question.

A strawberry plant can reproduce by sending horizontal stems, or stolons, outward along the ground. When a stolon finds nutrient-rich soil, it sends roots down into the soil, and a new strawberry plant begins to grow. Eventually the new plant may disconnect from the original plant. One plant has now become two separate—but genetically identical—plants.

4. Cite Textual Evidence What type of reproduction is described in this passage? What evidence supports your claim?

5. Reason Quantitatively In a certain greenhouse, short-day plants are grown in the winter. The short winter days mean the plants receive about 10 hours of natural light each day. A nearby greenhouse grows the same plants. The conditions are the same except that, during the night, maintenance workers inadvertently expose the plants to artificial light as they come and go, turning the lights on and off as they complete their work each night. Describe how the night length experienced by the plants differs between the first and second greenhouse, and predict which greenhouse will have plants that flower.

▶ REVISIT RAINFOREST CONNECTIONS

Gather Evidence Above ground, plants have various mechanisms for responding to stimuli and changes in their environment. One type of response, releasing volatile organic compounds, signals other organisms with information about the stimulus. The transfer of information enables interactions between individual plants and between plants and other species.

1. What types of stimuli might the root system of a rainforest plant encounter, and what types of responses might the plant have to these stimuli?

2. What other questions do you have about the ways in which rainforest plants interact?

CHAPTER 10
ANIMAL SYSTEMS

Bar-tailed godwits are large wading birds that belong to the sandpiper family. They often gather in large flocks at their wintering grounds or when preparing to migrate.

Nearly 40 percent of the world's bird species migrate. Many of these species spend a portion of the year at their breeding grounds in far northern climates. Then, before winter sets in, they migrate south in groups to warmer climates. Migratory behaviors are a dramatic example of the ways in which animals respond to changes in their environment.

Chapter 10 supports the NGSS Performance Expectations **HS-LS1-2, HS-LS1-3,** and **HS-LS2-8.**

CASE STUDY
THE INCREDIBLE NONSTOP FLIGHT OF THE BAR-TAILED GODWIT

HOW DO ANIMALS RESPOND TO CHANGES IN THE ENVIRONMENT?

In early February 2007, a female bar-tailed godwit, named E7 after its leg tag, was fitted with an internal battery-operated satellite transmitter, similar to the one shown in **Figure 10-1**. In March, E7 took off from its wintering grounds in New Zealand and landed eight days later in Yalu Jiang, China, in the Yellow Sea. E7 spent five weeks at this coastal wetland refueling before taking off again on May 1 for its breeding grounds in Alaska, where it landed on May 6 after flying nonstop for five days.

Although researchers only expected the bird's satellite transmitter to send out data for the northbound flight, the battery lasted long enough to record the bird's southbound flight back to New Zealand as well.

The researchers were surprised when the data showed that the bird made the flight from Alaska to New Zealand in one fell swoop. From August 29 to September 7, E7 flew 11,700 km (7270 miles)—the equivalent of flying round trip from New York City to San Francisco and then back to San Francisco again—without stopping once. E7 held the record for the longest nonstop migratory bird flight until 2020, when a male bar-tailed godwit (named 4BBRW after the color of bands on its legs) made a nonstop 12,000-km journey from Alaska to New Zealand over a period of 11 days. Scientists estimated that the bird flew at speeds up to 88.5 km/h (55 mph), aided by strong easterly winds.

Bar-tailed godwits prepare for their nonstop journey south by gorging on mollusks, worms, and crustaceans in their Alaskan habitat in the Yukon-Kuskokwim Delta. By doing so, they dramatically increase their fat reserves, doubling their mass. Their bodies are able to store more fat due to the shrinkage of their intestines and gizzard during their migration. Other characteristics that make this bird well adapted for such a long flight are its aerodynamically shaped body and long tapered wings.

Ask Questions *In this chapter, you will learn about animal systems. As you read, generate questions about how a bird's body systems interact to allow it to make its annual migration.*

FIGURE 10-1
This bar-tailed godwit, identified as Z0 from its leg tag, is also outfitted with a satellite transmitter (note the antenna extending beyond its tail feathers). Data sent back from this transmitter allowed researchers to track this individual bird's migratory flight path from New Zealand to Alaska and back.

ANIMAL DIVERSITY

You are an animal. So are gigantic blue whales larger than three buses stacked end to end and tiny rotifers smaller than the period at the end of this sentence. Despite their huge variety of shapes and sizes, all animals have a shared set of characteristics and common ancestry.

Identify *What are two characteristics common to all animals?*

Animal Characteristics

Scientists have identified over 1 million species of animals. However, the actual number of animal species on Earth is estimated to be closer to 7.7 million. Known animal species are categorized into more than 30 different phyla. You and some of the animals that are likely most familiar to you—dogs, birds, fish, frogs—are members of the **chordate** phylum. These animals (including you) all belong to a subgroup of the chordates called **vertebrates**, which have backbones. Animals that do not have a backbone are called **invertebrates**. The invertebrates make up more than 95 percent of known species and include diverse forms such as corals, sea stars, spiders, and insects. A variety of animals is shown in **Figure 10-2**.

FIGURE 10-2 ▽
Animals vary greatly in size and shape. Brown tube sponges (a) are simple animals. Rosemary beetles (b) have an iridescent exoskeleton. Panther chameleons (c) exhibit bright shades of color. Red pandas (d) are fur-covered mammals.

Tissue Organization
The earliest animals were probably clumps of cells, and this level of organization continues to exist in sponges. However, most other modern animals have cells organized as tissues. Tissue organization begins during early development in animal embryos. Embryos of jellies and other cnidarians have two tissue layers: an outer ectoderm and an inner endoderm. In other modern animals, embryonic cells typically rearrange themselves to form a middle tissue layer called the mesoderm. Evolution of a three-layer embryo allowed for an important increase in structural complexity. Most internal organs in animals develop from embryonic mesoderm.

Body Symmetry
Animals may be asymmetrical, radial, or bilateral. Sponges, which are animals with the simplest structural organization, are asymmetrical (**Figure 10-3a**). This means their body cannot be divided into halves that are mirror images. Jellies, sea anemones, and other cnidarians have radial symmetry (**Figure 10-3b**). Their body parts are repeated around a central axis, like spokes of a wheel. Radial animals attach to an underwater surface or drift along in the water. A radial body plan lets them capture food that can arrive from any direction. Animals that have a three-layer body plan typically have bilateral symmetry (**Figure 10-3c**). This means the body's left and right halves are mirror images. Bilateral animals such as worms, snails, praying mantises, and lobsters have a distinctive head end with a concentration of nerve cells. They usually move headfirst through their environment.

Developmental Differences
The two lineages of bilateral animals are defined in part by developmental differences. In protostomes, the first opening of the digestive cavity that forms in the embryo is the mouth. The anus is formed second. (*Proto*– means "first" and *stoma* means "opening.") In deuterostomes, the anus forms from the first opening and the mouth forms from the second opening. (*Deutero*– means "second.")

Body Cavities
Some animals, such as jellyfish and sea anemones, digest food in a saclike cavity with a single opening. Most animals, however, have a tubular gut, with a mouth at one end and an anus at the other. Parts of the tube are typically specialized for taking in food, digesting it, absorbing nutrients, or compacting wastes. While a tubular gut can carry out these tasks at the same time, a saclike cavity cannot.

FIGURE 10-3
A branching vase sponge (a) is a simple animal that lacks tissues and has an asymmetrical body plan. A white-spotted jellyfish (b) has two tissue layers and a radial body plan. A praying mantis (c) has three tissue layers and a bilateral body plan.

Animals share a set of common characteristics:

- All animals are multicellular eukaryotes. Unlike plant cells, animal cells do not have cell walls. Animals use a protein called collagen for structural support.

- All animals have specialized cells, and most are organized into tissues, organs, and organ systems with which they carry out specific functions.

- Animals are heterotrophs that eat food and digest it inside their body, usually within a digestive system.

- Animals have diverse body plans that are adapted to their methods of obtaining food and reproducing.

- Most animals can move from one location to another during some stage of their lives.

- Most animals reproduce sexually.

- Most animals have well-developed sense organs, nervous systems, and muscle systems that allow them to respond rapidly to stimuli and changing conditions.

Major Animal Groups

An evolutionary tree for the nine major animal groups is shown in **Figure 10-4**. These groupings are based on structural, developmental, and genetic comparisons. Like all evolutionary trees, this one is a hypothesis and is open to revision if new data or new interpretations arise.

CCC **Structure and Function** *Use **Figure 10-4** to determine which characteristics echinoderms and chordates share.*

FIGURE 10-4 ▼
This evolutionary tree shows the evolutionary relationships among the nine major animal groups. Of these groups, eight are invertebrates. Chordates are the only vertebrates.

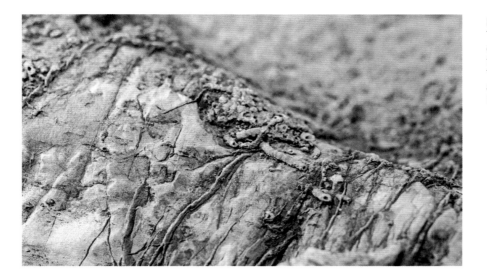

FIGURE 10-5
These tubular fossils are of *Cloudina carinata*. It was a worm-shaped organism that lived about 550 million years ago. These fossils were discovered at the archaeological site El Membrillar in Badajoz, Spain.

Animal Evolution

The oldest widely accepted evidence of animals dates to the final period of the Precambrian era (635 million–541 million years ago). Evidence from this time period includes many trace fossils—rocks with trails or burrows made when unidentified early animals moved across or tunneled through sediments on the ancient seafloor. There are also a variety of body fossils from this time period (**Figure 10-5**). All known animals from this period were soft bodied. Some were unlike any modern animal. Others resemble and may be related to modern invertebrates. Various late Precambrian fossils are considered possible relatives of sponges, cnidarians, annelids, mollusks, or arthropods. Thus, the origin of bilateral body plans and the divergence between protostomes and deuterostomes are thought to have occurred during this time period.

The abundance and types of animal fossils left behind rose dramatically with the onset of the Cambrian period (541 million–485 million years ago). The increase in the number and diversity of fossil animals resulted in part because the first animals with hard parts evolved. Remains of these animals were more likely to become fossils than soft-bodied animals. By the end of the Cambrian, representatives of every major animal phylum now known were present in the seas.

10.1 REVIEW

1. **Classify** Sort these animals by their symmetry: radial or bilateral.

   - anemone
   - butterfly
   - hammerhead shark
   - zebra mussel

2. **Describe** Which characteristics are common to ALL vertebrates? Select all correct answers.

   A. are autotrophs
   B. cells have nucleus
   C. early development occurs in stages
   D. have backbone
   E. multicellular

3. **Compare** Use **Figure 10-4** to identify the characteristics that are similar and different between mollusks and chordates.

4. **Explain** Why is there more evidence of animal life from the Cambrian period than from the end of the Precambrian era?

DEFINING ANIMAL SYSTEMS

Even the simplest animals—the sponges—are made up of specialized cells. More complex animals, such as you, are composed of a system of interacting cells, tissues, and organs.

Explain *What are two systems that interact in your body? How do they interact?*

Levels of Organization

In all animals, development produces a body with multiple types of cells. For most animals, these cells are organized into tissues. All vertebrates have four types of tissue: epithelial, connective, muscle, and nervous.

Typically, animal tissues are organized into organs. Recall that an organ is made up of two or more tissues that are arranged in a way that allows the organ to carry out specific tasks. Consider the cat heart, an organ that includes all four tissue types. The heart wall is made up mostly of cardiac muscle tissue. Epithelial tissue covers the heart's internal and external surfaces, heart valves are made of stretchy connective tissue, and nervous tissue delivers signals to and from the heart. Coordinated activities of these tissues let the heart undergo rhythmic contractions that move blood through the body at an appropriate pace.

As with plants, two or more organs in an organ system interact physically, chemically, or both to perform a common task. For example, in a cat's circulatory system, the pressure generated by a contracting heart (an organ) moves blood (a tissue) through blood vessels (organs), which transport gases and solutes to and from body cells (**Figure 10-6**).

FIGURE 10-6 ▷
Most animals can be organized into five levels. From smallest to largest, these levels are: cell, tissue, organ, organ system, and whole body.

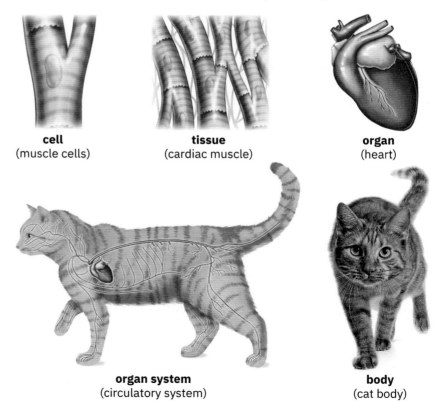

cell
(muscle cells)

tissue
(cardiac muscle)

organ
(heart)

organ system
(circulatory system)

body
(cat body)

Major Body Systems

Tissues interact structurally and functionally in organs. Organs, in turn, interact in organ systems. **Table 10-1** lists the major vertebrate body systems and their functions.

TABLE 10-1. Major Vertebrate Body Systems and Their Functions

Body system	Major organs and other parts	Major functions
circulatory	blood, blood vessels, heart, lymph nodes, lymphatic vessels	distributes materials and heat throughout the body
digestive	esophagus, gallbladder, large intestine, liver, mouth, pancreas, pharynx, small intestine, stomach	takes in food and water; breaks food down and absorbs nutrients, then eliminates food residues
endocrine	adrenal glands, hypothalamus, pancreas, parathyroids, pituitary, ovaries, testes, thyroid	secretes hormones that control the activities of other organ systems
integumentary	hair, nails, sweat and oil glands	protects body from injury, dehydration, pathogens; moderates temperature; excretes some wastes; detects external stimuli
lymphatic	lymph nodes, spleen, thymus	collects and returns excess tissue fluid to the blood; defends the body against infection and cancers
muscular	cardiac, skeletal, and smooth muscles	moves the body and its parts; maintains posture; produces heat to maintain body temperature
nervous	brain, peripheral nerves, spinal cord	detects external and internal stimuli; coordinates responses to stimuli; integrates organ system activities
reproductive	female: fallopian tubes, ovaries, uterus, vagina	female: produces eggs; nourishes and protects developing offspring
	male: ducts and glands, penis, testes	male: produces and transfers sperm to a female
respiratory	nasal cavity, nose, lungs, pharynx, trachea	takes in oxygen needed for aerobic respiration; expels carbon dioxide; helps maintain pH
skeletal	bones, cartilage, ligaments, tendons	supports and protects body parts; site of muscle attachment; produces blood cells; stores minerals
urinary	bladder, kidneys	maintains volume and composition of blood; excretes excess fluid and wastes; helps maintain pH

Body System Functions

Body systems interact together to accomplish tasks. For example, as shown in **Figure 10-7**, the circulatory system works with the respiratory, digestive, and urinary systems in delivering oxygen and nutrients to cells throughout the body, and clearing away their wastes. In this section, we will focus on a few vertebrate body systems and their interactions.

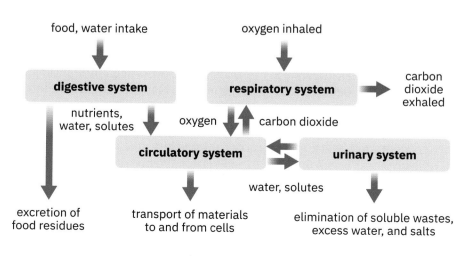

FIGURE 10-7
The organ system interactions shown here keep the body supplied with essential substances and eliminate unwanted wastes.

Nutrient Absorption Body systems involved with nutrient absorption include the digestive, muscular, and circulatory systems. Vertebrates have a complete digestive tract (**Figure 10-8**). Its various regions specialize in digesting food, absorbing nutrients, and concentrating and storing unabsorbed wastes.

FIGURE 10-8
Vertebrates, such as this dog, have a complete digestive tract. The processing of food begins in the mouth and ends when waste exits the body through the anus.

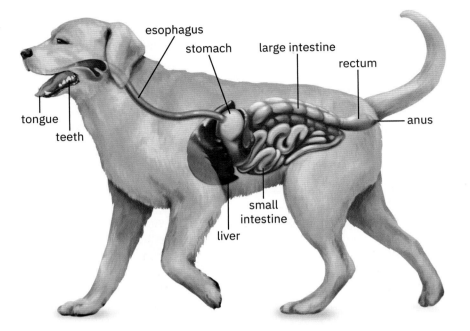

esophagus

stomach

large intestine

rectum

tongue

teeth

anus

small intestine

liver

- Processing of food begins inside the mouth. Salivary glands make saliva that moistens food and begins the process of chemical digestion. Swallowing moves the food–saliva mixture into the pharynx (throat), from which it continues into the esophagus.

- The wall of the esophagus and all portions of the digestive tract beyond it contain smooth muscle, part of the muscular system. By a process called *peristalsis*, waves of smooth muscle contraction propel material through the digestive tract.

- The esophagus extends into the abdominal cavity, where it connects to the stomach. The stomach has three main functions. First, it stores food and controls the rate at which food continues on to the small intestine. Second, it mechanically breaks down food. Third, it secretes substances that aid in chemical digestion.

- The stomach empties into the intestine, which has two regions that differ in their structure and function. The small intestine is the region that completes the process of chemical digestion and absorbs most nutrients. Secretions from the liver, gallbladder, and pancreas assist the small intestine in these tasks. The absorbed nutrients are transferred from the small intestine into the bloodstream, where they are transported around the body by the circulatory system.

- The large intestine is the region that absorbs water and salts and concentrates waste. At the end of the large intestine is the rectum, which stores waste until it is expelled from the body through the anus.

SEP **Develop a Model** *Draw a simple model that shows how the digestive system interacts with another body system during the process of nutrient absorption.*

Immunity and Defense The body's ability to resist and fight infections is called **immunity**. The immune system includes interactions among the integumentary, lymphatic, and circulatory systems. Major parts involved in the immune system are shown in **Table 10-2**.

TABLE 10-2. Immune System Parts and Their Functions

Part	Function
bone marrow	produces red blood cells, plasma cells, and white blood cells
lymph node	filters and destroys pathogens
skin, mucous membrane	serves as first-line defense against pathogens
spleen	stores white blood cells; filters blood
thymus	maturation site for specialized white blood cells
white blood cell	searches for, attacks, and destroys pathogens

Surface barriers usually prevent microorganisms from entering the body's internal environment. The tough outer layer of skin is an example. Microorganisms flourish on skin's waterproof, oily surface, but they rarely penetrate its thick layer of dead cells (**Figure 10-9**). The thinner epithelial tissues that line the body's interior tubes and cavities also have surface barriers. Sticky mucus secreted by cells of these linings can trap microorganisms. The mucus contains an enzyme that kills bacteria. In the sinuses and respiratory tract, the coordinated beating of cilia sweeps trapped microorganisms away before they have a chance to breach the delicate walls of these structures. These anatomical barriers are the body's first line of defense against pathogens.

A pathogen that breaches these barriers activates mechanisms of innate immunity, the second line of defense. *Innate immunity* is a set of immediate, general responses that help protect all multicellular organisms from infection.

FIGURE 10-9
This color-enhanced scanning electron microscope (SEM) image shows the layers of human skin. A thick, waterproof layer of dead skin cells at and just below skin's surface usually keeps microorganisms such as bacteria, fungi, and viruses from penetrating internal tissues.

Inflammation is a fast, local response that both destroys affected tissues and jump-starts the healing process. The primary function of inflammation is to form a physical barrier that prevents the spread of infection. Examples of inflammatory responses include swelling, redness, warmth, and pain.

The activation of innate immunity triggers mechanisms of adaptive immunity, which is the third line of defense. *Adaptive immunity* tailors an immune response to a vast array of specific pathogens that an individual encounters during their lifetime. For example, when a person recovers from chicken pox, the body develops a memory of the infection. That memory specifically protects the body from the virus that causes chicken pox if it is exposed to the virus again in the future.

White blood cells are active in both innate and adaptive immune responses. These cells circulate in blood and lymph and many populate the lymph nodes, spleen, and other solid tissues. White blood cells communicate by secreting and responding to chemical signaling molecules. These molecules, which include proteins and amino acids, allow cells throughout the body to coordinate activities during an immune response. As part of an immune response, white blood cells engulf and digest pathogens (**Figure 10-10**).

FIGURE 10-10 ▷
In this color-enhanced SEM image, a white blood cell (brown) is attacking a group of bacteria cells (blue).

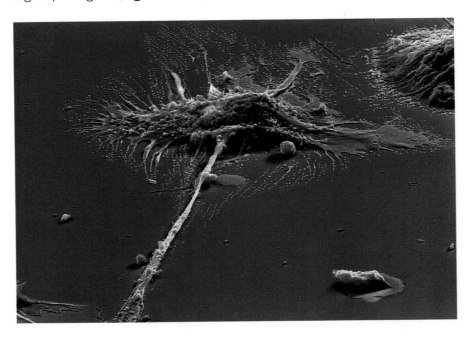

10.2 REVIEW

1. **Sequence** Order the terms to make a model of the levels of organization in animal bodies. List the terms from largest scale (top) to smallest scale (bottom).

   - body
   - cell
   - organ
   - organ system
   - tissue

2. **Distinguish** Describe an example of two organs working together in the human digestive, respiratory, circulatory, or urinary systems.

3. **Explain** Describe in your own words how the integumentary, lymphatic, and circulatory systems interact together to protect the body from pathogens.

COMPARING REACTION SPEED

SEP **Analyze and Interpret Data** Do body systems react to visual stimuli faster than auditory stimuli?

Many everyday activities you do, such as throwing a basketball or catching a flying disc, involve multiple body systems. To shoot a basket, the nervous system gauges the distance to the hoop and sends information to the musculoskeletal system, which then performs the throw. Catching an object, such as a flying disc, is even more complicated. The nervous system estimates where the disc will be and sends out information to the musculoskeletal system. This allows the catcher to put their hand in the path of the disc and gets them to close their fingers at the right time to grasp it.

In this activity, you will test the body's reaction time in catching a falling object. You will also determine whether the reaction time is faster with a visual stimulus compared to an auditory stimulus.

Athletes react to an auditory signal at the start of a race.

Materials
• meter stick

Procedure

1. Work in pairs for this experiment. To begin, Student A will release the meter stick and Student B will catch it. Develop a standard method for holding and dropping the meter stick. For example, the student dropping the meter stick could hold the meter stick from its top edge, while the student catching the meter stick could hold their finger and thumb loosely around the 10 cm mark of the meter stick.

2. To start the visual reaction test, Student A should indicate that a five-second window is starting. At some random time during that five-second window, Student A releases the meter stick.

3. In your biology notebook, record the distance the meter stick fell before being caught. Depending on where Student B initially placed their fingers around the meter stick, subtract any distance as necessary. Record the distance as the place just above where the fingers caught the meter stick.

4. Repeat Steps 2–3 three times and record the results in your biology notebook.

5. To start the auditory reaction test, use the same hand positioning you decided on in Step 1. This time, Student B will close their eyes.

6. Student A calls "drop" at the same time as they release the meter stick.

7. In your biology notebook, record the distance the meter stick fell before being caught.

8. Repeat Steps 5–7 three times and record the results in your biology notebook.

9. Switch roles to allow Student A to test their reaction time.

10. Use the formula $t = 0.045\sqrt{d}$, where d is distance in centimeters and t is time in seconds, to determine the reaction time for each trial.

Results and Analysis

1. **Sequence** Draw a model or flow chart showing the body systems involved in processing information for this experiment.

2. **Identify Patterns** Did you observe a pattern in the repeated trials of the visual part of this activity? For the auditory part? Explain possible reasons for whether a pattern was observed for either stimulus.

3. **Evaluate** Which stimulus, visual or auditory, had a faster reaction time? Why do you think this is the case?

KEY TERMS

control center
effector
negative feedback mechanism
positive feedback mechanism
sensory receptor

MAINTAINING HOMEOSTASIS

Internal and external factors, such as temperature, stress, and infection, can affect an animal's ability to maintain stable conditions in its body. For example, in humans, enzymes that control the chemical reactions that sustain life work best around 37 °C (98.6 °F).

Describe *What do you think happens to enzyme function when body temperatures are too high or too low?*

> **CASE STUDY**
> THE INCREDIBLE NONSTOP FLIGHT
> OF THE BAR-TAILED GODWIT
>
> **Ask Questions** *Generate questions about the body system interactions involved in the maintenance of homeostasis in migrating birds.*

Feedback Mechanisms

In animals, homeostasis involves interactions among sensory receptors, the brain, and muscles and glands. **Figure 10-11** shows the control systems involved in maintaining homeostasis.

- A **sensory receptor** is a cell or cell component that responds to a change in a specific stimulus such as temperature or blood pressure. Sensory receptors involved in homeostasis function like internal guards. They monitor the body for changes. When conditions within the body change, an imbalance occurs. This imbalance is a stimulus that signals to the body that conditions have changed.

- Information from sensory receptors throughout the body flows to a **control center**. The control center processes the incoming information. It compares this information to a set point, or normal condition in the body.

- If the information differs from the set point, the control center sends a message to the body's **effectors**—muscles and glands—to carry out the required response to return the body to the set point, or normal conditions.

FIGURE 10-11
When an imbalance occurs in an animal's body, information from sensory receptors is sent to the control center. The control center in turn sends a message that activates the body's effectors (muscles and glands) to return the body to stable, or balanced, conditions.

> **Go Online** **INTERACTIVE FIGURE**
>
> **FIGURE 10-11** Go online to see how an imbalance affects **Body Systems and Homeostasis**.

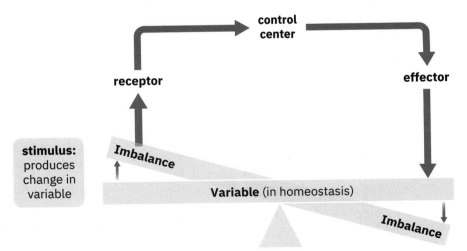

CCC **Stability and Change** *Use the terms shown **Figure 10-11** to describe how your body responds when you accidentally touch a hot surface such as a stovetop.*

In vertebrates, the nervous system is the body's main control center. The brain, spinal cord, and nerves are part of this system, as are sensory organs such as the eyes. The nervous system gathers information about the internal and external environment, integrates this information, and issues commands to muscles and glands. Neurons make up the communication lines of a nervous system.

The endocrine system consists of all the body's hormone-secreting glands and cells. Portions of the endocrine system and nervous system are so closely linked that scientists sometimes refer to the two systems collectively as the neuroendocrine system. Glands in the endocrine system and neurons in the nervous system receive signals from the hypothalamus, a structure that is the center for homeostatic control of the internal environment. Most organs respond to both hormones and signals from the nervous system.

Negative Feedback Mechanisms Homeostasis typically involves a **negative feedback mechanism**, in which a change brings about a response that reverses the change. An air conditioner with a thermostat provides a familiar nonbiological example of a negative feedback mechanism. A person sets the air conditioner to a desired temperature. When the temperature rises above this preset point, a sensor in the air conditioner detects the change and turns the unit on. When the temperature decreases to the desired level, the thermostat detects the change and turns off the air conditioner. (Note that the use of "negative" in this context does not mean the response is bad or undesirable, but rather that it negates the stimulus that caused it.)

A similar negative feedback mechanism operates when you exercise on a hot day (**Figure 10-12**). Muscle activity generates heat, and your body's internal temperature rises. Sensory receptors in the skin detect the increase and signal your brain. In response, the brain signals effectors. These signals increase the flow of blood from the body's hot interior to the skin. The shift maximizes the amount of heat given off to the surrounding air. At the same time, sweat glands in the skin increase their output. Evaporation of sweat helps cool the body surface. You breathe faster and deeper, speeding the transfer of heat from the blood in your lungs to the air. Your rate of heat loss increases, and your body's internal temperature decreases back to normal.

🧪 **CHAPTER INVESTIGATION**

The Effect of Exercise on Homeostasis
How does exercise affect homeostasis?

Go online to explore this chapter's design-your-own investigation about the feedback mechanisms that maintain homeostasis.

FIGURE 10-12 ▼
This diagram shows the negative feedback mechanism that maintains human body temperature under hot conditions.

Stimulus
Exertion on a hot day raises internal body temperature.

Sensory Receptors
Receptors monitor internal temperature and signal the brain when temperature increases.

Brain
The brain receives signals from sensory receptors and signals muscles and glands.

Muscles and Glands

Skeletal muscles in the chest wall contract more frequently, increasing the breathing rate.

Smooth muscle in blood vessels that supply the skin relaxes. More blood flows to the skin, and more heat radiates to the surrounding air.

Sweat glands secrete more sweat, which cools the body as it evaporates.

Endocrine glands that affect general activity levels slow secretion of hormones that stimulate activity.

Response
Body temperature declines.

FIGURE 10-13
The formation of a blood clot is an example of a positive feedback mechanism. Rather than returning the body to a set point, a positive feedback loop enhances the change away from a set point.

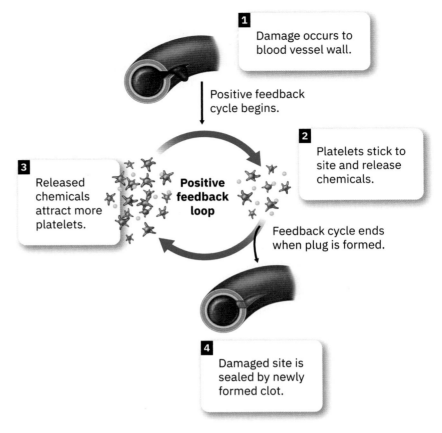

1 Damage occurs to blood vessel wall.

Positive feedback cycle begins.

2 Platelets stick to site and release chemicals.

Positive feedback loop

3 Released chemicals attract more platelets.

Feedback cycle ends when plug is formed.

4 Damaged site is sealed by newly formed clot.

Positive Feedback Mechanisms Unlike the negative feedback mechanisms that help to maintain homeostasis, a **positive feedback mechanism** maintains the direction of a stimulus, rather than stopping it. One example is blood clotting, shown in **Figure 10-13**. Once a clotting factor is triggered, it triggers the next factor in the sequence until a clot is formed. In the case of blood clotting, chemicals that attract platelets continue to be released by the body until a plug is formed by the accumulated platelets at the site of blood vessel damage.

CCC **Stability and Change** *What is the main difference between negative and positive feedback mechanisms?*

10.3 REVIEW

1. **Explain** Use the example of body temperature regulation to illustrate the role of a negative feedback mechanism.

2. **Identify** Describe the functions of a sensory receptor, control center, and effector in maintaining homeostasis. How are these three parts of a control system related?

3. **Distinguish** Identify each of the following response outcomes as part of a positive feedback or negative feedback mechanism.
   - response reverses a change
   - response enhances a change
   - response reinforces stability
   - response increases instability

THERMOREGULATION

SEP **Use Mathematics** Thermoregulation, or body temperature control, is an example of homeostasis. However, not all animals regulate body temperature in the same way. Animals called endotherms use internal mechanisms to maintain constant body temperature. Ectotherms are animals that can tolerate a variable body temperature and use behavior to regulate their temperature.

Tables 1 and **2** list the temperature responses, average mass, and average metabolic rate for various organisms.

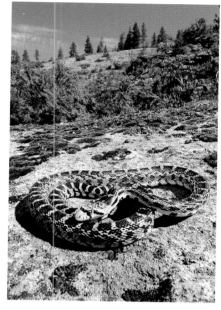

A gopher snake basks in the sun.

TABLE 1. Body Temperature Response for Four Model Organisms

Organism	Environmental temperature (°C)		
	0	15	30
	Body temperature (°C)		
bobcat	38	39	40
mouse	35	36	36
salamander	0	14	32
snake	5	16	29

TABLE 2. Average Mass and Metabolic Rates

Organism	Average mass (kg)	Average metabolic rate (kcal/hr)
bobcat	14	10^2
deer	180	10^3
dolphin	90	10^3
fish	5	10^{-1}
mouse	0.5	10^2
salamander	0.01	10^{-3}
snake	35	10^{-3}
turtle	160.01	10^{-3}

1. **Identify Patterns** Describe how the model organisms listed in **Table 1** respond to increases in environmental temperature.

2. **Classify** Label the model organisms in **Table 1** as endotherms or ectotherms.

3. **Analyze** Use the classification of the model organisms and the data in **Table 2** to compare the average mass and metabolic rate for endotherms and ectotherms. What correlation to thermoregulation does the data support?

4. **Predict** Classify the organisms in **Table 2** as endothermic or ectothermic based on the correlation supported by the data.

ANIMAL BEHAVIOR

KEY TERMS

altruism
eusocial
instinctive behavior
learned behavior
pheromone

In a colony of prairie dogs, one individual stands on its hind legs and scans the area for predators as the rest of the group forages for food. When a hawk soars above, the prairie dog issues a loud alarm call to warn the others. The rest of the colony members scurry into their burrow for safety.

Analyze *What is the function of an alarm call? Can you think of other examples of this type of behavior?*

Instinct and Learning

All animals have some **instinctive behaviors**—innate responses to a specific and usually simple stimulus. The life cycle of the cuckoo bird provides several examples of instinct at work. The common cuckoo is a brood parasite, meaning it lays its eggs in the nests of other birds. The female cuckoo scatters her eggs among the nests, leaving just one egg in each. A newly hatched cuckoo is blind, but contact with an object beside it stimulates an instinctive response. The cuckoo moves the object, which is usually one of its foster parents' eggs, onto its back, then shoves it out of the nest. The cuckoo will also shove its foster siblings over the side, if they hatched before it did. Instinctively shoving these objects out of the nest ensures that the cuckoo receives its foster parents' undivided attention.

Instinctive responses are adaptive, or beneficial for survival, when the triggering stimulus almost always signals the same situation and requires the same response. Getting rid of an egg or unrelated sibling always benefits a cuckoo chick because it rids the nest of future competitors for food. Instinctive responses sometimes open the way to exploitation. For example, most adult birds instinctively fill any wide-open mouth they see in their nest, a response that is clearly adaptive when those mouths belong to their chicks. However, this parental instinct opens the way to exploitation by cuckoos, which often look nothing like the chicks they displace (**Figure 10-14**).

FIGURE 10-14
A reed warbler feeds a dragonfly to a much larger common cuckoo chick. This is a behavioral response to a simple cue: the chick's gaping mouth.

FIGURE 10-15
Chimpanzees use sticks as tools for extracting tasty termites from a nest. The method of shaping the stick and catching termites is learned by imitation.

A **learned behavior** is a behavior that occurs only as a result of practice or experience. Some instinctive behaviors can be modified with learning. For example, a newly hatched toad instinctively tries to capture and eat any insect-sized moving object it sees. This behavior is modified after encounters with bees or wasps. The toad quickly learns that insect-sized objects with certain color patterns provide a sting rather than a meal. A genetic capacity to learn, combined with experiences in the environment, shapes most forms of behavior.

Some animals learn a behavior by imitation. Consider how a chimpanzee strips leaves from branches to make a "fishing stick" for use in capturing termites as food (**Figure 10-15**). The chimpanzee inserts a fishing stick into a termite mound, then withdraws the stick and eats the termites that cling to it. Different groups of chimpanzees use different methods of tool shaping and insect fishing. In each group, young chimpanzees learn by imitating the behavior of others.

SEP **Argue From Evidence** *What is the difference between a learned behavior and an instinctive behavior?*

Go Online VIRTUAL INVESTIGATION

Communication in the Rainforest
How do rainforest species communicate?

Explore how animals communicate in a Puerto Rican rainforest.

(▶) **VIDEO**

VIDEO 10-1 Go online to watch the courtship display of a male magnificent frigatebird.

FIGURE 10-16 ▶
The male magnificent frigatebird inflates its bright red throat pouch and clacks its slender beak to attract a mate. Large populations of these seabirds are found in the Galápagos Islands.

Animal Communication

Communication signals are cues that transmit information from one member of a species to another. A communication signal arises and persists only if it benefits both the signal sender and the signal receiver.

Chemical Signals A **pheromone** is a chemical communication signal that is secreted by one individual and brings about a change in another member of the same species. In many insects, a pheromone helps individuals locate a suitable mate. For example, a female silk moth releases a sex pheromone that a male silk moth can detect from as far as a kilometer away.

Sound Acoustic signals, or sounds, often announce the presence of an animal or group of animals. Many male vertebrates, some fish, and many insects make sounds to attract prospective mates. In numerous species, sounds made by males also function in territoriality. Some birds and mammals give alarm calls that inform others of potential threats. In many cases, the calls convey more information than simply "Danger!" A ground squirrel makes one type of bark when it detects an eagle and another when it sees a coyote. Upon hearing the call, other ground squirrels respond appropriately. They either dive into burrows (to escape an eagle's attack) or stand tall (to spot the coyote).

Sight Visual communication is most widespread in animals that have good eyesight and are active during the day. In most birds, mating is preceded by a courtship display that involves specific movements and actions (**Figure 10-16**). A courtship display assures a prospective mate that the displayer is of the correct species and in good health. When two potential rivals meet, a threat display demonstrates each individual's strength and how well armed it is. If the rivals are not evenly matched, the weaker individual retreats. Threat displays benefit both participants by allowing them to avoid an energetically costly fight that could lead to injury.

Touch With tactile communication, touch transmits information. For example, after discovering food, a foraging honeybee worker returns to the hive and dances on the honeycomb surrounded by a crowd of workers (**Figure 10-17**). The interior of the hive is dark, so the workers follow the dancer's progress by touch. The speed and orientation of a successful forager's dance provides information about the location of the food.

VIDEO

VIDEO 10-2 Go online to watch a honeybee perform a waggle dance.

FIGURE 10-17
The angle of the waggle run, in which the bee wiggles back and forth in a straight line, gives the direction of the food. The faster the dance is performed, the closer the food.

CONNECTIONS

CAN YOU HEAR ME NOW? Right whales, like other whales, use sound to communicate. The sound they make most frequently is a whoop-like contact call that informs other right whales of their presence.

Sound-recording devices attached to individual right whales show that the level of shipping noise influences the whales' calling patterns. Whales call more loudly and are shriller in the presence of a ship. The louder the ship noise, the louder the whales call. Such vocal alterations improve sound transmission, but vital information can still be drowned out. Scientists do not know if the changes the whales make to their voices are sufficient to let their calls be understood despite the noise.

For humans, chronic exposure to noise is stressful, and the same may be true for whales. It would be unrealistic to ask tankers to stop their engines for days to monitor how noise affects whales. However, a quiet period did occur immediately after the terrorist attacks of September 11, 2001, when all shipping traffic was halted for a short period of time. At the time, researchers were collecting whales' feces to measure hormone secretions, including glucocorticoids, a class of hormones excreted in response to stress.

When the data about ship-related noise and hormone secretions were combined, scientists found that the brief decline in shipping noise was accompanied by a significant drop in the whales' stress hormone level. There was no drop in stress hormone levels immediately after September 11 of other years. These data suggest that the normally high noise level related to shipping causes a chronic stress response in right whales. We know that, in other mammals, chronic stress dampens the immune response and impairs reproduction. Thus, noise-induced stress may slow the recovery of this highly endangered species.

Noise from cargo ships and other ocean traffic affects the ability of whales to communicate with one another.

Eavesdroppers and False Signals Predators can benefit by intercepting signals sent by their prey. For example, frog-eating bats locate a male tungara frog by listening for his mating call. This poses a dilemma for the male frog. Female tungara frogs prefer complex calls, but complex calls are easier for bats to locate. Thus, when bats are near, male frogs call less often and with less flair. This subdued signal is a trade-off between competing pressures to attract a mate and to avoid being eaten. Other predators lure prey with counterfeit signals. Fireflies are nocturnal beetles that attract mates with flashes of light. When a predatory female firefly sees the flash from a male of the prey species, she flashes back as if she were a female of his own species.

SEP **Construct an Explanation** *What is the function of animal communication?*

Parenting Behavior

Parental care requires time and energy that an individual could otherwise invest in reproducing again. It arises only if the genetic benefit of providing care (an increased chance of offspring survival) offsets the cost (reduced opportunity to produce more offspring). If the parental care provided by a single parent is sufficient to successfully rear an offspring, individuals who spare themselves this cost by leaving parental duties to their mate are at an advantage. Thus, whether parental care occurs and, if so, who provides it varies among species.

Most fish provide no parental care, but in those that do, this duty usually falls to the male. In many species, males guard eggs until they hatch. In some cases, males retain eggs or young on or in their body. Male seahorses have a special brood pouch. Mouth brooding, which refers to holding developing eggs in an organism's mouth, occurs in a variety of fish species, including the jawfish (**Figure 10-18**). The prevalence of male parental care in fish may be related to sex differences in how fertility changes with age. A female fish's fertility increases with age, whereas a male's does not. Thus, a female fish who invests energy in parental care forfeits more reproductive potential than does a male fish.

FIGURE 10-18 ▶
After a female jawfish lays an egg mass, the male fertilizes the eggs. The male then takes the eggs into its mouth, where the eggs are incubated until they hatch.

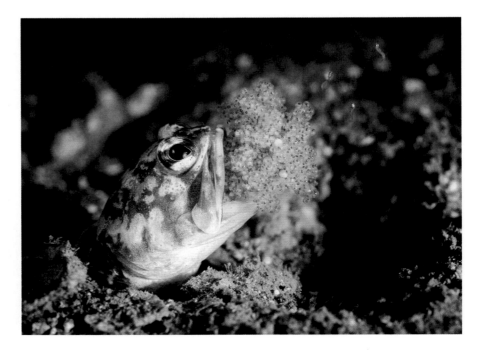

In birds, two-parent care is most common. Chicks of birds that cooperate in care of their young tend to hatch while in a relatively helpless state, so the chicks require the care of two parents to survive. In about 90 percent of mammals, the female rears young. In the remaining 10 percent, both sexes participate. Female mammals sustain developing young in their body, so they do not have the option of pursuing a new mate rather than providing care. Females also have a greater investment in newborns than males, and this investment continues with lactation.

Group Living and Social Behavior

Some animals live solitary lives, coming together only to mate. However, individuals of many species spend time in groups. Some groups are temporary, such as schools of fish. Others, such as prairie dog colonies or wolf packs, are more permanent. A tendency to group together, whether briefly or for the longer term, will occur only if the benefits of being near to others outweigh the costs.

Benefits of Group Behavior Whenever animals cluster together, individuals at the margins of the group inadvertently shield others from predators. The selfish herd effect describes how groups can emerge from the tendencies of individuals to reduce their risk of danger by drawing near one another. For example, starlings form large swooping flocks called murmurations in part to confuse and disorient a predator such as a falcon.

Once a group forms, multiple individuals can be on the alert for predators. In some cases, an animal that spots a threat will warn others of the threat's approach. Birds, monkeys, prairie dogs, and ground squirrels are among the animals that make alarm calls in response to a predator. Even in species that do not make alarm calls, individuals can benefit from the vigilance of others. Often, when an animal notices another group member beginning to flee, it will do likewise. In what is called the "confusion effect," a predator has more difficulty choosing an individual to pursue when a group of prey is scattering. Some animals stand their ground to present a united defense. For example, a group of threatened musk oxen forms a tight circle so a predator faces their sharp horns (**Figure 10-19**).

FIGURE 10-19 ◀
When threatened by predators, musk oxen stand shoulder to shoulder to form a defensive line or circle to protect their more vulnerable young.

FIGURE 10-20
An Arctic wolf pack works together to attack a herd of musk oxen on Ellesmere Island in Nunavut, Canada.

Wolves and lions are social animals that live in multigenerational groups and cooperate in hunting prey (**Figure 10-20**). Cooperative hunting allows a group of predators to capture larger or faster prey. However, on a per-hunter basis, cooperative hunting is usually no more efficient than hunting alone. In one study, researchers observed that a solitary lion catches prey about 15 percent of the time. Two lions hunting together catch prey twice as often as a solitary lion, but having to share the spoils of the hunt means the amount of food per lion is the same. Among carnivores that hunt cooperatively, hunting success is not the major advantage of group living. Individuals hunt together but also cooperate in fending off scavengers, caring for one another's young, and defending the group's territory.

Costs of Group Behavior Individuals that group together are easier for predators to locate. In addition, parasites and contagious diseases spread more quickly when individuals come into frequent close contact. Grouping also increases competition for food and mates, and the resulting conflict increases stress.

In most social groups, costs and benefits are not equally distributed among the group members. Many animals that live in groups form a hierarchy, a social system in which dominant animals get a greater share of resources and breeding opportunities than subordinates. Typically, dominance is established by physical confrontation. In wolf packs, the dominant male and dominant female are usually the only breeders.

All members of a wolf pack hunt and carry food back to individuals that guard the young in their den. Why would a wolf stay in a pack where it is subordinate? Belonging to a group enhances the subordinate's chance of survival, and some subordinates do get a chance to reproduce in periods when food is abundant. A subordinate may also one day move to the dominant reproductive role.

SEP **Argue From Evidence** *What is one cost and one benefit of social behavior?*

Evolution of Cooperation In many animal groups, individuals display **altruism**, which is behavior that decreases an individual's likelihood of survival and reproduction but increases the likelihood of survival and reproduction of other group members. Giving an alarm call is an example of an altruistic act (**Figure 10-21**). It puts the caller at an increased risk of predation but reduces the risk to others.

Field studies of social animals confirm that many altruistic behaviors are preferentially directed at relatives. For example, ground squirrels and prairie dogs are more likely to give an alarm call if they have close relatives living nearby. In hyenas, which often have intragroup fights, dominant females are more likely to risk injury by joining a fight to assist a relative than to assist a nonrelative.

Cooperative behavior can also arise through reciprocity, in which an individual assists group members who have previously assisted it or may assist it in the future. Consider vampire bats, which roost during the day in large groups. Hungry bats who have not successfully fed the night before are offered food (regurgitated blood) by other bats. Close kinship increases the likelihood of food sharing, but sharing also occurs among unrelated bats. Bats in need who previously offered food to many different recipients receive more offers of food than bats who were less generous.

 VIDEO

VIDEO 10-3 Go online to learn more about prairie dog alarm calls.

FIGURE 10-21
A black-tailed prairie dog makes a loud alarm call in response to an intruder. Such calls alert the prairie dog's relatives to take cover from potential danger, which aids in their survival.

Gather Evidence *Leaf-cutter ants are commonly found on the rainforest floor. Their trails can extend more than 200 meters in length. How do you think the ants communicate the location of a food source to other ants in their colony? Explain your reasoning.*

Eusocial Species Animals that are **eusocial** live in a multigenerational family group in which sterile workers carry out tasks essential to the group's welfare, while other members of the group reproduce. Many eusocial species are members of the order Hymenoptera, which includes ants, bees, and wasps. Leaf-cutter ants, shown in **Figure 10-22,** are a eusocial insect species that is commonly found in rainforest habitats. As their name suggests, worker ants cut leaves, which they bring back to their nest to use as a fertilizer to grow the fungus that is fed to ant larvae. In eusocial Hymenoptera, all workers are female. Workers forage for food, maintain the nest or hive, care for young, and defend the colony.

SEP **Construct an Explanation** *What is the genetic basis of altruistic behaviors?*

FIGURE 10-22
A leaf-cutter ant carries a leaf back to the colony's nest in Costa Rica's Manuel Antonio National Park. Leaf-cutter ant colonies are divided into several castes. Each caste serves a different function.

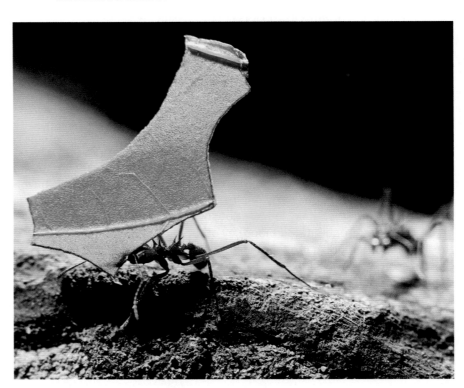

10.4 REVIEW

1. **Classify** Identify each animal behavior as an example of an instinct or a learned behavior.

   - Young coyotes find food sources by hunting with adult coyotes.
   - Rattlesnakes naturally rattle their tail as a warning to potential threats.
   - Migrating birds begin their journey to warmer climates at the start of fall.

2. **Identify** Which of the five senses are required for each type of animal communication?

   - acoustic signal
   - chemical signal
   - tactile signal
   - visual signal

3. **Explain** Which of these are the benefits of group behavior? Select all correct answers.

   A. assistance in raising young

   B. cooperation for hunting prey

   C. abundance of food resources

   D. increased defenses against predators

   E. protection from contagious disease

4. **Distinguish** Explain the difference between species that display altruism and species that are eusocial.

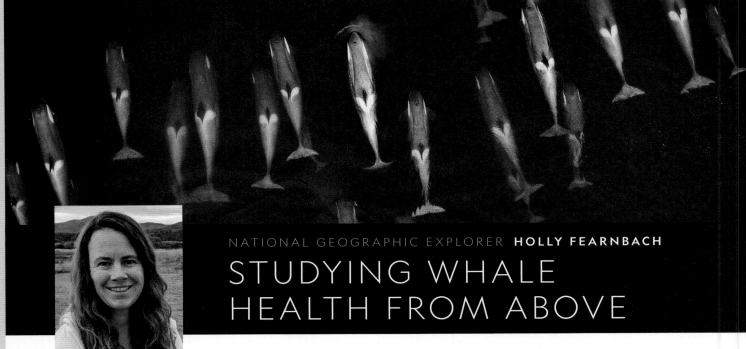

NATIONAL GEOGRAPHIC EXPLORER **HOLLY FEARNBACH**

STUDYING WHALE HEALTH FROM ABOVE

Dr. Holly Fearnbach is a leader in the field of marine mammal health.

▶ **VIDEO 10-4** Go online to view drone footage of Southern Resident killer whales captured by Fearnbach and a team of researchers.

Zoologist Dr. Holly Fearnbach's research focuses on assessing the health of whale populations around the world. "I've always been drawn to the ocean and fascinated by marine wildlife," Fearnbach says. Immediately after high school, Fearnbach decided to pursue a career in marine biology—and she has never looked back. Today, Fearnbach is the marine mammal research director of a Pacific Northwest nonprofit called SR³ (Sealife Response + Rehab + Research).

Fearnbach and her colleagues pioneered the use of drones to collect aerial images of free-ranging whales. They study the whales' health using photogrammetry, which is the science of making measurements from photographs. They fly the drone at an altitude of more than 30 meters above the whales and position their research boat several hundred meters away, enabling the team to collect aerial images without disturbing the whales.

Fearnbach spends most of her year assessing the health of Southern Resident killer whales (SRKWs). This endangered population of only 73 individuals has a core summer habitat in the Salish Sea between Puget Sound, Washington and Southern Vancouver Island, British Columbia. Three key threats have been identified for SRKWs: physical and acoustic disturbance from vessels, contaminants in their food and water, and declines in the availability of Chinook salmon, their primary prey.

Fearnbach and her team analyze the aerial images to assess the health of every whale in the population. They identify each whale using distinct pigmentation patterns on the white saddle patches on the whale's back and sides. Then they collect a series of biometric measurements that are used to estimate body length, monitor growth, and assess body condition. These measurements give a picture of the overall health of both the individual whale and the population as a whole. The datasets are also provided to management groups to help inform decisions aimed at population recovery.

"My greatest motivation is the hope that our research efforts will continue informing conservation and management measures to protect marine ecosystems around the world," Fearnbach says. ▓

THINKING CRITICALLY

Identify Patterns *Understanding the health of whales helps researchers understand the health of the ecosystem in which they live. Why are biometric measurements useful in assessing whale population health?*

TYING IT ALL TOGETHER
THE INCREDIBLE NONSTOP FLIGHT OF THE BAR-TAILED GODWIT

HOW DO ANIMALS RESPOND TO CHANGES IN THE ENVIRONMENT?

In this chapter, you learned how an animal's body systems interact to help it survive and respond to changes in its environment. You also learned about the benefits of social interactions and group behavior. The Case Study described migratory behavior in the bar-tailed godwit, a type of shorebird. On average, these birds fly 29,000 km (18,000 miles) annually. While the length of the bar-tailed godwit's annual migration is impressive, the Arctic tern (**Figure 10-23**) flies nearly 90,000 km (56,000 miles) annually. However, unlike the bar-tailed godwit, the Arctic tern makes several stops during its journey from the North Pole to the South Pole.

Much about bird migration remains unknown, including how birds are able to navigate long distances. It is thought that birds use a combination of tools to navigate. These tools include celestial clues, such as the position of the sun, moon, and stars, to help them find their way. Research also indicates a protein called Cry4 in the eyes of birds allows them to "see" Earth's magnetic fields.

This information can be used as a map and compass. Birds orientate themselves based on the strength of the magnetic field and its inclination, that is, the angle at which the magnetic field is tilted with respect to the surface of Earth.

In this activity, you will conduct research to identify the body system interactions involved in bird migration.

Obtain Information
1. Research the internal and external cues that trigger migratory behaviors in birds. Use your research to identify how these cues affect bird behavior.

Develop a Model
2. Choose a migratory bird species. Identify specific body systems and structures that support its migratory behavior. Use your research to describe how these body systems interact together.

3. Develop a model that illustrates these interactions.

Construct an Explanation
4. Make a presentation that uses digital media to share your findings, including your model, with your class.

FIGURE 10-23 ▽
Arctic terns have one of the longest migratory paths of all animals on Earth. Every year, these birds navigate from the Arctic Circle to Antarctica and back again.

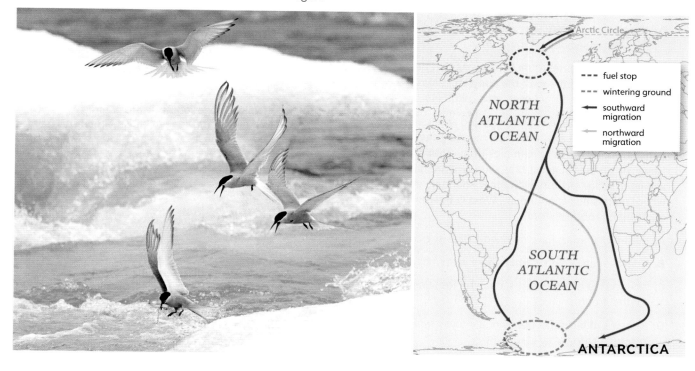

REVIEW KEY CONCEPTS

1. **Classify** Place each description of a tissue function into the appropriate category: nervous, connective, epithelial, or muscle.

   • lines, covers, and protects

   • sends and receives signals

   • provides structure and elasticity

   • contracts and relaxes to move body parts

2. **Classify** Label each role in maintaining homeostasis with the responsible body system. Choose from: sensory receptors; brain; and muscles and glands.

   • send(s) signals to effectors

   • monitor(s) body for changes

   • send(s) signals to control center

   • receive(s) signals from control center

   • take(s) action to restore homeostasis

3. **Identify** Which are examples of negative feedback mechanisms? Select all correct answers.

   A. A change in the external environment has an undesirable effect on the body.

   B. A body system operates to help the body maintain a stable internal environment.

   C. An increase in blood pressure triggers processes that decrease the blood pressure.

   D. An increase in body temperature triggers processes that decrease body temperature.

   E. A torn blood vessel attracts platelets that begin clotting around the tear; the platelets release chemicals that attract even more platelets.

4. **Explain** Wild pigs live in groups called sounders. Sounders are typically territorial, meaning they will not share their territory with pigs from other sounders. However, studies suggest that sounders are more willing to share territory with other sounders in areas where food is highly abundant. What is the most likely explanation for this?

   A. Well-fed animals have no need to live in groups.

   B. Competition is higher when there is abundant food.

   C. Abundance of food makes a habitat less desirable for the group.

   D. Benefits of territorial behavior are lower when resources are highly abundant

5. **Classify** Label each function with the animal body system that is primarily responsible for the function.

   • transports materials around the body

   • contains tissue where new blood cells are produced

   • helps maintain fluid and pH balance and excretes wastes

   • produces cells used for reproduction; may protect developing embryo

   • breaks down food so that nutrients can be absorbed; eliminates leftover wastes

   • brings in oxygen to be absorbed by the blood and exchanged with carbon dioxide

   • important in the immune response, returns fluid to the blood, and includes the spleen

   • produces hormones to cause the body to respond to stimuli and to control internal organs

   • moves bones; moves food through digestive tract and blood through blood vessels; helps generate heat

6. **Explain** Which statement reflects a typical cost of group behavior for animals that travel in herds?

   A. Individuals can alert other members of the herd when a predator is detected.

   B. When the herd flees, a predator may become confused and have trouble selecting an individual.

   C. Competition between group members for mates, food, and water can make it more difficult for some individuals to survive.

   D. All members receive the same benefits of living in the group, preventing stronger individuals from passing on their genes at a higher rate.

7. **Identify** Which of the following are chemical signals that convey information between individuals of the same species?

   A. pheromones

   B. neurotransmitters

   C. hormones

   D. releasers

8. **Explain** Describe how the circulatory and digestive systems interact so that nutrients from food can be transported through the body.

9. **Infer** Zebras live in large herds that roam the African savanna. Discuss two advantages and two disadvantages to zebras of living in a group.

CRITICAL THINKING

10. Explain Queen honeybees lay both fertilized and unfertilized eggs. The fertilized eggs become females and the unfertilized eggs become males. Except for the occasional female that becomes a queen, adult female honeybees are sterile workers. If an animal such as a bear threatens the hive, worker bees will sting the bear and die soon after. How does this altruistic behavior benefit the group? If the queen behaved the same way, would the same benefit occur? Explain why or why not.

11. NOS Scientific Investigations A group of students is conducting an investigation to provide evidence that feedback mechanisms maintain homeostasis during exercise. Why is it important that the group's experimental design is clear and easy to follow?

12. Synthesize Identify the two major animal body systems that work together to control the body's responses to stimuli. Explain how these systems work together and complement each other.

13. Predict On a cool day, a particular lizard can regulate its body temperature by increasing secretion of a hormone that stimulates melanocytes. Melanocytes are cells that contain melanin, a pigment that darkens the lizard's skin. Predict how this color change will affect the lizard's body temperature. Describe a possible negative feedback mechanism that could prevent the lizard's body temperature from changing too much.

MATH AND ENGLISH LANGUAGE ARTS CONNECTIONS

Read the Connections box titled "Can You Hear Me Now?" in Section 10.4. Use evidence from the passage to answer questions 1–3.

1. Cite Textual Evidence Do you think whale songs are instinctive or learned? Explain your answer and argue whether it is advantageous or disadvantageous when whales encounter loud noise from human activities.

2. Cite Textual Evidence What body system is responsible for producing the hormone that serves as evidence that whales experience stress from the noise of human activities? Explain how these hormones function in the body.

3. Reason Abstractly and Quantitatively Use the information in the article to construct a graph modeling whale hormone levels between June 2000 and June 2002. How do you think this curve would compare to other periods of decreased or increased shipping levels, such as during a pandemic or an economic boom? How could you test your hypothesis?

4. Write Explanatory Text Male tungara frogs adjust their calls in response to the presence or absence of bats. Explain why they do this and describe a situation in which these frogs would be highly likely to give conspicuous calls at a high frequency.

▶ REVISIT RAINFOREST CONNECTIONS

Gather Evidence In this chapter, you have seen how animal systems interact to help them perform specific functions essential for life. In Section 10.2, you learned that most animals can be organized into cells, tissues, organs, and organ systems. In Section 10.3, you learned that these organ systems work together to perform the functions animals need to maintain homeostasis. In Section 10.4, you learned that group behaviors often enhance an individual's and species' likelihood to survive and reproduce.

1. Choose an animal that inhabits a tropical rainforest and lives in a social group. Describe one behavior this species exhibits and explain how it aids in the species' overall survival.

2. What other questions do you have about the ways in which animals in the rainforest communicate? What else do you need to know to construct an explanation about the systems that allow animals to survive, grow, reproduce, and respond to their rainforest habitat?

INTERACTIONS IN LIVING SYSTEMS

CHAPTER 8
DIVERSITY OF LIVING SYSTEMS

How are the characteristics of an organism related to its place in an ecosystem?

- Phylogenetic analyses have allowed scientists to understand relatedness between species on the basis of genetic sequences.

- Genetic evidence has expanded the number of known bacteria and archaea species.

- Protists are incredibly diverse. Many protists are more closely related to plants and animals than to each other.

- Fungi participate in a wide range of ecological roles, ranging from symbioses that encourage plant growth and communication to parasitic relationships that cause other organisms to spread their spores.

- Viruses have DNA or RNA genomes surrounded by a protein capsid. Viruses require host cell processes to replicate their genomes and make proteins to assemble more viruses.

CHAPTER 9
PLANT SYSTEMS

How do plants respond to changes in the environment?

- Plant organization includes cells, simple and complex tissues, organs, and organ systems. Plants are categorized as vascular or nonvascular based on whether they have transport systems.

- Plants alternate between sporophyte and gametophyte generations.

- Passive and active mechanisms drive the movement of fluids through vascular tissue. Osmosis and active transport drive the movement of sugars through phloem cells.

- Plant hormones control growth, development, and homeostasis. Environmental cues trigger movement and other responses.

CHAPTER 10
ANIMAL SYSTEMS

How do animals respond to changes in the environment?

- All animals are multicellular eukaryotes. Most animals have specialized cells, tissues, and organ systems to carry out specialized functions.

- Negative and positive feedback loops help to maintain homeostasis.

- Behavior allows animals to respond to changes in their environment. All behaviors have costs and benefits. Social behaviors such as living in a group help to increase an individual's and species' chances to survive and reproduce.

Go Online	**VIRTUAL INVESTIGATION**

Communication in the Rainforest
How do rainforest species communicate?
Explore a Puerto Rican rainforest and discover the many species that live there.

HOW DO RAINFOREST SPECIES COMMUNICATE?

Argue From Evidence In this unit, you learned about the various categories into which scientists group living things based on similarities between the structures and systems their bodies employ for survival. An organism's survival in an ecosystem involves relationships, characteristics, and behaviors that communicate information about threats and resource availability. Organisms interact with their own species, but they also communicate with organisms of other species using sensory signals such as visual cues, sound, and smell, as well as by exchanging chemicals.

The El Yunque National Forest is the only tropical rainforest in the U.S. National Forest System. Its location on the small island of Puerto Rico exposes this forest to the recurring threat of hurricanes that can disrupt its ecosystems. In 2017, Hurricane Maria hit the island as a Category 4 storm with wind speeds as high as 250 kilometers per hour (155 mph) and a 1.5-meter (5-ft.) storm surge. Some scientists predict that recovery in the hardest hit areas of the rainforest will take a century.

National Geographic Explorer Dr. Nicole Colón Carrión studies how symbiotic fungi can support the restoration of the native forest. While fungi are not always visible, they send signals into the environment and communicate with other organisms by releasing chemical compounds. Some fungi form networks between the roots of different trees.

Endophytic fungi colonize plant tissues and produce substances that stimulate the plant's growth, improve its resistance to drought, and protect it from predators and pathogens. In turn, the plants provide the fungi with nutrients they need to grow and survive.

C **Claim** Make a claim about how interactions between rainforest organisms of different species transmit resources or information that help each species survive.

E **Evidence** Use the evidence you gathered throughout the unit to support your claim.

R **Reasoning** To help illustrate your reasoning, develop a model that illustrates how the organisms' systems enable them to interact.

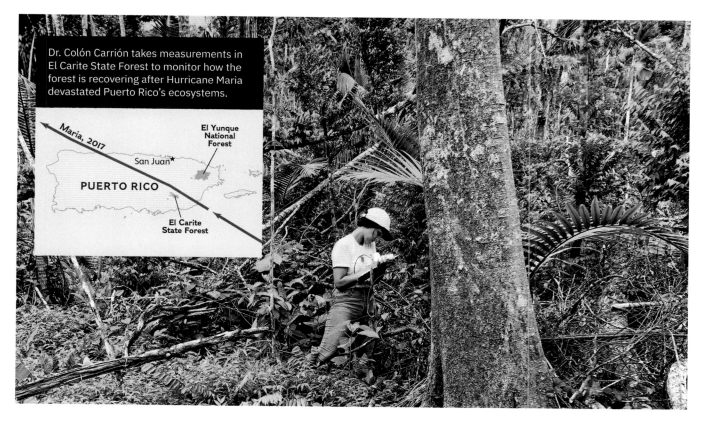

Dr. Colón Carrión takes measurements in El Carite State Forest to monitor how the forest is recovering after Hurricane Maria devastated Puerto Rico's ecosystems.

Maria, 2017

El Yunque National Forest

San Juan

PUERTO RICO

El Carite State Forest

GENETICS

A transmission electron microscopic image from a sample of the first U.S. case of COVID-19 coronavirus. The viral particles look like round structures in this cross section of their spherical form.

Severe acute respiratory syndrome coronavirus 2 (SARS-CoV-2) causes respiratory illness, along with a wide range of other symptoms, in an infection known as COVID-19. The virus spreads easily from human to human through the air. Its first known infection of a human occurred in December 2019. In March 2020, COVID-19 was declared a pandemic by the World Health Organization. In just over two years after SARS-CoV-2 emerged in the human population, more than 522 million patients contracted COVID-19, leading to more than six million deaths.

When scientists sequenced the SARS-CoV-2 genome in January 2020, they discovered the virus had a large RNA genome. The genome was similar to the SARS-CoV-1 virus, which had previously caused a much smaller global outbreak in 2003.

HOW CAN WE SLOW THE SPREAD OF A VIRUS?

In this unit, you will learn how scientific and technological advancement can help us better understand and respond to a viral pandemic.

CHAPTER 11
DNA, RNA, AND PROTEINS

CHAPTER 12
GENETIC VARIATION AND HEREDITY

CHAPTER 13
GENETIC TECHNOLOGIES

UNIT VIDEO 1 Go online to learn more about coronaviruses and COVID-19.

BLOOD DRIVE
VACCINATING VAMPIRE BATS IN THE PERUVIAN MOUNTAINS

It's the stuff legends are made of—a mammal that comes out at night to feed only after the moon sets. It flies flawlessly through the complete darkness, guided by sound and smell. Near a farm, it lands silently and skulks along the ground on long legs. When the bat finds its preferred prey, such as a cow, it hops or flies onto the cow's back, holding on tightly as the cow switches its tail and jerks its head around trying to dislodge the intruder, but to no avail. The bat's infrared sensors tell it where warm blood flows most closely to the surface of the skin. The cow, no longer bothered, goes back to sleep and the vampire bat prepares to feed.

Infectious disease ecologist Dr. Daniel Streicker marvels at how perfectly adapted the vampire bat is to its lifestyle of feeding only on blood. The mammal does not suck blood through its teeth as popularized by vampire folklore. Instead, its triangular teeth are tiny and as sharp as needles. Prey animals barely feel a pinch when a bat cuts a small divot in the skin. As the bat laps up blood, its tongue secretes an anticoagulant that prevents the blood from clotting. When it finishes feeding, the bat simply flies away.

Although Streicker admires the vampire bat's adaptations, he's more interested in studying them as a reservoir for the rabies virus. In biology, a reservoir is an organism that hosts a pathogen and spreads it to other species. For all mammals, the virus that causes rabies (*Rabies lyssavirus*) is deadly. Rabies has existed for thousands of years with no known cure once symptoms set in. Streicker researches vampire bats in Peru, where most colonies live in caves, mines, buildings, bridges, and wells. Infected vampire bats feeding on livestock create a perfect route for the virus to spread.

Streicker cites alarming data about the many thousands of livestock that die from rabies each year and the disturbing trend of the disease spreading to humans. In response, the Peruvian government and those of many other countries, from Mexico to Argentina, have killed vampire bats to reduce the spread. Their method involves a poison-laced petroleum jelly smeared on the back of captured bats. Treated bats return to the colony, where they are groomed by bats who ingest the poison and die. Streicker notes that little evidence exists that this method helps to control the spread of rabies. He proposes another solution—petroleum jelly mixed with an oral rabies vaccine instead of poison.

Streicker and his team have collected data that show where the disease might appear next. They found that rabies was moving in a steplike manner down one mountain valley and then down another. The patterns of old and new cases showed them how they could predict when rabies would reach an area so they could warn farmers. The farmers could then make decisions about getting the vaccine for their livestock and themselves.

Interest in the study of bats that harbor viruses resurfaced with the emergence of COVID-19, a virus thought to have crossed over from bats to humans. Streicker notes that many bats can live with viruses that are lethal in humans, such as SARS and Middle East respiratory syndrome (MERS). But, does bat tolerance of viruses result in genetic changes in viruses that cause them to be more dangerous to humans? That's something Streicker says needs more study. ▮

THINKING CRITICALLY

Research *Suggest ways that Streicker and other scientists might further study the question of whether viruses become more dangerous to humans after living in bat populations.*

Top: Although Dr. Daniel Streicker leads a lab in Glasgow, Scotland, he spends much of his time in the Amazon studying bats. **Bottom left:** Streicker has proposed that healthy virus-carrying bats could lead to the development of new treatments for humans. **Bottom right:** Vampire bats live in Central and South America, feeding mostly on the blood of livestock.

▶ **UNIT VIDEO 2** Go online to watch our interview with Streicker and learn more about his career and research.

CHAPTER 11

DNA, RNA, AND PROTEINS

The patterns on the wings of this *Heliconius erato notabilis* butterfly are the result of the different colors of individual scale cells.

11.1 GENETIC INFORMATION

11.2 REPLICATION, TRANSCRIPTION, AND TRANSLATION

11.3 REGULATING GENE EXPRESSION

The bright colors that make the patterns on this butterfly are determined by gene expression. The butterfly's genes ultimately code for proteins that affect the appearance of colors on its wings. The expression of those genes is a complex process that involves many factors.

Chapter 11 supports the NGSS Performance Expectations **HS-LS1-1** and **HS-LS3-1.**

CASE STUDY
EXPRESSING THE GENETIC CODE

HOW IS GENETIC INFORMATION TRANSFERRED AND REGULATED?

A butterfly's wing is covered with thousands of tiny scales that give the butterfly its characteristic colors and patterns. Each scale is produced by a single epithelial cell whose genes dictate the structure of the scale and the pigments produced. The scales' structures give some species their iridescent blue or purple colors, and pigments color the scales with shades and mixtures of red, yellow, and black. Scientists have long studied how these genes are expressed and what causes the similarities and differences in wing decorations between individual butterflies and between butterfly species.

Experiments performed in the early 1900s showed that temperature and light can influence gene expression during wing development. For example, when caterpillars of the genus *Vanessa* were placed under red, green, or blue light, differences in wing color emerged as the caterpillars matured into butterflies. Those that had been exposed to red light had brightly colored wings. However, exposure to green light resulted in dusky wings, and exposure to blue or no light resulted in pale wings.

Over a century has passed, yet questions remain about how and why butterfly wings vary. Scientists are now able to investigate them at much smaller scales due to major advancements in our knowledge of how gene expression works. In recent experiments with *Heliconius* butterflies, a genus that signals their toxicity to predators with dramatic multicolored wing patterns, researchers have identified four genes that control the color and pattern variations in all *Heliconius* species. Further investigation into how the same set of genes are expressed in different butterfly species may open up our understanding of how these species evolved.

Ask Questions *In this chapter, you will learn how the processes of gene expression transfer genetic information. As you read, generate questions about factors that affect these processes.*

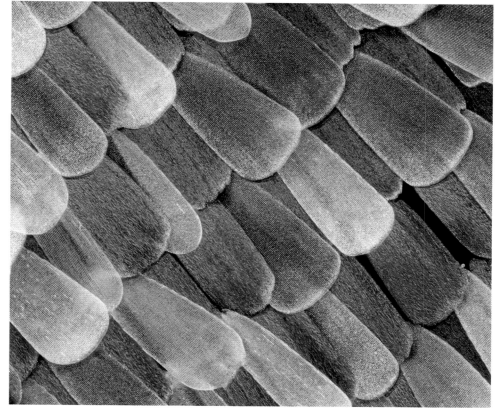

FIGURE 11-1
This light micrograph image shows the color and iridescence of scales on the wing of a butterfly.

KEY TERMS

gene
gene expression
replication
RNA
transcription
translation

GENETIC INFORMATION

Many sports competitions include multiple referees who watch the athletes from different angles and work together to make sure the game is played fairly. In a similar way, science questions are typically solved with input from multiple scientists from different research perspectives.

Infer *Consider what you already know about DNA. What different areas of science and techniques do you think might have been involved in understanding the structure and function of DNA molecules?*

DNA Discovery and Function

The substance that is now known as DNA was first described in 1869 by a Swiss biochemist named Friedrich Miescher. From experimentation, he knew it was not protein and that it was rich in nitrogen and phosphorus, but its function was unknown. Sixty years later, British bacteriologist Frederick Griffith unexpectedly found a clue to the function of DNA. Griffith was studying pneumonia-causing bacteria in the hope of making a vaccine. He isolated two strains (types) of the bacteria, one harmless (R), the other lethal (S). Griffith used R and S cells in a series of experiments testing their ability to cause pneumonia in mice (**Figure 11-2**). He discovered that heat destroyed the ability of lethal S bacteria to cause pneumonia, but it did not destroy their hereditary material. That hereditary material could be transferred from dead S cells to live R cells. The transformation was permanent and was passed onto offspring: even after several generations, descendants of transformed R cells retained the ability to kill mice.

FIGURE 11-2 ▽
Frederick Griffith discovered the hereditary information passed between two strains of bacteria (R and S).

Experiment 1
When R cells were injected into mice, the bacteria multiplied, but the mice remained healthy.

Conclusion
R cells were harmless.

Experiment 2
When S cells were injected into mice, the bacteria multiplied, and the mice died.

Conclusion
S cells caused mice to develop fatal pneumonia.

Experiment 3
When heat-killed S cells were injected into mice, the mice remained healthy.

Conclusion
Heat-killed S cells were harmless.

Experiment 4
When heat-killed S cells and live R cells were both injected into mice, the mice became fatally ill and contained living S cells.

Conclusion
The hereditary information from the heat-killed S cells was transferred to the R cells.

CONNECTIONS

WHAT IS IN A GENOME? It is well understood that genomes include the genes that code for important functions and the traits that make organisms unique. For example, the human genome has been estimated to include 20,000–30,000 genes, most coding for multiple proteins. (Learn how individual genes can code for more than one protein in Section 11.3.) Even with that tremendous number of genes, those coding sequences represent only about one percent of the three billion base pairs in the human genome.

What is the rest of the DNA in the genome doing? While most of the noncoding DNA does not have any understood function and has long been considered "junk DNA," scientists continue to work and improve our understanding of the origins and roles for those sequences. Here are some of the things scientists are learning about the rest of the human genome:

- **Small RNAs** Many parts of the genome code for small RNA molecules that are important for cell function and gene regulation. Some of these RNAs are introduced in Section 11.3.

- **Gene Expression Regulation** Specific DNA sequences in the genome regulate gene expression. A variety of sequences, including promoters, enhancers, silencers, and insulators have been identified to interact with other transcription factors described in Section 11.3.

- **Transposons** These sequences of DNA, which are hundreds or thousands of nucleotides long, can duplicate themselves and spontaneously "jump" between or within chromosomes.

- **Pseudogenes** These are copies of genes that are elsewhere in the genome and tend to be mutated so that they no longer produce a functional protein.

- **Endogenous Retroviruses** Scientists have estimated that 8 percent of the human genome originated with retroviruses. Retrovirus DNA is incorporated into the host genome as a part of the retroviral life cycle.

- **Telomeres** Sequences of DNA at the end of chromosomes are called telomeres. Each time a chromosome is copied, telomeres get shorter, which seems to be related to a shortening lifespan of a cell.

Canadian-American bacteriologist Oswald Avery and his colleagues subsequently sought to determine what substance "transformed" the R cells. They extracted lipid, protein, and nucleic acids from S cells and then used a process of elimination to determine which substance transformed bacteria. Treating the extract with enzymes that destroy lipids and proteins did not destroy the substance that transformed the cells. The researchers realized that the substance they were seeking must be a nucleic acid. That is, it must be either DNA or RNA. DNA-degrading enzymes destroyed the ability to transform cells, but RNA-degrading enzymes did not. Therefore, DNA must have been the substance that transformed the cells.

The result surprised the researchers, who, along with most other scientists, thought proteins passed genetic information from parent to offspring. They reasoned that individual characteristics are diverse, and proteins are the most diverse of all biological molecules. DNA was widely assumed to be too simple because it has only four nucleotide components. In 1944, after years of supporting results, scientists finally published the conclusion that DNA is the molecule that is inherited, passing genetic information from parent to offspring. Subsequent experiments by other scientists confirmed that the body cells of any individual of a species contain precisely the same amount of DNA.

CCC **Cause and Effect** *Describe at least one line of experimental evidence that confirmed DNA as the molecule that is inherited between generations of cells.*

Structure and Information in DNA, RNA, and Proteins

DNA DNA is the molecule that makes up the *genomes* of all living organisms and many viruses. DNA is a polymer of four types of nucleotides connected by a phosphate backbone (**Figure 11-3**). Each has a deoxyribose sugar, three phosphate groups, and a nitrogen-containing base: adenine (A), guanine (G), thymine (T), or cytosine (C). Nucleotide structure was understood in the early 1900s, but it took 50 years to puzzle out how they were arranged into the familiar double helix structure of DNA. British chemist Rosalind Franklin generated the breakthrough data, demonstrating the double helix and calculating the diameter and other characteristics of the molecule. These data ultimately led to American biologist James Watson and British biophysicist Francis Crick's first accurate model of DNA structure in 1953 (**Figure 11-3a**). Rosalind Franklin was not given credit for her contribution until after her death.

Notice how the two strands of DNA in **Figure 11-3b** match up. They are *complementary*. The base of each nucleotide on one strand pairs, through hydrogen bonding, with a partner base on the other. This base-pairing pattern (A to T, G to C) is the same in all molecules of DNA. How can just two kinds of base pairings give rise to the incredible diversity of traits we see among living things? Even though DNA is composed of only four nucleotides, the order in which the nucleotide bases occur along a strand— the DNA sequence—varies tremendously among species. DNA molecules can be hundreds of millions of nucleotides long, so their sequence can encode a massive amount of information. DNA sequence variation is the basis of traits that define species and distinguish individuals within a species.

FIGURE 11-3 ▼
A replica of the physical model generated by Watson and Crick (a) demonstrates how double-stranded DNA (b) twists into a double helix structure.

RNA The nature of information represented by the sequence of nucleotides in a DNA molecule occurs in hundreds or thousands of units called **genes**. The DNA sequence of a gene encodes (contains instructions for building) an RNA or protein product. Converting the information encoded by a gene into a product starts with RNA synthesis, which is called **transcription**. During transcription, enzymes use a strand of DNA as a template to synthesize a complementary strand of **RNA**.

Most of the RNA inside cells occurs in single strands that are similar in structure to single strands of DNA. For example, both are chains of four kinds of nucleotides. Like a DNA nucleotide, an RNA nucleotide consists of three phosphate groups, a sugar, and one of four bases. However, there are some differences (**Table 11-1**). The sugar in an RNA nucleotide is a ribose (ribonucleotide), and in a DNA nucleotide it is a deoxyribose (deoxyribonucleotide). Three bases—adenine, cytosine, and guanine— occur in both RNA and DNA nucleotides, but the fourth base differs between the two molecules. In RNA, the fourth base is uracil (U), which is only slightly different from the fourth base in DNA (thymine, T).

TABLE 11-1. Comparing DNA and RNA

Characteristic	DNA	RNA
form	double-stranded double helix	most are single stranded
monomers	deoxyribonucleotides	ribonucleotides
sugar	deoxyribose	ribose
bases	adenine (A), guanine (G), cytosine (C), thymine (T)	adenine (A), guanine (G), cytosine (C), uracil (U)
base pairing	A-T, G-C	A-U, G-C
variations	none	rRNA, tRNA, mRNA, and more
function	stores genetic information	protein synthesis, carries information, other roles

Small differences in structure between DNA and RNA give rise to very different functions. While DNA's critical function is to store a cell's genetic information, a cell makes several kinds of RNA, each with a different function. Three types of RNA have roles in protein synthesis, which will be detailed in the next section. Ribosomal RNA (rRNA) is the main component of ribosomes, which are the organelles that combine amino acids into polypeptide chains. Transfer RNA (tRNA) delivers the amino acids to ribosomes, one by one, in the order specified by a messenger RNA (mRNA). mRNA was named for its function as the "messenger" between DNA (stored in the nucleus) and the proteins encoded by it (synthesized in the cytoplasm).

CCC **Structure and Function** *RNA and DNA have very slight structural differences that generally make RNA strands less stable and more likely to participate in chemical reactions than DNA strands. How is this reflected in the typical functions of each molecule?*

FIGURE 11-4 ▼
At its simplest primary structure, a protein is a chain of peptides. Those peptides interact to form complex secondary and tertiary structures that are required to carry out reactions in cells.

Protein As described in Chapter 5, proteins are composed of chains of amino acids, known as polypeptides (**Figure 11-4**). Each amino acid in a protein chain is encoded by a three-nucleotide sequence on an mRNA. mRNA guides the assembly of the amino acid chain in a process of protein synthesis called **translation**. Proteins form complex structures and combine with other molecules to perform most of the work in cells.

primary structure

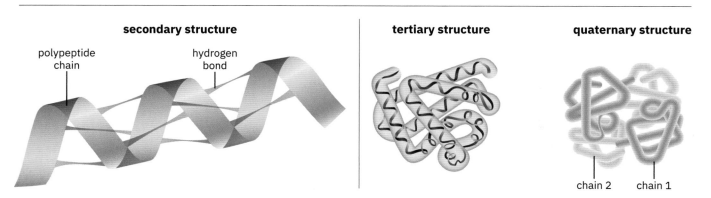

Information Transfer

Most genetic information in living organisms is decoded and transferred in the process of gene expression. In **gene expression**, information is transferred as the sequences of the DNA genome are transcribed into an mRNA intermediary. The mRNA is then translated to a protein product that performs functions in the cell (**Figure 11-5**).

However, the transfer of information in the cell is much more complicated than just the one path of gene expression. In this chapter, you will learn how RNAs serve many additional important functions in cells. You will also learn how DNA and protein structures serve complex functions beyond just being a sequence of informational nucleotides or amino acids.

FIGURE 11-5 ▶
In a typical model of gene expression, the information from DNA is transferred to RNA in transcription. That information in the RNA is then transferred into a protein through translation.

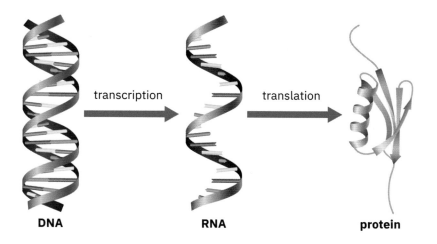

Figure 11-6 shows the ways we know genetic information can be copied and transferred. In normal cell processes, information is transferred by DNA **replication** (the copying of DNA), transcription of DNA to RNA, and translation of RNA to protein.

Additional paths for information transfer shown in the figure either have only been generated in special laboratory experiments outside living cells, or are used by infectious agents. For example, viruses exploit a variety of mechanisms and encode their own proteins that perform unique functions most living cells are not capable of, such as reverse transcription and RNA replication. *Prions* are infectious forms of normal cellular proteins that can multiply by inducing normal proteins to misfold and become infectious.

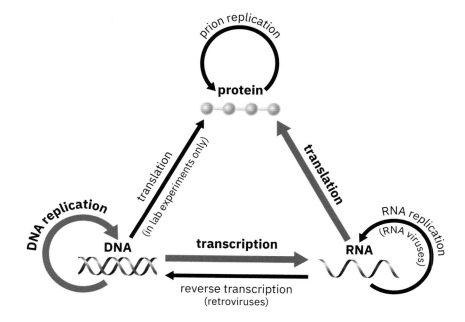

FIGURE 11-6
DNA replication, RNA transcription, and protein translation are emphasized with blue arrows to indicate they are the most important transfers of information in biological systems.

SEP **Use a Model** *How does the model in **Figure 11-6** demonstrate the transfer of information from DNA to protein in living cells? Notice there are no arrows pointing out from protein. What do you think that might mean?*

11.1 REVIEW

1. **Relate** A small segment of one DNA strand is made up of sugar, phosphate, adenine, and cytosine. Which components make up the matching segment in the second strand? Select all correct answers.

   A. adenine   C. guanine   E. sugar

   B. cytosine   D. phosphate   F. thymine

2. **Identify** Which processes are involved in normal gene expression? Select all correct answers.

   A. DNA replication   D. transcription

   B. prion replication   E. translation

   C. RNA replication

3. **Distinguish** Identify the type of RNA that fulfills each role.

   • assemble amino acids into polypeptide chains

   • deliver amino acids to ribosomes in a particular order

   • guide sequence of polypeptides during protein synthesis

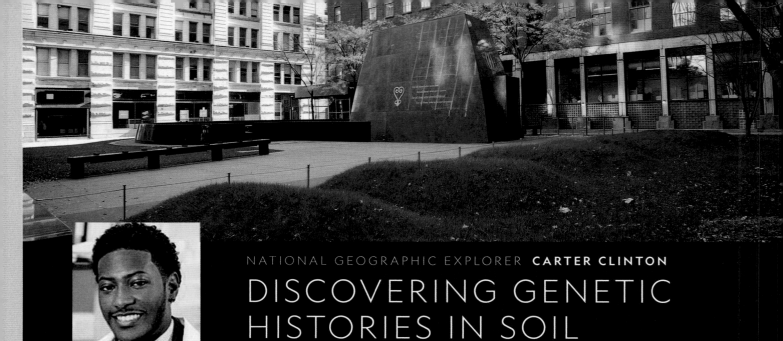

DISCOVERING GENETIC HISTORIES IN SOIL

Dr. Carter Clinton works to identify and analyze DNA from historic samples, to better understand the past and improve present disparities in genetic data.

▶ **VIDEO 11-1** Go online to learn more about Clinton's research and motivations.

It is dusk on a November evening in 1847. The travelers move swiftly but quietly through the brambles, avoiding the shrubs' prickly thorns as best they can. It's taken them a few weeks to reach this Maryland forest from the South Carolina plantation where they had been enslaved. They stop at the base of a huge tree, whose hollowed trunk provides shelter and traps the heat of a small fire so that they might rest before continuing northward.

Fast forward to a sunny day in November, 170 years later. Biological anthropologist Dr. Carter Clinton pauses before the very same huge tree that is hollowed out at the base. Clinton has studied the movements of people on the Underground Railroad and knows a location like this would have provided needed cover. He thinks that many people may have stopped here for the night, so it may be a good spot to collect DNA they left behind.

Back in the lab, Clinton extracts the DNA from the soil and then performs next generation sequencing to determine the genomic sequences isolated from these samples. From these data, he can tell where an individual was from as well as hair color, face shape, age, sex, and other details. Computer algorithms also tell him about how the people lived, and possibly how they died.

Clinton is continuing similar work in what he describes as the most out-of-the-ordinary project he's ever worked on: sampling DNA from the New York African Burial Ground in Lower Manhattan. First discovered in 1991, the New York City burial grounds were located about 8 meters below the surface and stretched over an area equivalent to five football fields. An estimated 15,000 individuals are buried there, more than half of them children. Researchers excavated 419 individuals, carefully cataloging each sample of soil gathered. Over six months, Clinton's team sifted and analyzed the samples, obtaining small particles on which to perform DNA analysis. Eventually, they were successful in detecting genomic DNA in burial soil samples. From those DNA analyses, Clinton was able to identify human-associated bacteria, including disease-causing bacteria that might have been a cause of death. He is currently working to identify human DNA in the samples. He hopes to use his research to address health disparities in African Americans and fill in data gaps for African-descended people in genomic databases. To do so, he'll keep digging for answers.

THINKING CRITICALLY

Ask Questions *Pose a question or problem that might be answerable using techniques similar to Clinton's research on detecting and analyzing DNA in soil.*

KEY TERMS

anticodon
codon
DNA polymerase
primer
RNA polymerase

REPLICATION, TRANSCRIPTION, AND TRANSLATION

The information in DNA is copied as cells replicate, slightly changed in transcription from DNA to RNA, and entirely recoded in the process of translation. The name for each process reflects a critical aspect of how the process occurs.

Explain *Generate an analogy to explain the general processes of replication, transcription, and translation.*

DNA Replication

As discussed in Sections 7.1 and 7.2, when a cell undergoes mitosis to reproduce, it divides (**Figure 11-7**). The two descendant cells must inherit a complete and accurate copy of their parent's genome, or they will not function like the parent cell. In preparation for division, the cell copies its chromosomes so that it contains two complete sets: one for each of its future offspring. The copying process, which is called *replication*, ensures the continuity of genetic information from one generation to the next.

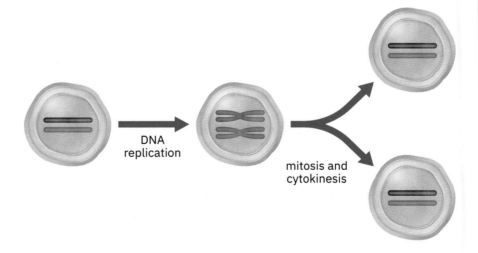

FIGURE 11-7
DNA must be replicated for cells to divide and pass on genetic information to offspring.

DNA replication

mitosis and cytokinesis

Separation of the DNA Strand Before DNA replication, a chromosome consists of one molecule of DNA—one double helix consisting of two complementary DNA strands (**Figure 11-8**). The replication process is triggered when an initiator complex assembles and begins to unwind the double helix. An enzyme called helicase breaks the hydrogen bonds that hold the two DNA strands together, forming a replication bubble as shown in **Figure 11-9**.

FIGURE 11-8
In DNA, C (cytosine) pairs with G (guanine) and A (adenine) pairs with T (thymine).

DNA C C T C T T T C A G C C T C T

DNA G G A G A A G T C G G A G A

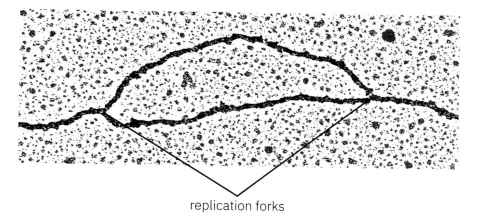

FIGURE 11-9
This colored transmission electron microscope image shows DNA from a HeLa cell undergoing DNA replication. Replication forks, where the DNA unwinds to allow new strands to be formed, are indicated.

replication forks

Assembling a New DNA Strand **Figure 11-10** shows many of the important factors involved in DNA replication. When the helicase separates the strands for replication, an enzyme attaches to each DNA strand to build a short sequence of nucleotides on which replication starts. This short sequence of nucleotides is called a **primer**. Multiple primers attach in different places along the original, or template, DNA strands.

DNA polymerases assemble around the primers and attach free-floating nucleotides to the new nucleotide chain. At each position, the nucleotide added has a nitrogen base complementary to the exposed base on the template strand: A (adenine) to T (thymine) and C (cytosine) to G (guanine). Hydrogen bonds connect each pair of complementary bases as DNA replication proceeds, ultimately producing two new double-stranded DNA molecules from one. The DNA sequence of each new strand is complementary to its template strand.

The unwinding of the DNA strand happens in both directions at the same time. Likewise, replication happens at both forks (both ends of the replication bubble) at the same time. On the leading strand, DNA replication begins at the primer and proceeds in one direction, building a continuous strand. On the lagging strand, replication occurs in segments in the opposite direction. On the lagging strand, primers attach at multiple locations, so multiple molecules of DNA polymerases can add nucleotides to each primer at the same time. The enzyme *DNA ligase* seals any gaps on the lagging strand, so the new DNA strands are continuous.

CCC **Structure and Function** *Identify the leading and lagging strand on the diagram in* **Figure 11-10**. *How do you know which strand is which?*

▶ **VIDEO**

VIDEO 11-2 Go online to see how molecular data has been used to model DNA replication.

FIGURE 11-10 ▼
At a replication fork, the helicase enzyme unwinds DNA. New DNA is generated as the strands of the original double helix are replicated.

primer

nucleotide

helicase

DNA polymerase

DNA ligase

Transcription

DNA stores the information for multiple forms of RNA (mRNA, rRNA, and tRNA). Transcription is the process by which information encoded in a gene, or DNA segment, is used to synthesize an RNA molecule. Similar to DNA replication, during transcription, a strand of DNA functions as the template for synthesis of a new RNA molecule. For RNA transcription, slightly different base-pairing rules are followed, compared with DNA replication, because uracil is substituted for thymine (**Figure 11-11**). Cytosine (C) pairs with guanine (G), and adenine (A) pairs with uracil (U). A nucleotide can be added to the end of a growing RNA molecule only if the base pairs with the corresponding nucleotide of the template DNA. Thus, the new RNA is complementary in sequence to the DNA template.

FIGURE 11-11
In RNA, C (cytosine) pairs with G (guanine), and A (adenine) pairs with U (uracil).

RNA C C U C U U C A G C C U C U

DNA G G A G A A G T C G G A G A

In contrast to DNA replication, only a defined region of the DNA strand is used as a template for transcription, not the entire strand. So, only the particular segment of DNA is transcribed when it is needed. Also, transcription produces a single strand of RNA, not a double strand as with DNA replication.

Similar in function to DNA polymerases, enzymes called **RNA polymerases** are used in transcription. A regulatory site, called a *promoter*, is a short DNA sequence that serves as a binding site for RNA polymerase.

Transcription begins when proteins that recognize a promoter help RNA polymerase bind to it (**Figure 11-12**). After binding, the polymerase starts moving along the DNA, unwinding the double helix to reveal the template DNA sequence. The enzyme adds free RNA nucleotides into a chain, in the order determined by the DNA sequence.

FIGURE 11-12
RNA polymerase binds a promoter sequence in the DNA. The DNA is unwound, and the polymerase adds nucleotides to form a new RNA strand as it moves along the gene sequence.

RNA polymerase

gene

promoter sequence in DNA

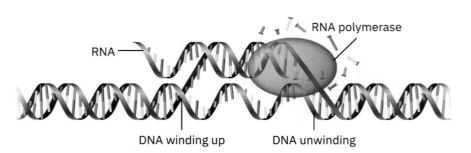

RNA

RNA polymerase

DNA winding up   DNA unwinding

When the RNA polymerase reaches the end of the gene region, it disconnects from the DNA template and the newly synthesized RNA strand. The DNA template re-forms a double helix, and the RNA product is processed according to its function (usually mRNA, rRNA, or tRNA). Messenger RNA (mRNA) is the molecule that codes for a protein to be produced. Unlike the model in **Figure 11-12**, many RNA molecules can be made at once from a single gene, as shown in **Figure 11-13**.

SEP **Construct an Explanation** *Describe the similarities and differences between replication and transcription.*

RNA molecules

DNA molecule

FIGURE 11-13
This electron micrograph shows RNA molecules being transcribed in huge numbers, with individual genes being transcribed multiple times simultaneously.

Translation

The information encoded by a gene is ultimately translated by ribosomes, using mRNA to direct synthesis of a polypeptide, or protein. This process is called translation. Translation occurs in the cytoplasm of all cells where there are many free amino acids, tRNAs, and ribosomal subunits available to participate in the process. Often, several ribosomes attach to a single mRNA to translate new protein molecules at one time (**Figure 11-14**).

mRNA Coding Messenger RNA (mRNA), transfer RNA (tRNA), and ribosomal RNA (rRNA) interact to translate DNA's information into a protein. mRNA is essentially a temporary, abridged copy of a gene. Its job is to carry the gene's protein-building information to the other two types of RNA during translation. The protein-building information carried by an mRNA is a sequence of genetic "words" that occur one after another along its length. Like the words of a sentence, a series of these genetic words can form a meaningful parcel of information—in this case, a sequence of amino acids that constitutes the primary structure of a protein.

▼
VIRAL SPREAD

Gather Evidence *SARS-CoV-2 is a virus with a single-stranded RNA genome that resembles a messenger RNA to a host cell. The genome encodes genes for the structural proteins to assemble new viruses as well as some additional enzymes. What molecules and processes does it need from the host cell to make new viruses? What additional enzymes do you think it needs to provide to replicate itself?*

FIGURE 11-14
This electron micrograph shows multiple ribosomes translating single mRNA molecules at one time. These are known as polysomes.

Each genetic "word" in an mRNA is three bases long, and each is a code—a **codon**—for a particular amino acid. The sequence of bases in a triplet determines which amino acid the codon specifies (**Figure 11-15**). For instance, the codon UUU specifies the amino acid phenylalanine, and UUA specifies leucine. With four possible bases (G, A, U, or C) in each of the three positions of a codon, there are a total of 64 mRNA codons. Collectively, the 64 codons constitute the genetic code. These codons specify a total of 20 naturally occurring amino acids, so some amino acids are specified by more than one codon. For instance, the amino acid tyrosine (tyr) is specified by two codons: UAU and UAC.

Other codons signal the beginning and end of a protein-coding sequence. The first AUG in an mRNA almost always serves as the signal to start translation. AUG is also the codon for methionine, so methionine is almost always the first amino acid in new polypeptides. The codons UAA, UAG, and UGA do not specify an amino acid. These are signals that stop translation, so they are called stop codons. A stop codon marks the end of the protein-coding sequence in an mRNA.

FIGURE 11-15 ▽
This chart describes which three-letter RNA codons match each of the 20 naturally occurring amino acids, as well as the stop codons that end translation.

		second base of codon							
		U		**C**		**A**		**G**	
U	UUU	phenylalanine (phe)	UCU	serine (ser)	UAU	tyrosine (tyr)	UGU	cysteine (cys)	U
	UUC		UCC		UAC		UGC		C
	UUA	leucine (leu)	UCA		UAA	STOP	UGA	STOP	A
	UUG		UCG		UAG		UGG	tryptophan (trp)	G
C	CUU	leucine (leu)	CCU	proline (pro)	CAU	histidine (his)	CGU	arginine (arg)	U
	CUC		CCC		CAC		CGC		C
	CUA		CCA		CAA	glutamine (gln)	CGA		A
	CUG		CCG		CAG		CGG		G
A	AUU	isoleucine (ile)	ACU	threonine (thr)	AAU	asparagine (asn)	AGU	serine (ser)	U
	AUC		ACC		AAC		AGC		C
	AUA		ACA		AAA	lysine (lys)	AGA	arginine (arg)	A
	AUG	methionine (met)	ACG		AAG		AGG		G
G	GUU	valine (val)	GCU	alanine (ala)	GAU	aspartic acid (asp)	GGU	glycine (gly)	U
	GUC		GCC		GAC		GGC		C
	GUA		GCA		GAA	glutamic acid (glu)	GGA		A
	GUG		GCG		GAG		GGG		G

first base of codon → (left side)
third base of codon → (right side)

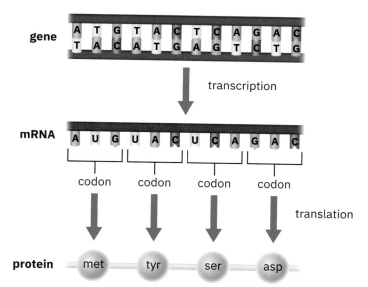

gene

transcription

mRNA

codon   codon   codon   codon

translation

protein   met   tyr   ser   asp

FIGURE 11-16
Use this model to trace the information in the DNA sequence as it is transcribed into an mRNA and then translated into an amino acid sequence of a protein.

SEP **Use a Model** *The DNA strand that is used to make an mRNA molecule is often referred to as the template strand. The other strand that is similar to the mRNA sequence is often called the complementary strand. In* **Figure 11-16**, *which DNA strand is the template strand and which is the complementary strand?*

tRNA and rRNA Codons occur one after the next in an mRNA. When the mRNA is translated, the order of its codons determines the order of amino acids in the resulting polypeptide. Thus, the DNA sequence of a gene is transcribed into the nucleotide sequence of an mRNA, which is in turn translated into an amino acid sequence (**Figure 11-16**).

Ribosomes interact with transfer RNAs (tRNAs) to translate the sequence of codons in an mRNA into a polypeptide. Each tRNA has two attachment sites. The first is an **anticodon**, which is a triplet of nucleotides that base-pairs with an mRNA codon. The other attachment site binds to an amino acid—the one specified by the codon. Transfer RNAs with different anticodons carry different amino acids. During translation, these tRNAs deliver amino acids to a ribosome. As the amino acids are delivered, the ribosome joins them into a new polypeptide.

A ribosome has two subunits, one large and one small (**Figure 11-17**). Each subunit consists of rRNA and associated structural proteins. During translation, a large and small ribosomal subunit come together to form a complete ribosome on an mRNA. Ribosomal RNA is one example of RNA with enzymatic activity. The rRNA components of a ribosome (not the protein components) catalyze the formation of peptide bonds that connect amino acids during protein synthesis.

Go Online **SIMULATION**

Gene Expression Go online to step through the processes of transcription and translation.

ribosome

large subunit

small subunit

binding sites

tRNA

met — amino acid

U A C

anticodon

FIGURE 11-17
The ribosome is a complex molecular machine made out of many proteins and RNAs. tRNAs match corresponding sequences of the mRNA sequence at binding sites within the ribosome.

FIGURE 11-18 ▼

The process of translation can be described as a series of
steps that repeats, adding peptides to the chain until a stop codon
is reached and translation is terminated.

1 Ribosomal subunits
and an initiator tRNA
converge on an mRNA at
a start codon. A second
tRNA binds to the
second codon.

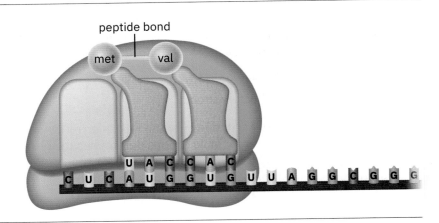

first amino acid
of polypeptide — met

initiator tRNA

start codon in mRNA

2 A peptide bond forms
between the first two
amino acids.

peptide bond

met — val

3 The first tRNA is
released and the
ribosome moves to the
next codon. A third tRNA
binds to the third codon.

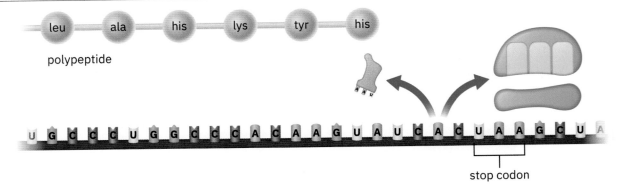

met — val

leu

polypeptide

leu — ala — his — lys — tyr — his

stop codon

Steps of Translation In a eukaryotic cell, ribosome biosynthesis occurs in the nucleus, and then subunits are transported through nuclear pores into the cytoplasm where translation occurs. In a prokaryotic cell, translation may begin on an mRNA even as it is still being transcribed.

▶ **VIDEO**

VIDEO 11-3 Go online to view a simulation of translation that is based on molecular modeling data.

- Translation begins when a small ribosomal subunit binds to an mRNA, and the anticodon of an *initiator tRNA* base pairs with the mRNA's first AUG codon. Then, a large ribosomal subunit joins the small subunit.

- The complex of molecules is now ready to carry out protein synthesis (**Figure 11-18**). The ribosome moves along the mRNA and assembles a polypeptide. Most initiator tRNAs carry methionine, so the first amino acid of most new polypeptide chains is methionine. Another tRNA joins the complex when its anticodon pairs with the second codon in the mRNA, bringing the second amino acid. The ribosome then catalyzes formation of a peptide bond between the first and second amino acids.

- As the ribosome moves to the next codon, it releases the first tRNA. Another tRNA brings the third amino acid to the complex as its anticodon base-pairs with the third codon of the mRNA. A peptide bond forms between the second and third amino acids.

- The second tRNA is released, and the ribosome moves to the next codon. Another tRNA brings the fourth amino acid to the complex as its anticodon base-pairs with the fourth codon of the mRNA, adding another peptide to the chain.

- The amino acid chain continues to elongate. Translation terminates when the ribosome reaches a stop codon in the mRNA. The mRNA and the polypeptide detach from the ribosome, and the ribosomal subunits separate from each other. Translation is now complete.

CCC **Structure and Function** *Ribosomes add as many as 20 amino acids per second. While the main functions of the ribosome are all performed by RNA, the process would proceed much more slowly without the protein components of the ribosome. How do you think those structures might contribute to the efficiency of the ribosome?*

11.2 REVIEW

1. **Analyze** For each segment of template DNA strand, determine the corresponding sequence of nucleotides that the DNA polymerase enzyme will synthesize during DNA replication.

   - TGA
   - CCT
   - CTC
   - GAC

2. **Analyze** For each segment of mRNA, determine the original sequence of nucleotides in the DNA strand before transcription.

   - ACU
   - GAA
   - GAG
   - CUG

3. **Contrast** Label each statement as being true for replication, transcription, or both.

   - Polymerase enzymes carry out this process.
   - This process produces one strand of nucleic acids.
   - Bases involved include the four nucleic acids A, C, G, T.
   - At least one part of a strand of nucleic acids serves as a template.

4. **Evaluate** Use **Figure 11-15** to convert the codons into amino acids.

   - ACU
   - GGA
   - GAG
   - CUG

MODELING DNA REPLICATION, TRANSCRIPTION, AND TRANSLATION

SEP **Asking Questions and Defining Problems** How can replication, transcription, or translation be demonstrated?

Modeling the process of DNA replication, transcription, and translation are good ways to gain a better understanding of these processes as well as to explain them to others. In this activity, you will work with a model of DNA and related components and determine a way to demonstrate DNA replication, transcription, or translation using your model.

Suggested Materials

- camera, tablet, computer
- craft paper, poster paper
- modeling clay, craft sticks, building blocks
- pipe cleaners, bendable wire
- scissors, glue, transparent tape

Procedure

1. Determine which one of these processes you will demonstrate: DNA replication, transcription, or translation.

2. Think about the steps involved in your process, and create a list of the components that are necessary for your demonstration. Not all details of the process need to be represented. Make a note of any steps you simplified or left out because of limited time and materials.

3. Working from your list, decide on the method and items you will use to demonstrate your process. Ideas include, but are not limited to, acting out the process with props, recording a video, or creating a stop-action animation.

4. Create your demonstration of the process you picked, either DNA replication, translation, or transcription. Include narration, if possible, or captions that explain the process.

5. Once you are done, clean up and return unused materials to the materials station.

Results and Analysis

1. **Identify** For the process you have chosen, what components are necessary in order to demonstrate your chosen process?

2. **Sequence** Describe the sequence of events represented by your demonstration.

3. **Evaluate** Consider the strengths and limitations of the model you presented. Which components and events of the process were you able to demonstrate most clearly? What elements or events did you choose to simplify or omit?

4. **Construct an Explanation** How does the process you demonstrated work with the other two processes to accomplish gene expression?

REGULATING GENE EXPRESSION

Pilots have many ways to adjust an airplane's speed in the air. They can adjust the engine's thrust, or they can change altitude and direction to fly with or against prevailing winds. An airplane's wings can change shape to increase or reduce drag through the air. Similarly, cells have many different mechanisms to speed up, slow down, or otherwise modify gene expression.

Infer *Considering what you know about gene expression, how do you think a cell is likely to increase or decrease the expression of particular genes?*

KEY TERMS

epigenetic
exon
intron
operon
RNA interference
transcription factor

Gene Expression Regulation in Prokaryotes

Although most prokaryotes do not have the need to express different genes for the purposes of differentiation, they do have a life cycle and the need to rapidly respond to changes in the environment. Prokaryotes respond to environmental changes by adjusting gene expression, mainly by changing the amount of transcription. For example, when a preferred nutrient becomes available, a bacterium begins transcribing genes whose products allow the cell to use the nutrient. When the nutrient is no longer available, transcription of those genes stops. Thus, the cell does not waste energy and resources producing gene products that are not needed.

In bacteria, genes that are used together often occur in a group, one after the next on the chromosome. One *promoter* sequence precedes the group, so all of the genes are transcribed together, producing a single RNA strand. Their transcription can be controlled in a single step. Typically, this control involves a *repressor* protein that can bind to an *operator* sequence in the DNA. A group of genes together with a promoter and one or more operators are collectively called an **operon**. Operons were discovered in bacteria, but they also occur in archaea and eukaryotes, including individual cells within multicellular organisms.

The *lac* Operon *Escherichia coli* (*E. coli*) bacteria live in the gut of mammals, consuming nutrients that travel past as food moves through the intestines. Their carbohydrate of choice is glucose, but they can make use of other sugars such as lactose, a disaccharide in milk.

The *lac* operon includes three genes that encode proteins involved in lactose metabolism and a promoter flanked by two operators (**Figure 11-19**). Bacteria make these three proteins only when lactose is present.

CHAPTER INVESTIGATION

Regulation of Gene Expression
How can genes be expressed and regulated in organisms?
Go online to explore this chapter's hands-on investigation to study how gene expression can be regulated in the bacteria *Serratia marcescens*.

lac operon in the *E. coli* chromosome

FIGURE 11-19
This *lac* operon model includes three genes under the control of one promoter and two operators.

20a Lactose absent

In the absence of lactose, a repressor binds to the two operators. Binding prevents RNA polymerase from attaching to the promoter, so transcription of the operon genes does not occur.

repressor protein

gene 1   gene 2   gene 3

20b Lactose present

When lactose is present, some is converted to a form that binds to the repressor such that it releases the operators.

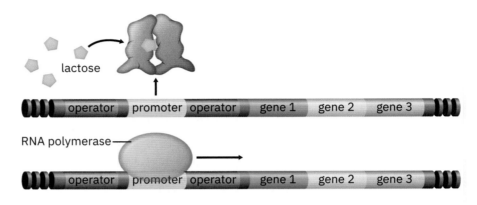

lactose

operator   promoter   operator   gene 1   gene 2   gene 3

RNA polymerase

RNA polymerase can now attach to the promoter and transcribe the operon genes.

operator   promoter   operator   gene 1   gene 2   gene 3

FIGURE 11-20
This model of the *lac* operon demonstrates how a repressor protein works to regulate expression of genes, depending on the presence or absence of lactose molecules.

When lactose is not present, a repressor binds to the two operators and twists the region of DNA with the promoter into a loop (**Figure 11-20a**). RNA polymerase cannot access the twisted-up promoter, so the *lac* operon's genes cannot be transcribed. When lactose is present (**Figure 11-20b**), some of it is converted to another sugar that binds to the repressor and changes its shape. The altered repressor releases the operators and the looped DNA unwinds. The promoter is now accessible to RNA polymerase, and transcription of lactose-metabolizing genes begins.

The presence of glucose also inhibits transcription of the *lac* operon. Because glucose metabolism is a shorter pathway than lactose metabolism, it requires less energy and fewer resources. Therefore, when both lactose and glucose are present, the cells will use up all of the available glucose before switching to lactose metabolism.

SEP **Use a Model** *Using the model of the lac operon, explain what you think might happen to its function if one of the operator regions was disrupted. What if the promoter region was broken in some way?*

> **CASE STUDY**
> EXPRESSING THE GENETIC CODE
>
> **Ask Questions** *Generate questions about how the mechanisms of gene regulation could help organisms express the particular genes they need, and how different factors in the environment might affect that regulation.*

Gene Expression Regulation in Eukaryotes

Responding to internal and external change is critical to life. Cellular responses often involve adjustments to the timing and rate of gene expression. Consider how a typical differentiated human body cell uses only about 10 percent of its genes. Cells differentiate during development as they begin to express different genes. The set of genes a cell expresses determines the molecules it will produce, and the type of cell it will be.

All steps of gene expression are regulated. Many of these regulation points are indicated in **Figure 11-21**. Each cell is a very complex system. Everything from the position of a gene in the nucleus to the stability of its final protein products can influence the level of expression for each gene.

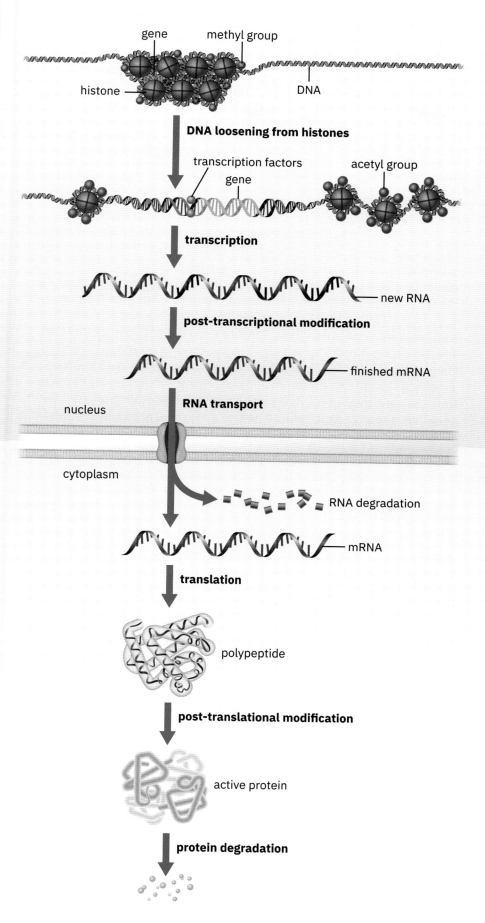

FIGURE 11-21 ◀
Getting from a gene to a final protein product includes many points at which a gene's expression might be changed and regulated.

gene   methyl group

histone   DNA

DNA loosening from histones

transcription factors   acetyl group
gene

transcription

new RNA

post-transcriptional modification

finished mRNA

RNA transport

nucleus

cytoplasm

RNA degradation

mRNA

translation

polypeptide

post-translational modification

active protein

protein degradation

DNA-Histone Interactions In eukaryotic cells, much of a DNA strand is tightly wrapped around *histones*. A histone is a type of protein that associates with DNA and helps organize and condense it into a smaller space. Only DNA regions that have been unwound from histones are accessible to RNA polymerase. Modifications to histone proteins make them loosen or tighten their grip on the DNA wrapped around them, and this influences transcription. For example, adding acetyl groups ($-COCH_3$) to histones loosens DNA so transcription can occur. Adding methyl groups ($-CH_3$) to histones (methylating them) tightens the DNA and prevents transcription.

Transcription Factors A cell can change the gene products it produces (and the rate of production) by changing the transcription factors it makes. **Transcription factors** are proteins that bind directly to DNA and affect whether and how fast a gene is transcribed. *Repressors* are transcription factors that slow or stop transcription, either by preventing RNA polymerase from accessing the promoter or by blocking the enzyme's progress. Some repressors work by binding directly to a *promoter* (**Figure 11-22**). Others bind to a DNA sequence called a *silencer* to reduce transcription. *Activators* are transcription factors that speed up transcription by helping RNA polymerase access a promoter. Many activators work by binding to the promoter. Others bind to DNA sequences called *enhancers*, which, like silencers, may be very far away from the gene they affect. A silencer or enhancer operating on a distant gene can inappropriately affect a nearby gene. Insulators prevent this from occurring. An *insulator* is a region of DNA that, upon binding a transcription

FIGURE 11-22 ▼
Repressors slow or stop transcription by binding to a promoter or silencer. Activators encourage transcription of nearby genes by binding to an enhancer. Insulators prevent activators or repressors from inappropriately affecting transcription of a neighboring gene.

gene · promoter · insulator · silencer · enhancer · promoter · gene

factor, can block the effect of a silencer or enhancer on a neighboring gene.

RNA Processing Transcription in eukaryotes occurs in the nucleus, and translation occurs in the cytoplasm. A newly transcribed mRNA can pass through pores of a nuclear envelope only after it has been modified appropriately. Mechanisms that delay these post-transcriptional modifications also delay delivery of the mRNA to the cytoplasm for translation.

Most eukaryotic genes (and many prokaryotic ones) consist of both exons and introns. **Exons** contain the actual coding information, with intervening sequences called **introns**. Introns are removed from a newly transcribed RNA through a process called splicing (**Figure 11-23**). Exons can be spliced together in different combinations, and this *alternative splicing* allows a single gene to encode multiple versions of a protein.

After alternative splicing, additional mRNA processing adds a guanine cap and a tail made out of a long stretch of adenine bases, known as a poly-A tail. The guanine cap is bound to the end of the mRNA in a way that prevents degradation of the messenger RNA, and it interacts with factors that help export mRNA from the nucleus. The poly-A tail is also important for the export of mRNA from the nucleus as well as translation and stability of the mRNA. Typically, the poly-A tail will shorten over time, eventually ending with the degradation of the mRNA.

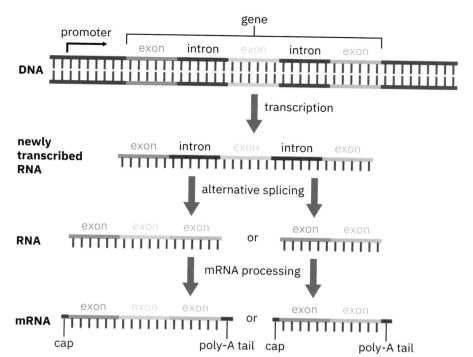

FIGURE 11-23
During post-transcriptional modifications, introns are removed, and exons are spliced together. Messenger RNAs are also given a tail made from a series of adenine bases and a cap made from a modified guanine.

SEP **Argue From Evidence** *In the human genome, there are an average of 8.8 exons and 7.8 introns per gene. Many genes code for several different proteins. If the gene in **Figure 11-23** codes for two different proteins, imagine how many different combinations could be generated by a gene with 9 exons and 8 introns. Why do you think this flexibility might be useful? Think about how cells need to react to changes and how different cells serve different functions.*

mRNA Stability and Translation Homeostasis in a cell depends on tight regulation of the proteins being produced in a cell at a given time, which in turn depends on the mRNA molecules available for translation. The longer an mRNA persists, the more protein molecules can be made from it. Some mRNAs last for several hours in cytoplasm, whereas others are degraded within a minute or two. How long a particular mRNA persists depends mainly on the proteins attached to it. Some binding proteins prevent translation until an mRNA has been delivered to its destination. Other proteins produced in response to environmental signals can attach to and stabilize (or destabilize) specific mRNAs.

Protein Stability and Modifications Some proteins last a long time in a cell, and others are broken down almost immediately after synthesis. The amount of a particular protein in a cell depends on the rate of synthesis and the rate of breaking down. Regulatory proteins such as transcription factors typically have a rapid turnover. A cell can shift its activities quickly by activating molecules that break down these proteins. Many newly synthesized polypeptide chains must be modified before they become functional. There are a variety of post-translational modifications that inhibit, activate, or stabilize many molecules, including enzymes that participate in transcription and translation.

CHAPTER INVESTIGATION

Investigating the Building Blocks of Life
How can we model the building blocks of life?

Go online to explore this chapter's hands-on investigation to design your own model of gene expression and its regulation.

FIGURE 11-24

Short pieces of noncoding RNA, often called microRNAs, serve important regulatory functions through processes such as this RNA interference pathway.

double-stranded RNA

Dicer protein

Double-stranded RNA is cut into short RNA pieces by the Dicer protein.

Multiple proteins and a short RNA segment form RISC.

RISC

RISC binds matching mRNA strands and destroys it.

mRNA

RNA Interference

RNA Interference Small regulatory RNAs can also impact mRNA stability and translation of specific transcripts. A microRNA is a short non-coding RNA molecule that is complementary in nucleotide sequence to part of the target mRNA. MicroRNAs can be generated by proteins such as Dicer, and these microRNAs combine with other proteins to form a complex such as RISC, as shown in **Figure 11-24**. Base pairing between the microRNA and mRNA transcript forms a small double-stranded region, triggering a cascade of events known as **RNA interference**. Depending on how the sequences match, the enzyme complexes that recognize the double-stranded RNA may either prevent translation or facilitate mRNA degradation. RNA interference is used by both prokaryotes and eukaryotes as a mechanism of gene regulation, and it is used by scientists to target genes of interest in research studies.

Epigenetics and Environmental Effects on Gene Expression

Recall that adding methyl groups to histones silences DNA transcription. Direct methylation of DNA nucleotides also suppresses transcription. In eukaryotes, methyl groups are usually added to a cytosine that is followed by a guanine (**Figure 11-25**). When the cytosine on one DNA strand is methylated, enzymes methylate the cytosine on the other strand. Once a particular nucleotide has become methylated in a cell's DNA, it will usually stay methylated in the DNA of the cell's descendants.

DNA methylation is necessary for cell differentiation, so it begins very early in embryonic development. Genes actively expressed in cells of a developing embryo become silenced as their promoters get methylated, and this silencing is the basis of selective gene expression that drives cell differentiation.

FIGURE 11-25

In the DNA of differentiated cells, a methyl group (the red CH$_3$ in the diagram) is most often attached to a cytosine nucleotide that is next to a guanine nucleotide. When the cytosine on one strand is methylated, enzymes tend to also methylate the other strand.

methyl
H$_3$C
NH$_2$
N
C=O
N
cytosine

During development, each cell's DNA continues to acquire methylations. Which sites are methylated in a genome varies by the individual. This is because methylation is influenced by environmental factors experienced during an individual's lifetime. Some of these factors increase methylation of particular genes and others reduce methylation. Patterns of DNA methylation in an individual's cells change after exposure to environmental contaminants. For example, cigarette smoke substantially alters methylation of certain promoters in a pattern that also occurs in cancer cells. Some other examples of factors that can affect methylation patterns include

- alcohol consumption
- BPA consumption
- cancer
- cigarette smoke
- heavy metal exposure
- lead exposure
- low nutritional intake

- obesity
- phthalate consumption
- radiation exposure
- stress
- sun exposure
- temperature

These and other factors that influence DNA methylation patterns can have multigenerational effects. When an organism reproduces, it passes its DNA to offspring. Methylation of parental DNA is normally "reset" in gametes (eggs and sperm) and after fertilization, but this reprogramming does not remove all of the parental methyl groups. Methylations acquired during an individual's lifetime can be passed to future offspring. Inheritable, stable changes in gene expression that occur through chromosomal changes rather than DNA sequence changes are **epigenetic**. DNA methylations are epigenetic, as are histone modifications, some proteins that modify histones, and some noncoding RNAs that influence gene expression.

SEP **Construct an Explanation** *Some methylation changes to DNA are reversible, including some effects of cigarette smoke, which causes a reduction in methylation in certain genes. Why do you think those changes might readily be reversed if an individual stops smoking?*

11.3 REVIEW

1. **Classify** Identify the types of proteins that enable or inhibit transcription.

   - activators
   - promoters
   - repressors
   - enhancers
   - silencers

2. **Infer** What is an advantage and a disadvantage of a long-living mRNA molecule?

3. **Explain** How is the regulation of gene expression different in eukaryotes versus prokaryotes?

4. **Apply** Which of the following statements apply to the *lac* operon?

   A. RNA polymerase converts lactose to glucose.

   B. Glucose binds the repressor to allow transcription.

   C. The repressor twists the promoter region into a loop.

   D. The genes encode three proteins needed for lactose metabolism.

DECAY OF mRNA MOLECULES

SEP **Mathematical Thinking** Gene expression occurs at different rates in the cells of different species.

One of the ways gene expression is controlled is through the timely destruction of mRNA molecules that are no longer needed. After a relatively short period of time, mRNA molecules will degrade into component parts that can be incorporated into new RNA molecules. The lifetime of mRNA is related to the time available for the translation of genetic information into proteins.

Scientists have studied mRNA degradation in the cells of many organisms to better understand the regulation of genetic processes. **Figure 1** and **Figure 2** show the results of three studies that measured the lifetime of mRNA molecules in a single-celled bacterium, a single-celled eukaryote, and a multicellular eukaryote. The half-life of mRNA molecules in all three species showed normal distributions, typically with single peaks and measurable ranges. The half-life is the time it takes for the amount of mRNA present to decrease by half.

FIGURE 1 ▽
This graph shows the frequency of mRNA molecule half-life in a prokaryote, the bacterium *Escherichia coli*.

FIGURE 2 ▽
These two graphs show the frequency of mRNA molecule half-life in the eukaryotes yeast (*Saccharomyces cerevisiae*) and humans (*Homo sapiens*).

---

1. **Analyze Data** Determine the most common, minimum, and maximum half-life for *E. coli*, *S. cerevisiae*, and *H. sapiens*.

2. **Identify Patterns** Use **Figures 1** and **2** to describe a relationship between the mRNA half-life and organism complexity.

3. **Predict** Why might it be advantageous for an *E. coli* cell to degrade most of its mRNAs so quickly, compared with a mature *H. sapiens* cell?

4. **Argue From Evidence** State a claim about the relationship between an mRNA's half-life and the amount of protein produced. What additional evidence would you need to support your claim?

TYING IT ALL TOGETHER
EXPRESSING THE GENETIC CODE

HOW IS GENETIC INFORMATION TRANSFERRED AND REGULATED?

In this chapter, you learned how genes are expressed by translating the information contained in the nucleotide sequence of DNA into instructions for building proteins that perform specific functions. The butterflies described in the Case Study are examples of organisms in which variations in the expression of genes that control their pigmentation can occur due to environmental factors.

The changing of seasons commonly affects the expression of color genes in animals that live in cold climates. Although many arctic animal species stay white all year, some, including weasels, arctic foxes, and snowshoe hares, have brown fur in summer that turns white in winter. Ptarmigans, a genus of chicken-like birds native to the northern tundra, molt from brown or gray to completely white plumage as the weather turns cold.

By analyzing snowshoe hare skin samples collected during molting stages, scientists have identified more than 600 genes that are expressed differently over time. Determining which of these genes dictate changes in the hare's coat color requires advanced genetic techniques, but the fundamental process of gene expression is the same for all of them.

In this activity, you will develop and use a model to construct an explanation of how an animal's fur color changes seasonally. Work individually or in a group to complete these steps.

Ask Questions

1. Review the questions you generated throughout the chapter about how genetic information is transmitted. Identify any questions whose answers help you understand how an animal's appearance is determined by its DNA. If needed, refine some of your existing questions or generate new questions to structure your explanation.

Develop and Use a Model

2. Make a model that describes how a gene that codes for an animal's color is expressed.

Construct an Explanation

3. Use your model of gene expression to explain how the animal's color changes with the seasons.

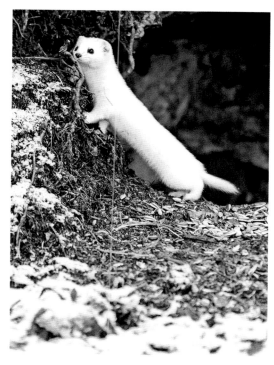

FIGURE 11-26 ◀
The fur of the least weasel (*Mustela nivalis*) changes color in winter, as its habitat turns white with snow and ice.

REVIEW KEY CONCEPTS

1. **Identify** In DNA, which nucleotide is complementary with adenine?

   A. cytosine (C)   C. thymine (T)

   B. guanine (G)   D. uracil (U)

2. **Classify** Indicate whether each characteristic describes RNA, DNA, or both.

   • uses the base uracil

   • uses the base guanine

   • uses the base thymine

   • is typically double stranded

   • has a sugar phosphate backbone

   • carries genetic information

3. **Label** Match the descriptions of the process in DNA replication to the enzyme that performs it: polymerase, helicase, primase, or ligase.

   • unwinds the DNA molecule

   • elongates the new DNA molecule

   • seals up gaps in the DNA backbone

   • builds a short starting nucleotide sequence

4. **Calculate** Using **Figure 11-15**, determine which amino acid is coded for by CAU.

   A. histidine   C. serine

   B. methionine   D. threonine

5. **Explain** Which describes the role of tRNA?

   A. holds the ribosome together

   B. brings the amino acid sequence from the DNA

   C. builds the peptide bond between the amino acids

   D. delivers the appropriate amino acid based on the codon

6. **Summarize** What role do histones play in gene regulation?

7. **Describe** How can genetic traits be affected epigenetically? Give a specific example to support your answer.

8. **Identify Patterns** If a DNA sequence is GGA CTA CCG, what would the order of the bases be on (a) the complementary DNA strand and (b) the mRNA built from the sequence? (c) What would be the amino acids in the polypeptide?

9. **Predict** Which statement best describes the status of the *lac* operon when a large amount of glucose is present?

   A. Genes of the *lac* operon are transcribed to metabolize glucose.

   B. The operators of the *lac* operon are bound to inhibit lactose metabolism.

   C. The repressor protein binds glucose, so the DNA in the *lac* operon is not accessible for transcription.

   D. Polymerase is attached to the *lac* operon promoter region, so lactose can be metabolized as well.

10. **Identify** What methods can a eukaryotic cell use to regulate gene expression? Select all correct answers.

    A. Adjust transcription factors.

    B. Destroy sections of DNA that are not needed.

    C. Break down mRNA molecules at different rates.

    D. Break down protein products at different rates.

    E. Prevent or promote the unwinding of DNA sections.

11. **Sequence** Two ribosomal subunits and a tRNA with methionine are positioned at the start codon of an mRNA. What is the next step in translation?

    A. A peptide bond is formed.

    B. The mRNA molecule unwinds.

    C. The tRNA releases the methionine.

    D. Another tRNA binds to the next codon.

12. **Compare** In which of these ways is DNA replication similar to transcription?

    A. It occurs inside the nucleus.

    B. It copies the entire strand of DNA.

    C. Another DNA molecule is produced.

    D. Uracil is incorporated into the molecule.

13. **Explain** What role do hydrogen bonds play in DNA replication? Select all correct answers.

    A. They make it easier to separate the strands.

    B. They enable the correct base pairings to occur.

    C. They signal the cell to know when to replicate itself.

    D. They assist the helicase molecule in unwinding the DNA.

    E. They hold the two strands of the DNA molecule together.

CRITICAL THINKING

14. **Explain** If DNA has only four different bases, how can it be used to produce so many different proteins?

15. **NOS** **Scientific Knowledge** Describe how the discoveries of Miescher, Griffith, and Avery built on each other to help advance our understanding of DNA.

16. **Explain** What happens when a ribosome reaches a stop codon?

17. **Contrast** Compare activators and repressors in gene regulation.

MATH AND ENGLISH LANGUAGE ARTS CONNECTIONS

1. **Synthesize Information** Describe what the words *transcription* and *translation* mean in other contexts outside of science, and relate those meanings to what they mean in protein synthesis.

2. **Write a Function** Write an equation to describe the relationship between the number of nucleotides (*n*) in a DNA sequence and the number of amino acids (*a*) in the resulting polypeptide.

3. **Infer from Statistics** If a codon is randomly generated, what amino acids are most likely to be coded for? Which are least likely? Refer to **Figure 11-15**.

4. **Write Explanatory Text** Francis Crick said, "Rather than believe that Watson and Crick made the DNA structure, I would rather stress that the structure made Watson and Crick." Using what you know about the history of the discovery of DNA and what DNA does, how do you interpret this quote?

5. **Reason Abstractly** In geometry, complementary angles fit together to form an angle that measures exactly 90 degrees. Use this mathematical definition and **Figure 11-3** to help explain why base pairs in nucleotides are called complementary.

► REVISIT VIRAL SPREAD

Gather Evidence In this chapter, you learned about how cells transfer information from their genomes to the RNA and protein products that are important for life. You have also learned here and in Section 8.4 that viruses have their own genomes. Viral genomes vary widely and require different help from their host cells to be expressed, but the overall goal remains the same: to express genes and replicate. Look at the structure of SARS-CoV-2, which was first presented in Section 8.4.

1. Observe the structures shown in the provided model of the SAR-CoV-2 viral particle. What are some of the genes that need to be encoded within the SARS-CoV-2 genome to make new virus particles? Which genes do you think code for proteins that are important for infecting a host cell?

2. What other questions do you have about how SARS-CoV-2 infects and replicates within host cells?

glycoprotein spike

membrane protein

envelope protein

lipid envelope

RNA and nucleocapsid protein

CHAPTER 12

GENETIC VARIATION AND HEREDITY

The American Kennel Club currently registers around 200 dog breeds. This number does not take into account the immense variety of mixed breeds that exist.

12.1 MEIOSIS

12.2 MUTATIONS

12.3 MENDELIAN INHERITANCE

12.4 OTHER PATTERNS OF INHERITANCE

Despite the great variety among dog breeds, they share 99.9 percent of their DNA. A dog's genome contains three billion base pairs. Though 0.1 percent might seem like a tiny difference, it actually adds up to three million base pairs. Within those base pairs lie the genetic variations that make each breed—and each individual dog—unique from all others.

Chapter 12 supports the NGSS Performance Expectations **HS-LS3-2** and **HS-LS3-3**.

CASE STUDY
FOR THE LOVE OF DOGS

HOW DOES GENETIC INFORMATION CHANGE AND GET PASSED FROM GENERATION TO GENERATION?

Large, small, long hair, short hair, perky ears, floppy ears—the list of dog trait variations goes on and on. However, despite their differences, all dogs belong to the same species, *Canis lupus familiaris*. Research indicates that all dogs descended from a gray wolf (*Canis lupus*) ancestor. Although how and why remain unclear, most scientists agree that dogs were likely domesticated sometime between 14,000 and 40,000 years ago.

Today, there are more than 340 recognized dog breeds around the world. Most of these breeds were developed within the past 150 years. Through selective breeding by humans, these dogs exhibit desired traits in both their appearance and behavior. For example, while some dogs are bred to exhibit certain physical traits, such as short legs or wiry hair, others are bred for certain skills, such as herding, retrieving, or guarding. These traits are embedded in a dog's genetic code. When dogs with the same traits are bred together, their resulting offspring will often—but not always—exhibit the same characteristics as their parents.

But if all domesticated dogs evolved from a wolf ancestor, what accounts for such a wide variety of traits seen today? One of the key characteristics of domesticated dogs is tameness. In the late 1950s, Dmitry Belyaev, a Russian geneticist, hypothesized that by initially selecting the tamest wolves to live with them, early humans were unknowingly choosing a single trait that could be genetically linked to a wide range of traits, including changes in body shape, behavior, and physical functioning. To test his hypothesis, Belyaev chose to work with wild foxes, a species related to dogs. He found that within only eight generations of domestication, the tamed fox population exhibited changes in fur color and developed floppy ears and curved tails, traits common in many dog species. Belyaev's team also discovered that an increase in tameness was associated with changes in two developmental milestones: the tamer fox kits opened their eyes several days earlier than those born in the wild, and their fear response appeared almost a month later than typically seen in wild foxes. The scientists hypothesize that these changes, if also exhibited by the first domesticated dogs, would have made them more open to interacting with humans without fear. Belyaev's population of tame foxes continues to be studied today. Recent discoveries include the finding that foxes bred for tameness and those bred for aggressiveness show a significant difference in gene expression related to neurologic processing.

Ask Questions *As you read this chapter, generate questions about the mechanisms that lead to genetic variation.*

FIGURE 12-1
The silver fox is a species that has been bred for tameness. Foxes and modern dogs belong to the canine group that also includes wolves, coyotes, and jackals.

▶ **VIDEO 12-1** Go online to watch a brief history of humans' relationship with dogs.

KEY TERMS

allele
asexual reproduction
gamete
meiosis
sexual reproduction
trait

MEIOSIS

Take a look around you. What living things do you see? When you are outside, you might see an even greater variety of organisms—plants, humans, and other animals. What makes every organism unique is its genetic code, or genome. Information encoded in DNA is the basis of visible traits that define species and distinguish individuals. Humans, trees, insects, and all organisms have a genome that is unique.

Make a Claim *Make and defend a claim about the basis of similarities and differences in characteristics of a particular species.*

Traits, Genes, and Alleles

Members of a species have the same **traits**, or inherited characteristics, because they have the same genes. A *gene* is a section of DNA that codes for a certain protein or RNA molecule. Genes are the most basic unit of heredity. A continuous piece of DNA is made up of many genes and is called a *chromosome* (**Figure 12-2**). Genes are the units of information that are passed from one generation to the next. Every gene has a locus, or specific position on a chromosome. All the genes of an organism are called its *genome*. A genome is a complete set of genetic instructions that include all the information needed to build the individual organism and allow it to develop and grow.

FIGURE 12-2 ▼
A strand of DNA is made up of many genes. In eukaryotes, DNA is organized into linear chromosomes that are duplicated.

In eukaryotes, a DNA molecule is organized into a chromosome contained in the nucleus of the cell. During cell division, a chromosome replicates. A replicated chromosome is made up of two identical DNA molecules, called sister chromatids, that are joined at the centromere.

In prokaryotes, DNA is contained in the cytoplasm of the cell. Most prokaryotes have a single, circular chromosome. The cytoplasm also contains plasmids, which are small circles of DNA that carry a few genes. Plasmid genes are not required for the survival and reproduction of the organism. However, a plasmid can provide advantages to the cell, such as resistance to antibiotics.

Your somatic, or body, cells contain pairs of homologous chromosomes. There are 23 homologous pairs of chromosomes in humans, shown in **Figure 12-3**. A karyotype is an image of an individual cell's chromosomes. To make a karyotype, cells taken from the individual are stained so the chromosomes can be distinguished under a microscope. The chromosomes are then digitally rearranged according to size, shape, and length.

Of the 23 pairs of chromosomes, 22 pairs are autosomes, or chromosomes that contain genes for characteristics that are not directly related to the sex of the individual. The last pair are called sex chromosomes because they directly control the development of sexual characteristics. The sex chromosomes are referred to as X and Y, or the XY system, and determine the biological sex of an individual. Typically, organisms with two X chromosomes (XX) are female, and organisms with XY chromosomes are male. The XY system occurs in humans, most mammals, and some reptiles and plants.

FIGURE 12-3
Humans have 23 homologous pairs of chromosomes. A karyotype shows the complete set of 23 chromosomes in the cells of humans. As shown in the inset scanning electron micrograph, the X chromosome is about three times the size of the Y chromosome.

The two chromosomes of each homologous pair have the same genes, but their DNA sequence is not identical. This is because an individual inherits chromosomes from each parent who differ genetically. Thus, the DNA sequence of any of an individual's genes may vary from a corresponding gene on a homologous chromosome.

Genes occur in pairs on homologous chromosomes. Different forms of the same gene are called **alleles** (**Figure 12-4**). Traits are inherited characteristics that derive from the genes that are inherited. However, almost every shared trait varies among individuals of a species. Alleles of the shared genes are the basis of this variation.

FIGURE 12-4 ▶
Corresponding colored patches indicate corresponding DNA sequences in a homologous chromosome pair.

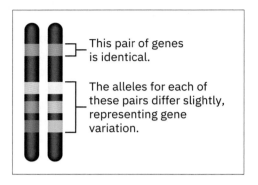

This pair of genes is identical.

The alleles for each of these pairs differ slightly, representing gene variation.

Asexual and Sexual Reproduction

Chapter 7 introduced mitosis and cytoplasmic division as part of the processes of asexual reproduction. Not all species can use this reproductive mode. Many eukaryotes reproduce sexually, either exclusively or most of the time. **Sexual reproduction** is the process in which offspring arise from two parents and inherit genes from both.

All organisms transmit genetic information to their offspring either through asexual reproduction or sexual reproduction. Sexual reproduction mixes genetic information from two parents. Such variation is almost always advantageous, because genetically diverse populations are more resilient to environmental change than populations with low genetic diversity.

Asexual reproduction produces genetically identical individuals, so populations of asexually reproducing organisms typically have low genetic diversity. This is because an asexually reproducing individual passes all of its genes to every one of its offspring. All the offspring are basically clones because they have the same alleles as their one parent. For comparison, only about half of a sexually reproducing organism's genes are passed to each offspring (**Table 12-1**).

TABLE 12-1. Comparison of Asexual and Sexual Reproduction

Attribute	Asexual reproduction	Sexual reproduction
type of cell division	mitosis	meiosis and mitosis
number of parents	1	2
parental cell(s)	diploid cell	haploid gametes
inherited genes	100% from 1 parent	50% from each parent
offspring genes	genetically identical	not genetically identical
advantages	does not require a partner	high genetic diversity
disadvantages	no genetic diversity	typically requires a partner
organisms	prokaryotes, such as bacteria and archaea, and eukaryotes, such as many plants, fungi, and some animals	eukaryotes, including most animals and some plants and fungi

Consistency is a good evolutionary strategy in a favorable, unchanging environment. Alleles that help an organism survive and reproduce in the environment do the same for its descendants. However, most environments are constantly changing, and change is not always favorable. Individuals that are identical are equally vulnerable to challenges.

In a changing environment, genetic diversity in sexual reproducers is an advantage. Sexual reproduction randomly mixes up the genetic information of two parents who have different alleles. The offspring of sexually reproducing organisms inherit different combinations of parental alleles, so they differ from one another and from their parents. Some of the offspring may be perfectly suited to a new environmental challenge. Thus, as a group, they have a greater chance of surviving environmental change than clones.

SEP **Analyze Data** *Table 12-1 identifies one advantage of asexual reproduction as not requiring a partner. Identify at least one other advantage of asexual reproduction.*

🧪 **CHAPTER INVESTIGATION**

Mapping Fruit Fly Genes Through Linkage
How can we map genes using traits that are inherited together?

Go online to explore this chapter's hands-on investigation to map some traits on fruit fly chromosomes.

BIOTECHNOLOGY FOCUS

FOLLOW THE MAP A karyotype is a collection of chromosomes in the cells of an individual. A genome map identifies all the genes and the distance between genes on a chromosome. Scientists map genomes to compare the DNA of closely related species to establish and analyze their genetic differences. The differences help scientists to catalogue the biodiversity of organisms on the planet. This process is called comparative genomics.

Comparative genomics includes comparing single genes and gene fragments to study their function and help establish relationships among species. Scientists are building databases of genome sequences to share knowledge and support the progress of this scientific

research. For example, researchers study where genetic variants associated with specific diseases or characteristics are located on the chromosomes. Genes or gene sequences with a known location on a chromosome are called genetic markers. Physical maps identify the physical distance between the known gene sequences. The distance is expressed as the number of base pairs between the sequences. This information helps scientists to identify and isolate genes.

As scientists learn more about a particular genome, its map becomes more accurate and detailed. A genome map is not a final product but a work in progress. Genetic mapping is a tool scientists use to identify genes and to understand their function.

There are two basic ways of mapping a genome: genetic mapping and physical mapping.

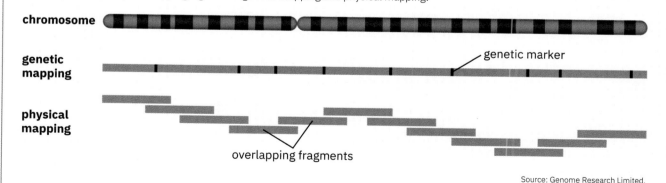

Source: Genome Research Limited.

FIGURE 12-5 ▼
During meiosis, a diploid (2n) cell divides
into four haploid (n) cells.

The Phases of Meiosis

Genetic variation occurs in many ways, including the recombination of genes during two processes: meiosis and fertilization by sexual reproduction. **Meiosis** is a nuclear division process. During meiosis, diploid cells become haploid sex cells, called **gametes**. Meiosis halves the number of chromosomes to maintain the proper number of chromosomes through successive generations (**Figure 12-5**).

Before meiosis begins, DNA is copied during the S phase of the cell cycle. During meiosis I, homologous chromosomes separate, producing two haploid cells with duplicated chromosomes. Meiosis I can be described in distinct phases, each of which is a series of gradual changes (**Figure 12-6**).

- **Prophase I** The chromosomes condense, and homologous chromosomes pair up. The nuclear envelope breaks up. Microtubules extend from opposite poles in all directions to form a spindle. The microtubules attach chromosomes of the homologous pair to opposite spindle poles.

- **Metaphase I** The microtubules push and pull the chromosomes until they are aligned midway between the spindle poles.

- **Anaphase I** Microtubules of the spindle move the homologous chromosomes of each pair away from one another and toward opposite spindle poles.

- **Telophase I** Two sets of chromosomes reach the spindle poles, and a new nuclear envelope forms around each set as the DNA loosens up. The two new nuclei are haploid (n); each contains one complete set of chromosomes. The sister chromatids stay together. The cytoplasm divides.

In some cells, meiosis II occurs immediately after meiosis I. In other cells, a period of protein synthesis—but no DNA replication—intervenes between the divisions.

FIGURE 12-6 ▼
During meiosis I, a diploid nucleus is
divided into two haploid nuclei.

prophase I metaphase I anaphase I telophase I

plasma membrane spindle

nuclear envelope breaking up

pair of homologous chromosomes

Meiosis II (**Figure 12-7**) proceeds simultaneously in both nuclei that formed in meiosis I.

- **Prophase II** The chromosomes condense, and the nuclear envelope breaks up. A new spindle forms. By the end of prophase II, microtubules attach each chromatid to one spindle pole, and its sister chromatid to the opposite spindle pole.

- **Metaphase II** The microtubules push and pull the chromosomes, aligning them in the middle of the cell.

- **Anaphase II** The spindle microtubules move the sister chromatids apart and toward opposite spindle poles.

- **Telophase II** The chromosomes reach the spindle poles. New nuclear envelopes form around the four clusters of chromosomes as the DNA loosens up. Each of the four nuclei that form are haploid (*n*), with one set of unduplicated chromosomes. The cytoplasm divides.

Comparing Mitosis and Meiosis Meiosis is an important process that produces new genetic combinations in each of the four daughter cells. Meiosis also ensures that offspring produced by sexual reproduction contain the correct number of chromosomes. If the chromosome number changes, so does the individual's genetic instruction.

The first part of meiosis is similar to mitosis. A cell duplicates its DNA before either nuclear division process begins. However, meiosis sorts the chromosomes into new nuclei not once but twice, so it results in the formation of four haploid nuclei.

CCC **Cause and Effect** *Why is it important that human gametes have half a set of DNA instead of a full set of DNA? Use evidence and scientific reasoning to support your claim.*

VIDEO

VIDEO 12-2 Go online to watch meiosis in action.

FIGURE 12-7 ▼
During meiosis II, two haploid nuclei divide into four haploid nuclei.

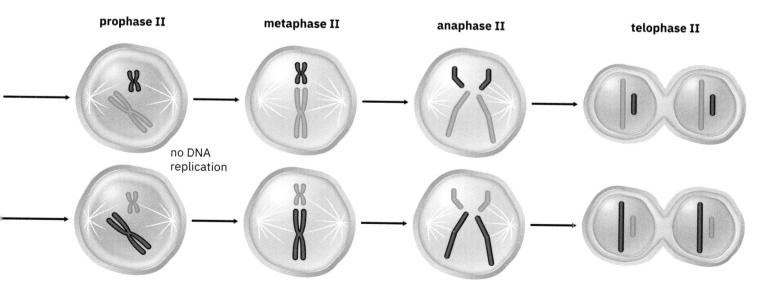

prophase II metaphase II anaphase II telophase II

no DNA replication

Mechanisms of Variation in Meiosis and Fertilization

In addition to the random mating that occurs in many species, there are a number of mechanisms at the cellular level that produce genetic variation.

Crossing Over Early in prophase I, all chromosomes in the cell condense. When they do, each is drawn close to its homologous partner, so that the chromatids align along their length. This tight, parallel orientation favors crossing over, a process in which a chromosome and its homologous partner exchange corresponding pieces of DNA (**Figure 12-8**). Homologous chromosomes may swap any segment of DNA along their length, although crossovers tend to occur more frequently in certain regions of a chromosome. Swapping segments of DNA shuffles alleles between homologous chromosomes. It breaks up the combinations of alleles that occurred on the parental chromosomes and makes new ones on the chromosomes that end up in gametes.

Crossing over introduces novel combinations of alleles among offspring. It is a required process—meiosis will not finish unless it happens. The rate of crossing over varies among species and among chromosomes.

FIGURE 12-8 ▽

During prophase I of meiosis, crossing over occurs.

In this example, one gene has alleles *A* and *a*; the other gene has alleles *B* and *b*.

Close contact between homologous chromosomes promotes crossing over, in which nonsister chromatids exchange corresponding pieces.

After crossing over, paternal and maternal alleles have become mixed up on homologous chromosomes.

Fertilization Sexual reproduction requires that diploid organisms produce haploid gametes through meiosis. Fertilization is the union of two haploid cells, one from each parent (**Figure 12-9**). When sexual reproduction results in fertilization, gametes unite to produce new, unique individual organisms. A male gamete fuses with a female gamete at fertilization to produce a diploid cell called a zygote. A zygote is the first cell of a new individual. Sexual reproduction results in increased genetic diversity within a species because of the random assortment of combined alleles from both parents.

FIGURE 12-9 ▷

At fertilization, two gametes meet to form a zygote. Meiosis halves the chromosome number, and fertilization restores it. If meiosis did not precede fertilization, the chromosome number would double with every generation.

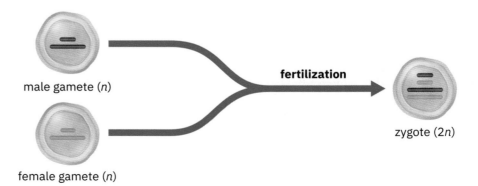

male gamete (*n*)

female gamete (*n*)

fertilization

zygote (2*n*)

Segregation The new nuclei that form in meiosis I receive a complete set of chromosomes, but whether a new nucleus ends up with the maternal or paternal version of a chromosome is random. The chance that the maternal or paternal version of any chromosome will end up in a particular nucleus is 50 percent because of the way the spindle segregates homologous chromosomes.

In prophase I, after crossing over has occurred, microtubules fasten homologous chromosomes of each pair to opposite spindle poles. There is no pattern to the attachment of the maternal or paternal chromosome to a particular pole. Microtubules extending from a spindle pole attach to the centromere of the first chromosome they contact, regardless of whether it is maternal or paternal (**Figure 12-10**).

FIGURE 12-10 ◄
Segregation of two chromosome pairs, one from each parent, occurs during meiosis. For simplicity, assume no crossing over, so all sister chromatids are identical.

The homologous chromosomes of two pairs can be divided between two spindle poles in four possible ways. There are eight possible combinations of maternal and paternal chromosomes in the two nuclei that form at telophase I. There are eight possible combinations of maternal and paternal chromosomes in the four nuclei that form at telophase II.

> **CCC** **Cause and Effect** *Explain how chromosome segregation during meiosis is one mechanism for why offspring are not exact replicas of their parents.*

Independent Assortment During meiosis, two alleles at one gene locus tend to be sorted into gametes independently of alleles at other loci. During metaphase I, the homologous chromosomes arrange themselves randomly in the center of the cell. This determines the genes each gamete will receive because only one of the two homologous chromosomes is moved into each newly forming cell.

In meiosis I, either chromosome of a pair may get attached to either spindle pole. With two pairs of homologous chromosomes, there are two ways in which the maternal and paternal chromosomes can become attached to the two spindle poles, as shown in **Figure 12-11**. Two nuclei from each scenario show four possible combinations of alleles in the nuclei that form after meiosis I. Thus, when sister chromatids separate during meiosis II, the gametes that result have one of the four possible combinations of alleles.

FIGURE 12-11 ▶
Independent assortment during meiosis results in new combinations of genes. Here, we can track alleles on different chromosomes.

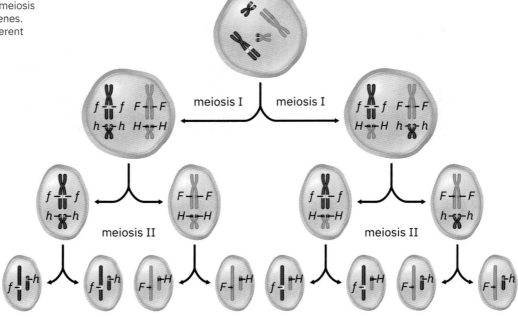

SEP **Argue From Evidence** *Describe two pieces of evidence to support the claim that sexual reproduction tends to give rise to greater genetic diversity among offspring.*

12.1 REVIEW

1. **Classify** Label each description as relevant to mitosis, meiosis, or both.

   • A cell's DNA is duplicated.

   • Cell division results in four daughter cells.

   • Offspring exhibit more genetic variation.

   • This process begins with diploid cells.

   • The products of the steps are gametes for sexual reproduction.

   • A single cell divides in a series of distinct phases.

2. **Explain** How do crossing over, segregation, and independent assortment provide evidence for increased genetic variation?

3. **Identify** Which statement represents an advantage of sexual reproduction over asexual reproduction?

   A. Reproduction occurs without a partner.

   B. Offspring are genetically identical to the parents.

   C. Genetic diversity increases from one generation to the next.

   D. Offspring have a decreased chance of surviving environmental change.

4. **Analyze** What is the difference between the genetic material on two sister chromatids and the genetic material on homologous chromosomes?

NATIONAL GEOGRAPHIC EXPLORER **KRISTEN RUEGG**

USING GENES TO MAP FLYWAYS

Biologist Dr. Kristen Ruegg sits on the ground among early spring grasses and pulls an American robin from a soft, cloth bag. She holds it in her left hand, belly up, with its head between her index and middle fingers. She then gently but firmly grasps it above the legs with her other hand and turns it upright. The bird looks up at her and chirps with a sharp "*peek-peek-peek.*" Ruegg looks it in the eyes and replies warmly, "Yes. I see you."

Dr. Kristen Ruegg's goal is to collect DNA from 100 species of migratory birds for the Bird Genoscape Project.

The American robin is one of the species in the Bird Genoscape Project, an effort Ruegg directs. The project is much like a human ancestry database—a collection of genetic profiles to which an individual's genes can be compared. Ruegg will go on to pluck two of the bird's tail feathers, which she says is easier than pulling a hair from your chin. Then, she opens her hand and the bird flies off. Birds lose and replace feathers regularly, so these will soon grow back.

Ruegg slips the feathers in clean envelopes, records the location and date, and places the envelopes in a cooler. She's extremely careful to not touch the tiny bit of flesh at the quill's tip where the DNA she wants for the Genoscape Project will be extracted. The goal of the project is to map the routes of 100 genetically distinct populations of migratory birds by 2025. The project's urgency is underscored by data that shows about 30 percent of North American birds have vanished over the last 50 years.

Ruegg thinks that mapping the migration routes of different populations based on their distinct genetic makeup holds keys to developing conservation strategies in Earth's changing climate. In actuality, many birds identified as "North American birds" spend only about three months in North America during their breeding season. The rest of the year they winter in warmer semitropical climates. An individual bird also tends to breed and winter in the same locations. A robin that breeds in eastern Canada likely winters in Florida, and one that breeds in Alaska likely winters in northern Mexico. Genetic markers from the DNA of an individual bird's tail feathers can tell where it is from and its migration route. Knowing the migration route helps to determine where environmental challenges exist and predict how bird ranges may change as the climate warms.

THINKING CRITICALLY

Identify Patterns *What are some reasons that populations of the same species might develop distinct genetic profiles?*

MUTATIONS

Genetic variation occurs in many ways. So far you have learned about recombination of genes during meiosis and by fertilization in sexual reproduction. Genetic variation also occurs via mutations. These happen randomly and cause a range of effects, from unnoticeable changes to structural and functional defects or genetic disease.

Predict *How could a change in the way a protein is made affect the trait of an individual?*

Causes of Mutations

Spontaneous errors during DNA replication are often repaired by enzymes. When proofreading and repair mechanisms fail, an error results in a permanent change in the DNA sequence of a chromosome. A **mutation** is a change in DNA. It can affect one or more nucleotides or large segments of genes on a chromosome. The consequences of these changes appear in the proteins made from the modified code instructions. Repair enzymes cannot fix a mutation after the altered DNA strand has been replicated. Thus, a mutation is passed on to the next generation.

In addition to spontaneous events, physical and chemical environmental agents, called **mutagens**, can increase the frequency of mutation in organisms. For example, ultraviolet (UV) radiation from sunlight exposure can cause long-term damage to DNA. Infectious agents, such as some viruses and bacteria, and chemical agents found in cigarettes and some preservatives in processed foods, have also been linked to mutations.

CCC **Cause and Effect** *Explain how mutations can affect protein synthesis, and, in turn, the expression of a trait.*

Gene Mutations

Some mutations occur from changes in the sequence of nucleotides of a single gene, typically during DNA replication. The result is a newly replicated DNA strand that is not exactly complementary to its parent strand. A nucleotide may get deleted during DNA replication, or an extra one may be inserted. Most of these replication errors occur simply because DNA polymerases work very fast. Mistakes are inevitable, and some DNA polymerases make a lot of them.

Frameshift Mutations When one or more nucleotides in a DNA sequence are either inserted or deleted, the reading frame is altered. As a result, the codon base sequences are altered, and the synthesized protein does not match the protein originally intended (**Figure 12-12**).

Luckily, most DNA polymerases proofread their work. They can correct a mismatch by reversing the synthesis reaction to remove the mispaired nucleotide and then resume synthesis in the forward direction. Replication errors also occur after DNA is broken or otherwise damaged because DNA polymerases do not copy damaged DNA very well. In most cases, enzymes and other proteins can repair damaged DNA before replication begins.

original sequence

T A A C T G C A G G T

base insertion

frameshift →

T A A C C T G C A G G T

base deletion

← frameshift

T A A C G C A G G T

T

Point Mutations

Point mutations are gene mutations caused by the substitution of one nucleotide for another (**Figure 12-13**). These nucleotide, or base, substitutions generally have three possible effects on the amino acid sequence, which may alter the structure and function of the resulting protein.

original sequence

T A A C T G C A G G T

T A A C C G C A G G T

base substitution

FIGURE 12-13
Point mutations occur when one base is substituted for another in a sequence.

- **Silent Mutation** The base substitution in the altered codon corresponds to the same amino acid. Although a silent mutation does not change the amino acid produced or present a visible change, it can still alter a protein's function.

- **Missense Mutation** The base substitution in the altered codon corresponds to a different amino acid. Sickle cell disease is caused by a missense mutation.

- **Nonsense Mutation** The base substitution in the altered codon corresponds to a stop signal. As a result, the protein is shortened and likely nonfunctional. Duchenne muscular dystrophy, cystic fibrosis, and hemophilia are different diseases caused by nonsense mutations.

Chromosomal Mutations

Chromosomal changes occur in either segments of chromosomes or whole chromosomes. These types of mutations result in changes to the amount of genetic material or the structure of the chromosome.

Gene Translocation In gene translocation, a chromosome segment moves to a nonhomologous chromosome. Often translocations are reciprocal in that the two nonhomologous chromosomes both exchange segments (**Figure 12-14**). Translocation is different from crossing over, in which homologous chromosomes swap segments during prophase I.

FIGURE 12-14
A segment of one chromosome moves to a nonhomologous chromosome during meiosis, resulting in gene translocation. Often segments are swapped, resulting in reciprocal translocation.

Gene Duplication During meiosis, crossing over results in homologous chromosomes exchanging DNA segments. Sometimes the chromosomes do not align with each other and the exchange of DNA segments is uneven, resulting in one chromosome with two copies of a gene or genes. This process is called gene duplication (**Figure 12-15**). The chromosome that lost the segment has undergone gene deletion.

FIGURE 12-15
A segment of a chromosome is repeated when homologous chromosomes do not align properly during meiosis, resulting in gene duplication.

Gene Inversion Sometimes genes on chromosomes switch places. A chromosome segment breaks off and reattaches in reverse order (**Figure 12-16**). This type of structural change, called a gene inversion, may not affect a carrier's health if the break point does not occur in a gene or control region. The individual's cells still contain their full complement of genetic material. However, fertility may be compromised because a chromosome with an inversion does not pair properly with its homologous partner during meiosis. Crossovers between the mispaired chromosomes produce other chromosome abnormalities that reduce the viability of offspring.

FIGURE 12-16
A segment of a chromosome is flipped in the opposite orientation during meiosis, resulting in gene inversion.

Genetic Variation

Mutations make new alleles, which results in small differences in DNA sequences that make every individual unique. Once new alleles arise, meiosis and sexual reproduction combine different alleles in new ways to increase genetic variation. Mutations account for the variation we see in human hair color, skin color, height, shape, behavior, and susceptibility to disease. The same is true for individuals in other species.

Fruit flies are a model organism for the study of genetic variation. Some common mutations seen in fruit flies include wing structure and eye color variations. Mutant wings may be short or backward. Fruit flies are known for their red eyes, although mutations cause certain individuals to have golden or white eyes (**Figure 12-17**).

Often mutation has a negative connotation. In contrast to variations that cause disease, there are many more examples of mutation variations that are neither beneficial nor harmful, just different.

FIGURE 12-17
Fruit flies typically have red eyes, though some mutant individuals have white eyes.

12.2 REVIEW

1. **Argue From Evidence** Use evidence to support the claim that genetic mutations can increase the genetic variation in populations of organisms.

2. **Explain** If a gene mutation changes the structure of a protein, how could it affect that organism's traits?

3. **Identify** Which statement is true of mutations?

   A. They only result from genetic factors.

   B. They always change the DNA sequence.

   C. They only result from environmental factors.

   D. They are always detrimental to the organism.

4. **Compare** Which type of mutation has the greater impact on the resulting proteins?

   A. point mutations because they always change the amino acid sequence

   B. point mutations because they can sometimes change the resulting protein

   C. frameshift mutations because they substitute one nucleotide for another

   D. frameshift mutations because they often shift the entire sequence following the mutation

ON ASSIGNMENT National Geographic photographer Shannon Wild spent 18 months pursuing this black panther in its forested habitat in southern India. A black panther is also known as a melanistic leopard. The color of this cat's fur coat is a recessive trait that results from a mutation that knocks out the gene that regulates the production of melanin. As a result, there is an overproduction of pigment, resulting in its black coat.

12.3

KEY TERMS

dominant
genotype
heterozygous
homozygous
phenotype
recessive

MENDELIAN INHERITANCE

In 1865, Austrian monk Gregor Mendel was carefully breeding thousands of pea plants. By keeping detailed records of how traits passed from one generation to the next, Mendel was collecting evidence of how inheritance works. At the time, no one knew that hereditary information (DNA) is divided into discrete units, called genes, an insight that is critical to understanding how traits are inherited.

Predict *Make a list of traits you could observe in a plant or animal to show how traits are passed down from one generation to another.*

(▶) VIDEO

VIDEO 12-3 Go online to learn more about the study of genetics.

Mendel's Experiments

Mendel cultivated garden pea plants. This species is naturally self-fertilizing, which means each plant's flowers produce male and female gametes that form a zygote that can develop into a viable embryo (Section 9.3). To study inheritance, Mendel had to carry out controlled mating between individuals with specific traits (**Figure 12-18**). Mendel kept individual pea plants from self-fertilizing by removing the pollen-bearing parts (anthers) from their flowers. He then cross-fertilized the plants by brushing the egg-bearing parts (carpels) of their flowers with pollen from other plants. He collected and planted seeds from the cross-fertilized individuals and recorded the traits of the resulting pea plant offspring.

FIGURE 12-18 ▶
Mendel cultivated and bred garden pea plants in his experimental procedure.

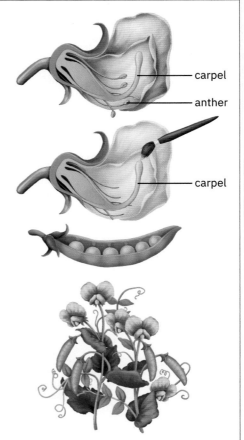

In this example, the white flower's pollen-producing anthers are cut off to prevent it from self-fertilizing. Then, pollen from the anther of the purple flower is brushed onto the egg-producing carpel of the white flower.

carpel

anther

carpel

Later, seeds develop inside pods of the cross-fertilized plant. When the seeds are planted, the embryo in each develops into a pea plant.

In this example, every plant that arises from the cross has purple flowers. Predictable patterns such as this are evidence of how inheritance works.

Many of Mendel's experiments, which are called crosses, started with plants of pure breed for particular traits, such as white flowers or purple flowers. Purebred for a trait generally means that all offspring have the same form of the trait as the parent(s), generation after generation. For example, all offspring of pea plants that are purebred for white flowers also have white flowers.

Mendel cross-fertilized purebred pea plants for different forms of a trait and discovered that the traits of the offspring often appear in predictable patterns. Mendel's meticulous work tracking pea plant traits led him to correctly conclude that hereditary information passes from one generation to the next in discrete units.

Mendel's Observations

Mendel discovered hereditary units, which we now call genes, almost a century before the discovery of DNA. Today, we know that individuals of a species share certain traits because their chromosomes carry the same genes.

Diploid cells have pairs of homologous chromosomes, so they have two copies of each gene. The two copies of any gene may be identical, or they may vary as alleles. **Genotype** is the particular set of alleles an individual carries. If two alleles at a specific locus on the gene are the same, they are **homozygous**. If two alleles at a specific locus on the gene are different, they are **heterozygous**. Genotype is the basis of **phenotype**, which refers to the individual's observable traits. Mendel studied seven traits in garden pea plants (**Table 12-2**).

TABLE 12-2. Mendel's Seven Pea Plant Traits

Trait	Dominant form	Recessive form
seed shape	round	wrinkled
seed color	yellow	green
pod texture	smooth	wrinkled
pod color	green	yellow

Trait	Dominant form	Recessive form
flower color	purple	white
flower position	along stem	at tip
stem length	tall	short

Go Online SIMULATION

Punnett Square Go online to generate your own test crosses.

Modeling Genetic Crosses

The phenotype of a heterozygous individual for a particular trait depends on its two different alleles. In many cases, the effect of one allele influences the effect of the other, and the outcome is reflected in the individual's phenotype. A **dominant** allele is the allele that is expressed when two different alleles or two dominant alleles are present. A **recessive** allele is the allele that is expressed only when two copies are present. A dominant allele is often represented by a capital letter, in this case *F*. A recessive allele is represented by a lowercase letter, such as *f* (**Figure 12-19**).

FIGURE 12-19
Genotype gives rise to phenotype. In this example, the dominant allele *F* specifies purple flowers and the recessive allele *f*, specifies white flowers.

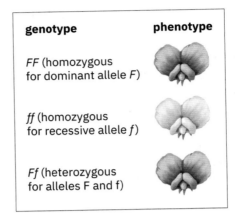

genotype   phenotype

FF (homozygous for dominant allele *F*)

ff (homozygous for recessive allele *f*)

Ff (heterozygous for alleles F and f)

A grid called a Punnett square is helpful for predicting the outcomes of crosses. This grid was developed by British geneticist R. C. Punnett in the early 1900s to track the combination of alleles possible from parental gametes to their offspring. In sexually reproducing organisms, fertilization occurs when a male and female gamete fuse. The gametes are haploid, but the resulting zygote is diploid. A Punnett square is a useful model to show this fusion and the probable outcomes for a specific gamete combination.

FIGURE 12-20
To make a Punnett square, parental gametes are placed on the top and left sides of a grid. Each square is filled with the combination of alleles that would result if the gametes in the corresponding row and column met up.

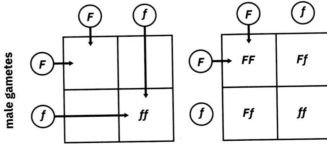

female gametes

male gametes

	F	f
F	FF	Ff
f	Ff	ff

Test Crosses We can determine whether an individual is homozygous (*FF* or *ff*) or heterozygous (*Ff*) for a trait using test crosses (**Figure 12-20**). For example, by crossing a known homozygous recessive (*ff*) individual with an individual having a dominant trait (but unknown genotype), the pattern of traits among the offspring of the cross can reveal whether the tested individual is heterozygous or homozygous. If all offspring of the test cross have the dominant trait, then the parent with the unknown genotype is homozygous (*FF*) for the dominant allele. If some of the offspring have the recessive trait, then the parent is heterozygous (*Ff*). Dominance relationships between alleles determine the phenotypic outcome of a monohybrid cross.

Monohybrid Cross To make a monohybrid cross, we would start with individuals that are purebred for distinct variations of a single trait. In pea plants, flower color (*F*, purple; *f*, white) is one example of a trait with two distinct variations. A cross between such individuals (*FF* × *ff*) yields hybrid offspring (*Ff*), all with the same set of alleles governing the trait. A cross between two of these F_1 (first generation) hybrids is the monohybrid cross (*Ff* × *Ff*). The frequency at which the two traits appear in the F_2 (second generation) offspring offers information about a dominance relationship between the two alleles (**Figure 12-21**).

The 3:1 pattern is evidence that purple and white flower color are specified by alleles with a clear dominance relationship: purple is dominant and white is recessive. In this example, there will be roughly three purple-flowered plants for every white-flowered one. This example illustrates a pattern so predictable that it can be used as evidence of a dominance relationship between alleles. The phenotype ratios in the F_2 offspring of Mendel's monohybrid crosses were all close to 3:1.

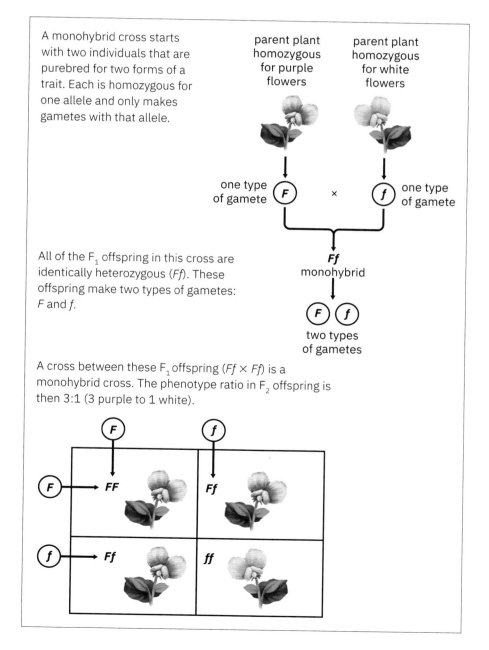

A monohybrid cross starts with two individuals that are purebred for two forms of a trait. Each is homozygous for one allele and only makes gametes with that allele.

parent plant homozygous for purple flowers

parent plant homozygous for white flowers

one type of gamete **F** × **f** one type of gamete

Ff monohybrid

F **f** two types of gametes

All of the F_1 offspring in this cross are identically heterozygous (*Ff*). These offspring make two types of gametes: *F* and *f*.

A cross between these F_1 offspring (*Ff* × *Ff*) is a monohybrid cross. The phenotype ratio in F_2 offspring is then 3:1 (3 purple to 1 white).

	F	**f**
F	**FF**	**Ff**
f	**Ff**	**ff**

FIGURE 12-21
A cross between F_1 offspring (*Ff* × *Ff*) is a monohybrid cross. The phenotype ratio in F_2 offspring is 3:1 (3 purple to 1 white) in this example.

Dihybrid Cross An individual heterozygous for two alleles at two loci is called a dihybrid. A cross between two such individuals is a dihybrid cross. As with a monohybrid cross, the frequency of traits appearing among the offspring of a dihybrid cross depends on the dominance relationships between the alleles.

To make a dihybrid cross, we would start with individuals that are purebred for two different traits. In pea plants, flower color (*F*, purple; *f*, white) and plant height (*H*, tall; *h*, short) are examples of two traits each with two distinct variations. Making a dihybrid cross using these genes begins with one parent purebred for purple flowers and tall stems (*FFHH*) and one parent purebred for white flowers and short stems (*ffhh*) (**Figure 12-22**).

FIGURE 12-22 ▷
A dihybrid cross starts with two individuals that are purebred for two different traits.

Individuals homozygous for alleles of two genes produce gametes with the same allele combination.

A cross between the two homozygous individuals yields offspring heterozygous for alleles of two genes (dihybrids).

Dihybrid individuals produce gametes with four possible combinations of alleles.

If two of the dihybrid individuals are crossed, the four types of gametes can combine in 16 possible ways: 9 that are purple-flowered and tall; 3 that are purple-flowered and short; 3 that are white-flowered and tall; and 1 that is white-flowered and short. Thus, the ratio of phenotypes is 9:3:3:1.

Calculating Genetic Probabilities

The frequency at which traits associated with alleles appear among the offspring depends on whether one of the alleles is dominant over the other. Scientists use probability, a branch of mathematics, to calculate the chances for a particular outcome. In genetics, scientists use probability to determine the genotype of offspring from a specific cross.

$$\text{Probability} = \frac{\text{the number of ways a specific outcome can occur}}{\text{the number of total possible outcomes}}$$

For example, the probability of human offspring having the *XX* or the *XY* sex chromosome is typically 50 percent or ½. The mother can donate only X chromosomes, so the father determines the sex of the offspring with the Y chromosome. The father, being *XY*, could donate either an X chromosome, in which case the offspring would be *XX*, or a Y chromosome, in which case the offspring would be *XY* (**Figure 12-23**).

	X	**Y**
X	XX	XY
X	XX	XY

FIGURE 12-23
The probability that a human offspring will be either *XX* or *XY* is typically 50 percent.

12.3 REVIEW

1. **Distinguish** Describe the differences between genotype and phenotype.

2. **Calculate** What is the genotypic ratio of homozygous dominant to heterozygous to homozygous recessive offspring in a cross between parents with the genotypes *Ff* × *Ff*?

3. **Identify** List the genotypes of possible gametes from a heterozygous organism *WwRr*.

4. **Relate** Why is a recessive allele only expressed when the organism is homozygous for that allele?

BLOOD TYPE COMPATIBILITY

SEP **Mathematical Thinking** Blood donors and recipients must have compatible blood types, even if they are close relatives.

Blood type is a heritable trait. The three alleles are I^A, I^B, and i. The antigens (I or i) expressed in the red blood cells contribute to the determination of an individual's blood type. **Table 1** shows how allele combinations result in an offspring's blood type.

TABLE 1. Blood Types and Alleles

Blood type	Allele combinations	
	Homozygous	Heterozygous
A	AA	AO
AB	n/a	AB
B	BB	BO
O	OO	n/a

FIGURE 1 ▲
A donor-recipient chart shows blood type compatibility between two individuals.

A donor-recipient chart that shows blood type compatibility is shown in **Figure 1**. Each square links a donor on the horizontal axis and a recipient on the vertical axis. Y means a blood transfer is medically safe while N means it is not. For example, a person with blood type AB can safely receive a blood transfusion from a family member with blood type O, A, B, or AB. However, a recipient with blood type B can only safely receive blood from a donor of blood type O or B.

Figure 2 shows the blood type pedigree chart for a fictitious family. Squares represent males, and circles represent females. The letters inside each shape represent the family member's blood type. In the first generation, a male (1) with blood type AB reproduces with a female (2) with blood type O. They produce three offspring in the second generation: one female of blood type B (4) and two males with blood type A (5, 6).

FIGURE 2 ▲
A blood type pedigree chart shows the blood types of family members.

---

1. **Analyze Data** Determine the probability of blood types in generation III for the offspring of the pairing of heterozygous male 3 with heterozygous female 4. Does the pedigree match the possibilities?

2. **Evaluate** Use the phenotypes of male 10 and female 11 in the pedigree to determine the genotype of their father and mother.

3. **Predict** A homozygous male with blood type A (10) and homozygous female (11) produce a female offspring with iron-deficiency anemia. Determine the offspring's blood type and identify all the family members who could donate blood to them.

OTHER PATTERNS OF INHERITANCE

KEY TERMS

codominance
incomplete dominance

Most human traits do not follow the rules of Mendelian inheritance with predictable outcomes. Long past the early days of genetic studies, we now know there is much more to genetic variation than the straightforward patterns of dominant and recessive relationships.

Predict *How might patterns of inheritance and environmental factors influence a trait, such as height in humans?*

Incomplete Dominance

In an inheritance pattern called **incomplete dominance**, one allele is not fully dominant over the other, so the heterozygous phenotype is an intermediate blend of the two homozygous phenotypes. One example is the gene that affects flower color in snapdragon plants (**Figure 12-24**). One allele of the gene (*R*) encodes an enzyme that makes a red pigment. The enzyme encoded by an allele with a mutation (*r*) cannot make any pigment. Plants homozygous for the *R* allele (*RR*) make a lot of red pigment, so they have red flowers. Plants homozygous for the *r* allele (*rr*) make no pigment, so their flowers are white. Heterozygous plants (*Rr*) make only enough red pigment to color their flowers pink.

homozygous parent   ×   homozygous parent   =   heterozygous offspring
         (rr)   (RR)   (Rr)

FIGURE 12-24 ◀
Snapdragons are a plant that demonstrate incomplete dominance. When a red-flowered snapdragon plant is crossed with a white-flowered one, the resulting offspring have pink flowers.

Codominance

In an inheritance pattern called **codominance**, two versions of an allele, one from each parent, are equally expressed in heterozygous individuals. Neither allele is dominant or recessive. Codominance means that neither allele can mask the expression of the other allele. The gene that affects hair color in shorthorn cattle is an example (**Figure 12-25**).

FIGURE 12-25
Shorthorn cattle are animals that demonstrate codominance. When a white-haired cow is crossed with a red-haired cow, the resulting offspring will have speckled white and red hair.

| white coat color homozygous parent (*WW*) | × | red coat color homozygous parent (*RR*) | = | roan coat color heterozygous offspring (*WR*) |

Multiple Alleles

Human blood type is controlled by multiple alleles (**Table 12-3**), two of which are codominant (*AB*). Alleles *A* and *B* are codominant when paired. The *O* allele is recessive when paired with either the *A* or *B* allele. The three alleles are called I^A, I^B and *i*. Both I^A and I^B result in a protein, called an antigen, on the surface of red blood cells. Allele *i* is recessive and does not result in an antigen.

TABLE 12-3. Combinations of Alleles (Genotype) for Human Blood Type (Phenotype)

Blood type (Phenotype)	Genotype	Can donate blood to:	Can receive blood from:
O	*ii* (*OO*)	A, B, AB, and O (universal donor)	O
AB	I^AI^B	AB	A, B, AB, and O (universal receiver)
A	I^AI^A or I^Ai (I^AO)	AB, A	O, A
B	I^BI^B or I^Bi (I^BO)	AB, B	O, B

If your genotype is *AA* or *AO*, your blood type is A. If your genotype is *BB* or *BO*, it is type B. If your genotype is *OO*, then your blood type is O. The antigens (*I* or *i*) expressed in the red blood cells also contribute to the determination of blood type.

CCC **Patterns** *Explain in your own words how incomplete dominance and codominance differ from what is called Mendelian inheritance, which involves dominant and recessive traits.*

Polygenic Traits

In a common inheritance pattern called polygenic inheritance, one trait is affected by multiple genes. Your height is an example of a polygenic trait, in which multiple genes contribute to the overall phenotype observed. The height genes you inherit from your parents accumulate, and the final height you are likely to reach is due in part to the cumulative effect of these genes. Scientists have discovered more than 600 genes that affect height. These complex traits show a continuous range of phenotypes from very short to very tall, making a bell-shaped curve when graphed.

In a phenomenon called *epistasis*, the expression of one gene is affected by the expression of one or more independently inherited genes. One example is genes related to pigments, called melanins, that produce different fur color in Labrador retriever dogs. The brown and black fur comes from a dark brown form of melanin and the yellow fur comes from a reddish form of melanin. Alleles of two of these genes determine whether the individual has black, brown, or yellow fur (**Figure 12-26**). The product of one gene (*TYRP1*) helps make the brown melanin. A dominant allele (*B*) of this gene results in a higher production of brown melanin than the recessive allele (*b*). A different gene (*MC1R*) affects which type of melanin is produced. A dominant allele (*E*) of this gene triggers production of the brown melanin. Its recessive partner (*e*) carries a mutation that results in production of the reddish form. Dogs homozygous for the *e* allele are yellow because they only make the reddish melanin.

FIGURE 12-26 ▽
In a phenomenon called epistasis, interactions among products of two genes affect fur color in Labrador retrievers.

Sex-Linked Traits

Recall that humans have 23 pairs of chromosomes: 22 pairs of autosomes, or nonsex chromosomes, and one pair of sex chromosomes. These sex chromosomes—X and Y—contain different genes, which make a unique pattern of inheritance. Many of the genes seen on the X chromosome do not have corresponding genes on the Y chromosome, simply because the Y chromosome is much smaller.

The genes located on an X or Y chromosome are referred to as sex-linked genes. Males have only one copy of the Y chromosome, so any recessive gene on a Y chromosome will be expressed. Any recessive gene on an X chromosome also will be expressed in males because there is no second X chromosome to mask the recessive allele's expression.

CHAPTER INVESTIGATION

Design an Organism
How do alleles determine the phenotype of an organism?
Go online to explore this chapter's hands-on investigation about variation in alleles and designing your own organism.

Females have double the number of genes located on an X chromosome, but they do not need double the number of their associated proteins. A process known as X inactivation solves this dilemma. Only one X chromosome is active, while the other is silenced or has very few active genes. X inactivation results in more balanced gene expression between males and females.

Red-green color blindness is an example of a trait caused by a sex-linked gene that occurs more often in males. The dominant allele that produces normal vision is represented by the C superscript (X^C). The recessive allele that is responsible for red-green color blindness is represented by the c superscript (X^c), as shown in **Figure 12-27**.

FIGURE 12-27 ▶
A cross between a female homozygous dominant for red-green color blindness and a male with normal vision.

	X^C	Y
X^c	$X^c X^C$	$X^c Y$
X^c	$X^c X^C$	$X^c Y$

SEP **Analyze and Interpret Data** *Using the Punnett square in Figure 12-27, determine the probabilities that a couple will have a son or daughter with color blindness.*

Environmental Factors

The environment affects the expression of many genes, which in turn affects phenotype, including physical and behavioral traits. Today, we understand that genetics (nature) and environmental factors (nurture) both play a substantial role in the behavioral traits of humans and other organisms.

In plants, a flexible phenotype gives immobile individuals an ability to thrive in diverse habitats. For example, genetically identical yarrow plants can grow to different heights at different altitudes. More challenging temperature, soil, and water conditions are typically encountered at higher altitudes. Differences in altitude are also correlated with changes in the reproductive mode of yarrow. Plants at higher altitude tend to reproduce asexually, and those at lower altitude tend to reproduce sexually.

Environmental cues trigger adjustments in gene expression that change an individual's form and function to suit its current environment. For example, a water flea that swims to the bottom of a pond can survive the low oxygen conditions by turning on expression of genes involved in the production of hemoglobin. Hemoglobin is a protein that carries oxygen, and it enhances the individual's ability to absorb oxygen from the water. Other environmental factors also affect water flea phenotype. For example, the presence of insect predators causes water fleas to form a protective pointy helmet and lengthened tail spine. Individual water fleas also switch between asexual and sexual modes of reproduction depending on the season.

Environmental cues trigger adjustments in gene expression that change an individual's form. In many mammals, seasonal changes in temperature and length of day affect the production of melanin and other pigments that provide skin and fur with their color. These species have different color phases in different seasons (**Figure 12-28**). Hormonal signals triggered by seasonal changes cause fur to be shed, and new fur grows back with different types and amounts of pigments deposited in it. The resulting change in phenotype provides the animals with seasonally appropriate camouflage from predators.

FIGURE 12-28
Environmental cues, such as temperature changes, can trigger changes in melanin and other pigments that can alter fur color between white (a) and brown (b) in hares.

12.4 REVIEW

1. **Calculate** If two pink-flowered snapdragons are crossed, what is the phenotypic ratio of the offspring? Support your ratio with the percentages for each phenotype.

2. **Distinguish** Why is a sex-linked trait on an X chromosome expressed differently in male and female offspring?

3. **Identify** Sort the examples of genetic and environmental factors that affect phenotype.

   • carcinogens
   • genotype
   • parental DNA
   • temperature

4. **Explain** Two species of hare occupy an area that experiences four seasons. Hare A has white fur in the winter and brown fur in the spring. Hare B has brown fur all year round. Which of these types of hare has a more beneficial phenotype? Explain your answer.

MODELING INHERITANCE

SEP **Analyzing and Interpreting Data** How can we model the probability of inheriting a trait?

Most organisms are diploid, meaning they carry two sets of chromosomes. In diploid organisms, an individual has two alleles for most genes. Each set of alleles includes an allele from the mother and an allele from the father. In this activity, you will use probability calculations to explain the variation and distribution of traits in a cross between two heterozygous individuals.

Fruit flies are model organisms for genetic study because they reproduce quickly and are easy to handle, among other reasons.

Materials

- coins, 2
- black marker

Procedure

The inherited gene you will model is red or white eye color in fruit flies. Red eye color (*R*) is dominant, and white eye color is recessive (*r*). For a cross between heterozygous parents, you will calculate the probability that the offspring will get either the red eye color allele or the white eye color allele from each parent.

1. Each coin represents the alleles from each parent. In this activity, the parents are heterozygous, so heads equals red eyes and tails equals white eyes.

2. Enter the possible genotypes for a heterozygous cross *Rr* × *Rr* in the data table.

Genotype	Phenotype	Offspring

3. Enter the corresponding phenotypes for the genotypes in the data table.

4. Flip both coins together. Enter a tick mark in the offspring column in the data table based on the outcome of the coin flip.

5. Repeat Step 4 an additional 24 times. In the end, you will have data for 25 offspring.

Results and Analysis

To calculate the probability of an event, use the formula

$$\text{Probability} = \frac{\text{number of ways a specific event can occur}}{\text{number of total possible outcomes}}$$

To calculate the probability of two independent events occurring together, multiply the probability of the individual events. So, the probability of flipping heads is 1/2. Therefore, the probability of flipping two heads together is $1/2 \times 1/2 = 1/4$.

1. **Calculate** What is the probability of each genotype?

2. **Calculate** What is the probability of each phenotype?

3. **Analyze** How do your calculations in Question 1 compare with the data you collected?

4. **Evaluate** Describe and evaluate the model used in this lab.

TYING IT ALL TOGETHER
FOR THE LOVE OF DOGS

HOW DOES GENETIC INFORMATION CHANGE AND GET PASSED FROM GENERATION TO GENERATION?

In this chapter, you learned how traits are passed from parents to offspring through the transfer of genes. You also learned how mutations can affect gene expression. The Case Study described how scientists learned that animal domestication through careful breeding can result in offspring with desired characteristics, such as certain physical characteristics or the ability to herd, retrieve, or hunt.

Today, several consumer brands offer genetic testing for dog owners interested in learning more about the ancestry of their pets. These genetic tests can not only help to pinpoint the breeds that make up a mixed-breed dog (**Figure 12-29**), but they can also provide insight into potential health issues. These companies only analyze a fraction of the billions of base pairs in a dog's genome, focusing on certain short sequences of base pairs that are known to be associated with a particular dog breed. However, there can be a significant amount of genetic variation even within a single purebred dog breed. For example, a Corgi bred for herding has different genes from one bred to be a household pet. The accuracy of breed identification continues to advance as more data are collected, analyzed, and added to a company's repository of genetic information.

In this activity, you will develop models and use evidence to explain how the genetic information passed from parents to their offspring determines which traits they exhibit. Work individually or in a group to complete these steps.

Gather Evidence

1. Choose a dog breed, and research the traits it was bred to have. Which of these traits are Mendelian?

Develop and Use a Model

2. Choose one of the Mendelian traits, such as coat color, and develop a model to predict the genotypes of the offspring from parents that are heterozygous for that trait.

Argue From Evidence

3. Agouti is a type of fur pattern that shows more than one color on each strand of fur. Research the four alleles that control this fur pattern. What can you conclude about the way this trait is inherited?

FIGURE 12-29 ▼

Leroy is a mixed-breed dog that was adopted from a small dog rescue in New Jersey. Leroy's adoption papers listed him as a Cairn terrier mix. Genetic test results showed otherwise.

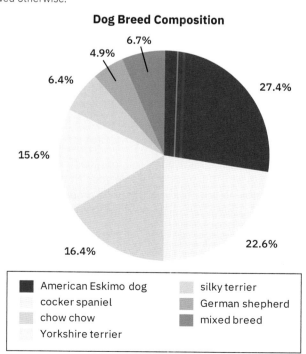

Dog Breed Composition

- 27.4%
- 22.6%
- 16.4%
- 15.6%
- 6.4%
- 4.9%
- 6.7%

Legend:
- American Eskimo dog
- cocker spaniel
- chow chow
- Yorkshire terrier
- silky terrier
- German shepherd
- mixed breed

REVIEW KEY CONCEPTS

1. **Describe** Which statements are true about alleles in a eukaryotic organism? Select all correct answers.

   A. They can be dominant or recessive.

   B. They are alternative forms of a gene.

   C. They are both inherited from the female parent.

   D. They contribute to the phenotype of an organism.

   E. They are located on the same chromosome.

2. **Contrast** Match each statement with either sexual reproduction or asexual reproduction.

   • Genetic variation is introduced.

   • Mitosis is the reproductive process.

   • All parental genes are passed to offspring.

   • Genetically identical offspring are produced.

   • Meiosis plays a role in the reproductive process.

   • Offspring from two parents inherit genes from both.

3. **Summarize** Which of the following is the outcome of meiosis for a parent cell?

   A. two diploid gametes   C. four diploid gametes

   B. two haploid gametes   D. four haploid gametes

4. **Classify** Match each statement to the type of mutation it describes: gene duplication, point mutation, gene translocation.

   • A faulty crossing over event results in a gene for one chromosome being swapped for a gene from another chromosome.

   • A misalignment of homologous chromosomes results in DNA segments of unequal size because one chromosome has two copies of a gene.

   • A replication error results in the insertion of an adenine in place of a cytosine in a DNA strand.

5. **Analyze** A plant that is purebred for blue flowers is crossed with a plant of the same species that is purebred for yellow flowers. Offspring produced from the cross all have yellow flowers. Explain this outcome.

   A. The yellow and blue traits are codominant.

   B. Yellow is a dominant trait, and blue is a recessive trait.

   C. Blue is a dominant trait, and yellow is a recessive trait.

   D. The yellow and blue traits demonstrate incomplete dominance.

6. **Predict** Sickle cell anemia is a genetic disease caused by an autosomal recessive mutation in the gene for hemoglobin. This means an individual must have two copies of the sickle cell mutation to be afflicted with the disease. Individuals who inherit only one copy of the sickle cell mutation are carriers of the disease but are not afflicted with any of the symptoms. If a woman who has sickle cell anemia has a child with a man who is a carrier, what is the probability that the child will have sickle cell anemia?

7. **Relate** In pea plants, the purple flower trait (*F*) is dominant, and the white flower trait (*f*) is recessive. Also, the tall stem trait (*H*) is dominant, and the short stem trait (*h*) is recessive. Which pairs of pea plants have the same phenotype? Select all correct answers.

   A. *FFhh* and *ffHH*   D. *FFHH* and *FFhh*

   B. *FfHh* and *FFHH*   E. *ffHh* and *ffHH*

   C. *ffhh* and *Ffhh*

8. **Identify** Keratin is a protein found in the hair of mammals. Dogs that are homozygous for a particular allele for keratin have very curly hair. Dogs that are homozygous for a different allele for keratin have straight hair. Dogs that are heterozygous for these two alleles have wavy hair. What type of inheritance pattern does this example represent?

   A. codominance

   B. epistasis

   C. incomplete dominance

   D. polygenic inheritance

9. **Describe** Which statements about sex-linked traits are true? Select all correct answers.

   A. Only females express sex-linked trait.

   B. Only males express sex-linked traits.

   C. Sex-linked traits are determined by genes found on X and Y chromosomes.

   D. An individual can be a carrier of a sex-linked trait without expressing the trait.

   E. Sex-linked traits follow the rules of Mendelian inheritance in a predictable pattern.

CRITICAL THINKING

10. Compare Describe one similarity and one difference between crossing over and segregation.

11. NOS Scientific Investigation Gregor Mendel conducted heredity experiments on pea plants. Thirty-five years later, Theodor Boveri and Walter Sutton used microscopes to study the behavior of chromosomes during gamete formation and fertilization. They concluded that chromosomes were likely responsible for carrying genetic information from parents to offspring. How do you think scientific understanding of heredity would have been affected if microscope technology had not been developed?

12. Compare How are gene mutations similar to and different from chromosomal mutations?

13. Explain Why is it possible for two organisms to have the same phenotype for a particular trait but different genotypes? Provide an example as part of your response.

14. Identify Cause and Effect Butterfly eggs from the same population were placed in different environments. The larvae hatched, grew, and underwent metamorphosis. The adult butterflies that emerged had different markings on their wings. How can this difference be explained?

MATH AND ENGLISH LANGUAGE ARTS CONNECTIONS

1. Reason Abstractly and Quantitatively How many different combinations are there with two pairs of homologous chromosomes? Explain your reasoning.

Read the following passage. Use evidence from the passage to answer the question.

The azoospermia factor (AZF) regions of the human Y chromosome contain genes that code for proteins critical to sperm development. Gene deletions sometimes occur in the AZF regions during meiosis. This leads to the production of sperm carrying these mutations. While these sperm are capable of producing healthy offspring, the mutations are carried to the next generation.

2. Cite Textual Evidence Explain how a man could be infertile from this type of mutation. Cite information from the text to support your answer.

3. Write Explanatory Text Mendel began his experiments with purebred parent pea plants. Purebred means that a purple-flowering pea plant only produces offspring that have purple flowers when allowed to self-fertilize. Why was this critical in allowing Mendel to conclude that traits were passed from one generation to the next in discrete units?

Read the following passage. Use evidence from the passage to justify your answer to the question.

A human female inherits one X chromosome from her father and the other from her mother. When the embryo reaches about 1000 cells, a process called X inactivation occurs. Each cell renders one of the two X chromosomes inactive. There is no preference for which X chromosome is inactivated; each is inactivated roughly 50 percent of the time. From that point on, all of the descendant cells continue to inactivate the same X chromosome.

4. Write an Argument How can you explain why a female who inherits the gene for color blindness from her father does not express the color-blind trait?

5. Reason Abstractly and Quantitatively A man has blood type A and is heterozygous for the I^A and i alleles. He fathers a child with a woman with blood type B who is heterozygous for the I^B and i alleles. What are the possible blood types that the offspring could have? Calculate the probability of each blood type. Probability is calculated by dividing the number of ways a specific outcome can occur by the total number of possible outcomes.

► REVISIT VIRAL SPREAD

Gather Evidence In this chapter, you learned about genetic variation that is introduced through processes related to meiosis and mutations. You also learned in Section 12.2 that a DNA mutation can alter the structure and function of the resulting protein. Similar to those mutations, errors in replicating the RNA genome of SARS-CoV-2 can introduce significant changes in the proteins that make up the virus particle.

1. The spike protein of SARS-CoV-2 enables the virus to infect human cells and is the target of most COVID-19 vaccines. The D614G mutation changes a single amino acid in the spike protein, making the spike proteins more stable. How do you think a mutation such as D614G can impact science, technology, and society?

2. What other questions do you have about how mutations can affect pandemics such as COVID-19?

GENETIC TECHNOLOGIES

Elizabeth Ann is a clone of an endangered species, the black-footed ferret, which is native to North America.

Over the past few decades, with increasing success, scientists have been able to study the effects of changing a gene by manipulating DNA. The application of genetic editing technology to problems involving conservation and human health is a major part of the field of genetic engineering.

Chapter 13 supports the NGSS Performance Expectation **HS-ETS1-1** and **HS-ETS1-3**.

CASE STUDY
GENETICS TO THE RESCUE!

HOW CAN GENETIC INFORMATION BE USED IN MEDICAL AND OTHER SCIENTIFIC APPLICATIONS?

An organism that is genetically identical to its parent, typically as a result of asexual reproduction, is a clone. Cloning is a widespread agricultural strategy for ensuring that crops bred for specific desirable traits continue to have those traits. For example, bananas in grocery stores are often clones of the Cavendish variety.

Animal cloning is being tested as a solution to global problems of species conservation. When most of the individuals in an isolated population are directly related, the genetic diversity needed to adapt to changing conditions is limited. One way to introduce more genetic diversity is to transplant individuals from elsewhere into the endangered population to breed. However, in cases where existing populations are so small that no such animals are available, conservation scientists explore cloning genetically distinct individuals from the cells of previous members of the species as an alternative.

A black-footed ferret was the first endangered animal to be cloned in the United States. The North American native species was thought to have become extinct in the 1970s due to the eradication of prairie dogs, their main prey, by hunters and ranchers. However, a small colony of 18 ferrets found in Wyoming in 1981 were used to start a captive breeding program. Only seven of them bred. Thus, all black-footed ferrets in the wild population of several hundred are closely related. This ferret population is additionally threatened by sylvatic plague, an often fatal flea-borne bacterial disease.

In 2020, scientists attempted to again rescue the species. They made a clone using the frozen cells of a female black-footed ferret named Willa that died in 1988. A surrogate domestic ferret, implanted with an embryo made from eggs containing genetic material extracted from these cells, gave birth to Elizabeth Ann, Willa's clone. The cloned ferret's DNA, while identical to its parent's DNA, differs from that of all other living black-footed ferrets. Breeding Elizabeth Ann and reintroducing her descendants into the wild is anticipated to widen the gene pool and improve the species' odds of survival.

Ask Questions *In this chapter, you will learn about fundamental tools and techniques for manipulating genetic material. As you read, generate questions that would help determine when genetic technology should be used to solve medical or scientific problems.*

FIGURE 13-1
Przewalkski's horse is a critically endangered species of wild horse native to Mongolia. It was successfully cloned in 2020.

13.1

KEY TERMS

bioinformatics
DNA cloning
DNA profiling
gel electrophoresis
genomics
microarray
polymerase chain reaction (PCR)
recombinant DNA
restriction enzyme

TOOLS IN GENETIC TECHNOLOGY

In a pastry chef's kitchen or an automobile mechanic's shop, there are a wide variety of very specialized tools, each designed to perform a particular task. A pastry chef uses one type of spatula to scrape batter in a bowl and a different type to apply frosting to a cake. An automobile mechanic needs the right type of wrench to remove an oil filter. Similarly, scientists have spent decades developing and honing a set of tools for use in genetic technology.

Analyze *What are some likely similarities and differences between kitchen or workshop tools and the tools used in a genetics lab?*

Working With DNA

The basic tools that unlock most genetic technologies start with the ability to manipulate DNA. Scientists have repurposed enzymes borrowed from nature as tools to cut, copy, paste, edit, sequence, and thus better understand DNA.

Restriction Enzymes In the 1950s, excitement over the discovery of DNA's structure gave way to challenges as scientists attempted to determine the order of nucleotides in a molecule of DNA. Identifying a single base among thousands or millions of others turned out to be a major technical challenge. Research in a seemingly unrelated field yielded a solution when scientists discovered how some bacteria resist infection by bacteriophage viruses. The defense mechanism of the bacteria involves enzymes that chop up any injected viral DNA. The enzymes restrict viral growth. Therefore, they were named **restriction enzymes**. A restriction enzyme cuts DNA wherever a specific nucleotide sequence occurs (**Figure 13-2**). For example, the enzyme *Eco*RI (named after *Escherichia coli*, the bacterium from which it was isolated) cuts DNA at the nucleotide sequence G-A-A-T-T-C. Other restriction enzymes cut at different sequences. The discovery of restriction enzymes made it possible to cut chromosomal DNA into manageable chunks.

FIGURE 13-2 ▶
The restriction enzyme *Eco*RI recognizes a specific base sequence in DNA and cuts it. *Eco*RI leaves single-stranded tails that are known as "sticky ends."

Recombinant DNA Many restriction enzymes, including *Eco*RI, leave single-stranded tails on DNA fragments. The tails are called "sticky ends" because two DNA fragments stick together when their matching tails base-pair. Scientists realized that because the chemical structure of DNA is the same in all organisms, complementary tails will base-pair regardless of the source of DNA. Another enzyme, *DNA ligase*, can be used to seal the gaps between hybridized DNA fragments, forming continuous DNA strands (**Figure 13-3**). Using appropriate restriction enzymes and DNA ligase, DNA can be cut and pasted to combine fragments from different sources. The result, a hybrid molecule that consists of genetic material from two or more organisms, is called **recombinant DNA**. This ability to use enzymes to manipulate DNA fragments was a major advance in genetic technology.

FIGURE 13-3
When DNA fragments from two sources are cut with *Eco*RI and mixed together, their matching sticky ends base-pair. DNA ligase seals the gaps between hybridized DNA fragments. The resulting hybrid molecules are called recombinant DNA.

DNA Cloning Making recombinant DNA is the first step in DNA cloning. **DNA cloning** is a set of laboratory methods that uses living cells to mass-produce specific DNA fragments. A fragment of DNA is cloned by inserting it into a *vector*, which in this context is a DNA molecule used to shuttle foreign DNA fragments into host cells. As shown in **Figure 13-4**, plasmids can be used as cloning vectors by introducing them into a bacterial host. When the bacterial cell divides, the recombinant plasmid is replicated and distributed to descendant cells in the same way as the bacterium's own genetic material. Recombinant vectors are introduced into cells that can be easily grown in the laboratory to yield huge populations of genetically identical descendants. Each of these clones contains a copy of the recombinant vector. The vector can be extracted in quantity, and the cloned DNA fragment can then be manipulated using restriction enzymes and other tools.

FIGURE 13-4
DNA fragments are inserted into plasmid vectors with the use of restriction enzymes and DNA ligase.

SEP **Construct an Explanation** *Plasmid DNA vectors often include a gene for antibiotic resistance. Why do you think that might be useful?*

Polymerase Chain Reaction Scientists often need to generate large quantities of a DNA sequence they want to study. Making recombinant DNA to grow in host bacteria is not necessarily the quickest or most precise method. **Polymerase chain reaction** (PCR) is a technique used to mass-produce, or amplify, copies of a particular section of linear DNA. One PCR cycle can double the number of copies of the targeted section of DNA. Thirty PCR cycles may amplify that number a billionfold (**Figure 13-5**).

FIGURE 13-5 ▶
In one cycle of PCR, each strand of DNA that contains the targeted section may be copied to form a new strand.

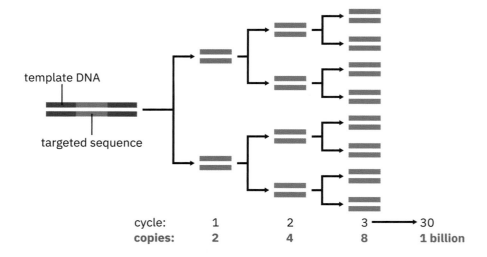

template DNA

targeted sequence

cycle: 1   2   3 ——→ 30
copies: 2   4   8   1 billion

The starting material for PCR is any sample of DNA with at least one molecule of the desired DNA sequence. The source of the DNA might be a mixture with multiple DNA samples, a hair left at a crime scene, or a mummy—essentially, any substance that has DNA in it.

PCR is DNA replication in a test tube (Section 11.2). Like replication in a cell, DNA strands are separated, primers bind the DNA, and a DNA polymerase enzyme builds complementary strands. However, rather than a helicase enzyme, the PCR technique uses high temperatures to separate DNA strands. The temperatures required to do this would damage the DNA polymerases of most organisms, so PCR reactions make use of *Taq* polymerase, which comes from the bacterial species *Thermus aquaticus*. These bacteria live in hot springs and hydrothermal vents, so their polymerase tolerates high temperatures. Like other DNA polymerases, *Taq* polymerase recognizes primers that have matched and hybridized with the DNA template as places to start DNA synthesis.

PCR requires two DNA primers designed to base-pair at opposite ends of the sequence of the sample DNA that scientists want to amplify. These primers are mixed with the DNA sample, nucleotides, and *Taq* polymerase (**Figure 13-6**). The reaction mixture is then exposed to repeated cycles of high and low temperatures. A few seconds at high temperature disrupts the hydrogen bonds that hold the two strands of the sample DNA together, so every molecule of DNA unwinds into single strands. As the temperature of the mixture is lowered, the single DNA strands hybridize with the primers, and the *Taq* polymerase builds complementary DNA strands. The newly synthesized DNA is a copy of the targeted section. When the mixture is reheated, all of the DNA strands separate to begin another cycle.

> ▼
> **VIRAL SPREAD**
>
> **Gather Evidence** *RT-PCR is a PCR technique that relies on reverse transcriptase (RT) to make a DNA copy of an RNA strand, which can then be amplified. How could this technology be used for diagnosing cases of SARS-CoV-2 infection?*

SEP **Develop a Solution** *How might PCR be used to diagnose whether a patient is infected with a particular pathogen?*

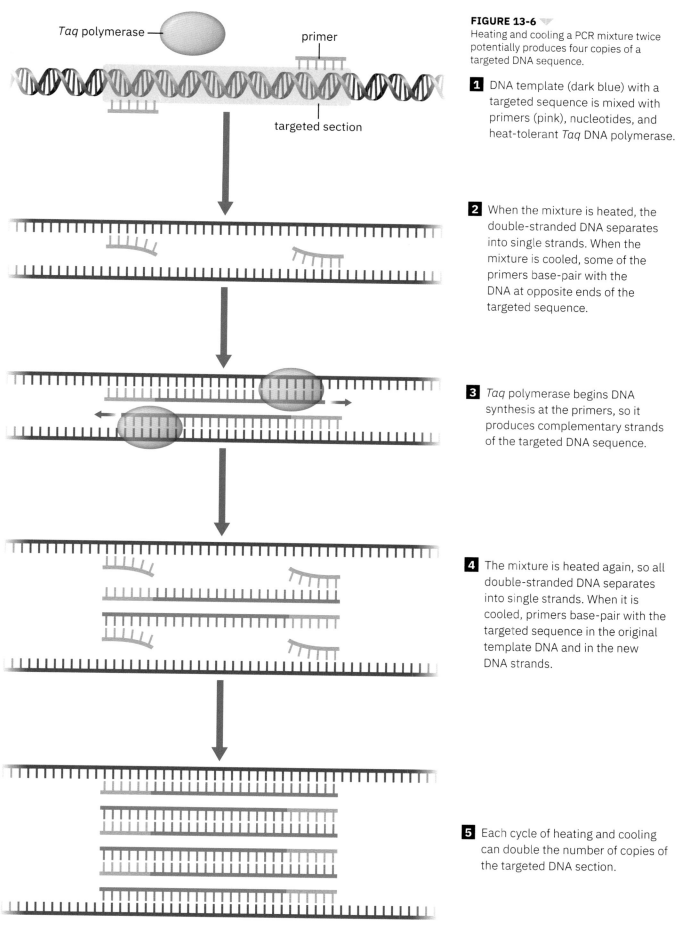

FIGURE 13-6 ▽
Heating and cooling a PCR mixture twice potentially produces four copies of a targeted DNA sequence.

1 DNA template (dark blue) with a targeted sequence is mixed with primers (pink), nucleotides, and heat-tolerant *Taq* DNA polymerase.

2 When the mixture is heated, the double-stranded DNA separates into single strands. When the mixture is cooled, some of the primers base-pair with the DNA at opposite ends of the targeted sequence.

3 *Taq* polymerase begins DNA synthesis at the primers, so it produces complementary strands of the targeted DNA sequence.

4 The mixture is heated again, so all double-stranded DNA separates into single strands. When it is cooled, primers base-pair with the targeted sequence in the original template DNA and in the new DNA strands.

5 Each cycle of heating and cooling can double the number of copies of the targeted DNA section.

Go Online SIMULATION

PCR and Gel Electrophoresis Go online to use PCR and gel electrophoresis to amplify DNA and check your results.

Gel Electrophoresis In a sample of DNA that has been cut into fragments by enzymes or that contains specific segments that scientists want to study, it is useful to separate the DNA fragments by length. A technique called **gel electrophoresis** uses an electric field and a semisolid, porous gel to accomplish this. Each gel has wells that hold samples of DNA. The wells position the samples so they can move through the gel material during the procedure.

Figure 13-7 shows the apparatus for gel electrophoresis. A power source generates the electric field by charging electrodes positioned at opposite ends of the gel slab positively at one end and negatively at the other end. The phosphate groups along the DNA backbone give DNA molecules an overall negative charge. When a charged particle is placed in an electric field, it is attracted toward the opposite charge. Thus, negatively charged DNA fragments placed in wells near the negative electrode will all be pulled through the gel toward the positive electrode. However, DNA fragments of different lengths travel through the gel at different rates. Smaller fragments move farther toward the positive electrode than larger fragments, which stay closer to the negative electrode. **Figure 13-8** shows a pattern resulting from a gel electrophoresis experiment. Each band represents a DNA fragment of a particular size from a sample.

FIGURE 13-7
Gel electrophoresis uses an electric field to separate fragments of DNA based on size. In the gel, smaller fragments will move farther than larger ones. Once they have been separated, specific fragments can be cut out of the gel to use in further studies. For the model shown, samples would be loaded into the wells shown on the left side of the gel, near the negatively charged black electrode. Samples would be pulled through the gel toward the positively charged red electrode.

sample wells in gel   gel slab

electrolyte solution

FIGURE 13-8
The patterns made by separated DNA fragments in the gel give scientists information about the sequences present in the sample. A solution of DNA molecules of various known lengths, called a DNA ladder, is typically placed in one of the wells next to experimental DNA samples. The pattern made by an unknown sample can be compared to the known solution to determine fragment sizes. In this image, the wells in the gel are at the bottom of the photo, so the smallest DNA fragments are toward the top of the gel.

Genomes and Genome Analysis

The manipulation and amplification of DNA led to other technologies. Most important were techniques to determine DNA sequences. Studying the DNA of many organisms and sequencing their genomes has generated huge quantities of data, leading to new fields of statistical analyses and a better understanding of evolutionary relationships among organisms.

Genomics With continuing improvements in DNA sequencing technology, scientists began to sequence entire genomes of living organisms, starting with the bacterium *Haemophilus influenzae* in 1995. Three years later, the first genome to be sequenced for a multicellular organism was that of the roundworm *Caenorhabditis elegans*. Meanwhile, the Human Genome Project was launched in 1990 and completed in 2003. Sequencing the human genome paved the way for many other projects, including efforts to determine gene function. Because all organisms are descended from shared ancestors, all genomes are related to some extent. We see evidence of such genetic relationships by aligning sequences. Some regions of DNA are extremely similar across many species (**Figure 13-9**). Similarities among genomes allow us to discover functions of human genes by studying their counterparts in other species.

FIGURE 13-9 This is a region of the gene that codes for a DNA polymerase. Nucleotides that are different from the human sequence are highlighted.

```
758 GATAATCCTGTTTTGAACAAAAGGTCAAATTGCTGAATAGAAA-GTCTTGATTAACTAAAAGATGTACAAAGTGGAATTA 836 Human
752 GATAATCCTGTTTTGAACAAAAGGTCAAATTGCTGAATAGAAA-GTCTTGATTAACTAAAAGATGTACAAAGTGGAATTA 830 Mouse
751 GATAATCCTGTTTTGAACAAAAGGTCAAATTGCTGAATAGAAA-GTCTTGATTAACTAAAAGATGTACAAAGTGGAATTA 829 Rat
754 GATAATCCTGTTTTGAACAAAAGGTCAAATTGCTGAATAGAAA-GTCTTGATTAACTAAAAGATGTACAAAGTGGAATTA 832 Dog
782 GATAATCCTGTTTTGAACAAAAGGTCAAATTGCTGAATAGAAA-GTCTTGATTAACTAAAAGATGTACAAAGTGGAATTA 860 Chicken
758 GATAATCCTGTTTTGAACAAAAGGTCAAATTGCTGAATAGAAA-GTCTTGATTAAGTAAAAGATGTACAAAGTGGAATTA 836 Frog
823 GATAATCCTGTTTTGAACAAAAGGTCAGATTGCTGAATAGAAAAGGCTTGATTAAAGCAGAGATGTACAAAGTGGACGCA 902 Zebrafish
763 GATAATCCTGTTTTGAACAAAAGGTCAAATTGTTGAATAGAGACGCTTTGATAAAGCGGAGGAGGTACAAAGTGGGACC- 841 Pufferfish
```

The study of whole-genome structure and function is called **genomics**. This field has yielded many insights into gene function and evolutionary relationships among organisms. For example, comparing primate genomes revealed a change in chromosome structure that occurred during the evolution of our species. Comparing genomes also showed us that structural changes in chromosomes are not entirely random. Some specific alterations are much more common than others. This is because chromosomes that break tend to do so in particular locations. Human, mouse, rat, cow, pig, dog, cat, and horse chromosomes have undergone several translocations at these breakage "hot spots" during evolution. In humans, chromosome abnormalities that contribute to the progression of cancer also occur at the very same breakage hot spots.

Studying the products of a genome is even more difficult than deciphering the genome itself because the genome is constant but gene expression is not. The amounts and types of mRNA and proteins in a cell can differ dramatically by cell type and over time—an outcome of gene expression regulation (Section 11.3). Scientists study the *transcriptome* (mRNAs) and the *proteome* (proteins) to observe all mRNAs and proteins expressed at a particular moment. Scientists may choose to study the full set of mRNA or proteins expressed by an organism, or they may choose to just observe the expression in a particular type of cell within an organism. Understanding patterns and shifts in mRNA and protein production gives scientists additional ways to view cellular function.

Bioinformatics Genomics and proteomics require computational tools for analyzing and interpreting biological data. The science of developing these tools is called **bioinformatics**. This field has profoundly shifted the focus of biology research. Instead of trying to understand a complex biological system by studying its parts, scientists can now study the system as a whole. Until recently, for example, the role of genetics in medicine was limited to the diagnosis of single-gene disorders. Bioinformatics is bringing us closer to unraveling conditions that have complex inheritance patterns, such as cancer, diabetes, and cardiovascular disease.

Microarrays One important tool for performing a large number of genetic tests at once is the **microarray**, which can test for the presence of thousands of DNA sequences in a sample at once. **Figure 13-10** demonstrates a simple model of the principle that underlies microarrays and similar genetic technologies. In a basic microarray, known sequences of DNA are fixed to wells or spots on a plate. A sample of DNA is introduced to many wells at once. When DNA sequences in the sample match a microarray spot and hybridize, a fluorescent probe is activated. Changes in the fluorescent light in each cell can be measured to identify matches. Microarray-related technology can be used in many applications. For example, it can be used to quickly test whole genomes for important mutations, or to detect what and how many mRNA molecules are present in a cell at a given time.

DNA Profiling About 99 percent of your DNA is exactly the same as everyone else's DNA. The shared part is what makes you human; the differences make you a unique member of the species. Identifying an individual by his or her DNA is called **DNA profiling**.

If you compared your DNA with another human's, regardless of race or ethnicity, an estimated 2.97 billion nucleotides of the two sequences would be identical. The remaining 30 million nonidentical nucleotides are sprinkled throughout your chromosomes. Conserved regions of DNA are those sequences that tend to be the same between individuals. Conserved sequences tend to vary at single nucleotides in particular locations.

FIGURE 13-10 ▶

Microarrays can detect a large number of specific DNA sequences in a sample at one time. Known test DNA sequences are attached to each well or spot on the array. When a sequence from the sample matches one of the test sequences, a fluorescent probe can be detected. Microarrays can use multiple types of fluorescent probes to generate different colors depending on the conditions of the test.

test DNA attached to the array

sample DNA

match

no match

A base pair substitution that occurs in a measurable percentage of a population is called a *single-nucleotide polymorphism*, or SNP (pronounced SNIP). Alleles of most genes differ by single nucleotides, and differences in alleles are the basis of the variation in human traits. Those differences are so unique that they can be used to identify you.

Another method of DNA profiling involves analysis of short tandem repeats in an individual's chromosomes. These repeated sequences of nucleotides usually occur at predictable locations, but the number of times a sequence is repeated differs among individuals. For example, one person's DNA may have 15 repeats of the nucleotides T-T-T-T-C at a certain location. Another person's DNA may have only four repeats. DNA polymerases may repeat or skip over these regions during DNA replication, so the number of repeats can increase or decrease from one generation to the next.

Unless two people are identical twins, the chance that they have identical short tandem repeats at even three locations is one in a quintillion (10^{18}), which is far more than the number of people who have ever lived. Therefore, an individual's array of short tandem repeats is unique.

Geneticists compare short tandem repeats on Y chromosomes to determine relationships among male relatives and to identify ethnic heritage. They also track mutations that accumulate in populations over time by comparing DNA profiles of living humans with those of people who lived long ago. These studies allow scientists to study population dispersals that happened in the ancient past.

SEP **Develop a Solution** *Construct a problem or a question related to genealogy or forensic science that could be solved with the help of DNA evidence. How could you use the genetic tools described in this section to solve the problem or answer the question? How would you begin if you had only a tiny sample of DNA available?*

> ### CHAPTER INVESTIGATION
>
> **DNA Evidence**
> *How can you use the properties of DNA to figure out who committed the "crime" of taking a bite out of a cookie?*
>
> Go online to explore this chapter's hands-on investigation about the use of DNA evidence in forensics.

13.1 REVIEW

1. **Sequence** Order the steps of DNA cloning.

   - Identify a segment of DNA to clone.

   - The segment is inserted into the plasmid.

   - Bacterium replicates the recombinant DNA.

   - Plasmid is taken up by a single-cell bacterium.

   - Restriction enzymes cut the DNA plasmid and segment.

   - DNA ligases seal the gaps between the segment and plasmid.

2. **Identify** Which of these qualities of DNA enables gel electrophoresis to work?

   A. double stranded

   B. negatively charged

   C. coils up into chromosomes

   D. contains only four types of nucleotide bases

3. **Justify** Which statement describes an advantage of PCR over DNA cloning for producing copies of a DNA segment?

   A. Hydrogen bonds that hold two strands of DNA together can be disrupted at high temperature.

   B. Polymerase from bacteria that thrive in hot springs and thermal vents is essential for the process to work.

   C. Genetic material can be exponentially mass produced very quickly without requiring living host cells to carry out replication.

   D. DNA polymerases of most organisms would be damaged at the high temperature required to separate double strands of DNA.

4. **Explain** Why can most individuals be identified using short tandem repeats in their chromosomes?

13.2

KEY TERMS

clone
CRISPR
gene drive
gene therapy
genetic engineering
genetically modified organism
somatic cell nuclear transfer

GENETIC ENGINEERING

Using a variety of techniques, scientists can modify an organism's genome in order to find the genetic basis of a trait or determine what traits arise from a specific change in a DNA sequence. Altering a gene may inhibit or inactivate a protein's function, or it may cause the protein to be more active or to perform a new function. Investigating these effects opens many new doors in our scientific understanding of the living world and unlocks numerous possible benefits to humanity. However, there are also many limitations and ethical considerations related to genetic engineering.

Analyze *What is one genetic trait or problem you have learned about in genetics that you think could probably be altered by changing an organism's genome? Can you think of any possible ethical questions that could arise from making the change?*

Genetically Modified Organisms

Intentional breeding of selected organisms can alter genomes over time, as was the case with Mendel's pea plants or the domestication of dogs. However, that works only if individuals with the desired traits will interbreed. The tools that allow scientists to manipulate DNA take gene-swapping to an entirely different level. **Genetic engineering** is a process by which an individual organism's genome is deliberately modified with the intent of changing the organism's phenotype. An individual with a genome that has been modified in this way is a **genetically modified organism**, or GMO. The processes that generate GMOs often change an organism's genome in a way that can be passed onto offspring.

Microorganisms Most genetic engineering involves the yeast *Saccharomyces cerevisiae* and various species of bacteria, often *Escherichia coli*. Both types of cells have the metabolic machinery to make complex organic molecules and are easy to cultivate in the lab. Both organisms also make excellent model organisms for research projects because of their well-understood genomes.

Genetically engineered microorganisms are common sources of medically important proteins. People with diabetes were among the first beneficiaries of such genetically modified organisms. Insulin for treatment of diabetes was once extracted from animals, but animal insulin provoked an allergic reaction in some people. Human insulin, which does not provoke allergic reactions, has been produced by *E. coli* engineered to express the human insulin gene since 1982. GMOs that have a gene from a different species inserted into their DNA, such as these bacteria with human genes, are called *transgenic* organisms.

Microorganisms are also engineered to make proteins used in foods. For example, we use enzymes produced by modified microorganisms to improve the taste and clarity of fruit juice, to slow bread staling, and to modify fats. Cheese was traditionally made with an enzyme (chymosin) extracted from calf stomachs. Today, many cheeses are made with calf chymosin produced by transgenic yeast.

Plants As crop production expands to keep pace with human population growth, many farmers have begun to rely on genetically modified crop plants. Genes are often introduced into plant cells by way of *Agrobacterium tumefaciens*, a bacterium that infects plants. *A. tumefaciens* carries a plasmid with genes that cause tumors to form on a host plant, so the plasmid is called the tumor-inducing (Ti) plasmid. Tumor-inducing genes are replaced with foreign or modified genes, and then the recombinant plasmid is used as a vector to deliver the genes into plant cells. Whole plants can be grown from cells that integrate a recombinant plasmid into their chromosomes (**Figure 13-11** and **Figure 13-12**).

FIGURE 13-11
When *A. tumefaciens* containing a recombinant Ti plasmid infects a plant cell, the Ti plasmid is able to insert DNA into the plant cell's genome.

Some genetically modified crops carry genes that impart resistance to plant diseases or pests. Farmers that follow organic growing methods often spray their crops with spores of *Bt* (*Bacillus thuringiensis*), a species of bacterium that makes a protein toxic to some insect larvae. Alternatively, farmers can grow crops that have been genetically modified to produce the toxic *Bt* protein. These crops include soybeans, corn, cotton, and even eggplants. Cells of the engineered plants produce the *Bt* protein, and larvae die shortly after eating their first and only GMO meal.

Worldwide, hundreds of millions of acres are planted in GMO crops. The majority of these crops are corn, sorghum, cotton, soybeans, canola, and alfalfa that have been genetically engineered to be resistant to the herbicide glyphosate. Rather than tilling the soil or spraying a variety of targeted herbicides to control weeds, farmers can spray their fields with glyphosate, which kills the weeds but not the GMO crops. Genes that confer glyphosate resistance have appeared in weeds and other wild plants, as well as in unmodified crops—which means that recombinant DNA can (and does) escape into the environment.

SEP **Construct an Explanation** *How do you think the genes for glyphosate resistance could become incorporated into wild plants?*

FIGURE 13-12
These rice plants have been modified with DNA introduced by Ti plasmids. The plants are first grown in nutrient agar. When the rice plants have grown large enough in the laboratory, the modified seedlings are transplanted into containers and eventually into controlled plots in a paddy field.

GOLDEN RICE While many GMO crops are engineered to confer herbicide or pesticide resistance, some other genetic modification efforts aim to solve problems associated with nutrition. Deficiency in vitamin A can cause blindness in children, often followed by death. In many parts of the world, vegetables that are rich in vitamin A are not readily available. Meanwhile, rice is a staple crop that is easy to obtain in many areas.

Since the 1990s, scientists have attempted to engineer a variety of rice that will address vitamin A deficiency. The original golden rice included two genes that are critical for the synthesis of beta-carotene, which is a precursor of vitamin A. One gene comes from a daffodil plant, and the other comes from the soil bacterium *Erwinia uredovora*. With later generations of golden rice, scientists have continued to hone the genes used to increase the synthesis and storage of beta-carotene.

Vitamin A deficiency is one of the most common nutrient deficiencies affecting children around the world, with an estimated thirty percent of children under five years old experiencing a deficiency. Despite many efforts to implement vitamin A supplement programs, this deficiency is still a tremendous global problem, requiring multiple approaches to solve. The World Health Organization estimates there are 500,000 cases of childhood blindness every year, and that half of those children die within a year of going blind.

Although golden rice has been reviewed and deemed safe by several countries, including Australia, Canada, and the United States, it has not been produced widely. In 2021, the Philippines was the first country to approve golden rice production on a commercial scale.

Beta-carotene gives golden rice its characteristic color.

Animals Genetically modified animals can be produced by a variety of methods. Two methods that have been used often in research either inactivate genes or add new genes. For example, "knock-out" mice are generated by inserting DNA into specific areas in the genome to inactivate targeted genes. Other genetically modified animals are made by injecting recombinant DNA into a fertilized egg and implanting the resulting embryo with its new gene into a surrogate to complete its development. More recently, scientists have utilized CRISPR techniques to modify animal genes. This method is described in detail later in this section.

Genetically modified mice are invaluable in research. Scientists have discovered the functions of many human genes by inactivating the same genes in experiments using knock-out mice. Genetically modified mice are also used as models of human diseases. For example, researchers inactivated the molecules involved in the control of glucose metabolism, one by one, in mice. Studying the effects of these modifications in mice resulted in much of our understanding of how diabetes works in humans.

Genetically engineered animals other than mice are also useful in research, and some make molecules that have medical applications. For example, various transgenic goats produce proteins used to treat cystic fibrosis, heart attacks, and blood-clotting disorders. Rabbits make human interleukin-2, a protein that triggers immune cells to divide and is used as a treatment for some cancers.

Some animals are genetically engineered to carry mutations associated with human disorders—multiple sclerosis, cystic fibrosis, diabetes, cancer, or Huntington disease, for example. Researchers produce engineered animals to study the disorders and potential treatments without experimenting on humans. However, the modified animals often suffer the same symptoms of the conditions as humans do.

Other genetic engineering experiments have attempted to tackle environmental issues. For example, endocrine disruptors are a group of chemicals that can interfere with endocrine, or hormone-related, systems in the body and cause negative health effects. These chemicals can enter the environment and water supplies from pesticides, plastics, and other wastes. As a method for detecting these pollutants, a gene from another organism has been inserted into the genome of a zebrafish (**Figure 13-13a**). This gene encodes a green fluorescent protein, thus engineering the zebrafish to glow green in the presence of endocrine disrupters (**Figure 13-13b**).

Scientists also engineer food animals. For example, genetic engineering has produced trout with extra muscle, pigs with environmentally friendly low-phosphate feces, chickens that do not transmit bird flu, and cows that do not get mad cow disease. In 2015, the FDA approved the first GMO animal for use as human food: a transgenic Atlantic salmon. These fish have been engineered to carry a gene promoter from ocean pout (a type of fish) that governs a growth hormone gene from a Chinook salmon. The engineered fish grow to full size about twice as fast as their unmodified counterparts. The engineered salmon are all female, are sterile, and have been approved only for specific aquaculture uses.

Many people do not think livestock should be genetically engineered. Others see it as an extension of thousands of years of acceptable animal husbandry practices. The techniques have changed, but the intent has not: humans continue to have an interest in improving our livestock. Either way, tinkering with the genes of animals raises a host of ethical dilemmas.

STSE **Science, Technology, and Society** *What ethical questions do you think scientists should consider when generating genetically modified organisms? Do the ethical considerations change depending on the goals of the technological application?*

FIGURE 13-13 ▲
Zebrafish (a) are an important model organism for genetic studies. Genetically modified zebrafish (b) glow with green fluorescent protein.

🧪 **CHAPTER INVESTIGATION**

Fluorescent Genes
Can we replicate the process scientists engineered to insert foreign DNA into bacteria?

Go online to explore this chapter's hands-on investigation about genetic engineering.

▶ **VIDEO**

VIDEO 13-1 Go online to learn about some of the many organisms that use fluorescent compounds in nature.

Cloning Organisms

All cells descended from the same fertilized egg inherit the same DNA. That DNA is like a master blueprint for directing the development of an individual's body. Consider how identical twins have identical DNA, so their bodies develop the same way. Identical twins are the product of a natural process called *embryo splitting*. The first few divisions of a fertilized egg form a tiny ball of cells that sometimes splits spontaneously. If both halves of the ball develop independently, identical twins result. Animal breeders have long exploited this phenomenon with a technique called artificial embryo splitting. A tiny ball of cells grown from a fertilized egg is teased apart into two halves that develop as separate embryos. The embryos are implanted in surrogate mothers, who give birth to identical twins.

Twins produced by embryo splitting are genetically identical to one another, but they are not identical to either parent. This is because in humans and other animals, twins get their DNA from two parents that typically differ in their DNA sequence.

Somatic Cell Nuclear Transfer "Cloning" means making an identical copy of something, and it can refer to deliberate interventions intended to produce an exact genetic copy of an organism. Animal breeders who want an exact copy of a specific individual use **somatic cell nuclear transfer** (SCNT), a laboratory procedure in which an unfertilized egg's nucleus is replaced with the nucleus of a donor's somatic cell (**Figure 13-14**). A somatic cell is a body cell, as opposed to a reproductive cell. If all goes well, the transplanted DNA directs the development of an embryo, which is then implanted into a surrogate mother. The animal born to the surrogate is a **clone**—a genetic copy—of the donor. Clones produced by SCNT have the same features as their adult donors, and there are other benefits. SCNT can yield many more offspring in a given time frame than traditional breeding, and offspring can be produced from a donor animal that is castrated or even dead.

FIGURE 13-14 ▽

Somatic cell nuclear transfer replaces the nucleus of an egg with a donor nucleus.

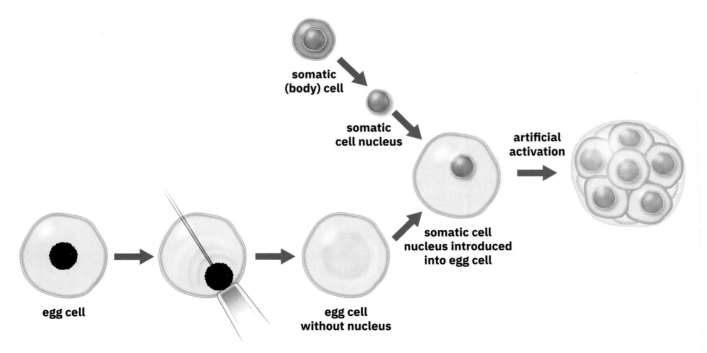

somatic (body) cell

somatic cell nucleus

artificial activation

somatic cell nucleus introduced into egg cell

egg cell

egg cell without nucleus

Reproductive cloning refers to SCNT and any other technology that produces clones of an animal from a single cell. SCNT has been used since 1997, when a lamb named Dolly (**Figure 13-15**) was cloned from a mammary cell of an adult sheep. Dolly looked and acted like a normal sheep, but she died early, most likely because she was a clone.

The outcome of SCNT is sometimes unpredictable. Depending on the species, few implanted embryos may survive until birth. For many of the initial attempts at SCNT, most of the clones that did survive had serious health problems such as enlarged organs and obesity. Cloned mice developed lung and liver problems, and almost all died prematurely. Cloned pigs tended to limp and have heart problems; some developed without important parts.

SCNT works because the DNA in a somatic cell contains all the information necessary to build the individual all over again. However, a somatic cell does not automatically start dividing to form an embryo. This is because during early development, an embryo's cells start using different subsets of their DNA. As they do, the cells become different in form and function through the process of differentiation. In animals, this process is usually a one-way path, which means that once a cell has become specialized, all of its descendant cells will be specialized the same way. By the time a liver cell, muscle cell, or other differentiated cell forms, many genes in its DNA are no longer expressed. To clone an adult, the DNA of a somatic cell must be reprogrammed. The parts that trigger embryonic development are turned back on so the cells have the same potential for gene expression as a normal developing embryo. Scientists still have a lot to learn, but SCNT techniques have improved to the extent that health problems are much less common in animals cloned today.

SEP **Construct an Explanation** *Consider what you know about DNA replication and other processes in the cell. What are some events that might occur after somatic cell nuclear transfer that could result in an unexpected outcome?*

Gene Therapy and Genome Editing

We know of more than 15,000 serious genetic disorders. Genetic disorders cause a large number of infant deaths each year, along with a significant number of hospitalizations for genetic disorders that are survivable. Drugs and other treatments can minimize the symptoms of some genetic disorders, but modifying the genome to correct the mutation would be the only real cure. **Gene therapy** is the transfer of DNA into an individual's body cells to correct a genetic disorder or treat a disease.

Genetic Disorders and Abnormalities Many genetic disorders are caused by single-gene mutations (**Figure 13-16**). Studying human inheritance patterns has given scientists many insights into how genetic disorders arise and progress, and how to treat them. Surgery, prescription drugs, hormone replacement therapy, and dietary controls can minimize and in some cases eliminate the symptoms of a genetic disorder. Some disorders can be detected early enough to start countermeasures before symptoms develop. Most hospitals in the United States now screen newborns for certain mutations. For example, one mutation causes phenylketonuria, or PKU, in one of every 10,000–15,000 newborns. The mutations affect an enzyme that converts one amino acid (phenylalanine) to another (tyrosine). Without this enzyme, the body becomes deficient in tyrosine, and phenylalanine accumulates to high levels. The imbalance inhibits protein synthesis in the brain, which can ultimately result in permanent intellectual disability. Restricting all intake of phenylalanine can slow the progression of PKU, so routine early screening has resulted in fewer individuals experiencing the symptoms of the disorder.

FIGURE 13-16 ▼
Autosomal abnormalities and disorders are caused by genetic problems that occur on the numbered chromosomes in the genome, as opposed to an X or Y sex chromosome.

Inheritance Pattern
autosomal
dominant

Disorder/Abnormality	Primary Symptoms
achondroplasia	dwarfism
aniridia	eye defects
Huntington disease	nervous system degeneration
Marfan syndrome	abnormal/missing connective tissue
progeria	drastic premature aging

Inheritance Pattern
autosomal
recessive

Disorder/Abnormality	Primary Symptoms
albinism	absence of pigmentation
cystic fibrosis	difficulty breathing, lung infections
Ellis-van Creveld syndrome	dwarfism, heart defects, polydactyly
phenylketonuria (PKU)	mental impairment
sickle cell anemia	anemia, swelling, frequent infection
Tay-Sachs disease	mental and physical deterioration, early death

Gene Therapy Gene therapy is being tested as a treatment for a wide variety of diseases and disorders, but not all diseases and disorders are readily treatable through these methods. Some disorders arise because a needed protein is not produced or is malfunctioning. Gene therapy can provide a healthy, working gene to replace that lost function. Other gene therapy techniques work by silencing mutated genes that are causing a disorder. Potential targets for gene therapy treatments include

- AIDS
- Alzheimer disease
- cancer (several types)
- cystic fibrosis
- heart failure
- hemophilia A
- inherited eye, ear, immune disorders
- muscular dystrophy
- Parkinson disease
- sickle cell anemia

The biggest challenge in gene therapy is developing a method that efficiently delivers functioning copies of genes to the affected tissue so the proteins can be produced in the cells where they are needed. For example, to treat leukemia, a potentially fatal cancer of bone marrow cells, scientists have used a viral vector to insert a gene into immune cells extracted from the leukemia patient. When the modified cells are reintroduced into the patient's body, the inserted gene directs the destruction of cancer cells.

Despite the successes, the outcomes of manipulating a gene for use in a living individual can be unpredictable. For example, X-linked severe combined immunodeficiency (SCID-X1) is a severe genetic disorder that stems from a mutated allele of the *IL2RG* gene on the X chromosome. The gene normally encodes a receptor important for signaling the immune system. Without treatment, people affected by this disorder can survive only in germ-free isolation tents because they cannot fight infections. Researchers used a genetically engineered virus to insert unmutated copies of *IL2RG* into cells taken from the bone marrow of 20 boys with SCID-X1. Each child's modified cells were infused back into his bone marrow. Within months of treatment, 18 of the boys were able to leave their isolation tents. Gene therapy had repaired their immune systems. However, five of the boys later developed leukemia and died. Developers of the gene therapy could not have known that the gene targeted for repair would cause cancer. The viral vector had inserted the gene into the chromosome at a site near a proto-oncogene (Section 7.1). The insertion triggered transcription of the gene, resulting in the onset of leukemia.

SEP **Evaluate a Solution** *Age-related macular degeneration (AMD) is a leading cause of blindness. Many genes are related to AMD, but scientists have identified just a few specific genes as potential gene therapy targets. One trial in particular is attempting to block an immune system gene that generates a protein that attacks cells of the retina. Do you think AMD is a disorder that is likely to be solved with gene therapy? What are some of the challenges? How do you think the treatment would be delivered?*

CRISPR Technology

Gene therapy with viral vectors has some risks. As was the case for the SCID-X1 treatments, a recombinant viral vector inserts randomly into the genome. This can have unpredictable consequences. By taking advantage of a system that prokaryotes use to defend themselves against viral infection, scientists have developed a powerful and precise method of editing DNA called **CRISPR** (pronounced CRISPER) that is safer. CRISPR is named for a DNA sequence that, when transcribed, helps a prokaryote combat viral infection through an RNA interference pathway that recognizes and destroys viral DNA (Section 11.3).

Editing Gene Sequences The CRISPR technique uses a combination of molecules, or a complex, that combines an RNA sequence, a *nuclease* enzyme (Cas9), and a DNA sequence. The RNA guides the complex to a specific sequence of DNA in the chromosome, where the nuclease enzyme cuts both strands of DNA (**Figure 13-17**). Then, the new DNA sequence is used to repair the break. The guide RNA and new DNA sequences can be designed to precisely target and change essentially any part of a genome in a living cell. Researchers deliver the guide RNA, the nuclease enzyme, and the new DNA into cells in the form of genes carried by a plasmid vector. A cell that expresses the edited genes will have both of its chromosomes edited, and the change will be passed to all of the cell's descendants.

CRISPR is more accurate and efficient than viral vectors or any other method of altering genomes. It is fast, easy, inexpensive, and works in almost any cell. The first generation of CRISPR techniques sometimes cut DNA in unintended locations. However, a newer generation of CRISPR base-editing techniques (**Figure 13-18**) improves accuracy and uses different enzymes to perform in-place editing of individual nucleotides without introducing unexpected breaks in the DNA.

FIGURE 13-17 ▷
The first generation of CRISPR technology cut target DNA strands to introduce new DNA sequences. The guide RNA leads the complex to the target sequence. The nuclease enzyme cleaves the DNA, and a new DNA sequence is inserted at the cleavage site.

CRISPR DNA insertion

guide RNA

cas9 nuclease enzyme

target DNA

site of cleavage

cleavage

new DNA

insertion

CRISPR base editing

guide RNA

cas9 nickase enzyme

target DNA

C to U change

base editor

A to I change

U
G

DNA replication

I
T

T
A

C:G to T:A substitution

G
C

A:T to G:C substitution

FIGURE 13-18

Newer CRISPR base-editing techniques can swap individual nucleotides. Unlike the cas9 nuclease that cuts both strands of DNA in earlier generations of CRISPR, the cas9 nickase enzyme cuts only one strand of the DNA at a targeted location. A base editor molecule can then change particular nucleotides on that side of the double strand. DNA replication then replaces the nucleotide on the opposite strand, completing the base editing process. The "I" in this diagram represents inositol, which serves as an intermediary in the conversion of A:T to G:C.

Applications of CRISPR These CRISPR methods pioneered by scientists such as American biochemist Jennifer Doudna (**Figure 13-19**) are useful in a variety of applications. For example, crop plants can be enhanced without leaving traces of the vector DNA. HIV DNA that has been integrated into an infected patient's cells (Section 8.4) can be edited out to prevent relapse after remission. Removing mutations from somatic cells can permanently cure many genetic disorders. The technique has been used successfully to repair mutations that cause muscular dystrophy, achondroplasia, and cancer in cells taken from human patients.

 VIDEO

VIDEO 13-2 Go online to see Dr. Jennifer Doudna discuss the CRISPR method.

FIGURE 13-19

In 2020, Jennifer Doudna (pictured) and Emmanuelle Charpentier were awarded the Nobel Prize in Chemistry for their discovery of the CRISPR method of genome editing.

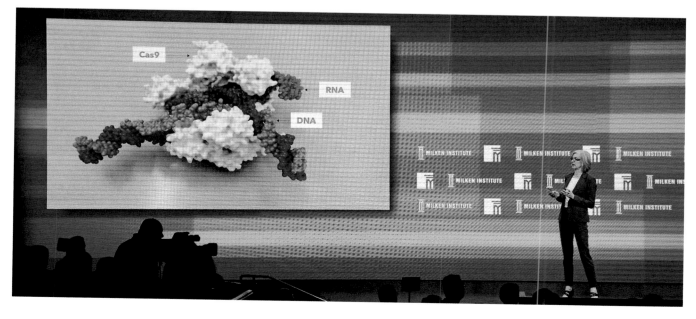

FIGURE 13-20 ▶
Plasmodium parasites (a) reproduce in the gut of the *Anopheles* mosquito (b) and are transferred to humans in the mosquito's saliva.

20a

20b

> **CASE STUDY**
> GENETICS TO THE RESCUE!
>
> **Ask Questions** *Generate questions that the scientific and medical communities should consider when determining whether a CRISPR method should be approved to treat a human disease or disorder.*

Gene Drives CRISPR was the first successful method of making **gene drives**, which are genes that can "drive" themselves into other chromosomes and spread through a population. The eradication of malaria is one possible application of this technology. This disease infects more than two million people each year, about one-fifth of whom die. Most are children under the age of five.

Already, mosquitoes have been engineered to carry genes that boost their immune systems to prevent *Plasmodium*, the malaria parasite, from growing in their guts (**Figure 13-20b**). With a typical gene therapy, the engineered genes are diluted out of a population because only some of the mosquito's offspring inherit them. However, the outcome is different in mosquitoes engineered with CRISPR and CRISPR-based gene drives. When one of the engineered mosquitoes mates with an unmodified mosquito, 100 percent of their offspring inherit the engineered genes. This is because the CRISPR system that delivered the modification is part of the engineered mosquitoes' chromosomes, and it also edits homologous chromosomes in zygotes. If the engineered mosquitoes were to be released in the wild, the worldwide population of mosquitoes would probably be modified within a few years, eliminating malaria.

SEP **Evaluate a Solution** Aedes aegypti *mosquitoes carry several viruses that cause deadly disease in humans. Scientists have produced mosquitoes with genes that prevent female offspring from surviving to adulthood. How might eliminating adult female mosquitoes affect an ecosystem, and what are some tradeoffs that would be made if we were to use genetically engineered* A. aegypti *to prevent human disease?*

13.2 REVIEW

1. **Identify** Which are common goals of genetically modifying plants? Select all correct answers.

   A. increasing crop productivity

   B. developing medicinal compounds

   C. growing crops resistant to herbicides

   D. spreading genes to animals that eat the plants

   E. cultivating plants that are resistant to insects

2. **Describe** What are some goals of scientists who clone animals?

3. **Explain** What characteristics make a genetic disorder a good candidate for gene therapy?

4. **Sequence** List the steps in the correct order for the process of using CRISPR to edit a gene.

   • The cas9 enzyme cuts the DNA.

   • A target DNA sequence to modify is identified.

   • A plasmid delivers DNA, RNA, and enzymes to a cell.

   • A new DNA sequence is inserted into the place where the DNA was cut.

   • The RNA guides the complex to the target DNA sequence and hybridizes.

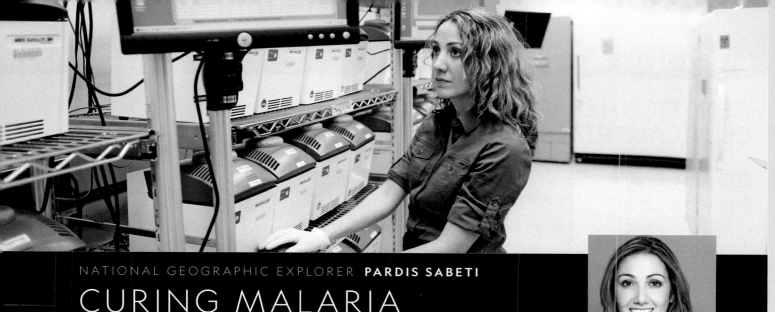

CURING MALARIA WITH MATH

Computational biologist Dr. Pardis Sabeti uses math to mine the human genome to solve problems in human health.

An individual suffering from malaria sweats with a high fever and shakes with chills. The *Anopheles* mosquito feasts. With its bite, the mosquito takes in a small amount of blood containing parasites that mix with its saliva. For its next meal, the mosquito lands on a young child and injects the parasite into the child's bloodstream. A few weeks later, the child falls ill with the same symptoms as the other infected individual, but the outcome is much worse. The young child has no immunity to the infection and will likely die.

Computational biologist Dr. Pardis Sabeti has long been on the trail of infections such as malaria. She develops computer algorithms that analyze changes in DNA related to the spread of infectious microbes. Because the malaria parasite's genetic makeup is extremely diverse, it can become drug resistant by adapting quickly to new environmental conditions that result from drug treatment. By studying microbial genetic diversity, Sabeti can predict where a disease outbreak might occur next and inform more effective drug strategies.

A person's genetic makeup may play a role in how sick they become if infected. Sabeti wanted to test whether gene mutations that had occurred recently in the human population might provide an evolutionary advantage, such as resistance to the malaria parasite. Differentiating between recent mutations and those that appeared much longer in the past would require analyzing DNA sequences in the surrounding regions. In 2001, Sabeti developed a breakthrough algorithm that enabled this analysis.

After identifying many mutations that indicated relatively recent natural selection, Sabeti had to determine which ones were relevant. She and her colleagues developed another algorithm that allowed them to narrow down a region of 10,000 mutations to only 10 or so that were biologically meaningful to test.

Sabeti has continued to extend her algorithms to study other diseases, including Ebola, Lassa fever, and COVID-19. Pinpointing mutations in survivors and infection-resistant individuals helps identify genes that are important in the human response to infection. "So much of the physical world has been explored," Sabeti says. "But the deluge of data I get to investigate really lets me chart new territory. Most of my work may happen at a computer, but it's still a new and very exciting frontier."

THINKING CRITICALLY

Explain *Why is computational analysis crucial for genomic analysis?*

GENETIC THERAPY CLINICAL TRIALS

SEP **Mathematical Thinking** Despite setbacks and increasing costs, development of genetic medical therapies is rising.

In 2021, a phase III trial for a gene therapy treatment of Huntington disease (a degenerative brain disease) was ended because no therapeutic effect was demonstrated, when comparing treated patients with a placebo group. The community of individuals affected by the disease was devastated because the treatment had produced promising initial results. Many treatments that enter clinical trials do not make it as far as phase III. Clinical trials are costly, but they perform the important function of determining what treatments are effective and safe for use in most patients.

There are several phases in most clinical trials. The preclinical phase includes laboratory research on animals, tissue, or cell samples. Institutional Review Boards vet the trial plans to ensure safety protocols are followed. Phase I begins with six to ten participants with special attention on treatment side effects. Phase II and phase III involve more participants, from 25–50 to 100–200, and are intended to evaluate safety, confirm benefits, and prove treatment is effective. Following these trial phases, the FDA conducts a thorough review prior to approving the treatment for public use. Some clinical trials continue into phase IV, in which they study long-term effects on all participants.

FIGURE 1 ▼

The number of clinical trials for genetic therapies by year over the last decade has shown a steady increase.

Source: American Society of Gene and Cell Therapy

Figure 1 shows the number of gene therapy clinical trials at different phases over the last decade. **Figure 2** shows the average cost breakdown of the phases in all clinical trials, including gene therapies and other treatment methods, for a selection of common therapeutic areas.

FIGURE 2 ▼

The cost of conducting a clinical trial ranges from tens of millions to hundreds of millions of dollars and depends on the phase and therapeutic area.

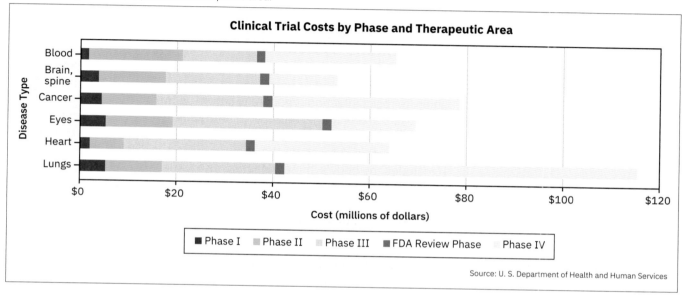

Clinical Trial Costs by Phase and Therapeutic Area

Disease Type: Blood, Brain/spine, Cancer, Eyes, Heart, Lungs

Cost (millions of dollars): $0, $20, $40, $60, $80, $100, $120

Legend: ■ Phase I ■ Phase II Phase III ■ FDA Review Phase Phase IV

Source: U. S. Department of Health and Human Services

1. **Identify Patterns** Approximately how many times more preclinical trials were there in 2021 than in 2010? Compare this to how clinical trials in at least two other phases have changed over the decade.

2. **Organize Data** For each therapeutic area, rank the phases of clinical trials by average cost. Which phases tend to be the most and least expensive?

3. **Compare** Rank the therapeutic areas by total cost.

4. **Argue From Evidence** Use the data to support or refute the claim that in the future, there will be many job opportunities in the research and development of gene therapies.

5. **Nature of Science** Why do you think so many phases are required before the FDA approves treatment for the public? Why do you think companies are willing to invest all this money before being able to sell the treatment?

KEY TERMS

antibody
antigen
immunity
pathogen
reservoir
vaccine

VACCINE DEVELOPMENT

The genetic technologies that underlie modern vaccines are complex. An idea that is simpler to understand is the human need to protect ourselves from discomfort and illness and to work together to help others in our communities. Vaccines require both thoroughly tested genetic technology and community cooperation to be most effective.

Identify *Name at least one way you use a tool or technology to make yourself safer or more comfortable. Then describe at least one way you have observed people working together to help a community.*

The Immune System

The human immune system protects an individual from **pathogens**—bacteria, viruses, or other organisms that can cause infection. The body's ability to resist infection is generally known as **immunity**. An immune response starts with the detection of **antigens**, which are molecules or particles that the immune system recognizes as being foreign to the host. The first level of defense for the immune system is called *innate immunity*. It includes the body's immediate responses, such as increasing body temperature and releasing general immune system cells that destroy foreign particles. The second level of immune response is less immediate and is known as *adaptive immunity*. It involves a different set of immune system cells and antibodies that target and respond to specific antigens.

Antigens and Antibodies The immune system employs a wide variety of specialized cell types and structures, but the components of the immune system most relevant to understanding vaccines are antibodies. An **antibody** is a Y-shaped antigen receptor protein made by specialized immune cells to help the body fight infections. Many antibodies circulate in blood, where they bind to antigens and activate pathways that destroy associated pathogens. Antibody binding can also prevent pathogens and toxins from attaching to body cells. An antibody molecule consists of four polypeptides (**Figure 13-21**). When polypeptide chains fold up together as an antibody, two antigen-binding sites form at the tips of the Y. These sites bind only to specific antigens that match their shape and charge patterns.

FIGURE 13-21 ▽
An antibody molecule includes four polypeptide chains joined in a Y shape. Two antigen-binding sites form at the tips of the Y.

binding site for antigen

antigen

antigen

CCC **Structure and Function** *Look at the structures in **Figure 13-21**. How do the shape and properties of the polypeptides that make up an antibody help it recognize and bind a specific antigen?*

When the immune system encounters a new antigen, its immune cells form a lasting antibody memory that allows the system to respond more readily the next time it detects the same antigen. This means that more immune cells and antibodies are available to quickly respond the second time the antigen invades (**Figure 13-22**).

FIGURE 13-22 ▽
Adaptive immunity generates a fast response after a second exposure to an antigen.

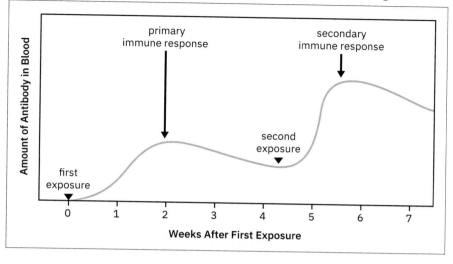

Vaccines and Public Health

Immunization refers to procedures designed to induce immunity. In active immunization, a preparation that contains an antigen—a **vaccine**— is injected or given orally. This immunization elicits a primary immune response, just as an infection would. A second immunization, or booster, elicits a secondary immune response for enhanced protection. Vaccines use a variety of technologies to modify and manipulate pathogen genomes to stimulate this immune response.

Discovery of Vaccines The first vaccine was developed as a result of desperate attempts to survive epidemics of smallpox, a severe disease that kills up to one-third of the people who contract it. Before 1880, no one knew what caused infectious diseases or how to protect anyone from getting them, but there were clues. For instance, survivors of smallpox only rarely contracted the disease a second time. At the time, the idea of acquiring immunity to smallpox was extremely appealing. People risked their lives by poking bits of smallpox scabs or pus from smallpox sores into their own skin. Some people survived these crude practices, but many others did not. This practice of deliberately infecting someone in hopes of contracting a mild infection to gain immunity is known as *variolation*, and it dates back to 15th-century China.

By 1774, it was known that women who milked cows usually did not get smallpox after they had contracted cowpox, a mild disease that affects humans as well as cattle. An English farmer collected pus from a cowpox sore on a cow's udder and poked it into the arms of his pregnant wife and two small children. All members of his family survived the smallpox epidemic, but their neighbors pelted them with rocks, convinced the family would turn into cows.

Twenty years later, British physician Edward Jenner introduced liquid from a cowpox sore into the arm of a healthy boy. Six weeks later, Jenner inoculated the boy with liquid from a smallpox sore. The boy did not get smallpox. Jenner's experiment and additional confirming studies showed directly that the cowpox virus elicits immunity to smallpox. Jenner named his procedure "vaccination," after the Latin word for cowpox (*vaccinia*). A smallpox vaccine that was developed later eradicated the disease, and the last known case of naturally occurring smallpox was in 1977.

NOS **Scientific Investigation** *How do you think ethical standards for medical research have changed since the time of Edward Jenner?*

Public Health Today, we know that the use of cowpox for immunization was effective against smallpox because the two diseases are caused by closely related viruses. Antibodies produced during an infection with one of the viruses recognize antigens of both. Building on this knowledge, vaccines for many other infectious diseases have since been developed. Vaccines greatly reduce rates of infection, the degree of associated suffering, and death as a result of infectious disease. Many nations where vaccines are available have very successful child vaccination programs that have nearly eliminated devastating diseases, such as measles.

Public confidence is a necessary part of vaccine success. When enough individuals refuse vaccination, outbreaks of preventable and sometimes fatal diseases occur. Measles had nearly been eradicated in the United States by the year 2010, with only 63 reported cases, but cases spiked to 1282 in the year 2019 (**Figure 13-23**). A significant number of parents are choosing not to vaccinate their children, most citing fears about vaccine safety. Safety concerns reported about one vaccine are sometimes applied to all vaccines, even those with millions of uses and proven safety. One concern that childhood vaccines cause an increased risk of autism has no scientific basis. The 1998 scientific paper that first proposed this risk was later shown to contain falsified data, and the lead author of the paper lost his medical license as a result of this fraud. The scientist was attempting to discredit one particular vaccine to sell more of a vaccine he was financially invested in. Rigorous studies of thousands of individuals have repeatedly failed to show a link between vaccinations and autism.

FIGURE 13-23 ▼
Measles outbreaks have occurred more often in recent years.

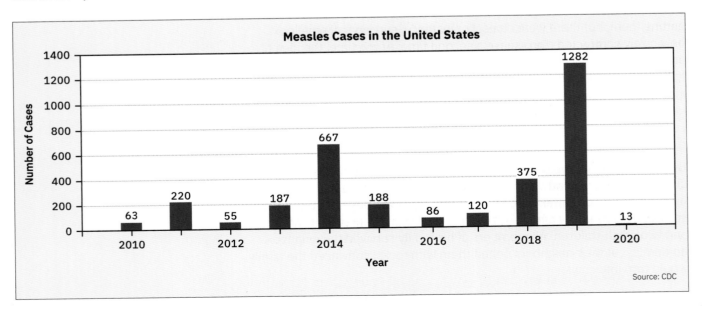

Source: CDC

Global Challenges of Vaccine Delivery Pathogens can be easily transmitted as people travel around the globe. However, most of the technology to develop and produce large quantities of vaccines exists primarily in countries with well-funded and established medical and science infrastructure. Other parts of the world do not have these resources or the money to purchase the vaccines. Solving a global problem such as a pandemic disease requires a robust global response that addresses this inequality. The support of international organizations is critical for the delivery of vaccines to the places that need them most (**Figure 13-24**).

FIGURE 13-24
Workers in Burundi unload donations of SARS-CoV-2 vaccines in October 2021.

Key regulatory agencies involved in vaccine distribution and policy in the United States and worldwide are the Centers for Disease Control and Prevention (CDC) and the World Heath Organization (WHO), respectively.

Vaccines are delivered in many ways, and the ideal method varies depending on the constraints of the situation. Many vaccines are delivered as part of childhood vaccination programs. Others, such as the seasonal influenza and COVID-19 vaccines, must be administered as needed. However, not every nation or area has robust vaccination programs or the infrastructure necessary to distribute vaccines.

Administering and distributing vaccines poses many challenges. Most vaccines are administered via injection into the muscle, which requires a trained nurse. Many vaccines have storage requirements, such as stable cold temperatures. A variety of approaches have been studied in attempts to address difficulties in storage, transportation, and administration of vaccines. Among these approaches are vaccines that are stable at a variety of temperatures, as well as vaccines that can be administered orally or inhaled. Other attempts have involved developing edible vaccines in genetically modified fruits or vegetables, as well as making a live bacterial vector that will spread through a population, expressing vaccine proteins but not causing illness.

STSE **Science, Technology, and Society** *Why is it important to ensure that all countries around the globe have access to sufficient quantities of vaccines, as well as resources for delivering them to the population?*

Vaccine Technologies

Since the smallpox vaccine was developed, vaccine technology and delivery has advanced immensely. Public health efforts and vaccine requirements have greatly reduced and nearly eliminated many diseases (**Table 13-1**). Smallpox is the only disease that has been eradicated—or eliminated—worldwide.

Vaccine Types Many different types of vaccines can be developed, depending on the nature of the pathogen and the body's immune response to infection. The following are types of vaccines that have been successfully developed and used:

- **Inactivated Vaccines** These vaccines involve delivering whole virus particles that have been inactivated so they cannot reproduce.

- **Live-attenuated Vaccines** These vaccines are made from whole live viruses that have been modified to not cause disease.

- **Messenger RNA (mRNA) Vaccines** These vaccines directly deliver mRNA (encoding a viral protein) in a lipid shell. The mRNA induces the body to produce an antigen that will elicit an immune response against the pathogen.

- **Subunit Vaccines** These vaccines directly introduce the antigen or nonreplicating parts of a pathogen, which will elicit an immune response against the pathogen.

- **Toxoid Vaccines** These vaccines elicit an immune response against a toxic component made during an infection instead of the infecting pathogen.

- **Viral-vector Vaccines** These vaccines introduce a different, safe virus to deliver genetic material that will then induce the body to make antigens that will elicit an immune response to the pathogen virus.

CCC **Structure and Function** *What is the difference between a viral pathogen and a vaccine that uses a virus or part of a virus to elicit an immune response?*

TABLE 13-1. Examples of Key Vaccines

Disease	Pathogen	Common vaccine type(s)	Outcomes
COVID-19	coronavirus	mRNA or viral-vector	varies by formulation, typically >90% effective at preventing infection, and a high rate of protection against severe illness
HPV	papillomavirus	subunit	results (2021) show 87% reduction in cervical cancer in the United Kingdom
measles	morbillivirus	live-attenuated	97% effective at protecting against infection (CDC)
polio	poliovirus	inactivated	eliminated in United States, 99.9% decrease in cases worldwide
seasonal influenza	influenza virus	inactivated, live-attenuated, subunit	CDC reports 40%-60% seasonal reduction in illness
smallpox	variola virus	live-attenuated	eradicated in 1977; samples exist only in laboratories
tetanus	*Clostridium tetani* (bacteria)	toxoid	WHO reported a 96% decrease in childhood deaths from 1988 to 2017
whooping cough	*Bordetella pertussis* (bacteria)	subunit	80%–90% effective at protecting against infection (CDC)

Influenza Vaccines There are four types of influenza viruses (A, B, C, and D). Types A and B are responsible for seasonal flu epidemics. Influenza A viruses are also responsible for historic pandemics as well as avian and swine influenza infections. Subtypes of influenza are determined by two different proteins on the surface of the virus, hemagglutinin and neuraminidase (**Figure 13-25**), indicated by H and N. Influenza has a genome with eight RNA segments, and different viruses often swap genome segments to generate new, unique virus subtypes that can consistently evade the human immune system. Each year, there are approximately one billion cases of influenza worldwide, resulting in 290,000–650,000 related deaths.

 VIDEO

VIDEO 13-3 Go online to learn about influenza subtypes and how the variety of subtypes affects vaccine development.

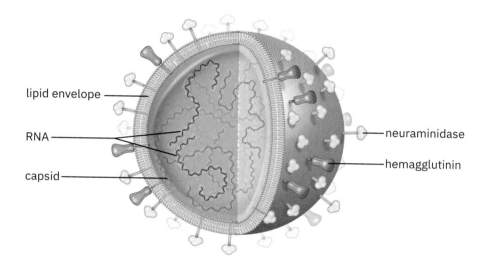

FIGURE 13-25
Influenza subtypes are referred to based on the types of hemagglutinin (H) and neuraminidase (N) proteins present on the surface of the virus.

lipid envelope

RNA

capsid

neuraminidase

hemagglutinin

Producing seasonal influenza vaccines is a year-round process (**Figure 13-26**). Scientists observe the dominant subtypes in the southern hemisphere's winter to anticipate the upcoming influenza season in the northern hemisphere, and vice versa. Vaccines are produced twice a year, for the southern and northern hemisphere influenza seasons. Influenza vaccines are produced through a variety of methods. For most vaccines, viruses are grown in eggs or mammalian cell lines, and they are then inactivated before purification for vaccine use. Live-attenuated influenza vaccines are also grown in eggs. Not all viruses or influenza subtypes are able to be grown using these methods.

FIGURE 13-26
Outside of tropical regions, influenza tends to peak every winter season. The data show positive specimens for the northern hemisphere. The 2009–2010 H1N1 swine flu pandemic and the 2020–2021 winter during the COVID-19 pandemic are both represented in this graph's timeframe.

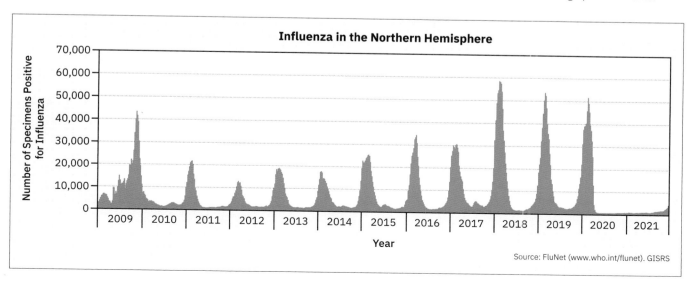

Influenza in the Northern Hemisphere

Source: FluNet (www.who.int/flunet). GISRS

Gather Evidence *Vaccines for SARS-CoV-2 were generated very quickly, compared with traditional methods of vaccine development that lead to inactivated, attenuated, and subunit vaccines. How do you think scientists' increased understanding of mRNA contributed to the rapid development of both mRNA and adenovirus-vector vaccines? How might this technology help us respond quickly to new variants or future epidemics and pandemics?*

Another type of influenza vaccine uses recombinant DNA technology. Large amounts of hemagglutinin protein are produced to make a subunit vaccine. Influenza vaccines typically cover multiple H and N subtypes, in hopes of more effectively protecting us against a variety of possible infections. Vaccines are key in combating seasonal influenza and providing better outcomes for most patients. They work best in combination with other precautions that can be taken to reduce the spread of illness when an individual is sick.

CCC **Patterns** *Why do you think influenza and other respiratory viruses tend to be transmitted more often in the winter season of each hemisphere? What measures could be taken to reduce transmission?*

COVID-19 Vaccines COVID-19 has caused millions of deaths, along with significant long-term health concerns for some patients who survived infection. Daily case data for the United States show the trends over the first two years of the pandemic (**Figure 13-27**). The COVID-19 pandemic demanded a more rapid response than traditional vaccine development allows. Vaccines have demonstrated effectiveness in reducing transmission and negative outcomes (such as hospitalization) for vaccinated individuals (**Figure 13-28**).

FIGURE 13-27 ▼
Spikes in the number of daily COVID cases in the United States were associated with the Delta (mid 2021) and Omicron (early 2022) variants of SARS-CoV-2.

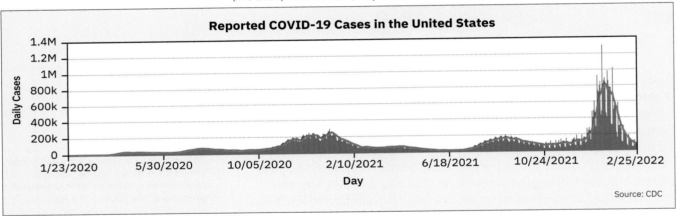

FIGURE 13-28 ▼
While the administration of vaccines in the United States did not stop all viral transmission for vaccinated individuals, particularly in the case of new variants, rates of hospitalization and death are significantly lower among the vaccinated population.

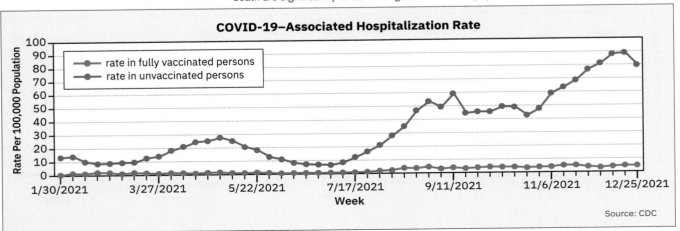

SARS-CoV-2 is the causative agent of COVID-19. The virus has a spike protein on its surface that is recognized as an antigen by the immune system. Adenovirus-vector and mRNA vaccine delivery methods were quickly developed and tested in an effort to slow down the virus's rapid transmission. Both methods rely on delivering genetic material into a host cell (**Figure 13-29**). The viral-vector versions of the COVID-19 vaccine deliver genetic material with an adenovirus that interacts with host cells to deliver DNA encoding the antigen. mRNA vaccines involve synthesizing an RNA molecule that encodes the viral spike antigen. The mRNA is delivered in lipid nanoparticles that can be absorbed by host cells, which then express the antigen and stimulate the production of antibodies to protect against the virus. The speed gained by delivering genetic material, rather than having to grow virus particles and purify their proteins, gives mRNA delivery a significant advantage over other vaccine preparation methods.

Although the mRNA and adenovirus-vector vaccines for COVID-19 were developed quickly, both use established technologies. Viral-vector technology has been successfully used in gene therapy, and mRNA vaccines and lipid nanoparticles have both been under study since 1990. It is likely that the success of the COVID-19 vaccine will lead to more scientific advancements and new vaccines that use mRNA. In addition to these newer genetic vaccine technologies, manufacturers have also developed more traditional inactivated and subunit vaccines for SARS-CoV-2.

FIGURE 13-29 ▽
COVID-19 vaccine mRNA encoding the viral spike protein antigen can be delivered using adenovirus vectors (a) or lipid nanoparticles (b).

29a   glycoprotein spike

virus

step 1

Gene encoding the viral spike protein is generated.

step 2

Adenovirus carrying the gene causes host cells to express the viral spike protein.

step 3

Viral spike proteins initiate an immune response.

step 4

Antibodies that recognize the viral spike protein are formed.

step 5

29b   glycoprotein spike

virus

step 1

mRNA that encodes the spike protein is synthesized.

step 2

mRNA is delivered to cells in a lipid nanoparticle, and cells express the viral spike protein.

step 3

Viral spike proteins initiate an immune response.

step 4

Antibodies that recognize the viral spike protein are formed.

step 5

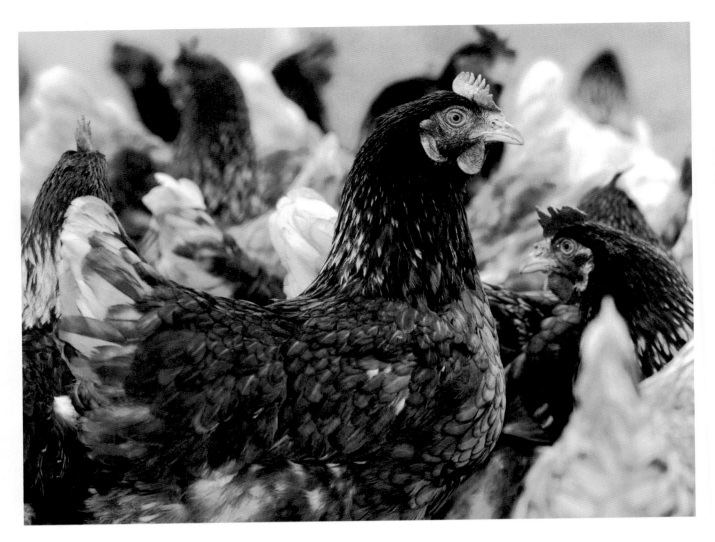

FIGURE 13-30 ▲
Chickens are often vaccinated to protect the flock from disease and to reduce transmission of certain pathogens to humans.

Vaccination of Reservoir Species Most human pathogens can also infect other species. Organisms that can be infected and transmit pathogens to humans are known as **reservoirs**. In some cases, vaccinating these reservoir species may be a method that can protect humans from infection. For example, animals raised as food sources may transmit pathogens to humans, and vaccinations of the animals have successfully been shown to protect humans who encounter them (**Figure 13-30**).

The challenge is different with wild populations of animals, however. For example, coronaviruses infect a variety of species. It is most likely that SARS-CoV-2 has a natural reservoir in bats, and the virus has also been shown to infect other species, such as white-tailed deer. For some pathogens, such as the virus that causes rabies, scientists are making efforts to vaccinate the natural reservoir (bats) to limit the spread of the virus to humans. While effective vaccines already exist for some pathogens in nonhuman hosts, it is difficult to vaccinate an entire bat population. To be effective, vaccines for wild reservoir species will have to distribute themselves. Scientists are working on several approaches. One way of generating transmissible vaccines is to make an attenuated pathogen that will elicit an immune response but not cause disease. Another approach involves putting part of the target pathogen genome into a safe vector virus that can spread through the population. Some successful examples of immunizations of pigs have been reported to limit transmission of an infection caused by *Salmonella enterica* from pigs to humans.

Supporting Vaccines With Other Measures

Slowing down the spread of disease requires multiple parallel efforts that involve everyone from individuals, to small communities, to international agencies and governments. A significant challenge with any public health crisis is related to communication of scientific ideas to the broader public. As an example of effective communication, **Figure 13-31** demonstrates the Swiss cheese model for mitigating the transmission of an illness that is spread through airborne droplets. Just one approach, such as vaccines, is often not enough to protect against illness. Depending on the type of disease and how it is transmitted, there are many factors to consider.

- **Infectious Dose** The amount of virus or other pathogen necessary to cause infection varies depending on the pathogen. Generally, the less pathogen an individual is exposed to, the less likely the individual is to be infected or experience severe illness.

- **Mode of Transmission** Solutions for reducing the spread of pathogens must reflect the mode of transmission. Different pathogens can be transmitted through blood, food, water sources, or droplets in the air.

- **Herd Immunity** For some pathogens, a level of immunity can be reached such that the infections become very rare, or even eradicated for some populations. Herd immunity is important because it enables a community to protect vulnerable individuals who cannot get vaccinated and most need protection from severe disease.

FIGURE 13-31 ▽
This model illustrates how each method of prevention against transmission of an airborne virus has holes, but together, they provide a robust defense against disease transmission. Notice how these prevention methods involve a variety of both shared and personal responsibilities.

STSE **Science, Technology, and Society** *What can you do to prevent transmission of diseases and protect other people in your community?*

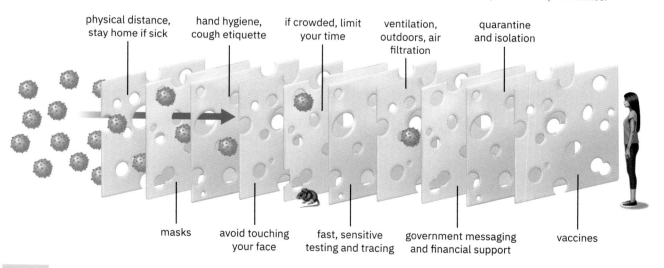

physical distance, stay home if sick | hand hygiene, cough etiquette | if crowded, limit your time | ventilation, outdoors, air filtration | quarantine and isolation

masks | avoid touching your face | fast, sensitive testing and tracing | government messaging and financial support | vaccines

13.3 REVIEW

1. **Distinguish** What is the relationship between vaccines and antibodies?

2. **Explain** Why is public participation and confidence necessary for the success of a vaccine?

3. **Identify** Which of the following statements accurately describes the COVID-19 vaccines?

   A. They deliver whole virus to host cells.

   B. They deliver genetic material to host cells.

   C. They can be transmitted between organisms.

   D. They deliver inactivated parts of a virus to the host's cells.

HERD IMMUNITY

SEP **Constructing Explanations and Designing Solutions** How does the percentage of people vaccinated impact the number of people infected with a disease?

Vaccines provide a "preview" of a specific pathogen that allows the immune system to prepare itself to recognize the pathogen when it sees it again. In this minilab, you will work with models of populations that have different percentages of vaccinations and explore how this affects the spread of a virus.

Materials
- opaque tubs (3)
- opaque plastic bags or lids (3)
- paper (3 pieces)
- 300 small objects of 2 different colors (suggestions include colored cotton balls, toy building blocks, small beads or beans, etc.)
- masking tape or labels
- marker
- scissors

Procedure

1. Set the three opaque tubs side by side.

2. Label one tub "30% vaccinated," one "50% vaccinated," and one "95% vaccinated." Each tub represents a population with a different percentage of vaccinated people.

3. Determine which color object represents vaccinated people and which represents unvaccinated people.

4. Place 30 "vaccinated" objects and 70 "unvaccinated" objects in the tub labeled "30% vaccinated."

5. Place 50 "vaccinated" objects and 50 "unvaccinated" objects in the tub labeled "50% vaccinated."

6. Place 95 "vaccinated" objects and 5 "unvaccinated" objects in the tub labeled "95% vaccinated."

7. Cover each tub with a lid or plastic bag and then cut a small opening in each lid so that a hand can reach into the tub.

8. Each student in a group should take a turn being a virus. The "virus" reaches into each tub, one at a time, and "infects" as many people as possible by grabbing a handful of the objects and pulling them out of the tub.

9. After the objects are drawn out of the tub, count the total number of objects you pulled out, and then count the number of unvaccinated individuals that became infected. Create a data table and record these data in your biology notebook.

10. Return the objects to the tub from which they were taken.

11. Repeat Steps 8 through 10 until everyone has had the opportunity to withdraw objects from all three tubs. Shake or stir up the objects in the container between students.

Results and Analysis

1. **Calculate** Based on the data you collected, what is the average infection rate of objects (people) for each of the tubs?

2. **Explain** Would it be realistic to have a tub with 0 percent vaccinated objects? Would it be realistic to have a tub with 100 percent vaccinated objects? Why?

3. **Identify** How do infected people spread disease in their community and when they travel outside their community?

4. **Compare** Imagine a real-life scenario where an infection is spreading in your community. What factors are represented well in your model, and what factors are not?

TYING IT ALL TOGETHER ENGINEERING
GENETICS TO THE RESCUE!

HOW CAN GENETIC INFORMATION BE USED IN MEDICAL AND OTHER SCIENTIFIC APPLICATIONS?

Somatic cell nuclear transfer (SCNT) was used to produce Elizabeth Ann, the black-footed ferret clone described in this chapter's Case Study. This chapter also introduced other techniques, including PCR, recombinant DNA, and CRISPR. These are commonly used in studying genetics and can also be applied to tackle a variety of problems. When considering genetic engineering as part of a solution, there are often ethical concerns associated with changing the genes of living and future organisms. There are also trade-offs to be made between the effectiveness of the solution and the potential impact of unpredictable outcomes.

For instance, genetic disorders in animals are usually observed in domesticated species that have been bred to have specific traits. These disorders occur more frequently in certain breeds as a consequence of the increased likelihood of offspring inheriting a recessive trait from both parents. Genetic engineering can rapidly produce livestock animals with traits that make them profitable in the marketplace but may render them susceptible to genetic disorders. This poses ethical dilemmas regarding the role of humans in preserving the value and quality of animal life.

In this activity, you will develop genetic engineering solutions for conserving a hypothetical wild animal population. Work individually or in a group to complete these steps.

Define the Problem

1. Consider a hypothetical wild animal species whose global population is endangered by a deadly pathogen. Suppose that it is possible, at a reasonable cost, to genetically engineer an individual of the species to resist infection by the pathogen. List some criteria and constraints that should be met by a solution designed to conserve this species. Include time, safety, social, ethical, and environmental factors in your list.

Design Solutions

2. Design at least two different solutions to the conservation problem, using genetic technologies you learned about in this chapter.

3. Construct and use models to explain how each solution would work.

Evaluate Solutions

4. Evaluate each solution in terms of how well it satisfies the criteria and constraints you defined. Decide which is the best solution according to your evaluation.

FIGURE 13-32
Naked foal syndrome is caused by a recessive trait that renders offspring mostly hairless and causes other health issues. Typically offspring with this disorder die within weeks or months of birth. This Akhal-Teke colt shown survived longer than most affected horses.

REVIEW KEY CONCEPTS

1. **Identify** A molecular biologist uses restriction enzymes to cut a section of genomic DNA, inserts the fragment into the plasmid of a bacterium, and then allows the bacterium to reproduce. The offspring of the bacterium all contain the recombinant plasmid. Which of these procedures best describes the scientist's method?

   A. DNA cloning

   B. DNA profiling

   C. Gel electrophoresis

   D. Polymerase chain reaction (PCR)

2. **Compare** Two samples of DNA migrate the same distance on an electrophoresis gel. What must be true about the DNA molecules in the two samples? Select all correct answers.

   A. They have the same length.

   B. They have the same charge.

   C. They have the same sequence.

   D. They have the same number of cytosine bases.

   E. They have the same number of nucleotides.

3. **Describe** Decide whether each of these statements best describes the template, the primer, or the polymerase in a PCR reaction.

   • It is an enzyme.

   • It is single stranded.

   • It is double stranded.

   • It separates when the reaction is heated.

   • It adds new nucleotides to the end of DNA molecules.

4. **Contrast** Which of these statements correctly describes how the genomes of two unrelated humans would most likely differ? Select all correct answers.

   A. The chemical composition of their genomes would differ.

   B. They would have different numbers of short tandem repeats.

   C. The genomic content inherited from ancestral species would differ.

   D. The sequence of the nucleotide bases in their genomes would be different.

   E. The single-nucleotide polymorphisms (SNPs) in their genomes would differ in length.

5. **Define** Which statement best describes how clones are produced through somatic cell nuclear transfer (SCNT)?

   A. A somatic cell's nucleus is removed, and then the nucleus of a fertilized egg is transferred to the somatic cell.

   B. A fertilized egg's nucleus is removed, and then the nucleus of a somatic cell is transferred to the fertilized egg.

   C. An unfertilized egg's nucleus is removed, and then the nucleus of a fertilized egg is transferred to the unfertilized egg.

   D. An unfertilized egg's nucleus is removed, and then the nucleus of a somatic cell is transferred to the unfertilized egg.

6. **Identify** Which of these conditions would most likely be treatable with gene therapy? Select all correct answers.

   A. muscle loss due to advanced age

   B. congestion caused by a respiratory virus

   C. mental impairment due to phenylketonuria

   D. difficulty breathing caused by cystic fibrosis

   E. an infection of the stomach lining by bacteria

7. **Compare** How is cloning an organism different from genetically engineering an organism?

8. **Identify** Which of these vaccine technologies involve the delivery of whole viruses to a patient? Select all correct answers.

   A. toxoid vaccines

   B. subunit vaccines

   C. inactivated vaccines

   D. viral-vector vaccines

   E. live-attenuated vaccines

   F. messenger RNA vaccines

9. **Describe** Explain how vaccines are able to induce immunity without causing severe illness in the patient.

CRITICAL THINKING

10. **Reason Quantitatively** AluI is a restriction enzyme that recognizes the sequence AGCT and makes a single cut between the guanine and cytosine of both DNA strands. A researcher adds AluI to a sample of DNA with the following sequence:

TCAGCTTAACAGCTGG
AGTCGAATTGTCGACC

After the reaction is complete, she separates the products by gel electrophoresis. How many bands will appear on her gel?

11. **Explain** Single-nucleotide polymorphism mutations are more likely to occur in noncoding DNA rather than in coding DNA. Why do you think stable unique polymorphisms are more likely to be in noncoding regions rather than in the middle of gene sequences?

12. **Explain** In somatic cell nuclear transfer (SCNT) experiments, scientists have found that the clones do not always look or behave like the parent from which they are cloned. Why might this be the case?

13. **Evaluate** People with diabetes are unable to produce enough insulin, a hormone that regulates blood sugar levels. To combat the disease, diabetics are often prescribed insulin that is produced by bacteria that have been genetically engineered to produce human insulin. Scientists have also investigated alternative methods for producing insulin, such as using recombinant DNA technology to engineer cows to secrete human insulin in their milk. This insulin can then be isolated from the milk and purified for use as treatment. What is one possible advantage of manufacturing recombinant insulin in cow's milk as opposed to using bacteria?

14. **Analyze** Measles is a highly contagious disease that is caused by a virus. In the United States, most people are vaccinated against measles as children, and cases are extremely rare. However, in recent years, outbreaks of measles have become more common in the United States. Some scientists hypothesize that these increases are due to the reluctance of some people to vaccinate their children. What data should scientists collect to test this hypothesis? What would the data show if the hypothesis is correct?

MATH AND ENGLISH LANGUAGE ARTS CONNECTIONS

1. **Model With Mathematics** A scientist is using PCR to amplify a segment of DNA. The initial sample contains five copies of a segment of DNA that can hybridize with the pair of primers added to the reaction. After six cycles, how many copies will be produced by the reaction?

2. **NOS** **Science, Technology, and Society** In 2018, a Chinese scientist used CRISPR technology to produce the world's first known genetically engineered humans. In the experiment, a gene conferring resistance to HIV was edited into the genomes of human embryos. This experiment was extremely controversial and instigated great debate among medical ethicists. What is one question that medical ethicists should answer before recommending this procedure for wider practice?

3. **Use Sources in Multiple Formats** Examine the base sequences in **Figure 13-9**. Suppose a laboratory wants to determine whether a sample of DNA came from a frog or a rat. Based on the information in the chapter, would it be possible to make this determination by using PCR to amplify this location followed by gel electrophoresis of the products? Explain your answer.

4. **Synthesize Information** During the first year of the COVID-19 pandemic in 2020, governments around the world imposed restrictions on travel and policies to encourage masking and social distancing in public. These policies were intended to reduce community spread of the COVID-19 virus. During this time, public health experts observed a much lower-than-usual incidence of seasonal influenza, which is caused by a different virus than COVID-19. What conclusions can be drawn from these observations?

▶ REVISIT VIRAL SPREAD

Gather Evidence In this chapter, you learned about how genetic technologies are employed in research and to help solve problems facing society, including viral pandemics.

1. How many genetic technologies can you identify that may have played an important role in understanding and developing a response to the COVID-19 pandemic?

2. What additional questions do you have about genetic technologies and their role in public health?

GENETICS

CHAPTER 11
DNA, RNA, AND PROTEINS

How is genetic information transferred and regulated?

- A series of independent experiments proved that DNA is the hereditary molecule in cells.

- Replication, transcription, and translation are mechanisms by which genetic information is moved and changed in living organisms.

- Transcription converts DNA to mRNA. Ribosomes translate RNA into proteins.

- Regulation of gene expression occurs at many points in the cell and can adjust to environmental and developmental conditions.

CHAPTER 12
GENETIC VARIATION AND HEREDITY

How does genetic information change and get passed from generation to generation?

- Sexually reproducing organisms distribute chromosomes to offspring through meiosis, which introduces genetic variation.

- Nucleotide and chromosomal mutations may be silent or may result in advantageous or disadvantageous changes.

- Gregor Mendel described basic rules of inheritance.

- The proportion of genes and traits passed from one generation to the next can often be modeled with Punnett squares.

- Complex inheritance patterns and gene expression include codominant, incomplete dominant, and sex-linked traits.

- Environmental factors can affect the expression of many genes.

CHAPTER 13
GENETIC TECHNOLOGIES

How can genetic information be used in medical and other scientific applications?

- Scientists use restriction enzymes and polymerases to cut, paste, and duplicate DNA through DNA cloning and PCR.

- Genome analyses help scientists study relatedness of organisms, understand how different genes work, and identify individuals.

- Scientists use genetic tools to modify or clone animals and plants.

- Gene therapy techniques, such as CRISPR, can replace gene function or repair gene sequences.

- Vaccine technologies take advantage of immune system functions to protect against disease.

Go Online | **VIRTUAL INVESTIGATION**

Fighting a Viral Pandemic
How can we slow the spread of a virus?
Enter the situation room and make decisions to protect your community from a deadly virus.

HOW CAN WE SLOW THE SPREAD OF A VIRUS?

Argue From Evidence In this unit, you learned how genetic information functions in organisms and how it is used in technological applications. You have learned how many of these mechanisms apply to COVID-19 and the SARS-CoV-2 virus that causes it.

The human immunodeficiency virus (HIV) is an RNA retrovirus (Section 8.4). HIV is transmitted through contact with bodily fluids. It attacks immune cells of the human host, making the infected individual susceptible to other infections. This condition is known as acquired immunodeficiency syndrome (AIDS). AIDS was first recognized as a global epidemic in the 1980s.

In 2020, approximately 37.7 million people worldwide were living with HIV. About 73 percent of those individuals had access to medical treatments. Antiretroviral therapies allow people with HIV to live longer and healthier lives, with a significantly reduced risk of transmission. Both new HIV infections and AIDS-related deaths per year have decreased significantly since the early 2000s, but there are still many challenges worldwide.

Numerous efforts by organizations, such as the United Nations and the World Health Organization, have been important in curbing the AIDS epidemic through education and the distribution of treatments. Education is a critical aspect of the international response to HIV and AIDS. It leads to reduced transmission and increased adherence to treatment regimens. The more scientists and the public understand a virus, the easier it is to stop its spread. Efforts to develop an effective vaccine have been ongoing since the virus was isolated and characterized in 1984, with an mRNA vaccine in development.

HIV and SARS-CoV-2 are viruses with different modes of replication and transmission, but many of the same factors apply. Both viruses spread easily and mutate in a way that can potentially dodge vaccines. Slowing the spread of any virus relies on global cooperation as well as individuals caring for their community and working together to take precautions.

 Claim Make a claim about the role of science and technology in combating SARS-CoV-2 and the COVID-19 pandemic.

 Evidence Use the evidence you gathered throughout the unit to support your claim.

 Reasoning Use your understanding of genetic mechanisms, mutations, and genetic and antiviral technology to address the goals and challenges associated with stopping a pandemic.

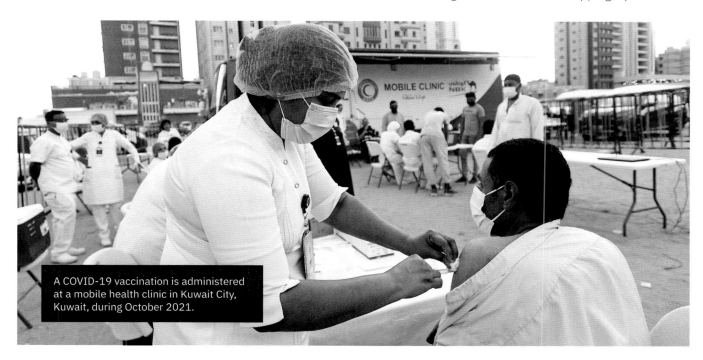

A COVID-19 vaccination is administered at a mobile health clinic in Kuwait City, Kuwait, during October 2021.

EVOLUTION AND CHANGING ENVIRONMENTS

The sword-billed hummingbird (*Ensifera ensifera*) has the highest bill-length-to-body-length ratio of any bird species. Its name comes from the Latin words *ensis* (sword) and *ferre* (to carry).

The sword-billed hummingbird is a species uniquely adapted to its ecological niche. It feeds on the nectar found deep within long-flowered plants. Sword-billed hummingbirds are one of more than 330 species that inhabit the Western Hemisphere. The majority of hummingbirds are found in South America, with over 140 species endemic to the Andes Mountain region alone.

A number of superlatives apply to this exceptional family of birds: smallest body, tiniest egg, fastest heart rate, quickest wingbeat, highest metabolism. Hummingbirds have the unique ability to fly in any direction. Their rapid wingbeats allow them to hover in place for an extended period of time.

▼

HOW DID HUMMINGBIRDS BECOME ADAPTED TO THEIR ENVIRONMENTS?

In this unit, you will evaluate how natural selection and changing environmental conditions, including those caused by human activities, affect populations of species.

▶ **UNIT VIDEO 1** Go online to observe adaptations hummingbirds have for survival.

THE HUMMINGBIRD'S SECRET TO SURVIVAL

EXAMINING EXTREME ENERGY CONSERVATION

As they flit and fly through the air, hummingbirds seem to defy the laws of gravity. They hover in midair, floating above the delicate flowers that provide them with nectar. According to ecologist Dr. Anusha Shankar, hovering is one of the most energetically expensive activities in the animal world. Because hovering uses up so much energy, hummingbirds have an enormous appetite. In order to survive, many species must consume two to three times their body weight in nectar and small insects every day.

MAXIMIZING ENERGY CONSERVATION One of Shankar's primary research goals is to understand how hummingbirds balance their daily energy needs. As part of her dissertation research, Shankar studied hummingbird energy budgets. She focused particularly on their use of torpor, an evolutionary strategy some animals use to conserve energy. Hummingbirds lapse into torpor at night or when their energy stores are very low. If sitting on a branch, the bird appears unresponsive and hunched up. Its beak is in the air, its eyes are closed, and it is barely breathing. Unlike hibernation that can last for days or weeks, daily torpor is short term. It typically lasts for only a few hours.

Shankar studies how different species of hummingbirds use torpor as an energy-saving strategy in different climates. Torpor saves the bird energy by drastically lowering its metabolism and body temperature. A hummingbird's normal body temperature is around 40 °C (104 °F). When it enters torpor, its body temperature lowers to that of its surroundings or less. The bird's body temperature could be as low as 3–10 °C (37–50 °F). Research indicates that a hummingbird conserves 65 to 92 percent of its energy every hour it is in torpor. The longer it is in torpor, the more energy it conserves.

Unlike during sleep, the body doesn't repair and regenerate itself during torpor. Shankar wondered exactly how much time hummingbirds spent in energy-saving torpor versus regenerative sleep. More recent research indicates that hummingbirds are able to regulate their body temperature at an intermediate state between deep torpor and sleep. This state is called shallow torpor. She hopes that further research in this area will help scientists to understand the physiological functions of sleep compared to torpor in both birds and other animals.

SURVIVAL IN A CHANGING CLIMATE In addition to her research focused on torpor, Shankar is interested in understanding how changing environmental conditions could affect hummingbird populations. As nectar feeders, hummingbirds play a primary role as pollinators for many plant species. Shankar's collaborators are combining plant distribution maps, climate data, and research on hummingbird behavior to model how a warming planet could affect hummingbird survival. Shankar hopes to expand this research to study the health of other bird species. ▮

THINKING CRITICALLY

Infer *What is the evolutionary benefit of an energy-conserving mechanism such as torpor?*

Top: Dr. Anusha Shankar transfers a hummingbird's waste into a clean tube. The sample will be used to identify gut microbes and analyze any changes that may be related to torpor. **Bottom:** A series of infrared photos shows a hummingbird moving from a state of normal body temperature (left) into the lethargic state of torpor (right), with low metabolism and body temperature.

(▶) UNIT VIDEO 2 Go online to watch our interview with Shankar and learn more about her career and research.

CHAPTER 14

EVIDENCE FOR EVOLUTION

Three-toed sloths are found throughout the tropical forests of Central America and South America.

14.1 LINES OF EVIDENCE

14.2 FOSSIL AND GEOLOGICAL EVIDENCE

14.3 DEVELOPMENTAL, ANATOMICAL, AND GENETIC EVIDENCE

A sloth is a slow-moving mammal that spends most of its lifetime living within the branches of its tropical treetop habitat. Algae that live within its fur help to camouflage the sloth from predators. While sloths may in some ways look similar to monkeys, they are actually more closely related to anteaters and armadillos.

Chapter 14 supports the NGSS Performance Expectation **HS-LS4-1.**

CASE STUDY
SOLVING THE MYSTERY OF SLOTH EVOLUTION

HOW DO WE KNOW HOW SPECIES HAVE EVOLVED?

If sloths physically resemble monkeys, why have scientists concluded that they are more closely related to armadillos? Looking beyond surface-level resemblances, scientists have found evidence in the anatomical and molecular makeup of these animals, as well as in the history revealed by fossils. Modern and extinct sloths, anteaters, and armadillos are members of a superorder called Xenarthra. The name *Xenarthra* derives from Greek words meaning "strange joints" and refers to extra joints found in the lower spines of all members of this group. All Xenarthrans have fewer teeth compared to other mammals their size. Sloths and armadillos have simple teeth that lack enamel and anteaters have no teeth at all. In addition, genetic evidence shows that all Xenarthrans have the same three consecutive amino acid deletions in a particular eye protein.

Xenarthrans are one of the oldest groups of mammals. Fossil evidence indicates they originated in South America 55 million to 65 million years ago. They diversified into numerous species while the continent was geographically isolated. The different species spread to Central and North America eight million years ago.

Ancient Xenarthrans flourished until about 10,000 years ago when the majority of species became extinct during the Ice Age, likely due to overhunting by humans.

Unlike their modern tree-dwelling equivalents, the ancient ancestors of sloths were giant ground dwellers. The first giant ground sloth fossil (**Figure 14-1**) was discovered in Argentina by Manuel Torres in 1788. This elephant-sized species was named *Megatherium americanum*. In 1797, a naturalist presented a paper to the American Philosophical Society about the discovery of a large claw and limb bone found in a cave in West Virginia. The naturalist initially identified the fossils as belonging to an extinct Ice Age cat species. However, upon recognizing similarities between the fossils and *M. americanum*, they were recategorized as belonging to a species of giant ground sloth. The ox-sized species was named *Megalonyx jeffersonii* in honor of the naturalist, Thomas Jefferson, then vice president of the United States. Fossils of *M. jeffersonii* have been recovered from 150 sites across the United States as well as from sites in northwestern Canada and western Mexico.

Ask Questions *As you read, generate questions about the lines of evidence scientists use to determine the evolutionary history of a species.*

FIGURE 14-1
Megatherium americanum means "great beast from America." This vegetarian mammal could stand and walk on its hind legs. With a standing height of 3.5 m (12 ft.), it is the largest bipedal mammal of all time.

LINES OF EVIDENCE

You may already know that whales are mammals, but you may not know that biologists have concluded that whales are descended from an ancient ancestor that lived on land. What types of evidence do you think scientists might have found that led them to this conclusion? What types of evidence and thought processes do scientists use to determine the evolutionary relationships among different species?

Ask Questions *What questions do you have about how biologists study the history of living things?*

Connecting Genetic Variation With Evolution

Evolution is the means by which all of Earth's species have descended from a single common ancestor. From the time the first living cell appeared on this planet billions of years ago to the incredible variety of both simple and complex organisms we know today, the process of evolution has been at work.

Genetic variation provides the raw material of evolutionary change. The main sources of variation are the mutations that occur within genomes as well as the new genetic combinations made during meiosis when crossover occurs. These processes result in a stockpile of unique alleles within a population's gene pool, any of which can suddenly be favored if environmental conditions change.

Consider also the effects of sexual reproduction on evolution. Though sexual reproduction produces no new alleles, the sheer number of genes that are shuffled during the formation of a zygote produces an enormous range of different combinations. If conditions change, any one of the genotypes produced could suddenly become advantageous.

Evolution Occurs at Different Scales

Evolutionary change occurs in populations at both large and small scales. Whether evolution occurs over a long period of time (macroevolution) or in a relatively short period of time (microevolution), the underlying mechanisms remain the same.

Macroevolution refers to major evolutionary events that occur in groups of species over geological time, or millions of years. Macroevolution can be thought of as the accumulation of microevolutionary change over an incredibly long period of time. These events are large phenotypic changes, such as the appearance of wings with feathers that evolved in birds. The phenotypic changes are so great that the organisms (and their descendants) that possess them are assigned to a whole new taxonomic category, such as the changes that caused transition from fishes to amphibians, or amphibians to reptiles. Macroevolution involves the origin of major taxonomic categories more general than the species level.

In contrast to macroevolution, **microevolution** is change in allele frequency within a single species or population. Microevolution accounts for the differences among the various populations of a species and, in some cases, can account for the origin of new species.

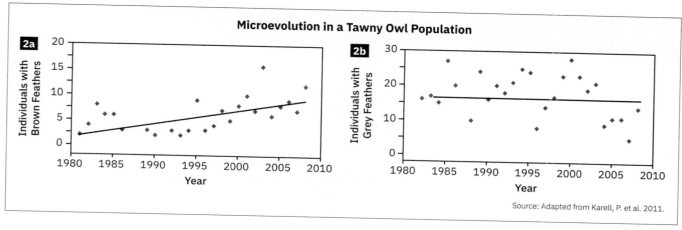

Microevolution in a Tawny Owl Population

Source: Adapted from Karell, P. et al. 2011.

FIGURE 14-2
Brown feathers (a) are becoming more common in populations of tawny owls in Finland, as grey feathers (b) become less advantageous in a warming climate.

Feather color in a population of tawny owls in Finland provides one example of microevolution in action (**Figure 14-2**). This heritable trait has two variations: dominant brown feathers and recessive grey feathers. In the past, brown feathers had been selected against, as grey feathers helped the owls to better camouflage themselves in Finland's snowy conditions. However, as the climate warms, milder winters are producing less snow in Finland. As a result, brown-feathered owls are becoming more common in the population.

Empirical Evidence

Scientific knowledge is based on empirical evidence, which is information acquired by observation or experimentation. Because most evolutionary change occurs over thousands to millions of years, much of the evidence for evolution is based on observations, such as comparisons between ancient and modern organisms. Evolutionary biologists are a bit like detectives, using clues to piece together history that no human witnessed. Five lines of evidence that support evolution include

- **Fossils** The fossil record connects long-dead organisms with their modern-day counterparts.

- **Developmental Patterns** Some animal embryos share similarities during early development.

- **Anatomy** Evidence for actual modification of species is found by comparing the anatomy of various organisms.

- **Molecular Biology and Genetics** A shared genetic code supports the idea that life-forms descended from a common ancestor.

- **Biogeography** The global distribution of plants and animals helps identify when and where species originated and evolved.

HUMMINGBIRD EVOLUTION

Gather Evidence *Multiple lines of evolution support the evolution of hummingbirds. Identify three types of evidence that scientists have used to determine the evolutionary history of hummingbirds.*

Piecing Together Evolutionary Evidence

Our knowledge of evolution is based on making logical inferences from the best available evidence. This knowledge has been greatly enhanced by our understanding of genetics and recent advancements in biotechnology.

Whales provide one example of how scientists have pieced together fossil, anatomical, and molecular evidence to fully understand their evolutionary history. Whales and their relatives such as dolphins and porpoises make up the group called cetaceans. Modern cetaceans have skeletons with remnants of a pelvis which would have at one time connected to hind limbs (**Figure 14-3a**), so evolutionary biologists had long inferred that the ancestors of this group walked on land. However, no one had found fossils demonstrating a clear link between cetaceans and ancient land animals, so the rest of the story remained hypothetical.

Intact fossil skeletons of extinct whalelike *Dorudon atrox* had been discovered, but these animals were clearly cetaceans with little resemblance to land animals. *Dorudon* lived about 37 million years ago and like modern whales, it was a tail swimmer and fully aquatic. Its tiny hind limbs could not have supported the animal's huge body out of water (**Figure 14-3b**).

In the early 1990s, DNA sequence comparisons suggested that modern cetaceans are more closely related to artiodactyls than to other groups. Artiodactyls are hooved mammals with an even number of toes (two or four) on each foot. Modern representatives of the lineage include camels, hippopotamuses, pigs, antelopes, and sheep.

The DNA findings were controversial at the time. Some scientists thought the ancestors of cetaceans were Mesonychids, a lineage of carnivorous mammals. The ancestors of artiodactyls were a lineage of herbivores that looked a bit like tiny deer with long tails. Either way, a seemingly unimaginable number of skeletal and physiological changes would have been required for small, land-based animals to evolve into whales with gigantic bodies uniquely adapted to swimming in the deep ocean.

Then, in 2000, paleontologist Philip Gingerich and his colleagues unearthed complete fossilized skeletons of two cetaceans from a 47-million-year-old rock formation in the Sulaiman Mountains in central Pakistan. Later named *Artiocetus clavis* and *Rodhocetus balochistanensis* (**Figure 14-3c**), both animals had whalelike skulls and robust hind limbs. The bodies of both animals were built for swimming with their feet—not their tails as whales do—and their ankle bones had clearly distinctive features of artiodactyls. This evidence settled the debate about cetacean ancestry. *Rodhocetus* and *Artiocetus* were not direct ancestors of modern whales, but their telltale ankle bones mean they were long-lost relatives. Both ancient cetaceans were offshoots of the artiodactyl-to-modern-whale lineage as it transitioned from life on land to life in water.

The oldest ancestor of living whales is considered to be *Pakicetus attocki* (**Figure 14-3d**), which lived around 50 million years ago. Fossils of this strange mammal with a whalelike head, webbed feet, and a wolf-sized body were discovered in 1983. The mammal was later found to have an ear bone similar to whales and ankle bones similar to artiodactyls, clearly linking it to modern cetaceans.

SEP **Communicate Information** *Summarize the evidence that modern whales evolved from animals that lived on land.*

FIGURE 14-3

The ancestor of whales was an artiodactyl that walked on land. Over millions of years, the lineage transitioned from life on land to life in water, and as it did, bones of the hind limb (highlighted in blue) became smaller.

A Modern cetaceans such as the sperm whale have remnants of a pelvis and hind limbs, but they do not walk.

B *Dorudon atrox*, a cetacean, lived about 37 million years ago. Its hind limbs worked, but they were tiny and were not connected to the backbone, so they would not have supported the weight of the animal's huge body on land. Thus, *Dorudon* was fully aquatic.

Ankle bones

2 cm

Rodhocetus   Antelope

C *Rodhocetus balochistanensis*, a cetacean that lived about 47 million years ago, was capable of walking (or dragging itself) on land but probably spent most of its time in water. Distinctive ankle bones are evidence of a close evolutionary connection to artiodactyls. Artiodactyls are defined by the unique "double-pulley" shape of the bone that forms the lower part of their ankle joint.

D *Pakicetus attocki*, a small animal that lived about 50 million years ago, was semiaquatic, but its body was specialized for running. *Pakicetus* belonged to the artiodactyl lineage, but it also had some traits unique to cetaceans. It is considered to be one of the earliest cetaceans.

Connecting Evolutionary Relationships

Classifying life's tremendous diversity into a series of taxonomic ranks (Chapter 1) is a useful endeavor, in the same way that it is useful to organize a contact list in alphabetical order: The result is convenient. Traditional (Linnaean) classification schemes have ranked species into successively higher groups based on shared traits—birds have feathers, cacti have spines, and so on. However, these rankings do not necessarily reflect evolutionary relationships.

Phylogeny Today's biologists work from the premise that every living thing is related if you just look back far enough in time. Grouping species according to evolutionary relationships is a way to fill in the details of this bigger picture of evolution. Thus, reconstructing *phylogeny*, which is the evolutionary history of a species or a group of species, is a priority. Phylogeny is a kind of genealogy that follows evolutionary relationships through time.

Humans were not around to witness the evolution of most species, but as you will see in this chapter, there is plenty of evidence to help us understand ancient events. Consider how each species bears traces of its own unique evolutionary history in its characters. A *character* is a quantifiable, heritable trait such as the number of segments in a backbone, the nucleotide sequence of ribosomal RNA, or the presence of wings. Evolutionary biologists group (rather than rank) species based on shared characters. They focus on what makes the species share the traits in the first place: a common ancestor. Common ancestry is determined by a *derived trait*—a character that is present in a group under consideration, but not in any of the group's ancestors.

A grouping whose members share one or more defining derived traits is called a *clade*. This grouping consists of an ancestor (in which a derived trait evolved) together with all of its descendants. It is the relative newness of a derived trait that defines a clade. Humans and bacteria use some of the same proteins to repair DNA, for example, but humans and bacteria are not close relatives. As another example, consider how alligators look a lot more like lizards than like birds (**Figure 14-4**). While the similarity in appearance does indicate shared ancestry, it is a more distant relationship than alligators have with birds. A unique set of traits that include a gizzard and a four-chambered heart evolved in the lineage that gave rise to alligators and birds, but not in the lineage that gave rise to lizards.

FIGURE 14-4 ▽

Lizards (a) look quite similar in appearance to alligators (b). However, alligators share more derived traits with, and are more closely related to, birds (c).

Cladistics All species are interconnected in the big picture of evolution. An evolutionary biologist's job is to figure out where the connections are. Making hypotheses about evolutionary relationships among clades is called *cladistics*. A *cladogram* is an evolutionary tree that visually summarizes a hypothesis about how a group of clades are related (**Figure 14-5**). Each line is a lineage, which may branch into two lineages at a node. The *node* represents a common ancestor of two lineages, and the two lineages that emerge from a node are called *sister groups*.

Evolutionary history does not change because of events in the present. A species' ancestry remains the same no matter how it evolves. However, as with traditional taxonomic rankings, we can make mistakes when we group organisms based on incomplete information. Thus, a clade or cladogram may change when new discoveries are made. As with all hypotheses, the more data in support of an evolutionary grouping, the less likely it is to require revision.

FIGURE 14-5 ▼
Evolutionary connections among clades are represented as lines on a cladogram. Sister groups emerge from a node, which represents a common ancestor (a). A cladogram can be viewed as "sets within sets" of derived traits. Each set, which includes an ancestor together with all of its descendants, is a clade (b).

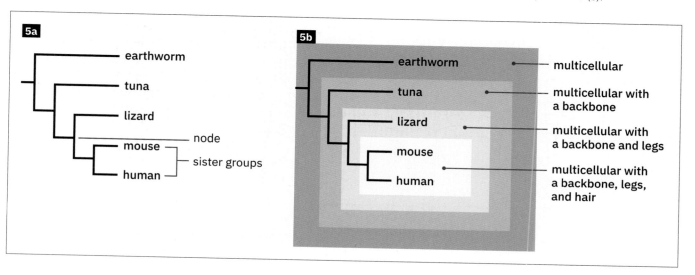

14.1 REVIEW

1. **Define** What is empirical evidence?

   A. information that is based on opinions

   B. information that is common knowledge

   C. information that is found in popular literature

   D. information that is gathered by observation or experimentation

2. **Identify** Which lines of evidence support evolution? Select all correct answers.

   A. common anatomical structures

   B. similarities in physical appearance

   C. comparable developmental stages

   D. matching genetic sequence patterns

   E. sequence of fossils in geologic record

3. **Compare** What is the difference between microevolution and macroevolution?

4. **Apply** Which scenario is an example of microevolution?

   A. A tadpole develops into a frog.

   B. A tree loses its leaves in the fall.

   C. A population of bacteria is resistant to antibiotics.

   D. A brown dog has a puppy that is white with brown spots.

ORGANIZING FOSSIL EVIDENCE

SEP **Construct Explanations** How can you form an evolutionary tree of related species based on fossils?

Trilobites are a group of extinct sea animals that existed over a period of millions of years. They were arthropods that had an exoskeleton, a segmented body, and segmented legs. Trilobites fossilize well, so scientists have been able to classify and study tens of thousands of trilobite species.

In this activity, you will study images of fossils that are related to trilobites. You will consider which species could have given rise to other species in order to form an evolutionary tree.

1   2   3   4   5   6

Suggested Materials

- computer/tablet
- poster board or paper
- scissors
- ruler
- glue
- craft materials

Procedure

1. Study the fossil images. These fossils are related species of trilobites.

2. Based on the physical forms you see, make an evolutionary tree that orders the species from oldest to most recent. Redraw the fossil images as necessary. As you make your tree, consider that your tree may have multiple branches. Some species tend to evolve into more specialized and complex shapes if it benefits their chance for reproduction and survival. For this activity, use the most basic trilobite as your oldest species.

3. Add the appropriate labels to your evolutionary tree using the following list. Some of these labels will be used more than once, and some may not be needed at all. Note: *mya* means "million years ago."

- Cambrian period trilobite—521 mya
- Ordovician period trilobite—460 mya
- Devonian period trilobite—400 mya
- Carboniferous period trilobite—300 mya
- Permian period trilobite—255 mya

Results and Analysis

1. **Analyze** Describe the reasoning for how you organized the fossils to represent an evolutionary pathway. What linked each species to the next?

2. **Predict** Study the trilobite that is the most recent in your evolutionary pathway. Draw a sketch of a trilobite that might have evolved from that species. Describe how your species is different from its ancestor and what change in conditions may have led to those differences.

3. **Predict** Study the trilobite that is the oldest in your evolutionary pathway. Draw a sketch that could be the ancestor of this species. Describe how your ancestor species is different from its descendants and what change in conditions may have led to those differences.

FOSSIL AND GEOLOGICAL EVIDENCE

Trilobites were marine animals that first appeared at the beginning of the Cambrian period, about 542 million years ago. These prolific arthropods persisted for 300 million years, more than double the length of time dinosaurs roamed our planet. Fossilized remains of trilobites have been found on every continent.

Infer *What do you think the discovery of trilobite fossils in the Midwest region of the United States tells us about how that region's environmental conditions have changed over geologic time?*

14.2

KEY TERMS

fossil
gradualism
half-life
index fossil
radiometric dating
trace fossil
uniformitarianism

Fossil Formation

Fossils have long been recognized as rock-hard evidence of earlier forms of life. Not only do they give us clues about what certain organisms looked like, but they also give us a glimpse of what environmental conditions were like millions of years ago. **Fossils** are mineralized bones, teeth, shells, seeds, spores, or other long-lasting parts of an organism that lived in the past. **Trace fossils** such as footprints and other impressions, nests, burrows, trails, eggshells, or feces are evidence of activities. For example, the spacing between fossilized footprints provides evidence of how an ancient animal moved. Fossilized feces, called coprolites, provide evidence of an extinct animal's diet. **Figure 14-6** shows a variety of fossil types.

 VIDEO

VIDEO 14-1 Go online to learn more about fossils and how they are formed.

FIGURE 14-6

Examples of fossils include fossilized dinosaur tracks (a), molds or casts of fossil shells (b), petrified wood (c), and insects preserved in amber (d).

The organism dies.

The soft parts of the body decompose, but bones remain. The remains are covered by layers of sediment.

Over millions of years, repeated layering of sediment buries the remains far below the surface. Groundwater then seeps into the remains, filling spaces around and inside of them. Minerals dissolved in the water gradually replace minerals in bones and other hard tissues, forming fossils.

Erosion exposes the fossilized remains.

FIGURE 14-7 ⬆
Very few organisms become fossils. A particular set of conditions is required for the fossilization process to occur.

The process of fossilization is shown in **Figure 14-7**. This process typically follows these steps:

- Fossilization begins when an organism or its traces become covered by sediments, mud, or ash.

- Groundwater then seeps into the remains, filling spaces around and inside of them.

- Minerals dissolved in the water gradually replace minerals in bones and other hard tissues.

- Mineral particles that settle out of the groundwater and crystallize inside cavities and impressions form detailed imprints of internal and external structures.

- Sediments that slowly accumulate on top of the site exert increasing pressure. After a very long time, extreme pressure transforms the mineralized remains into rock.

- Over time, the fossilized remains may become exposed as a result of the geologic processes of uplift and erosion.

The Fossil Record

We have fossils for more than 250,000 known species. Considering the current range of biodiversity, there must have been many millions more, but we will never know all of these species. Why not? The odds are against finding evidence of an extinct species. Few individuals of any species become fossilized.

Typically, when an organism dies, its remains are destroyed quickly by scavengers. Organic materials decompose in the presence of moisture and oxygen. Thus, remains that escape scavenging endure only if they dry out, freeze, or become encased in a material such as sap, tar, or mud. Most remains that do become fossilized are crushed or scattered by erosion and other geologic processes.

CASE STUDY
SOLVING THE MYSTERY OF SLOTH EVOLUTION

Ask Questions *Generate questions about the evidence the fossil record provides in support of the evolution of sloth species.*

For us to know about an extinct species that existed long ago, we have to find a fossil of it. At least one specimen had to be buried before it decomposed or something ate it. The burial site had to escape destructive geologic events and end up in a place we can find today. Most ancient species had no hard parts to fossilize, so we do not find much evidence of them. For example, there are many fossils of bony fishes and mollusks with hard shells, but few fossils of the jellyfish and soft worms that were probably much more common. Also, think about relative numbers of organisms. Fungal spores and pollen grains are typically released by the billions. By contrast, the earliest humans lived in small bands and few of their offspring survived. The odds of finding even one fossilized human bone are much smaller than the odds of finding a fossilized fungal spore.

Most fossils are found in layers of sedimentary rock that form as rivers wash silt, sand, volcanic ash, and other materials from land into the sea. Mineral particles in the materials settle on the seafloor in horizontal layers that vary in thickness and composition. After many millions of years, the layers of sediments become buried and compacted into layered sedimentary rock. Geologic processes can tilt the rock and lift it far above sea level, where the layers may become exposed by the erosive forces of water and wind (**Figure 14-8**).

Biologists study sedimentary rock formations to understand the historical context of ancient life. Rock layers provide a kind of clock or timing device for scientists to date fossils. In a multilayered formation, the more recent layers lie on top of the older layers. Knowing the rate of sediment deposition allows scientists to provide relative dates for given fossils. If, for example, you know it took 20 million years for each rock layer to form, then a dinosaur fossil found four layers down was alive approximately 80 million years ago.

CCC **Patterns** *What characteristics do you think are shared by species that are more likely to be represented in the fossil record?*

FIGURE 14-8 ▼

It takes thousands, even millions, of years for sedimentary rock layers to form out of sand, soil, and other materials. The youngest rock layer that makes up the Grand Canyon is 270 million years old. The oldest layers date back 1.8 billion years.

Index Fossils

Scientists use a number of different sources of evidence to connect rocks of the same age. **Index fossils** are useful pieces of evidence because they can be used to precisely determine sedimentary rock ages. The most useful index fossils share the following characteristics:

- The fossils are abundant in rock layers.

- The fossils are found all over Earth.

- The organisms existed as a species or genus for a relatively short period of geologic time.

- The fossils are easily identified in the field.

Marine organisms are some of the best index fossils because they spread rapidly and widely throughout their watery environments. Species that existed only for a short period of geologic time enable scientists to more precisely date the rock layers in which they are found.

Fossils of *Neptunea tabulata* (**Figure 14-9a**) date to the Quaternary period. Ammonites, trilobites, and brachiopods were particularly widespread over geological time. Today, many species from these groups are used as index fossils to determine the relative age of rock layers. The ammonite genus *Dactylioceras* (**Figure 14-9b**) is dated to the Jurassic period, the trilobite genus *Paradoxides* (**Figure 14-9c**) is dated to the Cambrian period, and the brachiopod genus *Mucrospirifer* (**Figure 14-9d**) is dated to the Devonian period.

FIGURE 14-9 ▽
Examples of index fossils include *Neptunea tabulata* (a) ammonites (b), trilobites (c), and brachiopods (d).

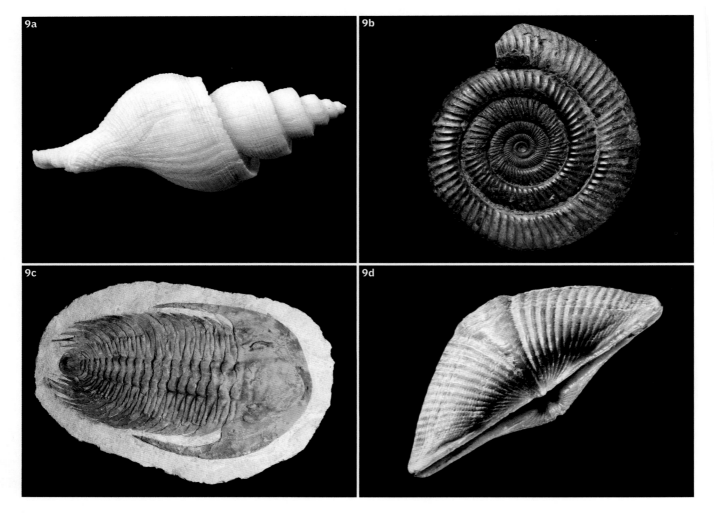

9a

9b

9c

9d

Radiometric Dating

Researchers use the predictability of radioactive decay to reveal the age of a fossil or other ancient object. This method, called **radiometric dating**, reveals the age of a material by measuring its radioisotope content (**Figure 14-10**). Each type of radioisotope decays at a constant rate into predictable products called daughter elements. The time it takes for half of the atoms in a sample of a radioisotope to decay is called its **half-life**.

Almost all carbon on Earth is in the form of ^{12}C. A tiny but constant amount of ^{14}C forms in the upper atmosphere and becomes incorporated into molecules of carbon dioxide. The ratio of ^{14}C to ^{12}C in atmospheric CO_2 is relatively stable. Because carbon dioxide is life's main source of carbon, the same ratio is maintained in the body of a living organism. After the organism dies, no more carbon is incorporated into its body. The ratio of ^{14}C to ^{12}C in the organism's remains declines over time as the ^{14}C decays. The half-life of ^{14}C is known (5730 years) so the ratio of ^{14}C to ^{12}C in the organism's remains can be used to calculate how long ago it died. Carbon isotope dating can be used to find the age of a biological material less than 60,000 years old. In older material, all of the ^{14}C has decayed. The age of older fossils can be estimated by dating volcanic rocks in lava flows above and below the fossil-containing layer of sedimentary rock.

The original source of most rock on Earth is magma, a hot, molten material deep under Earth's surface. When magma cools, it hardens and becomes rock. As this occurs, the atoms in the magma join and crystallize as different kinds of minerals, each with a characteristic structure and composition. Zircon is a mineral that consists mainly of zirconium silicate molecules. Some of the molecules in a newly formed zircon crystal have uranium atoms substituted for zirconium atoms. Uranium is a radioactive element with a half-life of 4.5 billion years. Its daughter element, thorium, is another radioactive element. Thorium decays at a predictable rate into another radioactive element, and so on until the atom becomes lead, a stable element. Over time, uranium atoms disappear from a zircon crystal, and lead atoms accumulate in it. The ratio of uranium atoms to lead atoms in a zircon crystal can be used to calculate its age. Using this technique, we know that the oldest known terrestrial rock, a tiny zircon crystal from the Jack Hills in Western Australia, is 4.404 billion years old.

SEP **Interpret Data** *According to **Figure 14-10**, what percentage of any radioisotope remains after two of its half-lives have passed?*

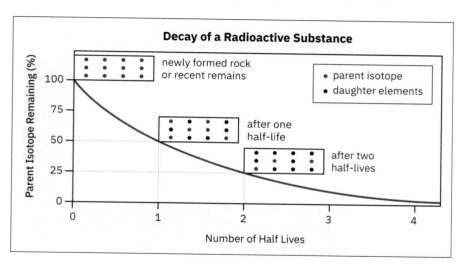

FIGURE 14-10
This generalized graph shows how the ratio of parent isotope and daughter elements changes as each half-life has passed.

Reconstructing Earth's Climate History

Scientists can also use other data to support the fossil record and radiometric findings. Proxy data, such as ice cores and tree rings, provide an indirect view of past conditions on Earth.

- **Ice Cores** Over hundreds and thousands of years, ice on mountaintops and at the Poles forms from the accumulation of snowfall. Scientists can drill deep into the ice to collect ice cores. These ice cores are made up of distinct layers. Each layer contains air bubbles, oxygen isotopes, and dust that scientists can analyze to determine past volcanic activity, atmospheric composition, temperature, precipitation, and wind patterns.

- **Tree Rings** Long-lived tree species such as redwoods and bristlecone pines add wood over centuries, typically one ring per year. If you know the year in which the tree was cut, you can determine when a particular ring formed by counting the rings backward from the outer edge. Tree-ring cores can also be taken from living trees. Tree rings can be used to estimate average annual rainfall; to date archaeological ruins; and to gather evidence of wildfires, floods, landslides, and glacier movements. Thickness, isotope content, and other features of a ring offer clues about the environmental conditions that prevailed during the year it formed. For example, during periods of drought, the rings are thinner compared to periods of heavy precipitation, when the rings are thicker.

CONNECTIONS

REFLECTIONS OF A DISTANT PAST The foundation for scientific understanding of the history of life is this premise: Natural phenomena that occurred in the ancient past can be explained by the same physical, chemical, and biological processes that operate today. Consider what caused the dinosaurs to become extinct at the end of the Cretaceous period. Most scientists accept the hypothesis that dinosaurs died in the aftermath of a catastrophic meteorite impact. No humans were around 66 million years ago to witness the impact, so how could anyone know what happened? The event is marked by an unusual, worldwide formation of sedimentary rock called the Cretaceous–Paleogene (or K–Pg) boundary sequence. There are plenty of dinosaur fossils below this formation. Above it, in layers of rock that were deposited more recently, there are no dinosaur fossils, anywhere.

The K–Pg boundary sequence consists of an unusual clay that is rich in iridium, an element rare on Earth's surface but common in meteorites. The clay also contains shocked quartz and small glass spheres called tektites. Both form when quartz or sand (respectively) undergoes a sudden, violent application of extreme pressure. The only processes on Earth known to produce these minerals are nuclear explosions and meteorite impacts.

Geologists hypothesized that the K–Pg boundary layer must have originated with extraterrestrial material. The geologists began looking for evidence of a meteorite that hit Earth 66 million years ago—one big enough to cover the entire planet with its debris. In 1991, they found it: an impact crater roughly the size of Ireland off the coast of the Yucatán Peninsula. To make a crater this big, a meteorite 10 km (6.2 miles) wide would have slammed into Earth with the force of 100 trillion tons of dynamite—enough to cause an ecological disaster of sufficient scale to wipe out almost all life on Earth.

The K–Pg boundary sequence (dark band) is a global sedimentary rock formation that formed 66 million years ago.

The Geologic Time Scale

Similar sequences of sedimentary rock layers occur around the world. The geologic time scale is a chronology of Earth's history that correlates these sequences with time (**Figure 14-11**). Transitions between layers of rock mark boundaries between time intervals. Each layer's composition offers clues about conditions that prevailed on Earth when the layer was deposited. For example, fossils are a record of life during the period of time that sediments in a layer accumulated.

Similar to how a year is divided into smaller increments including months, weeks, and days, so too is the geologic time scale split into smaller intervals. Units of geologic time include the following:

- Eons, which extend over 500 million years or more, are the longest interval of geologic time.

- Eras extend over several hundred million years.

- Periods extend over ten to several hundred million years. Periods are associated with specific layers of rock.

- Epochs last tens of millions of years.

- Ages extend over several million years.

Era	Period	Epoch	Millions of years ago	Major events
Cenozoic	Quaternary	Holocene	* 0.01	humans
		Pleistocene	1.65	new mountains
	Tertiary	Pliocene	5.3	early humans
		Miocene	23.7	apes
		Oligocene	36.6	monkeys
		Eocene	57.8	grasslands
		Paleocene	66.4	early primates
Mesozoic	Cretaceous		*	flowering plants, insects, and reptiles diversify
	Jurassic		144	first birds
	Triassic		208	first mammals
Paleozoic	Permian		245 *	first conifer trees
	Carboniferous		286	first reptiles and forests
			320	age of amphibians
	Devonian		360	first insects and amphibians
	Silurian		408	first jawed fishes
			* 438	
	Ordovician			first land plants
	Cambrian		* 505	first fishes
			545	
	Precambrian		900	first invertebrate animals
			3500	photosynthesis in bacteria
			4600	origin of Earth

* mass extinctions

FIGURE 14-11

This diagram shows the history of life on Earth. Note that the great expansion of life-forms occurred during the Cambrian period more than 500 million years ago.

The Present Is the Key to the Past

During the 18th and 19th centuries, prior to the advent of radiometric dating, it was commonly thought that Earth was only several thousand years old and the species and landforms on Earth were the same as they ever had been. The discovery of fossils and other geological evidence made many scientists of the time question this viewpoint.

In the late 1700s, Scottish geologist James Hutton reasoned that the changes he observed in landforms were the result of changes that occurred over a long period of time. This became known as the principle of **gradualism**. Unlike the theory of *catastrophism*, which states that major catastrophic events such as floods and volcanoes shaped Earth's surface, Hutton argued that many of Earth's features, such as deep canyons, resulted from slow processes.

British geologist Charles Lyell was also a proponent of gradualism. In the 1830s, he expanded on Hutton's work by proposing what is now known as the principle of **uniformitarianism**. This principle states that geologic processes that shape Earth's surface, such as erosion, are the same today as they were in the past. Lyell published his ideas in *The Principles of Geology*, a three-volume book. This book would prove to be quite influential on other scientists of the time, including Charles Darwin, which is described in detail in Chapter 15.

NOS **Scientific Knowledge** *Why do you think Lyell's principle of uniformitarianism proved to be so influential on scientists' understanding of evolution?*

14.2 REVIEW

1. **Compare** Use the descriptions to determine whether each organism would be ideal or not ideal as an index fossil.

   - Organism is abundant in rock layers.

   - Organism was limited to a single area.

   - Organism was widespread geographically.

   - Organism lived for hundreds of millions of years.

   - Organism is similar in appearance to other fossils.

2. **Calculate** Based on its carbon-14 to carbon-12 ratio, a fossil is determined to be 11,500 years old. Use the half-life of carbon-14 (5730 years) to determine the percentage of original carbon-14 that remains in the fossil.

3. **Contrast** Explain the differences between the geologic principles of uniformitarianism and catastrophism.

4. **Sequence** A rock formation that contains four layers with fossils has been greatly changed by geologic forces. Assuming the fossils are near the oldest possible age limit, use **Figure 14-11** to sort the layers into chronological order based on the fossils they contain.

Layer M – bird and amphibian fossils	Layer P – mammal and fish fossils
Layer O – fish fossils only	Layer T – primate and flowering plant fossils

5. **Identify** Which are examples of trace fossils? Select all correct answers.

   A. fossilized claw

   B. fossilized burrow

   C. dinosaur footprints

   D. fossilized leaf

   E. insects trapped in amber

FORENSIC RADIOMETRIC DATING

SEP **Analyze and Interpret Data** Traditionally, carbon dating has been considered an archaeological tool, not a forensic one. It is used to date tree, plant, and animal fossils that are between 500 and 50,000 years old. However, since the mid-1950s, forensic scientists have been able to use the same technique to date skeletal and tissue remains.

The concentration of ^{14}C relative to ^{12}C atoms in the atmosphere has remained relatively constant for thousands of years. In 1955, the radiometric carbon ratio began to rise sharply just 10 years after the first atmospheric nuclear tests by the United States. Nuclear testing creates neutrons that can interact with ^{14}N to produce the unstable ^{14}C isotope. **Figure 1** shows the measured atmospheric $^{14}C/^{12}C$ relative to the natural level up to the turn of the century. **Figure 2** shows the number of nuclear weapon tests by all countries since 1945.

FIGURE 1 ▽
The relative atmospheric radiometric carbon ratio $^{14}C/^{12}C$ has changed since the 1950s.

Source: Lawrence Livermore National Laboratory

FIGURE 2 ▽
Nuclear tests by all countries were conducted above ground between 1945 and 1962.

Source: Arms Control Association

1. **Compare** In which years did the atmospheric $^{14}C/^{12}C$ and number of above-ground nuclear tests peak?

2. **Relate** Describe the relationship between atmospheric $^{14}C/^{12}C$ and the number of above-ground nuclear tests conducted during the period.

3. **Explain** The half-life for spontaneous decay of ^{14}C is 5730 years. How does radiometric dating work and why does this nuclear lifetime make dating bones from organisms that died very recently a challenge?

4. **Infer** Scientists argue that as excess atmospheric ^{14}C continues to be incorporated into the biosphere and hydrosphere, future radiocarbon dating will underestimate the age of fossil remains of organisms alive today. Why might this be the case?

analogous structure
homologous structure
vestigial structure

DEVELOPMENTAL, ANATOMICAL, AND GENETIC EVIDENCE

Fossil evidence helped scientists begin to put together a picture of the history of life on Earth. Biological evidence such as developmental patterns and anatomical similarities helps scientists visualize the evolutionary connections between different species. Advancements in molecular and genetic sequencing techniques have allowed scientists to get an even clearer picture of the evolutionary relationships among organisms.

Infer *What genetic evidence might scientists use to analyze evolutionary relationships among species?*

⚗ CHAPTER INVESTIGATION

What Lived Here?
How can you use biological evidence to identify ancient organisms?

Go online to explore this chapter's hands-on investigation about the biological lines of evidence that support evolution.

Developmental Evidence

In general, the more closely related animals are, the more similar their development is. For example, all vertebrates go through a stage during which a developing embryo has four limb buds, a tail, pharyngeal arches, and divisions of the body that give rise to the backbone and associated skin and muscle (**Figure 14-12**).

While these structures look similar to one another during early stages of development, over time they diverge in structure and function. For example, pharyngeal arches, which form as a series of pouches on the side of a developing embryo's head, differentiate into gills in fish and ear and throat structures in mammals. Also, like all vertebrate embryos, humans have a tail early in development. The tail is typically absorbed by about eight weeks, forming the coccyx, or tailbone. Vertebrates have similar patterns of embryonic development because the same master regulator genes direct the process. Embryonic development in animals is coordinated by layer after layer of master gene expression.

FIGURE 14-12 ▼
The embryos of a mouse (a), alligator (b), and chicken (c) all share similarities during early development.

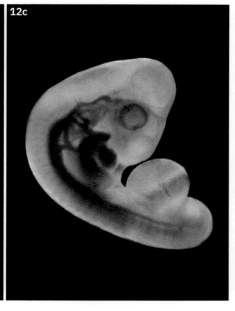

12a

12b

12c

The failure of any single master regulator gene to function properly can result in a drastically altered body plan, an outcome that often has severe consequences on the organism's health. Because a mutation in a master gene can unravel development completely, these genes tend to be highly conserved. This means the genes have remained relatively unchanged for a long period of time. Even among lineages that diverged a very long time ago, many master regulator genes retain similar sequences and functions.

SEP **Construct an Explanation** *How do similar structures during development provide evidence of a common ancestor among all vertebrates?*

Anatomical Evidence

Similarities in developmental patterns provide one source of biological evidence for common ancestry among organisms. Comparisons of body structures and their functions are another strong source of evidence. These sources are used to support scientists' understanding of evolutionary relationships among organisms.

Homologous Structures Comparing the anatomy of various organisms can provide evidence for descent from a common ancestor, or in other words, a shared evolutionary lineage. **Homologous structures** are body parts that appear similar in separate lineages because they evolved in a common ancestor. These structures may be used for different functions in different groups, but the same genes direct their development.

For example, the forelimbs of a bird, a human, and a sea lion, though quite different in appearance, have a strikingly similar arrangement of internal structures (**Figure 14-13**). Bird wings, human arms, and sea lion flippers are used in entirely different ways for different functions—flying, lifting, swimming, to name just a few. Given these different functions, there is no mechanical reason for them to be similar. However, they mirror each other in the structure and positioning of internal elements such as bones, nerves, blood vessels, and muscles. The similarities in these forelimb structures suggest that these organisms all share a common ancestor. In other words, this forelimb structural pattern was so useful that it was retained as new species evolved over time.

Go Online **INTERACTIVE FIGURE**

FIGURE 14-13 Go online to learn more about the evolutionary evidence left behind in the anatomy of different organisms.

FIGURE 14-13
Bird, human, and sea lion limbs all function in different ways. However, their underlying structures are very similar in appearance.

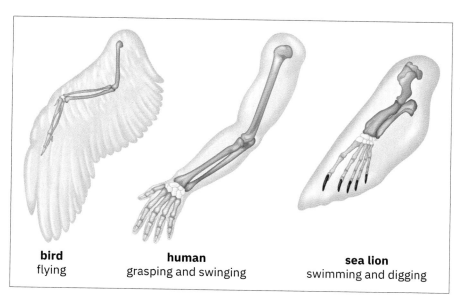

bird
flying

human
grasping and swinging

sea lion
swimming and digging

Analogous Structures Body parts that have a similar function but did not arise from a common ancestor are called **analogous structures**. The wings of insects, for example, perform the same function as the wings of birds (**Figure 14-14**). However, bird wings are supported by bone structure, while insect wings have no underlying skeletal support. Analogous organs are of evolutionary interest because they show that organisms with different ancestries can adapt in similar ways to similar environmental demands. This process is called *convergent evolution*.

FIGURE 14-14 ▼
Though the functions of the insect wings and bird wings are the same, their underlying structures are very different. This is an example of convergent evolution.

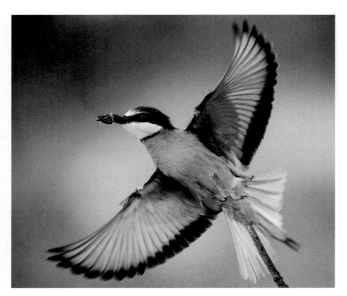

Vestigial Structures Body parts that no longer have a function are called **vestigial structures**. Humans, for example, have vestigial tail bones and muscles for moving the ears. Blind cavefish (**Figure 14-15**) live in total darkness where eyesight is not necessary for survival. In these unusual fish, the fish embryos initially have eyes during development. The eyes later disintegrate and become covered by skin and connective tissue.

FIGURE 14-15 ▶
The nonfunctional eyes of a blind cavefish are an example of vestigial structures.

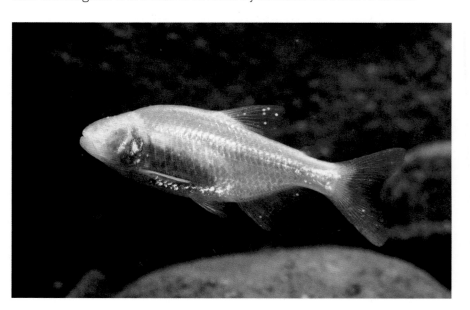

SEP **Construct an Explanation** *Why do you think vestigial structures do not entirely disappear from a population?*

Genetic Evidence

Over time, mutations change a genome's DNA sequence. Most of these mutations are neutral. In other words, they have no effect on an individual's survival or reproduction. The more recently two lineages diverged, the less time there has been for unique mutations to accumulate in the DNA of each one. This is why the genomes of closely related species tend to be more similar than those of distantly related species, a general rule that can be used to estimate relative times of divergence. Thus, similarities in the nucleotide sequence of a shared gene (or in the amino acid sequence of a shared protein) can be used to study evolutionary relationships. Biochemical comparisons like these may be combined with structural comparisons, in order to provide data for hypotheses about shared ancestry.

Pseudogenes Recall from Section 11.1 that pseudogenes are copies of genes that exist elsewhere in the genome but no longer produce a functional protein. Pseudogenes can sometimes reveal information about ancient genes and the rate of gene duplication over long periods of time.

mRNA Extremely strong evidence in support of common ancestors for almost all life-forms comes from the genetic code. For example, the codon UUU in mRNA, which codes for the amino acid phenylalanine, occurs in organisms as diverse as shrimp, humans, bacteria, and tulips. This kind of molecular evidence strongly suggests that all life descended from common ancestors, one-celled organisms, that originally developed the genetic code. Once initiated, the code was found to be so useful that it was never abandoned over billions of years.

Mitochondrial DNA As shown in **Figure 14-16**, the mitochondria in most animals are inherited intact from only one of the parents (most often the mother, in humans). Mitochondrial chromosomes are circular pieces of DNA that do not undergo crossing over, so any changes in their DNA sequence occur only by mutation. Thus, in most cases, differences in mitochondrial DNA (mtDNA) sequences among maternally related people are due to new mutations. mtDNA has been a particularly useful tool in tracing the origin, evolution, and migration of human populations.

CHAPTER INVESTIGATION

Comparing Genetic Information Among Organisms
How can you use genetic information to determine how closely related organisms are?
Go online to explore this chapter's hands-on investigation about the genetic evidence that supports evolution.

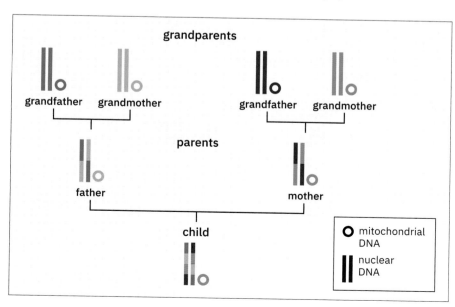

FIGURE 14-16
Mitochondrial DNA is typically passed from one generation to the next only through the maternal line. In contrast, each generation inherits a unique combination of nuclear DNA from both their parents. Because of the reduced complexity, mitochondrial DNA is much easier to trace through generations than nuclear DNA is.

```
...CRDVQFGWLIRNLHANGASFFFICIYLHIGRGIYYGSYLNK--ETWNIGVILLLTLMATAFVGYVLPWGQMSFWG...honeycreepers (10)
...CRDVQFGWLIRNLHANGASFFFICIYLHIGRGIYYGSYLNK--ETWNVGIILLLALMATAFVGYVLPWGQMSFWG...song sparrow
...CRDVQFGWLIRNIHANGASFFFICIYLHIGRGLYYGSYLYK--ETWNVGVILLLTLMATAFVGYVLPWGQMSFWG...Gough Island finch
...CRDVNYGWLIRYMHANGASMFFICLFLHVGRGMYYGSYTFT--ETWNIGIVLLFAVMATAFMGYVLPWGQMSFWG...deer mouse
...CRDVHYGWIIRYMHANGASMFFICLFMHVGRGLYYGSYLLS--ETWNIGIILLFTVMATAFMGYVLPWGQMSFWG...Asiatic black bear
...CRDVNYGWLIRNLHANGASFFFICIYLHIGRGLYYGSYLYK--ETWNIGVVLLLLVMGTAFVGYVLPWGQMSFWG...bogue (a fish)
...TRDVNYGWIIRYLHANGASMFFICLFLHIGRGLYYGSFLYS--ETWNIGIILLLATMATAFMGYVLPWGQMSFWG...human
...MRDVEGGWLLRYMHANGASMFLIVVYLHIFRGLYHASYSSPREFVWCLGVVIFLLMIVTAFIGYVLPWGQMSFWG...thale cress (a plant)
...ETDVMNGWMVRSIHANGASWFFIMLYSHIFRGLWVSSFTQP--LVWLSGVIILFLSMATAFLGYVLPWGQMSFWG...baboon louse
...MRDVHNGYILRYLHANGASFFFMVMFMHMAKGLYYGSYRSPRVTLWNVGVIIFTLTIATAFLGYCCVYGQMSHWG...baker's yeast
```

FIGURE 14-17 ▲

Partial amino acid sequences of cytochrome *b* from 19 species are aligned in this diagram. The honeycreeper sequence is identical in 10 species of honeycreeper. Amino acids that differ in the other species are shown in red. Dashes indicate insertion or deletion mutations.

Proteins Another form of evidence is found in the proteins of various organisms. For example, even organisms that are only remotely related, such as humans, baker's yeast, and a type of bird called the honeycreeper, all have the protein cytochrome *b*. This protein functions in all these species' mitochondria (**Figure 14-17**). In fact, because this protein developed billions of years ago, mutations have built up during that enormous time period to make different versions of cytochrome *b*.

SEP **Analyze Data** *Based on the amino acid sequences shown in* **Figure 14-17**, *which species is the most closely related to honeycreepers?*

Scientists use these differences to map evolutionary pathways. The scientists assume that the longer it has been since two organisms diverged, or took separate evolutionary pathways, the greater the differences in their cytochrome *b* molecules. Thus, two species that have very different cytochrome *b* molecules can be identified as having diverged in the far distant past. On the other hand, species with similar cytochrome *b* molecules are characterized as being more closely related and therefore sharing a more recent common ancestor.

DNA Sequencing With DNA sequencing, scientists have also discovered that the more similar two genomes are with respect to nucleotide sequences, the more closely related the organisms are that share those sequences. As **Table 14-1** shows, humans and chimpanzees are thought to be closely related and share a recent common ancestor because their genomes are so similar. Humans and lemurs, on the other hand, are not as closely related. Researchers use data from DNA sequencing to map which organisms are more closely related and to determine when different species diverged. Molecular evidence continues to provide many missing puzzle pieces to help us understand the evolution of species on our planet.

TABLE 14-1. Differences in Nucleotide Sequences Between Humans and Other Species

Species pair	Percentage difference in nucleotide sequences
human-chimpanzee	2.5%
human-gibbon	5.1%
human-Old World monkey	9.0%
human-New World monkey	15.8%
human-lemur	42.0%

Body Development and Homeotic Genes

Homeotic genes are master regulator genes that control the development of anatomical structures in animals, plants, and fungi. *Hox* genes are a subset of homeotic genes in some animals that direct the head-to-tail formation of body segments and structures during embryonic development (**Figure 14-18**). Insects have 10 *Hox* genes, and vertebrates have multiple versions of all of them. One insect *Hox* gene, called *antennapedia*, triggers leg formation in insect embryos. Thus, it normally determines the identity of the thorax (the part with legs). Humans and other vertebrates have a version of *antennapedia* called *HoxC6*. Expression of *HoxC6* in a vertebrate embryo causes ribs to develop on a vertebra, so it normally determines the identity of the back. Without *HoxC6* expression, vertebrae of the neck and tail develop, but ribs do not.

SEP **Construct an Explanation** *How could mutations in* Hox *genes lead to the diversification of animal species?*

VIDEO

VIDEO 14-2 Go online to learn how genetic evidence helped scientists understand snake evolution.

FIGURE 14-18 ▼
The genes that direct the development of structures in a fruit fly are variations of the same genes that determine a human's head-to-tail development, but they are expressed in different patterns.

14.3 REVIEW

1. **Compare** Label the statements as consistent with analogous structures or homologous structures.

   • The organisms with a similar structure share a common ancestor.

   • The structures develop in the same way in the compared organisms.

   • A body part has the same function but different structures in the compared organisms.

   • A body part has the same structures but different functions in the compared organisms.

2. **Explain** How do similarities in DNA or protein sequences provide evidence that two species share a common ancestor?

3. **Identify** Which types of data are most effective as evidence for shared ancestry?

   A. vestigial structures

   B. amino acid sequences

   C. DNA from mitochondria

   D. analagous structures

   E. embryonic development patterns

4. **Explain** Why might a mutation in a *Hox* gene result in a major difference in an organism's adult form?

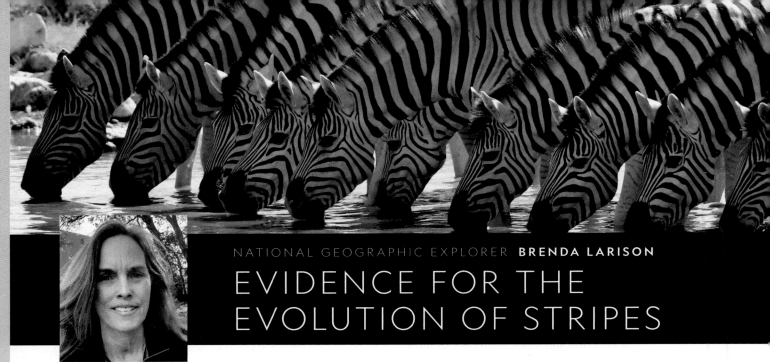

EVIDENCE FOR THE EVOLUTION OF STRIPES

Dr. Brenda Larison's research, which focuses on populations of plains zebras in sub-Saharan Africa, addresses questions related to both evolution and conservation.

Zebras, which are most closely related to wild donkeys, stand out in the genus *Equus* mainly because of their distinctive coats. What environmental changes spurred the survival of ancestors with stripes of any kind? What genetic changes resulted in such a bold trait with several variations? Biologist Dr. Brenda Larison studies plains zebras to answer those questions.

Larison has been revisiting some of the more popular explanations for the zebras' striped patterns that scientists have tested over time. Among these hypotheses are that stripes support social behaviors, aid in thermoregulation, help in the evasion of predators, or in the avoidance of biting flies that carry fatal diseases. As part of her research, Larison and her team devised a test that pitted some of the hypotheses against one another.

"Providing evidence in support of one hypothesis does nothing to disprove other hypotheses unless the hypotheses are mutually exclusive," Larison says. "The various hypotheses for why zebras have stripes are not mutually exclusive. It can be true that stripes deter biting flies, and that they also aid in other ways, such as predator avoidance or thermoregulation. The only way to eliminate the other hypotheses is to disprove them and no one has successfully done that as yet."

Larison's team collected and analyzed data about the relationship between stripe patterns and the environment from 16 sites across the plains zebras' range. The team looked at stripe numbers, thickness, length, and boldness of color to develop a stripe index. While their data provided support for the thermoregulation hypothesis, the reason for this correlation remains unclear. Many factors may be involved, but it is possible that stronger stripe patterns are beneficial in warmer tropical areas where flies carry more disease.

Because individual striping patterns are as unique as fingerprints, Larison can collect tissue samples and connect an individual's stripe phenotype to the genetic variation related to that stripe pattern. This information might help shed light on the advantages striping provides. Researchers are trying to determine whether genes related to striping are selected differently for zebras in different environments. This genetic evidence may at last provide a definitive answer to why striping evolved in zebras.

THINKING CRITICALLY

Justify *Why might scientists revisit problems even if others have tested and drawn logical conclusions?*

TYING IT ALL TOGETHER
SOLVING THE MYSTERY OF SLOTH EVOLUTION

HOW DO WE KNOW HOW SPECIES HAVE EVOLVED?

In this chapter, you learned about the lines of evidence that support evolution and how scientists use this evidence to build the evolutionary history of a species. The Case Study described some of the evolutionary history of sloths and their relatives.

Modern-day sloths include six species that are divided into two main groupings: *Choleopus* and *Bradypus*. Members of each genus are distinguished by the number of toes on their front feet: *Bradypus* have three toes and *Choleopus* have two toes. Initially it was thought that these two groups branched from the same common ancestor. However, while both their appearance and behavior are quite similar, it turns out the two groups are only distantly related (**Figure 14-19**).

In 2019, the results of two independent studies about the evolution of sloths were published. One relied on ancient DNA data while the other used ancient collagen (protein) sequence information. Both studies confirmed that three-toed sloths were in fact not a sister group to two-toed sloths. Instead, they are more closely related to a group of extinct ground sloths that includes *Megatherium* and *Megalonyx*.

Two-toed sloths, on the other hand, are more closely related to a group of extinct ground sloths called *Mylodontidae*. The evolution of three-toed and two-toed sloths therefore is an example of convergent evolution, in which the two lines, though similar in appearance, evolved independently of one another.

In this activity, you will research how advancements in technology have aided our understanding of evolutionary relationships among organisms. Work individually or in a group to complete these steps.

Gather Evidence
1. Research the field of paleoproteomics. Compare the reliability of ancient protein evidence and ancient DNA evidence, taking into consideration the environments in which different fossils are found.

Scientific Knowledge
2. Find out how scientists used proteomic data to change our understanding of the evolutionary relationships among sloth species. What other species' evolutionary histories have been revised due to advancements in molecular techniques?

Communicate Information
3. Develop a multimedia presentation to present your findings to your class.

FIGURE 14-19 ▽

Comparisons of DNA and protein sequences among extinct and living sloth species changed scientists' understanding of how sloths were related. 19a shows the old scheme and 19b shows the new scheme.

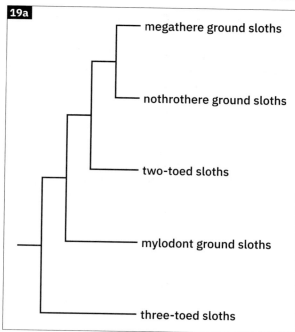

19a
- megathere ground sloths
- nothrothere ground sloths
- two-toed sloths
- mylodont ground sloths
- three-toed sloths

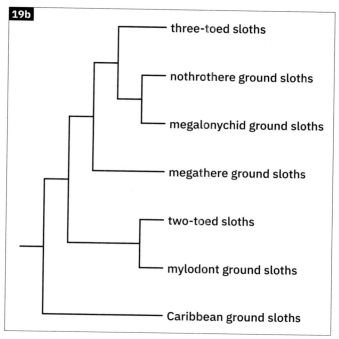

19b
- three-toed sloths
- nothrothere ground sloths
- megalonychid ground sloths
- megathere ground sloths
- two-toed sloths
- mylodont ground sloths
- Caribbean ground sloths

REVIEW KEY CONCEPTS

1. **Classify** Determine whether each statement represents an example of microevolution or macroevolution.

   - Whales descended from an ancestor that lived on land.

   - Over millions of years, numerous species of dinosaurs lived on Earth.

   - Brown owls become more common as climate change diminishes snow cover.

   - A strain of bacterium with antibiotic resistance becomes more common after treatment with antibiotics.

2. **Define** Which line of evidence for evolution involves observing the formation and growth of an embryo?

   A. anatomy

   B. biogeography

   C. developmental patterns

   D. genetics

3. **Classify** Sort the examples into fossils and trace fossils.

   - bone

   - coprolite

   - footprint

   - nest

   - tooth

4. **Explain** What factors increase the likelihood that a species will be represented in the fossil record? Select all correct answers.

   A. The species had hard body parts such as bones, seeds, or shells.

   B. The species lived in an area with many predators and scavengers.

   C. The species had a large population and existed over a long period of time.

   D. The species lived in an area where there are very few sedimentary rocks.

   E. The species lived in an area protected from destructive geologic events.

5. **Classify** Indicate whether the following pairs of structures are homologous or analogous.

   - the fin of a fish and the flipper of a whale

   - the leg of a caterpillar and the leg of a dog

   - the wing of a bat and the flipper of a whale

   - the leg of a kangaroo and the leg of a chicken

6. **Contrast** The embryos of fish and humans both have pharyngeal arches. In fish, they develop into gills. What happens to the pharyngeal arches as a human embryo develops?

   A. They develop into lungs.

   B. They disappear as the embryo develops.

   C. They have no function; they are vestigial.

   D. They develop into ear and throat structures.

7. **Explain** Why is carbon-14 dating an ineffective way to determine the age of a rock?

   A. The daughter isotope of carbon-14 decay is not detectable.

   B. Carbon-14 does not decay, so it cannot be used for radioactive dating.

   C. Carbon is present only in living things, so it cannot be measured in rocks.

   D. Most rocks are too old to be measured using the half-life of carbon-14 atoms.

8. **Explain** Which statements are supported by the evidence for evolution? Select all correct answers.

   A. All life on Earth descends from a common ancestor.

   B. Genetic variation among living organisms cannot be explained.

   C. Species never truly go extinct; they simply evolve and adapt, taking new forms.

   D. Populations of species change over long periods of time as they adapt to their environment.

   E. All organisms alive today are closely related to a common ancestor from a few million years ago.

9. **Justify** Why do vestigial structures, such as eyes in a blind cavefish, not fully disappear?

CRITICAL THINKING

10. **Analyze** How does sexual reproduction contribute to evolution?

11. **Predict** As a river erodes a canyon, it exposes layers of rock that are different in color and composition. Which rock layers would you expect to contain the oldest fossils? The youngest? Justify your prediction.

12. **Relate** Does the presence of the K-Pg boundary support or challenge the principle of gradualism? Explain your reasoning.

13. **Contrast** A scientist compared the DNA sequence of a master gene for development among many different bird species. Then she compared the DNA sequence of a gene for feather color. How would these two comparisons differ? Explain.

14. **Explain** Why are amino acid sequences used to determine evolutionary relationships between species?

15. **NOS** **Scientific Knowledge** How do multiple lines of evidence provide support for biological evolution? Use examples in your explanation.

MATH AND ENGLISH LANGUAGE ARTS CONNECTIONS

1. **Reason Quantitatively** Carbon-14 dating is used to determine that a fossil is about 28,650 years old. Given that the half-life of C-14 is 5730 years, what percentage of the original C-14 is left in the sample?

2. **Reason Quantitatively** A fossil is determined to have 12.5% of the original carbon-14. The half-life of carbon–14 is 5730 years. How old is the fossil in years?

3. **Write an Argument** A scientist is comparing the cytochrome *b* gene sequences of three species. Species X and Y have nearly identical sequences, with only a few differences, whereas the sequence of species Z is quite different. What does this suggest about the evolutionary relationships between the three organisms? Explain your reasoning.

4. **Write Informative Text** Define "convergent evolution" using an example.

► REVISIT HUMMINGBIRD EVOLUTION

Gather Evidence In this chapter, you have seen multiple lines of evidence that support common ancestry and biological evolution. In Section 14.2, you learned about fossil and geological evidence. In Section 14.3, you learned about the developmental, anatomical, and genetic evidence.

1. Which lines of evidence best support the evolution of hummingbirds over time?

2. What other questions do you have about the evidence that supports common ancestry and the evolution of hummingbirds?

CHAPTER 15

THE THEORY OF EVOLUTION

Bedbugs are not known to transmit or spread disease but they can cause itchiness, secondary skin infection, and anxiety to anyone dealing with an infestation.

15.1 DEVELOPING THE THEORY OF EVOLUTION

15.2 EVOLUTION IN POPULATIONS

15.3 OTHER MECHANISMS OF EVOLUTION

Bedbugs are found all around the world. Scientists are studying various bedbug species to better understand the evolutionary relationships among them. Bedbugs have existed since at least the time of dinosaurs, and each species tends to be specialized to a single host type.

Chapter 15 supports the NGSS Performance Expectations **HS-LS3-3**, **HS-LS4-2**, **HS-LS4-3**, and **HS-LS4-4**.

CASE STUDY
DON'T LET THE BEDBUGS BITE!

WHY DO POPULATIONS EVOLVE OVER TIME?

Insects represent about 80 percent of animal species on Earth. They provide the best example of biodiversity on the planet with at least 900,000 documented species. The historical success of insect evolution, which has persisted over enormous spans of geologic time to develop such diversity, is remarkable. Two factors that contribute to their survival success include their ability to adapt to changing environments and their high reproductive capacity. In other words, most insects can reproduce quickly and have a huge number of offspring.

Like all organisms, insects are just trying to survive. Take, for example, the bedbug (*Cimex lectularius*). These pesky prowlers are attracted to warmth, feed on blood, and can be hard to find given their small size and their habit of staying hidden (**Figure 15-1**). They are a public health pest because they cause a variety of health issues such as minor to severe allergic reactions to their bites, secondary infections of the skin from the bite reaction, and even mental health impacts for those living in an infested home. The United States Environmental Protection Agency includes bedbugs on their official List of Pests of Significant Public Health Importance.

Bedbugs were nearly eradicated in the United States in the 1950s through the use of a pesticide called DDT, which was banned in the 1970s. A new type of pesticide called pyrethroids works by attacking an insect's nervous system, but over a very short time bedbugs evolved resistance to them. Bedbugs (as well as all insects and humans) have tiny pores in cell membranes that trigger nerve impulses. Pesticides bind to the pores, locking them in an open position, which leads to paralysis.

Biologists have discovered that only a couple of specific mutations in one pore protein gene are enough to make a bedbug 250 times more resistant to pyrethroids. These mutations may change the pore so that the insecticide can no longer bind to it effectively and may change the way the pore responds when the insecticide binds. Such mutations arise randomly and are favored when the environment in which a population lives changes, such as when a bed is sprayed with pesticide.

If only a couple bedbugs in a population carry mutations that cause resistance, they will be better able to survive and reproduce and will pass the mutations on to their offspring. As this process continues through several generations, the population may evolve such that every individual carries the resistance mutations, surviving the changing pesticides. However, if the population does not carry any of the advantageous resistance mutations, the pyrethroid treatment will wipe out the bedbug population.

Ask Questions *In this chapter, you will learn how the theory of evolution was developed based on evidence in population evolution over time. Generate questions and gather evidence to support the claim that natural selection leads to adaptations in populations.*

FIGURE 15-1
Bedbugs resemble many other types of bugs. Finding bugs in your bed might be a clue that you have a bedbug infestation. Before you panic, there are many internet resources to help identify region-specific bedbug characteristics.

▶ **VIDEO 15-1** Go online to learn more about bedbugs.

adaptation
biogeography
fitness
natural selection

DEVELOPING THE THEORY OF EVOLUTION

When you are developing an idea about how a process works, you might start with a basic question you want to answer. You might predict a certain outcome, behavior, or response to a stimulus or a change to a situation. The main role of a scientist is to ask questions to develop an understanding about a phenomenon. Gathering evidence is part of understanding and explaining a phenomenon. For example, hundreds of years ago naturalists and scientists were asking questions about and documenting observations of relationships among organisms. They developed many different theories based on their evidence to explain why and how organisms change over time.

Predict *How do we know that organisms evolve over time to adapt to a changing environment?*

Early Ideas About Evolution

Biologically, evolution can be described as genetic changes in a population over many generations. Recall that a population is a group of the same species that lives in the same geographical area at the same time.

British naturalist Charles Darwin is widely recognized as the individual who proposed the theory of evolution. He defined evolution as "descent with modification." However, related ideas were developing long before his time (**Figure 15-2**).

FIGURE 15-2
Many proposals over the course of several hundred years have led to our current understanding of evolution.

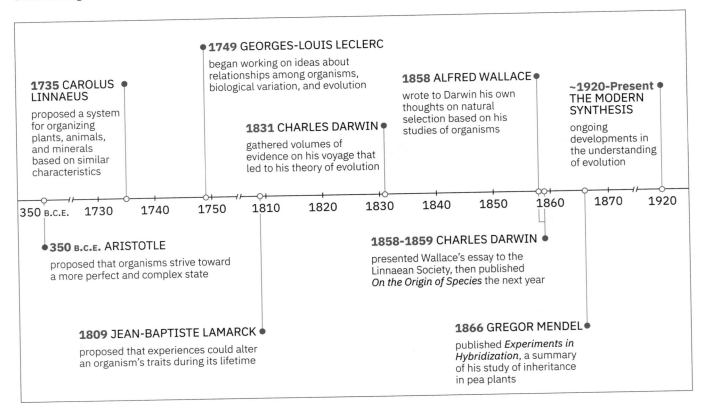

1749 GEORGES-LOUIS LECLERC
began working on ideas about relationships among organisms, biological variation, and evolution

1735 CAROLUS LINNAEUS
proposed a system for organizing plants, animals, and minerals based on similar characteristics

1831 CHARLES DARWIN
gathered volumes of evidence on his voyage that led to his theory of evolution

1858 ALFRED WALLACE
wrote to Darwin his own thoughts on natural selection based on his studies of organisms

~1920-Present THE MODERN SYNTHESIS
ongoing developments in the understanding of evolution

350 B.C.E.   1730   1740   1750   1810   1820   1830   1840   1850   1860   1870   1920

350 B.C.E. ARISTOTLE
proposed that organisms strive toward a more perfect and complex state

1858-1859 CHARLES DARWIN
presented Wallace's essay to the Linnaean Society, then published *On the Origin of Species* the next year

1809 JEAN-BAPTISTE LAMARCK
proposed that experiences could alter an organism's traits during its lifetime

1866 GREGOR MENDEL
published *Experiments in Hybridization*, a summary of his study of inheritance in pea plants

In the 1900s, people had different thoughts about heredity. For example, some thought that hereditary material must be a type of fluid that was blended at fertilization and passed on to offspring. Today we know that DNA stores hereditary information and that genes are the units passed on from one generation to the next.

Darwin did not know how heredity worked, but his detailed observations led him and others to recognize and question changes in organisms over time. Meanwhile, the little-known Austrian monk, Gregor Mendel, was developing what would become the fundamental laws of inheritance.

NOS **Scientific Knowledge** *How does the abbreviated time line in* **Figure 15-2** *support the idea that theories can be revised over time as new evidence is discovered?*

Asking Questions In the 1800s, European naturalists traveled the globe exploring tens of thousands of plants and animals. Their observations and records showed patterns in where species live and similarities in body plans. These explorers were pioneers in **biogeography**, the study of patterns in the geographic distribution of species and communities. Some of the patterns raised questions that could not be answered within the framework of how they thought species came to be.

- How could a flightless bird species have similar features to species living on the other side of impassable mountain ranges or across vast expanses of open ocean (**Figure 15-3**)?

FIGURE 15-3 ▽
The emu, rhea, and ostrich are native to three different continents but share a common ancestor.

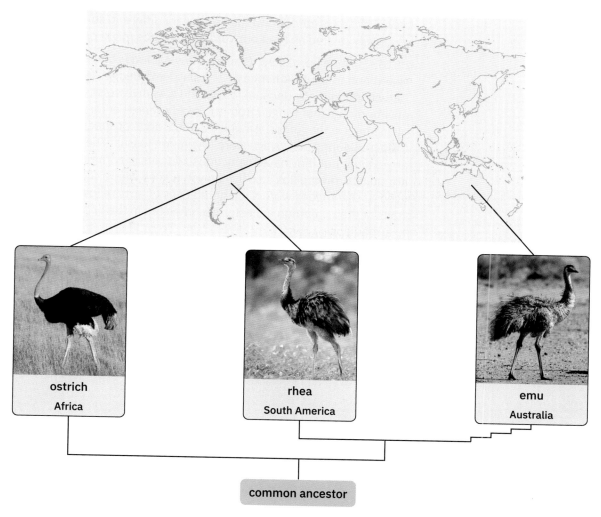

ostrich
Africa

rhea
South America

emu
Australia

common ancestor

Subgroups of these birds are related species, but they are native to very distant geographic locations. They are unlike most other birds in several unusual anatomical features, including long, muscular legs and an inability to fly. They also share strikingly similar DNA sequences. All these data provide evidence to support the evolutionary relationship of these birds.

- How could organisms be very similar in some features but very different in others (**Figure 15-4**)?

FIGURE 15-4 ▷
The saguaro cactus (*Carnegiea gigantea*) is native to the Sonoran Desert of Arizona (a) and the African milk barrel plant (*Euphorbia horrida*) is native to the Great Karoo desert of South Africa (b) share similarities in appearance though are unrelated species.

The saguaro cactus and the African milk barrel plant live in hot deserts where water is seasonally scarce. Both have rows of sharp spines that deter herbivores, and both store water in their thick, fleshy stems. However, their reproductive parts are very different, so these plants are not as closely related as their outward appearance might otherwise suggest.

In 1831, when he was 22, Charles Darwin joined a five-year survey expedition to South America on the ship HMS *Beagle*. During his voyage, Darwin found many unusual fossils and saw diverse species living in environments that ranged from the sandy shores of remote islands to plains high in the Andes. Among the thousands of specimens Darwin collected during his voyage were *Glyptodon* fossils. These mammals are extinct, but they have many unusual traits in common with modern armadillos. Armadillos also live only in places where *Glyptodons* once lived. If *Glyptodons* were ancient relatives of armadillos, then perhaps traits of their common ancestor had changed in the line of descent that led to armadillos.

FIGURE 15-5 ▽
The *Glyptodon* (a) and armadillo (b) are ancient relatives. Though separated in time by millions of years, these animals share a limited geographic distribution and unusual traits, including a shell and helmet of keratin-covered bony plates similar to crocodile and lizard skin.

- How could extinct *Glyptodons* have so many unusual traits in common with modern armadillos (**Figure 15-5**)?

FIGURE 15-6
Darwin's voyage aboard the HMS *Beagle* was a five-year trip that went around the world.

Looking at the Evidence During Darwin's journey on the HMS *Beagle*, he read *Principles of Geology*, a new and popular book by Charles Lyell. Lyell, a British geologist, was a proponent of what became known as the theory of uniformitarianism, the idea that gradual, everyday geologic processes such as erosion could have sculpted Earth's current landscape over great spans of time. The theory challenged the prevailing belief that Earth was 6000 years old. By Lyell's calculations, it must have taken millions of years to sculpt Earth's surface. Darwin's exposure to Lyell's ideas gave him insights into the history of the regions he encountered on his journey (**Figure 15-6**).

The first stop for the HMS *Beagle* journey was the Cape Verde Islands. It was there that Darwin observed sediments enclosed by lava flows and raised above the sea level, but with fossils similar to the shells in the sea nearby (**Figure 15-7**). These layers held fossils of simple marine organisms that were clearly related to one another, but their form changed slightly from one layer to the next. With these observations and Lyell's principles in mind, Darwin became convinced that the surface of Earth changes slowly and gradually over time.

SEP **Construct an Explanation** *Darwin considered the geologic theory of uniformitarianism as support for his theory of how new species emerge. What do you think led him to this conclusion?*

FIGURE 15-7 ▽
In different layers of sediment high above the waters of the Cape Verde Islands (a), Darwin observed simple marine organism fossils (b).

The Theory of Natural Selection

Reflecting on his journey, Darwin started thinking about how individuals of a species often vary a bit in the details of shared traits such as size, coloration, and so on. He saw such variation among finch species on isolated islands of the Galápagos archipelago. This island chain is separated from South America by hundreds of kilometers of open ocean, so most species living on them had little to no opportunity for interbreeding with mainland populations. The birds on the Galápagos Islands resembled finch species in South America, but unique traits suited many of them to their particular island habitats (**Figure 15-8**).

FIGURE 15-8 ▼
On his voyage to the Galápagos, Darwin noticed differences in finch beaks that were related to function in terms of food eaten.

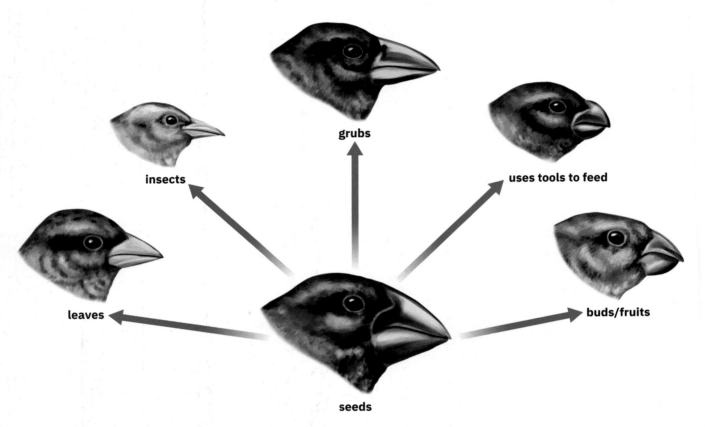

VIDEO

VIDEO 15-2 Go online to learn more about Galápagos finches.

 SEP **Argue From Evidence** *Darwin thought that the development of these different types of finches was not a random process. Use the evidence from the food sources and beak types in Figure 15-8 to support this claim.*

Darwin was familiar with *artificial selection,* which is intentionally breeding individuals with desired or advantageous traits over generations. In artificial selection, humans act as the selective agent. Darwin reasoned that natural environments could similarly "select" certain traits. Naturalists and scientists before him thought that organisms changed as a result of need or experience. The key to Darwin's insight was that individuals did not change but that individuals were selected because of favorable characteristics that matched changes in their environment. If a trait favors survival and reproduction, then individuals with that trait would mate and have a higher probability of passing on the favorable trait to their offspring than would individuals that do not carry that trait.

Principles of Natural Selection Darwin realized that individuals with adaptive traits would tend to leave more offspring than their less-fit rivals, a process he named **natural selection.** He understood that natural selection causes a population to change—in other words, it drives evolution. **Table 15-1** summarizes this reasoning.

If an individual has an adaptive trait that makes it better suited to an environment, then it is better able to survive. If an individual is better able to survive, then it has a better chance of living long enough to produce offspring. If individuals with an adaptive trait produce more offspring than other individuals, then the frequency of the adaptive trait in the population will increase over successive generations—the population will evolve.

TABLE 15-1. Summary of Darwin's Main Principles of Natural Selection

competition in populations	• Natural populations have an inherent capacity to increase in size over time.
	• As a population expands, resources that are used by its members (such as food and living space) eventually become limited.
	• When resources are limited, members of a population compete for them.
genetic variation	• Individuals of a species share certain traits.
	• Individuals of a natural population vary in the details of those shared traits.
	• Shared traits have a heritable basis in genes. Slightly different forms of those genes (alleles) give rise to variation in shared traits.
overproduction	• A certain form of a shared trait may make individuals with that trait better able to survive.
	• Individuals of a population that are better able to survive tend to leave more offspring.
adaptation	• An allele associated with an adaptive trait tends to become more common in a population over time.

CASE STUDY
DON'T LET THE BEDBUGS BITE!

Ask Questions *Generate questions about the role of natural selection in the evolution of pesticide resistance in bedbug populations.*

Darwin wrote out his hypothesis of evolution by natural selection in the late 1830s but was so conflicted about its implications that he collected evidence for 20 years without sharing it. Meanwhile, British naturalist Alfred Wallace, who was studying wildlife in the Amazon Basin and the Malay Archipelago, wrote to Darwin and Lyell about patterns in the geographic distribution of species. When he was ready to publish his own ideas about evolution, he sent them to Darwin for advice. To Darwin's shock, Wallace had come up with the same hypothesis: that evolution occurs by natural selection.

In 1858, the hypothesis of evolution by natural selection was presented at a scientific meeting. Darwin and Wallace were credited as authors, but neither attended the meeting. The next year, Darwin published *On the Origin of Species by Means of Natural Selection*, which presented detailed evidence in support of the hypothesis, which eventually became the theory of natural selection.

CCC **Patterns** *Why might a particular beak shape or size become more common in a finch species over time? Use the four principles of natural selection from* **Table 15-1** *to support your answer.*

PUT DOWN THOSE PHONES! Technology has helped us to advance in many different ways. Some technology has reduced human's needs to rely on some genetic adaptations. For example, humans can generally live in most any climate by using various types of shelter and clothing. Humans can also travel great distances thanks to many types of transportation that help us to move about. Our ancestors did not have the variety of shelter, clothing, and transportation we have today.

Over time, different technologies have changed some of the work and behavior patterns of our lives. We rely on machines more and more to do physical and mental work that humans used to do. For example, a calculator can complete complex mathematics within seconds. Smartphones allow us to access libraries of information with just a word search. As a result, there is less of a burden to retain as much information.

As we adapt to life with more sophisticated technologies, certain physical and mental activities we have done may no longer be essential. Over time, the brain could favor analyzing skills and rely less on its capability to retain information. The changes in our behavioral patterns that are caused by these technological advances could prove to be the primary driving forces behind the next stage of evolution for our species. It is worth noting, however, that we are still limited in part by our biology and genetics despite greater flexibility that some technological advances permit.

Technology can be a powerful source of information and distraction.

Go Online   **VIRTUAL INVESTIGATION**

Hummingbirds on the Move
How did hummingbirds become adapted to their environments?
Grab your binoculars and head into the field to gather evidence about hummingbird adaptations.

Fitness and Adaptation In any natural population, some individuals have variations of shared traits that make them better suited to their environment than other individuals. In nature, the environment generates the selective pressure that determines if a trait is passed on or not. The ability of populations to undergo adaptive evolution depends on the presence of genetic variation for advantageous traits. An **adaptation** is a heritable trait that improves an organism's chances of surviving and producing offspring in a particular environment. **Fitness** is a measure of an individual's ability relative to other members of its population to survive and produce offspring.

A population tends to grow until it exhausts resources in its environment. As that happens, competition for those resources intensifies among the population's members. Individuals with forms of shared, heritable traits that make them more competitive for the resources tend to produce more offspring. Thus, adaptations impart greater fitness and become more common in a population over generations. This process in which environmental pressures result in the differential survival and reproduction of individuals of a population is natural selection. In turn, natural selection is one of the mechanisms that drives evolution, or the change in a population over time. Natural selection drives adaptive evolution.

The Modern Synthesis

Charles Darwin launched evolutionary biology with the help of Alfred Wallace, Charles Lyell, and many other scientists before them. Darwin's work considered evidence from a wide range of sciences including geology, paleontology, and genetics (inheritance) to show that living things are related to one another by common descent. Despite having no idea what a gene was or how heredity worked, Darwin successfully introduced natural selection as a mechanism of evolution.

Darwin supported his hypothesis of natural selection on a foundation of evidence he and others gathered over time from observations and experiments. Recurring evidence confirmed that each generation of a species was full of variations. Some variations helped organisms survive and reproduce, and those were passed on to their offspring. Heredity was later understood to be the transmission of genes from generation to generation.

The modern synthesis is a unified explanation for the theory of evolution that combines natural selection with modern genetics. The theory of evolution is a fundamental framework in which we scientifically explain phenomena of living things. Scientists today use the modern synthesis as a tool for asking questions about biology and the history of life.

SEP **Argue From Evidence** *Explain how modern evidence confirms the theory of evolution.*

CHAPTER INVESTIGATION

Evolution of Antibiotic Resistance in Bacteria

Why do we need different types of antibiotics?

Go online to explore this chapter's hands-on investigation about the evolution of antibiotic resistance in bacteria.

15.1 REVIEW

1. **Relate** Define the term *biogeography* in your own words and explain how the science initiated the study of evolution.

2. **Compare** Describe the key difference between artificial selection and natural selection.

3. **Apply** Classify each factor as essential or nonessential for natural selection to occur.

   • adaptations

   • environmental change

   • geographic isolation

   • inheritance of traits

   • migration

4. **Identify** What are the main principles of natural selection? Select all correct answers.

   A. Some organisms are resistant to environmental changes.

   B. Many species' traits are based on genes that were inherited from parents.

   C. Organisms, even those within the same species, compete for resources.

   D. Certain traits make organisms better suited for reproduction and survival.

   E. Adaptations to the conditions in the environment increase an organism's fitness.

HAWKS AND MICE

SEP **Analyze Data** How does fur color impact a prey population?

Any population of organisms has variance within it. Organisms that have favorable variations are better adapted to their environment and will survive and reproduce in greater numbers. In this activity, you will simulate the effect of predation by a hawk on a population of field mice.

Materials

- newspaper, sheet (2)
- paper square, white, 3 x 3 cm (50)
- paper square, black, 3 x 3 cm (50)
- paper square, black-and-white speckled, 3 x 3 cm (90)
- container, clear, small
- container, dark, small
- timer

Procedure

1. Spread the sheets of newspaper open at one end of a table.

2. Mix and randomly spread out 30 of each color of paper squares (mice) on the newspaper (field).

3. Place the clear container, which represents the hawk's nest, at the other end of the table or on a different table. It should be far enough away that several steps need to be taken to get from the newspaper to the container.

4. Select one person to be the hawk (have them stand by the nest), another to operate the timer, and another to count the mice caught by the hawk.

5. The hawk has one minute to pick up as many mice as possible. The hawk may only pick up one mouse at a time and must place it in the nest before returning to pick up another mouse.

6. When the time is up, record the number of mice of each type left in the field (newspaper) in your biology notebook.

7. Switch roles within the group, return all the squares to the field, and repeat Steps 5 and 6. Do this as many times as necessary for each person within the group to play the role of the hawk.

8. Remove all the squares from the newspaper.

9. Using the data collected from each hawk, determine the average number of mice for each color remaining in the field.

10. Using the averages, place an equivalent number of each color of squares in a dark container.

11. Draw out 10 squares at random from your extra squares (those not in the containers or in the field) and place them on the newspaper.

12. Repeat Step 11 until you have 90 squares on the newspaper.

13. Repeat Steps 5 through 7 as many times as necessary for each person in your group to play the role of the hawk.

14. Using the data collected, determine the average number of mice for each color remaining in the field.

15. Clean up and return materials to their stations.

Results and Analysis

1. **Calculate** Based on the data you collected, what is the average number of each color of mice left after the hawk has captured the mice? Do the results surprise you? Explain why or why not.

2. **Explain** Were there any similarities or differences between the data collected from the first population of mice and the second population of mice?

3. **Draw Conclusions** How might the mouse population change over time from natural selection?

EVOLUTION IN POPULATIONS

You may have noticed patterns in your everyday environment. For example, there are weather patterns associated with the four seasons, daily patterns involving the moon and tides, and patterns tied to animal behaviors, including your own!

Analyze *What environmental changes suggest that patterns can be explained by evolution?*

KEY TERMS

allele frequency
directional selection
disruptive selection
gene pool
stabilizing selection

Genetic Variation

Evolution occurs in populations, not individuals. Individuals do not evolve during their lifetimes. Populations evolve over generations as heritable differences become either common or rare in a population. There are five known ways that populations can evolve. You learned about natural selection in the previous section. Natural selection acts on genetic variations that introduce different traits in an individual organism. If the trait is advantageous and helps the individual survive and reproduce, the trait is more likely to be passed to the next generation.

Gene Pool of a Population A population's **gene pool** is the total genetic material of all the individuals that make up that population at a given time (**Figure 15-9**). The gene pool includes all possible alleles, or variations of individual genes, within the population. Recall that an allele is a variation of a gene for a trait (Section 12.1). Genetic variation occurs when genes are recombined during meiosis and sexual reproduction. Recombination introduces genetic variation at the cellular level. Sexual reproduction results in increased genetic diversity within a species because of the random assortment of combined alleles from both parents.

FIGURE 15-9 ▽
Variation in shared traits among individuals is mainly an outcome of variations in alleles that influence those traits (a). Snail species, such as *Cepaea nemoralis* (b), provide an example of shell color variations.

9a

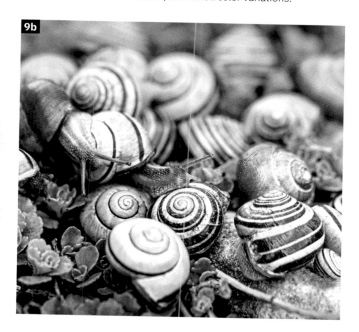

9b

Mutations Genetic recombination by sexual reproduction is a source of genetic variation. However, mutations in gametes are the ultimate source of genetic variation in an organism's genome. Changes in the environment favor mutations that provide even a slight advantage, such that the frequency of that mutation tends to increase in a population over time. Thus, mutations are another way that populations can evolve because they are a source of new alleles in a gene pool.

Allele Frequency Members of a population in the same area breed with one another more often than they breed with members of other populations, so their gene pool is basically isolated. Different combinations of alleles in a gene pool can be formed when organisms mate and have offspring. For example, deer mice chromosomes have different alleles for fur color. A change within a deer mouse population gene pool would be a new variation of fur color within the population (**Figure 15-10**).

FIGURE 15-10
Differences in allele combinations cause differences in fur color in mice.

The frequency of a particular allele for fur color depends on the environment in which the population lives. **Allele frequency** is the proportion of one allele relative to all the alleles for that trait in a population's gene pool. Allele frequency is expressed as a percentage or a fraction. For example, if half of the chromosomes carried by members of a population have a particular allele, then the frequency of that allele in the population is 50 percent, or 0.5.

$$\text{allele frequency} = \frac{\text{number of a particular allele}}{\text{total number of alleles}}$$

Allele frequency can also be expressed as a percentage by multiplying the frequency by 100. The frequencies of all the different alleles in a population should equal 1.0, or 100 percent.

SEP **Analyze Data** *Calculate the allele frequency of the B gene in* ***Figure 15-10*** *expressed as a percentage. Explain the frequency result in terms of the population of mice in that environment.*

Types of Natural Selection

Natural selection affects the frequency of alleles that influence a trait by increasing, decreasing, or maintaining particular variations of the trait in a population. The genetic variation on which natural selection acts may occur randomly, but natural selection itself is not random at all. The survival and reproductive success of an individual is directly related to the ways its inherited traits function in the context of its local environment.

Natural selection is a major driver of evolution, but it is not the only one. Allele frequencies in a population can also change for other reasons. Individuals moving into and out of populations bring their alleles with them. Environmental events and other factors that reduce the number of individuals in a population can also affect allele frequencies.

Normal Distribution A normal distribution of traits across a population looks like a bell curve (**Figure 15-11**). The shape of the curve shows that the traits of the majority of the individuals in a population are close to the mean, and there are fewer individuals have extreme traits.

FIGURE 15-11 ▽

Normal distribution is a bell curve, showing a distribution that occurs naturally in many situations.

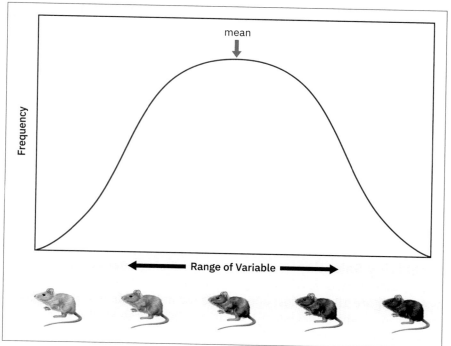

In populations, natural selection favors advantageous phenotypes that increase reproductive success. This results in favorable genes becoming more widespread in a population over time. *Microevolution* is the observable change in allele frequency in a population over time. It occurs constantly on a small scale within a single population. Microevolution occurs because natural selection acts on an organism's phenotype, which is often largely a product of genotype. When a phenotype produced by certain alleles helps individuals in a population survive and reproduce more successfully than other individuals, natural selection can increase the frequency of the helpful alleles from one generation to the next. Natural selection can shift the phenotype distribution in a population in three basic ways.

Directional Selection In **directional selection**, some phenotypes are favored over others as the environment changes over time. A classic case of directional selection occurred in Galápagos finches (**Figure 15-12**). As available food sources changed over time, so did the beak lengths of finches in the population. When there were fewer insects and the birds relied on seeds as food sources, finches with larger beaks that could break seeds survived. When more insects were available for food, finches with smaller, longer beaks were better able to catch insects and survive.

FIGURE 15-12 ▼
With directional selection, forms of a trait at one end of a range of variation are adaptive to environmental changes.

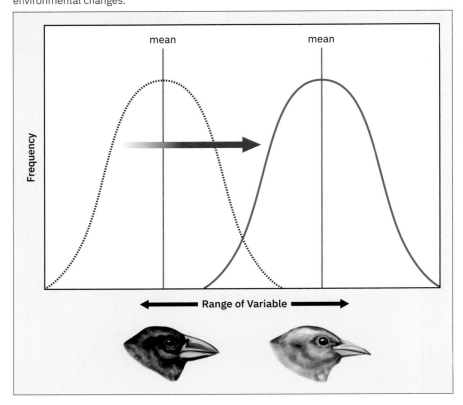

Stabilizing Selection In the case of **stabilizing selection**, an intermediate form of a trait is adaptive, and extreme forms are selected against (**Figure 15-13**). Most populations are at least fairly well adapted to their environment, so scientists think that stabilizing selection is the most common form of natural selection.

For example, environmental pressures maintain an intermediate body mass in populations of sociable weavers, which are birds that build large communal nests in the African savanna. Studies indicate that optimal body mass in sociable weavers is a trade-off between the risks of starvation and predation. Birds that have less fat are more likely to starve than plump birds. However, birds that have more fat spend more time eating, which in this species means foraging in open areas where they are easily accessible to predators such as snakes and birds of prey. Birds with more fat are also more attractive to predators and not as agile when escaping. Thus, predators are agents of selection that eliminate the individual birds with the most fat. Birds of intermediate weight have the selective advantage, and as a result they make up the bulk of sociable weaver populations.

FIGURE 15-13 ▼

With stabilizing selection, extreme forms of a trait are eliminated, and an intermediate form is maintained.

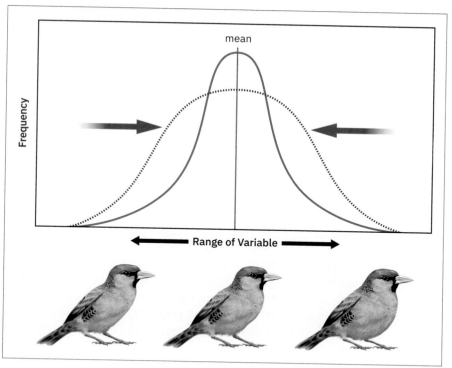

Disruptive Selection

Disruptive Selection The opposite of stabilizing selection, **disruptive selection** favors the extremes rather than the center of the population (**Figure 15-14**). For example, beak sizes of black-bellied seedcracker birds in central Africa are either 12 millimeters wide or wider than 15 millimeters. Birds with a bill size between 12 and 15 millimeters are uncommon. Large-billed and small-billed seedcrackers inhabit the same geographic range, and they breed randomly with respect to bill size.

FIGURE 15-14 ▼
Disruptive selection eliminates midrange forms of a trait and maintains extreme forms at both ends of the range of variation.

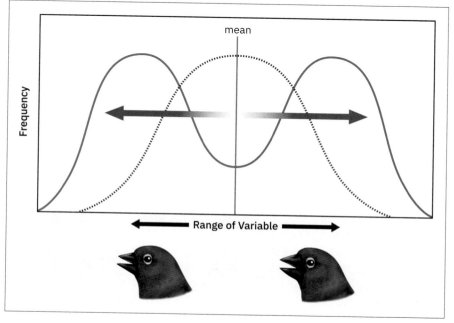

The existence of both forms of individuals arises from environmental factors that affect feeding performance. The birds feed mainly on the seeds of two types of sedge, a grasslike plant. One sedge produces hard seeds and the other produces soft seeds. Small-billed birds are better at opening the soft seeds, but large-billed birds are better at cracking the hard ones. Both hard and soft sedge seeds are abundant during the semiannual wet seasons. At these times, all seedcrackers feed on both seed types. During the region's dry seasons, the seeds become scarce. As competition for food increases, each bird focuses on eating the seeds that it opens most efficiently. Small-billed birds feed mainly on soft seeds, and large-billed birds feed mainly on hard seeds. Birds with intermediate-sized bills cannot open either type of seed as efficiently as the other birds, so they are less likely to survive the dry seasons.

Genetic Equilibrium

Evolutionary changes occur in a population due to natural selection, mutations, genetic drift, gene flow, and sexual selection. In contrast, the Hardy-Weinberg principle states that if a population is not undergoing evolutionary change, frequencies of each allele in the gene pool remain constant from generation to generation. This is called genetic equilibrium, or stability, in a population. It is an unrealistic and idealized state that does not happen in nature. A Hardy-Weinberg equilibrium, in which allele and genotype frequencies stay constant from generation to generation requires the following conditions:

- **Random Mating** Individuals within the population must mate with one another at random and not select their mates on the basis of genotype.

- **No Mutations** There can be no new alleles generated by mutations, nor duplication or deletion of genes.

- **Large Population Size** A large population size prevents random fluctuations that are more likely to occur in a small population.

- **No Migration or Immigration** No individuals enter or leave the population, a situation that could change allele frequency.

- **No Natural Selection** If natural selection were to occur, certain genotypes would be favored over others, and the allele frequencies would change.

15.2 REVIEW

1. **Explain** Why is it that populations, not individuals of a species, evolve?

2. **Justify** Support the claim that natural selection is not random.

3. **Identify** The sets of graphs show how the normal distribution of traits in three populations (L, M, O) changes over time. Identify the type of natural selection underway in each population.

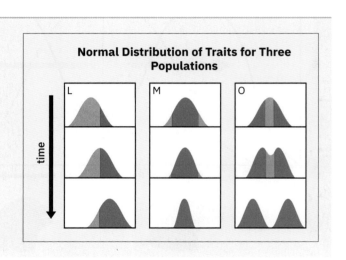

Normal Distribution of Traits for Three Populations

ON ASSIGNMENT These vibrant sea snails (*Nerita versicolor*) get their name from the varied colors and patterns on their shells. This image was captured by National Geographic photographer Gabby Salazar. In addition to her work as a conservation photojournalist, Salazar is also a social scientist who studies the influence environmental images have on people's attitudes and behaviors.

TRACKING EVOLUTION

SEP **Mathematical Thinking** The population of deer mice in areas of Nebraska where glaciers once deposited light-colored soil tend to have a large proportion of individuals with homozygous recessive coat color. Coat color is based on a single gene where dark brown is the dominant allele (**Figure 1**). Allele frequencies can be predicted mathematically using a Punnett square and the Hardy-Weinberg equation. The Hardy-Weinberg principle states that genotype frequencies in any population remain constant over time in the absence of evolutionary influences. Mathematically, this equilibrium is represented with two equations

$$p^2 + 2pq + q^2 = 1$$

$$p + q = 1$$

where p^2 represents the frequency of the homozygous dominant genotype, q^2 represents the frequency of the homozygous recessive genotype, and $2pq$ represents the heterozygous genotype. The corresponding allele frequencies are then p and q. The frequency of all possible genotypes in a population must equal 1. If allele frequency can be found using the equation $p + q = 1$, then $p^2 + 2pq + q^2 = 1$.

Figure 2 shows a graphical model of this principle for a single-gene trait based on dominant *A* and recessive *a* alleles. The area of the square represents all the possible genotypes in the population and must be equal to 1.

A summary of the variables in this Hardy-Weinberg model is as follows:

- p = the frequency of dominant allele *A*
- q = the frequency of recessive allele *a*
- p^2 = the frequency of homozygous dominant genotype *AA*
- q^2 = the frequency of homozygous recessive genotype *aa*
- $2pq$ = the frequency of heterozygous genotype *Aa*

For example, a population of 100 deer mice (generation M) has five deer mice with light brown coat color. The frequency q^2 will be

$$q^2 = 5/100 = 0.05$$

Therefore, five percent of the population has the genotype *aa*.

The allele frequency $q = \sqrt{0.05} = 0.22$. Then, using the second equation

$$p + q = 1$$
$$p = 1 - q$$
$$p = 1 - .22 = 0.78$$
$$p^2 = (0.78)^2 = 0.60$$

FIGURE 1
Peromyscus maniculatus have two main coat colors. Mice with light brown coats (a) are found in Nebraska Sand Hills and mice with dark brown ones are found elsewhere (b).

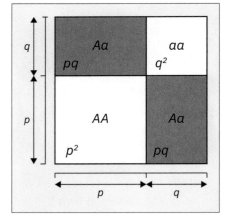

FIGURE 2
The Hardy-Weinberg equation using a Punnett square model shows allele distribution.

Therefore, 60 percent of the population has the homozygous genotype *AA*.

The predicted allele frequencies are p = 0.78 and q = 0.22. To calculate the predicted genotypic frequencies from the predicted allele frequencies, we use

$$2pq = 2(0.78)(0.22) = 0.35$$

Therefore, 35 percent of the population has the heterozygous genotype.

Generation M is made up of 60 homozygous dark brown deer mice, 35 heterozygous dark brown deer mice, and 5 homozygous light brown deer mice. If the population is not evolving, the genetic variation remains in equilibrium and these proportions will remain constant over time.

Table 1 shows the number of deer mice of different coat colors across three additional generations. The generations are not consecutive but cover the gene pool over dozens of years.

TABLE 1. A Deer Mouse Population Over Time

Population	Number of dark brown mice	Number of light brown mice
generation O	1976	104
generation T	6115	2621
generation W	27,824	28,960

1. **Calculate** Use the population data to determine the percentage of dark brown coat color and light brown coat color in deer mice of each generation. Round your answer to the nearest percent.

2. **Analyze Data** Calculate the genotype frequency (q^2) for homozygous recessive deer mice in each generation. Round your answer to the nearest percent.

3. **Use a Model** Calculate the expected percentage of homozygous dark brown (p^2) and heterozygous dark brown ($2pq$) deer mice expected in each generation using the Hardy-Weinberg equations.

4. **Evaluate** Which is the earliest generation that shows evidence for evolution from generation M? Explain how you know.

5. **Summarize** Why does looking at the observable traits of a population over time not give a complete picture of evolution occurring in a population?

6. **Infer** What are the possible reasons for a change in the coat color of deer mice populations over time?

bottleneck effect
founder effect
gene flow
genetic drift
sexual selection

OTHER MECHANISMS OF EVOLUTION

When you spend time figuring out how something works, one thing that you do (whether or not you realize it!) is gain an understanding of the mechanisms involved. This occurs whenever you learn how to play a video game, use a computer application, or create a new art piece. Mechanisms, such as rules, variables, materials, and environmental conditions, affect how things work.

Scientists also study mechanisms as part of their understanding of natural processes and developing theories. For example, measuring the selection of certain traits in populations that allow species to adapt and thrive over time has helped researchers to more fully understand the processes of evolution.

Explain *Identify one concept or phenomenon in science where your understanding changed after you came across new evidence.*

Gene Flow

Natural selection and genetic variation (mainly mutations) are two mechanisms of evolution. In this section, you will learn about the remaining three mechanisms: gene flow, genetic drift, and sexual selection. All of these mechanisms can cause a population to evolve over time. All of the mechanisms of evolution may act to some extent in any natural population. Changes in a population's allele frequency across generations may result from several evolutionary mechanisms acting at the same time. For example, a mutation may produce a new allele, which is then favored (or disfavored) by natural selection.

Individuals tend to mate or breed most frequently with other members of their own population. However, not all populations of a species are completely isolated from one another, and nearby populations may occasionally interbreed. Also, individuals sometimes leave one population and join another. **Gene flow** is the movement of alleles between populations. Whether individuals from nearby populations of the same species interbreed or move from one population to the other, gene flow occurs, and it can change or stabilize allele frequencies.

Genetic Drift Allele frequencies also change within a population by random chance events. For example, consider a population of 10 individuals in which an allele for a particular trait exists with a frequency of 20 percent. That means two of the 10 individuals in the population are likely to carry that allele. Because of the very small sampling size, there is a reasonable chance that those two individuals could be eliminated purely by accident, thus losing the allele permanently.

Now consider a second population of 10,000 individuals with the same allele that has the same frequency of 20 percent. That means 2000 individuals in the population are likely to carry that allele. The chances that all 2000 individuals that carry this allele would be eliminated is much less likely than in the first population.

From this situation, we see that there is a greater likelihood that the allele will be lost from the smaller population than from the larger population. This phenomenon is called **genetic drift**, or the change in allele frequency due to chance alone. A population can "drift" toward or away from certain alleles purely by chance, regardless of whether they provide an advantage.

CCC **Cause and Effect** *Why does the loss of genetic diversity have a greater effect in a small population compared to a large population?*

Bottleneck Effect A reduction in population size so severe that it reduces genetic diversity is called the **bottleneck effect**. For example, northern elephant seals underwent a bottleneck during the late 1890s, when overhunting left only about 20 individuals of this species alive. The bottleneck effect is an extreme example of genetic drift because with so few individuals, the frequency of alleles is either greatly reduced or some alleles are eliminated (**Figure 15-15**).

Hunting restrictions have allowed the population of the northern elephant seal to recover (**Figure 15-16**), but genetic diversity among its members has been greatly reduced. The bottleneck and subsequent genetic drift eliminated many alleles that had been present in the population.

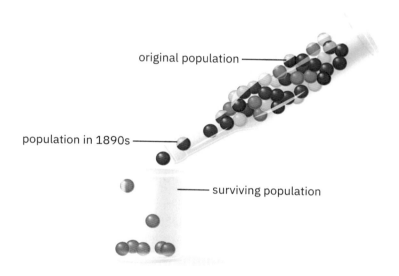

original population

population in 1890s

surviving population

FIGURE 15-15
Beads in a bottle is one way to model the bottleneck effect. Random chance determines which individual beads fall out of the bottle when it is tipped.

FIGURE 15-16
The northern elephant seal suffered from the bottleneck effect when most were killed for their blubber, which was used in lamp oil.

Founder Effect The **founder effect** occurs when a few individuals break off from an established population and form a new colony that is fully separated from its original population (**Figure 15-17**). In this case, the new population can drift in unexpected ways. For example, if the small group happens to possess very unusual alleles, those alleles will have a high frequency in the new colony, much greater than that in the original population.

FIGURE 15-17 ▶
Genetic variation of a new founding population compared to the original population will vary. The different colored beads represent different alleles in the populations.

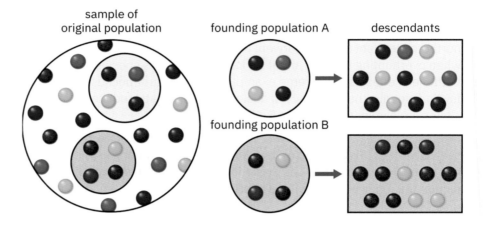

Sexual Selection

Apart from the genetic mechanisms (mutations, gene flow, genetic drift) that introduce variations in a population, random mating introduces variation as well. Not all evolution is driven by selection for traits that enhance survival. Competition for mates is another selective pressure that can shape form and behavior. In some species, individuals of one sex (often males) are more colorful, larger, or more aggressive than individuals of the other sex. These traits can take energy and time away from activities that enhance survival, and some actually compromise survival.

Sexual selection is a mechanism of evolution in which the evolutionary winners out-reproduce others of a population because they are better at securing mates. With this mode of natural selection, the most adaptive forms of a trait are those that help individuals defeat rivals for mates or are most attractive to the opposite sex.

For example, the females of some species cluster in defensible groups when they are sexually ready, and males compete for sole access to the groups. This is called lekking, and is a classic model for studies of sexual selection because males compete with one another to attract a female, and the female chooses her mate (**Figure 15-18**).

FIGURE 15-18 ▶
A female sage grouse (center) judges the courtship displays of three male sage grouse as they call and dance around her.

 VIDEO

VIDEO 15-3 Go online to learn more about the behavior called lekking.

Males or females that are choosy about mates act as selective agents on their own species. The females of some species shop for a mate among males that display species-specific cues, such as a highly specialized appearance or courtship behavior. The cues often include flashy body parts or movements—traits that attract predators and in some cases are a physical hindrance. However, to a female member of the species, such displays may imply health and vigor, two traits that are likely to improve her chances of bearing healthy, vigorous offspring. Selected males pass alleles for their attractive traits to the next generation of males, and females pass alleles that influence mate preference to the next generation of females. Highly exaggerated traits, such as a male peacock's tail, can be an evolutionary outcome (**Figure 15-19**).

CCC **Cause and Effect** *Why is the trade-off of an individual expending energy to find a mate worthwhile for a population?*

CHAPTER INVESTIGATION

Genetic Drift
How can genetic drift affect a population?
Go online to explore this chapter's hands-on investigation about the ways in which population's gene pool can change.

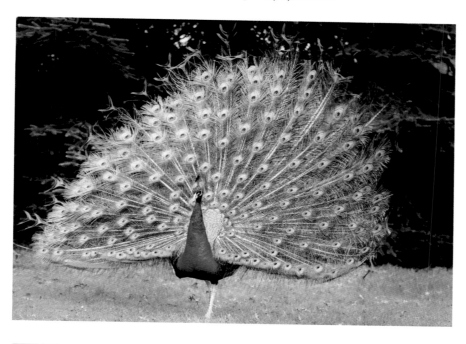

FIGURE 15-19
A male peacock displays his elaborate tail to attract a female mate.

15.3 REVIEW

1. **Classify** Sort the processes into those that can affect the allele frequencies and those that do not.

   - asexual reproduction
   - gene flow
   - genetic drift
   - meiosis
   - mitosis
   - mutation
   - natural selection
   - sexual selection

2. **Explain** How does the bottleneck effect lead to evolution?

3. **Identify** Which mechanism of evolution can keep two distinct populations genetically alike?

   A. gene flow

   B. genetic drift

   C. mutations

   D. natural selection

4. **Explain** Why does sexual selection often result in the evolution of elaborate traits, such as a male peacock's tail?

NATIONAL GEOGRAPHIC EXPLORER **CHRISTOPHER C. AUSTIN**

PUZZLING OUT THE ADVANTAGE OF GREEN BLOOD

Dr. Christopher Austin's research focuses on the use of molecular genetic data sets to answer evolutionary questions.

More than 100 species of skinks live on New Guinea, an island off the coast of Australia. Their smooth-scaled, slender appearance and behavioral habits are not especially different from those of other skinks. But biologist Dr. Christopher Austin took a special interest in certain ones in 1990. What made them so unique? Their bright, lime-green blood.

Until recently, the few described green-blooded skink species on the island have been grouped together in the genus *Prasinohaema*. Yet, Austin's research shows that the species are not closely related. They live in very different habitats and some lay eggs while others give birth to live young. He thinks the trait arose in all members of this group from a common red-blooded ancestor. But what advantage did it confer that caused its selection?

While not common, green blood in animals is not unique to these skink species. It occurs in some species of insects, frogs, and fish as well. However, it doesn't occur in any other reptiles or in any birds or mammals. The green color is caused by the green bile pigment called biliverdin that overwhelms the red color of the red blood cells present. This and other liver pigments are toxic in even small amounts in all other reptiles, birds, and mammals. The green bile present in the skinks is 15 to 20 times higher than the level that would kill a human. The high concentration of biliverdin in the blood colors not only the blood green but also the muscles, bones, and tongues of the skinks.

Austin's team examined 51 species including six with green blood. They could determine which species were those that had evolved on New Guinea and which descended from Australian lineages. By comparing segments of DNA, they reconstructed the evolutionary history of those relationships that included the green-blooded skinks. Surprisingly, based on the branching indicated by the DNA analysis, the trait arose independently four different times in species with a strict New Guinea heritage.

To solve the puzzle of green blood's evolutionary advantage, Austin's team is currently investigating how it might protect the skinks against blood parasites such as malaria. A similar human bile pigment, bilirubin, is toxic to human malaria parasites.

THINKING CRITICALLY

Infer *Even though the green-blooded skink species are not closely related, why do you think Austin states they all descended from a red-blooded ancestor?*

TYING IT ALL TOGETHER
DON'T LET THE BEDBUGS BITE!

WHY DO POPULATIONS EVOLVE OVER TIME?

In this chapter, you learned how natural selection and other mechanisms drive adaptation in populations over time in response to changes in the environment. The bedbugs described in the Case Study are an example of a species that adapts relatively quickly to its changing environment (**Figure 15-20**).

Natural selection occurs when there is genetic variation in the population. Scientists recognize that bedbug populations have been primed with the right sort of genetic variation by their evolutionary history of extensive exposure to DDT. Like pyrethroids, DDT kills insects by acting on certain pores in their nerve cells, causing paralysis. Many of the same mutations that protect bedbugs against DDT also protect it from pyrethroids. Though such mutations were probably extremely rare at the outset, the widespread use of DDT in the 1950s and 1960s drove such mutations to be more common in bedbugs through the process of natural selection. While DDT is rarely used today because of its harmful environmental effects, these mutations are still present in modern bedbug populations. Because of the action of natural selection in the past (favoring resistance to DDT), many bedbug populations today evolve resistance to pyrethroids rapidly.

In this activity, you will use evidence you gather to explain how a population can evolve over time.

Ask Questions
1. Review the evidence you gathered and the questions you generated throughout the chapter about the mechanisms of evolution. Relate these questions to what you have learned about bedbugs.

Analyze Data
2. Research data on the reproduction rate of bedbugs.

Construct an Explanation
3. Explain how a mutation causing resistance to pyrethroids would spread through a population of bedbugs that are being treated with the pesticide. Make sure to include the concepts of genetic variation, natural selection, and inheritance in your explanation.

FIGURE 15-20 ▽

The total development process of bedbugs takes about 37 days at optimal temperatures above 22 °C (72 °F) and with readily available blood meals.

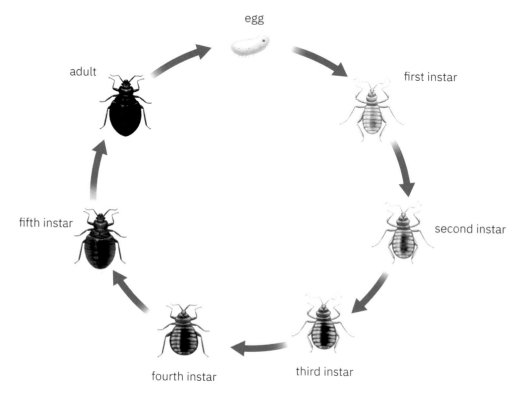

REVIEW KEY CONCEPTS

1. **Identify** Which of these ideas helped Darwin formulate his theory of evolution? Select all correct answers.

   A. Individuals develop different traits during their lifetime.

   B. DNA is a molecule that passes inherited traits from parents to offspring.

   C. Fossils of ancient organisms share features with some modern animals.

   D. Features of Earth's surface gradually change over very long periods of time.

   E. Similar species living in different habitats have unique traits suited for where they live.

2. **Analyze** Which is an example of a change that has resulted from natural selection?

   A. a racehorse that runs faster after training on a practice track for a year

   B. a population of wildflowers that produces more nectar than previous generations

   C. a flock of seagulls that searches for food scraps in human garbage left on the beach

   D. a new variety of apple produced by crossing a sweet variety with a drought-resistant variety

3. **Contrast** In evolutionary biology, how is fitness related to adaptation? How are they different?

4. **Define** What does overproduction mean in the context of natural selection?

   A. More individuals are produced than can be supported by the environment, so competition occurs.

   B. More genes than necessary are produced in an organism's genome, so some genes are not expressed.

   C. More mutations are produced than can be supported by a population, so some mutations will be less fit.

   D. More resources than necessary are produced by the environment, so a population will grow more fit over time.

5. **Define** What is a gene pool?

   A. all of an individual's genetic material

   B. the total genetic material in an ecosystem at a given time

   C. the total genetic material of all species on Earth at a given time

   D. the total genetic material of all individuals in a population at a given time

6. **Classify** Peppered moths are commonly found in the British Isles. Most are either black in color, which provides camouflage on dark surfaces, or white in color, which provides camouflage on light surfaces. Gray moths also exist but are extremely rare. What could explain this?

   A. artificial selection   C. disruptive selection

   B. directional selection   D. stabilizing selection

7. **Identify** During a heavy rainstorm, several rabbits are carried away by rushing floodwaters and deposited several miles downriver from their original habitat. A handful of survivors establishes a new population there. Why might the new population have less genetic diversity than the original population?

   A. bottleneck effect   C. genetic drift

   B. founder effect   D. sexual selection

8. **Classify** A wildfire burns through part of a forest, killing most of the Eastern white pine trees (*Pinus strobus*) in the population. Fifty years later, the area has a large number of Eastern white pine trees, most less than fifty years old. Compared to other areas of the forest, a very large percentage of these trees has an allele that causes them to grow short needles. What evolutionary effect does this demonstrate? Justify your answer.

9. **Define** Which description best fits gene flow?

   A. the transfer of alleles between two populations

   B. the transfer of alleles from parents to offspring

   C. the change in allele frequency when a population is greatly reduced in size

   D. the change in allele frequency when a small population loses an allele randomly

CRITICAL THINKING

10. Analyze Deuteranopia is a form of color blindness in humans that affects a small percentage of males. It can result from a single mutation on the X chromosome. Individuals who inherit this condition have trouble distinguishing red and green colors. Explain why natural selection may not have yet eliminated this trait from the human gene pool.

11. Explain The Hardy-Weinberg equilibrium model can be used to predict the frequency of alleles in a gene pool. Is this model applicable to most natural populations? Explain why or why not.

12. Explain The first organisms on Earth reproduced asexually. It was not until about two billion years ago that sexual reproduction began to evolve in prokaryotes. Today, nearly all eukaryotes reproduce sexually. How does sexual reproduction increase the reproductive fitness of organisms?

13. NOS Scientific Knowledge In Darwin's research, he examined many fossils to explain how organisms evolve into new species. Why is it necessary for evolutionary biologists to study the fossil record to learn about how species evolve?

MATH AND ENGLISH LANGUAGE ARTS CONNECTIONS

Darwin, in On the Origin of Species, *writes:*

The laws governing inheritance are for the most part unknown; no one can say why the same peculiarity in different individuals of the same species, or in different species, is sometimes inherited and sometimes not so; why the child often reverts in certain characteristics to its grandfather or grandmother or more remote ancestor; why a peculiarity is often transmitted from one sex to both sexes, or to one sex alone, more commonly but not exclusively to the like sex.

1. Cite Textual Evidence What clues suggest that Darwin did not have an understanding of modern genetics when he wrote this passage?

2. Write an Argument Human activity has resulted in the introduction of many species into new environments. In some cases, this results in invasive species that quickly colonize the new ecosystem and outcompete native species. Using what you know about evolutionary fitness, explain what factors would make a particular species likely to become invasive.

3. Reason Abstractly Suppose a herd of goats colonizes an area and starts eating the foliage. Before the goats arrived, shrub A and shrub B had approximately the same height distribution. However, because the goats cannot reach very high, shrubs with an allele that makes them tall prove to be more reproductively fit over time. In addition, the goats have a slight preference for shrub A over shrub B because its leaves taste better. Identify the type of selective pressure exerted by the goats on the shrubs and compare how the two populations of shrubs would likely evolve over a long period of time.

4. Use Mathematics A biologist surveys the alleles of a gene that affects fur color in a population. She finds four alleles at this locus in total. In her survey, she finds 74 copies of allele *A*, 115 copies of allele *B*, 65 copies of allele *C*, and 146 copies of allele *D*. What is the allele frequency of allele *A*? Express your answer as a percentage rounded to the nearest tenth of a percent.

▶ REVISIT HUMMINGBIRD EVOLUTION

Gather Evidence In this chapter, you learned about changes in populations over time. In Section 15.1 you learned about natural selection as a mechanism for adaptive evolution. In Section 15.2 you learned about mutations as a mechanism of genetic variation. In Section 15.3 you learned about other mechanisms of evolution including genetic drift, gene flow, and sexual selection.

1. Hummingbirds have adapted to survive in very specific habitats. Describe how flowers may have also adapted over time to suit hummingbirds. How would those adaptations benefit the flowers?

2. What other questions do you have about adaptations in hummingbirds?

CHAPTER 16
SURVIVAL IN CHANGING ENVIRONMENTS

This herd of savanna elephants, led by a tuskless matriarch, lives in Addo Elephant National Park in Eastern Cape, South Africa.

16.1 SPECIATION

16.2 EXTINCTION

16.3 HUMAN IMPACT ON THE ENVIRONMENT

16.4 REDUCING HUMAN IMPACT ON THE ENVIRONMENT

Chapter 16 supports the NGSS Performance Expectations **HS-LS4-5**, **HS-LS4-6**, **HS-LS2-7**, and **HS-ETS1-4**.

Although all African elephants were once grouped together as a single species, DNA analysis has shown that forest elephants (*Loxodonta cyclotis*) and savanna elephants (*Loxodonta africana*) are two different species that diverged millions of years ago. Forest elephants are smaller in size and live in smaller family groups than elephants that live in the grassy, open savanna.

CASE STUDY
TRACKING TUSKLESS ELEPHANTS

WHY DO NEW SPECIES EMERGE WHILE OTHER SPECIES DISAPPEAR?

Along with a trunk and large floppy ears, an elephant's tusks are one of its most characteristic features. Elephants use their tusks for a variety of essential tasks, including digging for water, removing edible bark from trees, and self defense.

The ivory in elephant tusks has long been prized for its appearance and durability, and it is easily carved and polished into practical and ornamental objects. In some traditions, ivory powder is believed to have healing properties. Poachers seeking to profit from selling ivory illegally hunt and kill elephants to remove their tusks. Older, larger elephants are preferred for their longer, heavier tusks. Despite long-standing international regulations banning the trade of ivory, poaching continues to endanger many elephant populations.

A 2014–2015 aerial census of savanna elephants in 18 African countries found a 30 percent decline in the region's elephant population. In Mozambique alone, the population declined by 53 percent in just five years.

Poaching not only decreases the size of a population. It can also influence the animals' traits. Although both male and female African elephants typically have tusks, between 2 and 4 percent of female elephants are naturally tuskless. In Mozambique's Gorongosa National Park, scientists have observed a change in this trait over several generations. Using historical film footage, they estimated that prior to Mozambique's civil war, which began in 1977, 18 percent of the park's female elephants had no tusks. Over 15 years of war, the conflicting sides turned to poaching to finance their efforts. Ultimately, they killed 90 percent of the park's elephants. Counts taken in 2018 determined that about half of the female elephants that survived the war were tuskless, and 33 percent of the survivors' daughters were also tuskless (**Figure 16-1**). These findings suggested that not having tusks increased the likelihood that an elephant would survive the war. Genetic analysis indicates that one of the genes for tusklessness is linked to the X chromosome.

Preliminary data indicate that elephants without tusks eat different types of plants than tusked elephants. Because elephant herbivory shapes the landscape of the savanna, these differences may have further implications for how African elephant populations evolve in a changing environment.

Ask Questions *In this chapter, you will learn how new species emerge and why species become extinct. As you read, generate questions about how human activity can influence a population's genetic makeup.*

FIGURE 16-1 ▼

The poaching of tusked elephants in Mozambique during the country's civil war led to an increase in the number of tuskless females in the population following the war's end.

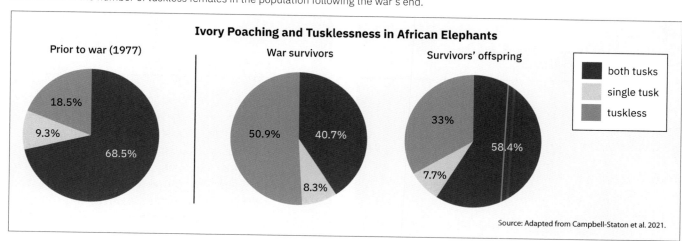

Ivory Poaching and Tusklessness in African Elephants

Prior to war (1977): 18.5%, 9.3%, 68.5%

War survivors: 50.9%, 40.7%, 8.3%

Survivors' offspring: 33%, 7.7%, 58.4%

both tusks / single tusk / tuskless

Source: Adapted from Campbell-Staton et al. 2021.

adaptive radiation
coevolution
reproductive isolation
speciation

SPECIATION

Earth is inhabited by millions of species that evolved over long stretches of time. All of the species alive today have not always existed. In fact, the vast majority of species that have ever existed on Earth are now extinct. Even species such as *Homo sapiens* (modern humans) are evolved versions of ancestor species. Evolutionary processes lead to adaptations within species and sometimes result in new species. The driving force behind evolutionary change is survival to reproduce.

Identify *What factors could lead to a species diversifying into a new species?*

CHAPTER INVESTIGATION

Modeling Speciation
What effect does environmental change have on speciation?
Go online to explore this chapter's hands-on investigation about speciation.

Mechanisms of Speciation

When two populations of a species do not interbreed, the number of genetic differences between them increases because mutation, natural selection, and genetic drift occur independently in each population. Over time, the populations may become so different that we classify them as different species. The emergence of a new species is an evolutionary process called **speciation**.

Reproductive Isolation Every time speciation happens, it occurs in a unique way. This means that each species is a product of its own unique evolutionary history. However, there are recurring patterns. **Reproductive isolation** is the end of gene flow between populations and occurs when members of those populations can no longer sexually reproduce. Several mechanisms of reproductive isolation prevent successful interbreeding, and, thus, reinforce differences between diverging populations.

- **Ecological Isolation** Adaptation to different environmental conditions may prevent closely related species from interbreeding. For example, there are over 90 species of manzanita (**Figure 16-2**). One species that lives on dry, rocky hillsides is better adapted for conserving water. Another species, which requires more water, lives in coastal regions where water stress is not as intense. The physical separation makes interbreeding unlikely.

FIGURE 16-2 ▽
Manzanita occupy diverse habitats including the Sierra Nevada mountain range (a) and coastal Southern California (b).

- **Temporal Isolation** Some closely related species cannot interbreed because the timing of their reproductive behaviors differ. One example is the periodical cicada. Three cicada species reproduce every 17 years. Each has a sibling species with nearly identical form and behavior that emerges on a 13-year cycle instead of a 17-year cycle. Sibling species have the potential to interbreed, but they can only get together once every 221 years.

- **Behavioral Isolation** Differences in behavior can prevent mating between related animal species. For example, many animal species engage in courtship displays before mating. In a typical pattern, the female recognizes the sounds and movements of a male of her species as the start of mating, but females of different species do not.

- **Mechanical Isolation** The size or shape of an individual's reproductive parts can prevent it from mating with members of related species. For example, closely related species of sage plants grow in the same areas, but their flowers are specialized for different animal pollinators, so cross-pollination rarely occurs.

Allopatric Speciation Genetic changes that lead to a new species can begin with ecological or physical separation between populations. With allopatric speciation, a physical barrier arises and separates two populations, ending gene flow between them. Whether a geographic barrier can block that gene flow depends on how the species moves, such as by swimming, walking, or flying. It also depends on how it reproduces, such as internal fertilization or pollen dispersal.

A geographic barrier can arise over millions of years, such as when mountains form, or it can happen much quicker. The Great Wall of China (**Figure 16-3**) is an example of a barrier that arose relatively abruptly. DNA sequence comparisons show that trees, shrubs, and herbs on either side of the wall are diverging genetically.

FIGURE 16-3
The longest stretch of the Great Wall that still exists today cuts across 8850 km (5500 miles) of land. It was built during the Ming dynasty (1368–1644).

Natural geographic barriers usually arise much more slowly. For example, it took millions of years of tectonic plate movements to bring the two continents of North and South America close enough to collide. The land bridge where the two continents now connect is called the Isthmus of Panama. When this isthmus formed about three million years ago, it cut off the flow of water and gene flow among populations of aquatic organisms. It separated one large ocean into what are now the Pacific and Atlantic Oceans (**Figure 16-4**).

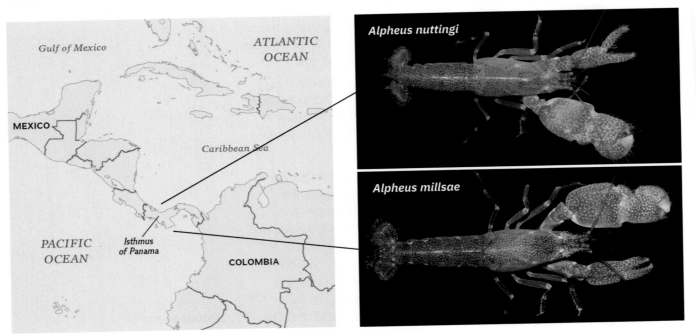

This geographic isolation led to the speciation of snapping shrimp. The species on either side of the Isthmus of Panama appear to be very similar to one another. However, without the ability to cross the geographic barrier, the species have become genetically distinct. For example, *Alpheus nuttingi* are found in the western Atlantic Ocean while *Alpheus millsae* inhabit the eastern Pacific Ocean. Instead of mating when they are brought together, male and female shrimp snap their claws at one another aggressively. Because they are unable to successfully mate together, the snapping shrimp are considered to be separate species.

Sympatric Speciation In this type of speciation, a new species arises within the same range as its ancestral population. Sympatric speciation is common only in plants. During meiosis, the chromosomes of some plants fail to separate and incorrectly produce diploid (2n) gametes. This condition, called polyploidy, refers to the possession of more than the proper complement of chromosomes. Polyploidy is a major factor in plant evolution. Polyploid gametes can develop into mature plants, even though they have double the number of chromosomes that a gamete should have. These individuals can self-fertilize and reproduce with themselves and other polyploid individuals. But they cannot sexually reproduce with any plants from the original parent generation because the two organisms now have different numbers of chromosomes.

SEP **Communicate Information** *Describe a possible scenario in which two populations of the same species might become reproductively isolated from one another.*

Adaptive Radiation

With **adaptive radiation**, one lineage rapidly diversifies into several new species. Adaptive radiation can occur after a population colonizes a new environment that has a variety of different habitats and niches and few competitors. Speciation occurs as adaptations to the different habitats evolve. Hawaiian honeycreepers arose by adaptive radiation (**Figure 16-5**).

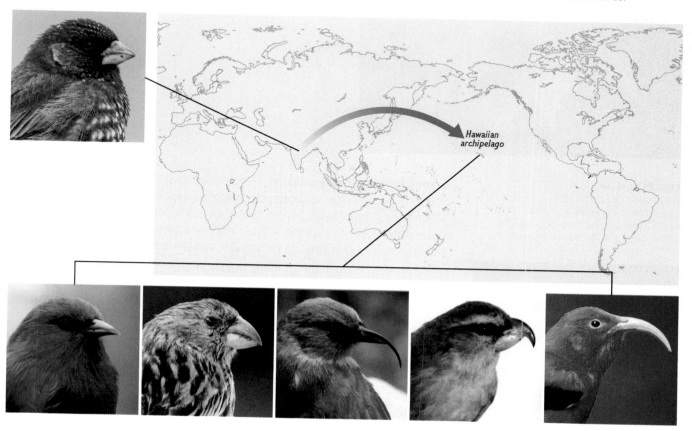

SEP **Argue From Evidence** *How do the Hawaiian honeycreepers shown in* ***Figure 16-5*** *provide evidence for adaptive radiation?*

A geologic or climatic event that eliminates some species from a habitat can spur adaptive radiation. Species that survive the event then have access to newly opened niches and resources from which they had previously been excluded. This is the way mammals were able to undergo an adaptive radiation after the dinosaurs were eliminated 66 million years ago. Adaptive radiation may also occur after a key innovation evolves. A key innovation is an adaptive trait that allows an organism to exploit a habitat more efficiently or in a new way. The evolution of lungs offers an example, because lungs were a key innovation that opened the way for an adaptive radiation of vertebrates that could live on land.

Patterns in Evolution

Evolution happens over a long time period. Environmental changes influence evolutionary processes, and organisms can sometimes adapt to such changes to survive and reproduce. Sometimes environmental changes, such as a physical barrier, result in the emergence of a new species. In other rare cases, two or more species competing for resources in shared habitats develop an evolutionary connection that leads them to independent adaptions in response to each other.

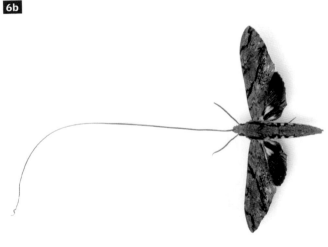

FIGURE 16-6 ▲
The Darwin's star orchid has a 30-cm-long nectar tube called a spur (a). It can be accessed only by the especially long proboscis of a Wallace's sphinx moth (b).

▼
HUMMINGBIRD EVOLUTION

Gather Evidence *Explain the role of coevolution in the diversification of hummingbird species.*

Coevolution In **coevolution**, two species that have close ecological interactions evolve in response to changes in each other. One species acts as an agent of selection on the other, and each adapts to changes in the other. Over evolutionary time, the two species may become so interdependent that they can no longer survive without the other.

One example of coevolution is the development in some insects of an especially long proboscis, a long narrow mouthpart used to sip nectar from a flower (**Figure 16-6**). The plant has likewise developed an adaptation called a floral nectar spur, which holds nectar deep within the flower.

The development of these complementary structures is beneficial to both organisms. The plant benefits by pollinator specialization, maintaining a narrow range of pollinators that can access the nectar deep within the flower. Animals must either be small enough to enter the spur or have a sufficiently long and narrow mouthpart to sip nectar from the spur. Charles Darwin observed this phenomenon in Madagascar orchids during his voyage. He correctly predicted the existence of a moth with a sufficiently long proboscis to pollinate the flower.

SEP **Argue From Evidence** *When is coevolution an example of a mutualistic symbiotic relationship?*

Evolutionary Arms Race In some cases, coevolution occurs between two species that compete with one another, particularly those that are in predator-prey relationships. For example, the thick shells of modern snails were an evolutionary response to predation by crabs. The crabs, in turn, have evolved to have sharper teeth and more powerful claws to crack the shells of the snails' thicker shells.

Punctuated Equilibrium How fast does evolution occur? The traditional model is one of gradualism, or incremental change, in which change takes place over millions rather than thousands of years. Gradualism presumes that favorable mutations take a long time to develop. Thus, the sequence in which, for example, giraffes' necks were to elongate might take dozens of mutations that occur only after millions of years.

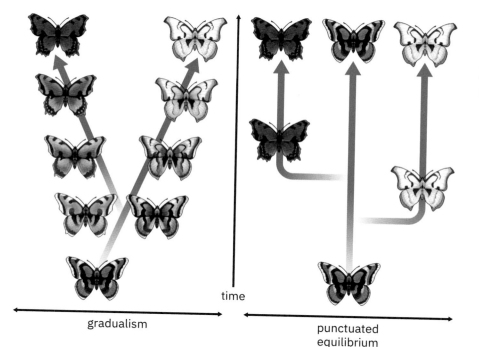

time

gradualism

punctuated
equilibrium

FIGURE 16-7
Gradualism assumes a large number of intermediate forms in the development of a species. With punctuated equilibrium, the change occurs rapidly with only a minimal number of intermediate forms.

The *punctuated equilibrium* model of evolution proposes that change is in fact quite rapid, occurring over a short period of time (a few thousand rather than millions of years) as ecological niches open up. Once these spurts of change occur, they are followed by much longer periods of stasis, or no change.

In fact, there is evidence that both models (**Figure 16-7**) might be correct for different time periods in the past. In some cases, noticeable change occurs only after millions of years. In others, the changes might have taken place in a much shorter period of time followed by a period of no change.

16.1 REVIEW

1. **Classify** Sort the examples into the type of reproductive isolation each represents.

   - Left-coiling snails cannot mate with right-coiling snails.

   - A male *Maratus nemo* spider conducts a ritual dance before mating and being killed by his mate.

   - *Rana boylii* mate during spring and summer while the co-existing *Rana draytonii* mate from winter into spring.

   - The common blackbird lives and breeds in forests while the closely related ring ouzel prefer to breed in open land.

2. **Explain** How can natural selection lead to speciation?

3. **Identify** Which factors are required for allopatric speciation in which a population becomes separated? Select all correct answers.

   A. migration

   B. natural selection

   C. a physical barrier

   D. genetic mutations

   E. development of adaptations

4. **Distinguish** How are allopatric speciation and adaptive radiation similar and different?

EXTINCTION

The passenger pigeon population once numbered in the billions across the United States and Canada. However, by the early 1900s, the bird had disappeared from the wild as a result of unrestricted hunting. The last known passenger pigeon died in captivity at the Cincinnati Zoo in 1914.

Explain *What could be an ecological consequence of a species going extinct?*

Types of Extinction

Extinction occurs when a species is eliminated from Earth. It is a critically important concept for evolution. While extinction marks the end of the existence of a species, it also presents opportunity for existing species to fill niches that become vacant. Extinction stimulates diversification into new species.

A low, steady level of extinction has continuously taken place throughout Earth's history. This type of extinction is called **background extinction**. Due to random events such as earthquakes, floods, or the introduction of new predators or competitors, some species simply do not survive under new environmental conditions and become extinct.

By current estimates, more than 99 percent of all species that ever lived are now extinct. In addition to continuing extinctions of individual species, the fossil record indicates that there have been more than five **mass extinctions** during which entire lineages were wiped out. These include five catastrophic events in which the majority of species on Earth went extinct (**Figure 16-8**). In most cases, these mass extinctions probably were caused by a massive environmental catastrophe. In other cases, there might be biological causes of extinctions, such as the introduction of a destructive new species. Humans, in fact, are a species that already has disrupted Earth's ecosystems and has been responsible for many thousands of extinctions. In the past, each period of mass extinction has been followed by a period of increasing diversity, in which thousands of new species have developed to fill newly emptied niches.

FIGURE 16-8 ▽
Geologic fossil evidence indicates that five major extinctions (indicated by the vertical bars) have occurred on Earth. They caused great loss but also greater biodiversity.

SEP **Construct an Explanation** *Why is mass extinction correlated with increased diversity?*

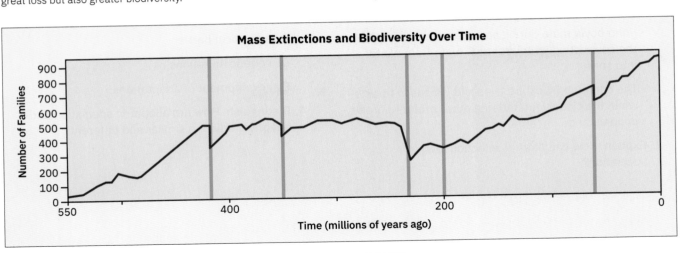

Mass Extinctions and Biodiversity Over Time

Number of Families (y-axis: 0, 100, 200, 300, 400, 500, 600, 700, 800, 900)

Time (millions of years ago) (x-axis: 550, 400, 200, 0)

Scientists estimate that the current extinction rate is about 1000 times that of the typical background extinction rate. Unlike most previous mass extinctions, which resulted from a massive catastrophe such as an asteroid impact, humans are driving the current rise in extinctions. Our actions will determine the extent of the losses.

A species is considered extinct if repeated, extensive surveys of its known range fail to turn up signs of any individuals. A species is "extinct in the wild" if the only known members of the species are in captivity. Some species are difficult to find, so occasionally a population of species previously thought to be extinct or extinct in the wild is rediscovered. However, this does not happen very often.

Endangered and Threatened Species

An **endangered species** is one in which its population has dwindled to the point where it is in imminent danger of extinction. Species whose populations are extremely low and are of concern for possible extinction in the future are called **threatened species**.

The International Union for Conservation of Nature (IUCN) manages a Red List of Threatened Species. This global list was first established in 1964. Listed species are sorted into three categories: critically endangered, endangered, and vulnerable. Several criteria are assessed to determine whether a species should be added to the list, such as the current species population and whether the species has a restricted geographic range.

In many ways, Earth's living species are its most valuable resources. Consider, for example, the more than 120 known medically effective substances derived from plants. Examples include morphine and other pain relievers from poppy plants, colchicine from the meadow saffron that treats gout and some types of cancer (**Figure 16-9**), and quinine from a tropical tree bark that treats malaria.

Scientists estimate that as many as one-third of all plant families might be lost by the end of the 21st century, in most cases because of human activity. With perhaps millions of plant species still undiscovered, who knows how many more critically important medicines and foods will be lost forever from the world because of extinction. Additionally, countless animals are also likely to disappear.

FIGURE 16-9
Colchicine, a compound derived from flowers of the meadow saffron, has potent anti-cancer properties.

Causes of Species Decline

In the United States, the listing and management of threatened and endangered species is managed by the U.S. Fish and Wildlife Service (USFWS). Keep in mind that not all rare species are threatened or endangered. Some species have always been uncommon.

Habitat Loss and Fragmentation Humans harm species indirectly by altering or destroying species' habitats. Because most species require a specific type of habitat, any degradation, fragmentation, or destruction of that habitat reduces population numbers.

An *endemic species* occurs only in the area in which it evolved. Endemic species are more likely to go extinct as a result of habitat degradation than species that have spread to many areas. For example, Pyne's ground plum (**Figure 16-10a**) is a flowering plant that lives only in a cedar forest near the rapidly growing city of Murfreesboro in middle Tennessee. The plant is threatened by conversion of its habitat to homes and industrial use. Texas blind salamanders (**Figure 16-10b**) are among the species endemic to Edwards Aquifer, a series of water-filled, underground limestone formations located in the Texas Hill Country. Excessive withdrawals of water from the aquifer, in combination with water pollution, threaten the salamander and other species in the aquifer.

Habitat fragmentation forms islands of suitable habitat scattered across what was once a continuous range. Buildings, roads, and fences can fragment a habitat. Thus, a large population can be broken into smaller populations in which inbreeding is more likely to occur. Inbreeding can have deleterious genetic effects. Fragmentation also prevents individuals from accessing essential resources. For example, roads, fences, and houses prevent spotted turtles endemic to the eastern United States from moving among wetlands to feed and hibernate. The wetlands still exist, but turtles cannot safely move between them.

CCC **Scale, Proportion, and Quantity** *Why is it important to maintain all parts of a species' habitat?*

FIGURE 16-10 ▽
Both the Pyne's ground plum (a) and the Texas blind salamander (b) are rare endemic species that exist in only an extremely limited range.

FIGURE 16-11
The critically endangered white abalone is one of seven abalone species that live off the coast of California.

▶ **VIDEO**

VIDEO 16-1 Go online to learn more about the overharvesting of white abalone.

Overharvesting In some cases, people directly reduce a species' number. Consider that when European settlers first arrived in North America, they found more than 30 million bison roaming the Western plains. By the late 1800s, that population had been reduced to less than 1000 individuals. It was only through the maintenance of captive populations, the development of nature reserves, and protective measures that restricted hunting that bison were able to rebound. Today, the bison population is around 500,000, although many live on private property. Only about 20,000 bison roam without restriction on tribal, state, and federal lands.

We continue to overharvest many species. One such species is the white abalone (**Figure 16-11**), a type of mollusk native to kelp forests off the coast of California. Heavy harvesting of this species during the 1970s reduced the population to about one percent of its original size. As a result, the white abalone fishery was closed in 1996. In 2001, it became the first invertebrate to be listed as endangered by the USFWS.

Although some white abalone remain in the wild, their population density remains too low for effective reproduction. The species' only hope for survival is a program of captive breeding, which began in 2001. After major setbacks, including the loss of 95 percent of the initial population of captive-bred juveniles due to bacterial infection and other factors, the first population of captive-bred juvenile white abalone were released back into the wild in 2019.

Species are overharvested not only as food, but also for use in traditional medicine, for the pet trade, and for ornamentation. Some orchids prized by private collectors have become nearly extinct in the wild. Rhinoceroses are killed by poachers to obtain their horns. The majority of rhinoceros horns are used to make traditional Chinese medicines. Possessing a whole rhinoceros horn is also seen by some people to be a status symbol.

Non-Native Species A community can change dramatically after the introduction of a non-native species. As described in Chapter 3, a **non-native species** is a species that evolved in one community and then dispersed from its home and became established elsewhere. The rate of non-native species introductions has accelerated along with the pace of global travel. Florida is home to more than 500 non-native species. In Hawaii, it is estimated that more than 45 percent of plant species are non-native. Some of these species were brought in as food crops, as ornamentals for gardens, or as a source of textiles. Other species arrived as stowaways along with cargo from distant regions.

Invasive Species Many non-native species have little impact on their adoptive community, but some of them are invasive. An invasive species is a non-native species that harms members of its new community. In some cases, the arrival of a non-native species can lead to the extinction of endemic species. Invasive species often have a far greater impact in their new community than they did in the region from which they originated. For example, invasive feral cats in Australia have had a devastating impact on endemic populations of ground-dwelling birds and small mammals. In fact, it is estimated that feral cats consume two billion reptiles, birds, frogs, and mammals each year.

When a species leaves its community of origin behind, it also leaves behind the competitors, predators, and parasites that coevolved with it and that helped keep its population in check. If the invasive species is a parasite, predator, or herbivore, it also leaves behind hosts or prey that had coevolved with it and had defenses against it. Its new hosts are often defenseless against it. As a result, an invasive species often reaches a higher population density in its new home than it achieved in its old one.

16.2 REVIEW

1. **Describe** Use the data provided in **Figure 16-8** to support the claim that life has thrived and diversified on Earth, despite extinction of species.

2. **Compare** What is the difference between background extinction and mass extinction?

3. **Explain** Why are native species more at risk of extinction than non-native species that have spread to many areas?

4. **Sequence** Rank the scenarios from least to most destructive for organisms living in a habitat. Use 1 to designate the least destructive scenario.

- repaving existing walking and biking paths
- developing a network of natural walking paths
- building a narrow one-way road with a slow speed limit
- designating the land as a protected conservation area
- constructing a road with high walls to protect wildlife from crossing

MONITORING BIRD POPULATIONS IN A CHANGING CLIMATE

Ornithology professor Dr. Çağan Şekercioğlu cites alarming statistics: By the year 2100, as many as 25 percent of the world's bird species could go extinct. This adds up to around 2800 unique bird species. Şekercioğlu cites two main reasons for the potential extinctions—climate change and habitat loss. And he notes that it's not a question of whether these species will become extinct, but how quickly.

Professor Çağan Şekercioğlu is not only a biologist; he is also an accomplished nature photographer. He thinks people need to feel the personal, emotional connection photography can provide to support facts and figures.

In 2000, Şekercioğlu developed a database of all the world's bird species, and he has been updating and analyzing it constantly since then. He collects extensive data about the ecology, conservation, distribution, and biogeography of species from field data and literature. The database allows him to analyze specific factors related to population changes. From that, he tries to answer questions about which species are more likely to go extinct based on climate change's impact on habitat availability. He warns that as the environment warms over 2 °C, the number of bird extinctions increases significantly.

Şekercioğlu notes that most of the world's bird species live in the tropics. However, very little data from those regions exists, so he says that their risk of extinction is greatly underestimated. He's watching tropical mountain birds in Costa Rica very closely. As the climate warms, the birds move higher and higher up the mountain in search of habitat and into smaller and smaller ranges. He monitors birds in farming areas as well to determine the effects of forest loss and land use. His study shows that populations of insect-eating birds are shrinking fast. He notes that the birds are so specialized in the habitats in which they feed that individuals will not cross a small field to get to a larger forested area. He says that when birds are lost, so are the ecosystem services they provide. As a result, the ecosystem deteriorates.

Today, despite all the environmental setbacks occurring around the world, Şekercioğlu strongly believes that it's the general public's lack of environmental awareness that is the biggest problem. Far too many people are unable to realize the grave nature of the issues facing birds and biodiversity in general. He is committed to improving this situation.

THINKING CRITICALLY

Analyze *How does Şekercioğlu use data analysis to draw his conclusions about the potential for bird species extinctions?*

16.3

KEY TERMS

deforestation
desertification
ecological footprint
pollutant

HUMAN IMPACT ON THE ENVIRONMENT

Humans rely on natural resources, such as food, energy, and building materials sourced from the ecosystems in which we live. Like other organisms, we need basic things like food and shelter. However, as humans have advanced over time, so have our needs and expectations. In modern times, we have the ability to prepare a variety of foods, construct elaborate buildings, and travel long distances in relatively short time using multiple modes of transportation. Every decision we make can have a lasting impact on Earth's ecosystems and the species that live within them.

Identify *List some decisions you made today that have an impact on the ecosystem in which you live.*

Human Population Growth and Resource Use

For most of its history, the human population grew very slowly (**Figure 16-12**). The growth rate began to pick up about 10,000 years ago, and it soared during the past two centuries. Three trends promoted the large increases. First, humans expanded into new habitats. Second, they developed technologies that increased the carrying capacity of their habitats. Third, they sidestepped limiting factors that typically limit population growth.

What is Earth's carrying capacity for humans? There is no simple answer to this question. For one thing, we cannot predict what new technologies may arise or the effects they will have. For another, different types of societies require different amounts of natural resources to sustain them. *Natural resources* are natural materials used by humans, such as water, forests, animals, and minerals.

FIGURE 16-12 ▼
The graph shows that where it once took hundreds or thousands of years to add one billion people to the population, it now takes a little over a decade.

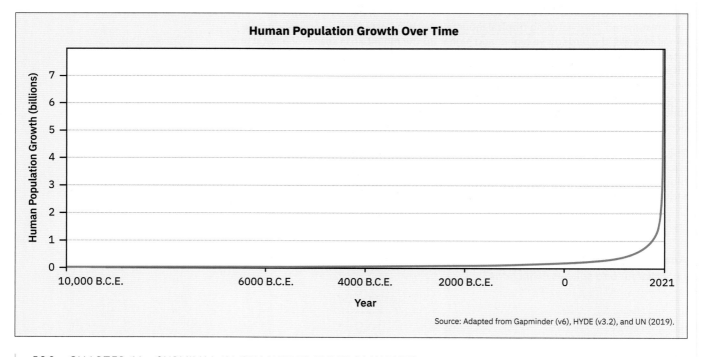

Source: Adapted from Gapminder (v6), HYDE (v3.2), and UN (2019).

On a per capita (per individual) basis, people in highly developed countries use far more natural resources than those in less developed countries, and they also generate more waste and pollution.

Renewable and Nonrenewable Resources Natural resources can be categorized as either renewable or nonrenewable.

- *Renewable resources* are natural resources that can be replenished at the same rate at which they are used. Some examples are wind energy, solar energy, hydroelectric energy, and geothermal energy.

- *Nonrenewable resources* are natural resources that cannot be replenished at the same rate at which they are used. Some examples are fossil fuels and minerals.

Figure 16-13 compares the global consumption of energy, including both renewable and nonrenewable sources of energy. As shown in the graph, the consumption of nonrenewable energy sources, such as oil, coal, and gas, has risen dramatically since the 1950s. Renewable energy sources, such as wind and solar energy, have become significantly more popular within the past few decades.

The local availability of natural resources influences the type of energy generated and used in a particular region. For example, coal has historically been a significant source of energy in the Appalachian coal region and Wyoming, where coal deposits are abundant. Areas that receive large amounts of sunlight are excellent candidates for solar power generation. Locations that experience high or constant winds are ideal sites for wind farms.

SEP **Analyze Data** *Explain the trend in energy consumption shown in* **Figure 16-13** *in terms of human population growth. Include the terms* renewable energy *and* nonrenewable energy *in your explanation.*

FIGURE 16-13 ▼

This graph shows how global energy consumption has changed over time for 10 different energy sources.

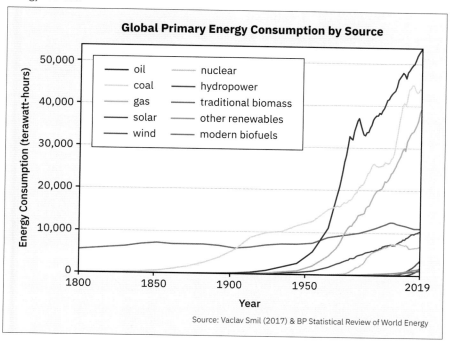

Water Pollution

Natural or synthetic substances released into the soil, air, or water in greater than natural amounts are called **pollutants**. The presence of a pollutant disrupts the biological processes of organisms that evolved in its absence or that are adapted to lower levels of the pollutant.

As shown in **Figure 16-14**, water pollution originates from many sources.

- *Point sources* are easily identifiable sources of water pollution. For example, a factory or wastewater treatment plant that discharges pollutants into water is a point source. These pollutants are easiest to control because the location of the source is known, and action can be taken to contain it.

- *Nonpoint sources* come from the widespread release of pollutants. For example, leaked motor oil that pollutes waterways originates from vehicles on many roads and driveways. Because of their widespread nature, it is much more difficult to eliminate nonpoint sources of water pollution than it is to eliminate point sources of water pollution.

FIGURE 16-14 ▽
Point sources of water pollution are easily identified. In contrast, it is difficult to pinpoint from where nonpoint sources of water pollution originate.

SEP **Scale, Proportion, and Quantity** *Explain how a point or nonpoint source of water pollution could affect an ecosystem far away from where you live.*

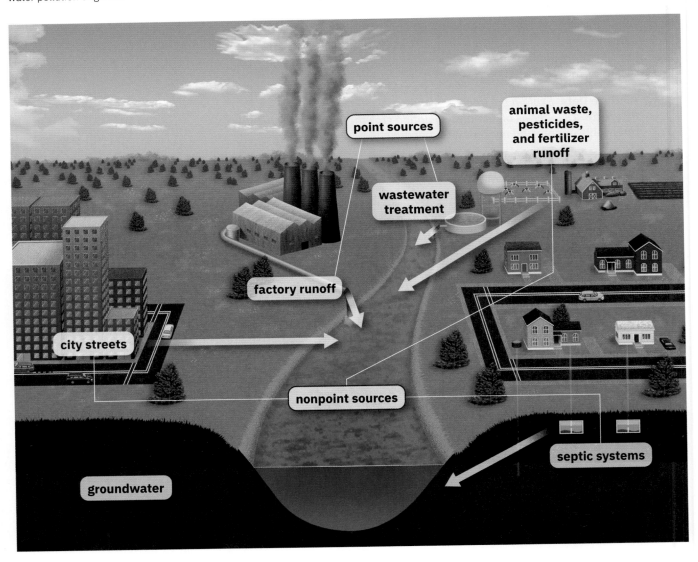

Solid Waste Seven billion people use and discard a lot of material. Where does all the waste go? Historically, much of it was buried in the ground or dumped out at sea. We now know that these practices have negative impacts on both biodiversity and human health.

Piling up or burying garbage on land can contaminate groundwater, such as when lead from discarded batteries seeps into aquifers. Modern landfills in developed countries are lined with clay or plastic to prevent toxins in the trash from reaching the groundwater. However, many landfills in less-developed countries have no such barrier. Toxins leached from trash enter the groundwater and can turn up in waterways and in wells that supply drinking water.

Discarding solid waste in oceans threatens marine life. In the United States, it is no longer legal to dump solid waste into the sea. Nevertheless, trash constantly enters coastal waters. Scientists estimate that the world's oceans currently contain 269,000 tons of floating plastic. The Great Pacific Garbage Patch is part of the five offshore plastic accumulation zones in the world's oceans and is located halfway between Hawaii and California. It covers an approximate surface area of 1.6 million square kilometers. This area is twice the size of Texas and three times the size of France. Much of the solid waste that ends up in the ocean is made up of discarded fishing gear (**Figure 16-15**). It is estimated that 640,000 tons of this type of waste is dumped or lost in the ocean every year.

VIDEO

VIDEO 16-2 Go online to learn how National Geographic Explorer Dr. Heather Koldewey implemented a solution for discarded fishing nets.

FIGURE 16-15 ▽
Lost or discarded fishing gear, which includes rope, nets, traps, crab pots, and fishing line, is a major source of ocean pollution.

Air Pollution

Fossil fuels such as petroleum, natural gas, and coal supply most of the energy used by developed countries. Burning these nonrenewable fuels contributes to climate change and acid rain. Natural gas that leaks from wells and pipes contributes to global warming. Pollutants that enter the atmosphere can harm organisms when they fall to Earth as dust or in precipitation. Common air pollutants include sulfur dioxides that are released by coal-burning power plants and nitrogen oxides that are released by combustion of gasoline and oil.

Global Climate Change Ongoing climate change affects ecosystems worldwide. As you learned in Chapter 2, average temperatures are increasing, with the more pronounced rise at temperate and polar latitudes. This rising temperature is elevating sea level by melting sea ice and glaciers, adding meltwater to the sea. In the past century, sea level has risen about 20 cm. As a result, some coastal wetlands and low-lying islands are disappearing under water.

Temperature changes are important cues for many species. Abnormally warm spring temperatures are causing deciduous trees to produce leaves earlier, and spring-blooming plants to flower earlier. Animal migrations and breeding seasons are also shifting. The variety of species in communities is changing as warmer temperatures allow some species to expand their range to higher latitudes or elevations that were once too cold for them. Not all species can move or disperse quickly to a new location, and warmer temperatures are expected to drive some of these species to extinction.

Temperature affects evaporation, winds, and currents, so many weather patterns are expected to change as the world continues to warm. For example, warmer temperatures are correlated with extremes in rainfall patterns: periods of drought interrupted by unusually heavy rains. In addition, warmer seas tend to increase the intensity of, and thus the damage incurred by, hurricanes (**Figure 16-16**).

FIGURE 16-16 ▼
Hurricane Laura, a Category 4 storm that made landfall in southwestern Louisiana on August 27, 2020, caused a total of $19 billion in damages. Winds at speeds up to 241 kph (150 mph) and a storm surge of more than 4.5 m (15 ft.) resulted in extensive coastal and inland damage.

Some species actually might thrive in a changed climate. For example, the growing season in Canada might increase because of climate change, resulting in more productive farming and more species diversity. Southern regions, on the other hand, might be devastated by heat, drought, and dramatic and unpredictable changes in precipitation patterns.

Ozone Depletion Ozone (O_3) is a form of oxygen that is a pollutant in the lower atmosphere where we live, but it blocks ultraviolet radiation from the sun in the stratosphere. Ultraviolet radiation is linked to several health problems in humans, including cataracts, skin cancer, eye problems, and a weakened immune system.

Scientists determined that excessive use of chlorofluorocarbons (CFCs) had significantly destroyed the stratospheric ozone. CFCs were widely used as aerosol-can propellants, air conditioner/refrigerator coolants, and industrial solvents. As the ozone layer became thinner, more ultraviolet radiation was reaching Earth's surface. Researchers reported declining populations of microscopic algae and fish around Antarctica that were related to the increased radiation. The good news is that by the 1990s, most nations agreed to ban and phase out CFCs and other harmful compounds by the end of the century. Since that time, the ozone layer has gradually recovered, but scientists estimate that it might take 50 years to determine whether the problem is completely solved.

Near-Ground Ozone Pollution While ozone does not naturally occur in the lower atmosphere, it can form when compounds released by burning or evaporating fossil fuels are exposed to sunlight (**Figure 16-17**). Warm temperature speeds this reaction, so ground-level ozone varies daily (it is higher in the daytime) and seasonally (it is higher during the summer). The ozone that forms in the lower atmosphere never reaches the ozone layer where it would be useful. Instead, ozone that forms in the lower atmosphere acts as a harmful pollutant. It irritates the eyes and respiratory tracts of animals and interferes with plant growth.

FIGURE 16-17 ▽
Ozone in the lower atmosphere forms from the interaction between air pollutants and sunlight. These air pollutants originate from a variety of sources.

Land Degradation and Habitat Loss

Many human activities related to obtaining resources threaten species by degrading land or destroying habitats. Obtaining resources for the global population requires large-scale operations that greatly impact ecosystems and biodiversity.

Mining Minerals are mined worldwide, and global trade makes it difficult to know the source of the raw materials in products you buy. Also, resource extraction in developing countries is often carried out under regulations that are less strict or less stringently enforced than those in the United States. As a result, the environmental impact of mining is even greater in these countries. There are four main methods of mining.

- In-situ mining involves dissolving a mineral resource underground and then processing it at the surface.

- Placer mining involves sifting minerals from sediments in streambed deposits.

- Surface mining includes open-pit mining (**Figure 16-18**), strip mining, and mountaintop removal. In this mining method, mineral deposits are removed near Earth's surface.

- Underground mining involves extracting mineral resources from deep within Earth.

Surface mining strips an area of vegetation and soil, forming an ecological dead zone. Mining typically puts particulate matter into the atmosphere, makes mountains of rocky waste, and contaminates nearby waterways.

FIGURE 16-18 ▽
The Cowal gold mine is a large open-pit mine in New South Wales, Australia.

SEP **Cause and Effect** *Identify two ways that mining affects the ecosystem in which it is located.*

Deforestation The clearing of forest areas is called **deforestation**. It causes enormous damage to both local and global environments. Forests cover 30 percent of Earth's land surface. Trees perform an important service in the storage of carbon. Tropical rainforests in particular play an important role in the removal of carbon dioxide from the atmosphere. Nevertheless, half of the world's rainforests are now gone, and an area of forest equal to about 20 football fields is being cut down on Earth every minute. At this rate, the world's rainforests will be eliminated in 100 years, if left unchecked. The prime causes of deforestation are agriculture, logging, and ranching with subsistence agriculture (**Figure 16-19**).

The Amazon is the world's largest rainforest and has sustained damage from subsistence farming, logging, ranching, and other destructive practices. Other areas, especially in Southeast Asia, are facing similar losses from destructive practices, such as burning and fragmenting forests and replacing them with vast plantations. The destruction of rainforests seriously damages the environment in many ways:

- Forests hold enormous amounts of water in the roots and trunks of trees. Areas that have been cleared suffer from floods that wash away or erode soil and cause great destruction.

- Trees release a large amount of water into the atmosphere through transpiration, which evaporates and returns as precipitation. Once cleared, an area becomes prone to drought as it has no way to retain water, and rainfall declines.

- Once a tropical forest has been logged, the resulting nutrient losses and drier, hotter conditions can make it impossible for tree seeds to germinate or for seedlings to survive. Thus, deforestation can be difficult to reverse.

FIGURE 16-19 ▽
This aerial view of a portion of the Amazon rainforest in Brazil shows a patch of forest surrounded by farmland deforested for use as cattle pasture.

FIGURE 16-20 Large sand dunes form from the deposition of silt and sand along the riverbanks of the Brahmaputra River Basin in the Shannan Region of Tibet.

Desertification Although deserts naturally expand and contract over geological time as climate conditions vary, human activities sometimes result in the rapid conversion of a grassland or woodland to desert. This process is called **desertification**. As human populations increase, greater numbers of people are forced to farm in areas that are not suitable for agriculture. In other places, people allow livestock to overgraze in grasslands. In both cases, the result can be habitat degradation. Drought encourages desertification, which results in more drought (**Figure 16-20**). Plants cannot thrive in a region where the topsoil has blown away.

16.3 REVIEW

1. **Explain** What factors have allowed the human population to grow exponentially?

2. **Classify** Categorize each resource as a renewable or nonrenewable resource.

   • forests

   • minerals

   • fossil fuels

   • Earth's internal heat

   • naturally flowing water

3. **Argue** How does global climate change affect biodiversity?

4. **Predict** Which suggested actions would likely decrease land degradation and habitat loss? Select all correct answers.

   A. increasing water use

   B. planting cover crops to prevent erosion

   C. implementating rotational grazing to prevent overgrazing

   D. implementing climate change initiatives that reduce fossil fuel use

   E. reusing or recycling materials that are made from mined resources

ECOLOGICAL FOOTPRINTS

SEP **Analyze and Interpret Data** Ecological footprint analysis is one widely used method of measuring and comparing resource use. An **ecological footprint** is the amount of Earth's surface required to support a particular level of resource production, consumption, and waste processing. It includes the amount of area required to grow crops, graze animals, produce forest products, catch fish, construct and maintain buildings, and take up any carbon emitted by burning fossil fuels.

In 2021, the per capita global footprint for the human population was 2.7 hectares, or about 6.7 acres. That is the area of just over five football fields per person. Ecological footprint analysis by the Global Footprint Network, a nonprofit research organization, suggests that the human population is currently living well beyond its ecological means, and is in the process of racking up a deficit that will take its toll on future generations. **Table 1** compares the ecological footprints of nine countries. **Table 2** compares their human populations.

TABLE 1. Comparing Ecological Footprints

Country	Hectares per capita (1 hectare = 2.47105 acres)
Brazil	3.11
Canada	8.17
China	3.38
France	5.14
Great Britain	7.93
India	1.16
Japan	5.02
Mexico	2.89
United States	8.22

Source: Global Footprint Network

TABLE 2. Comparing Populations

Country	Population (in thousands)
Brazil	212,559.41
Canada	38,005.24
China	1,410,929.36
France	67,391.58
Great Britain	67,215.29
India	1,380,004.39
Japan	125,836.02
Mexico	128,932.75
United States	329,484.12

Source: World Bank

1. **Organize Data** Sort the data in **Table 1** by ecological footprint size. Which country has the largest ecological footprint? Which has the smallest?

2. **Analyze** Sort the data in **Table 2** by population size. How does each country's population size compare to the size of its ecological footprint?

3. **Construct an Argument** Use the information provided in the passage and your analysis of the data to construct an argument for reducing a country's ecological footprint. In which two or three countries should maximum efforts to reduce their populations' ecological footprint be focused? Explain why.

4. **Predict** Which suggested changes in behavior would likely increase a country's ecological footprint? Select all correct answers.

   A. using waterways in addition to roadways

   B. eating less meat and more plant-based foods

   C. ridesharing and using more public transportation

   D. replacing paper and wood products with plastic products

   E. transporting waste to the deep ocean rather than burying it

ecological restoration
ecosystem service
sustainability
wildlife corridor

REDUCING HUMAN IMPACT ON THE ENVIRONMENT

An understanding that all life on Earth draws upon the same limited resources and that the health of the environment affects human well-being has given rise to a call for more sustainable practices. The first step is to recognize the environmental impact of every action we take.

Identify *What is one practice that could be implemented at your school to reduce the human impact on the environment?*

Managing Limited Resources

Living sustainably begins with recognizing the environmental impact of every action we take. **Sustainability** means using resources in a way that meets the needs of the current human population without harming the environment so that future generations will also be able to meet their own needs (**Figure 16-21**). People in industrial nations use large quantities of resources that must be extracted, produced, and transported before they are consumed and eliminated as waste. All these actions use energy, impact the environment, and have negative effects on biodiversity. However, we rely on many of these resources, and we can establish ways to minimize their use as part of living sustainably and preserving biodiversity. Sustainability begins with being aware of the problems, learning about the causes, and designing solutions.

FIGURE 16-21 ▽
Many fisheries, including the salmon fishery in Alaska, have strict enforcement of regulations to prevent the overharvesting of fish populations.

Managing Air and Water Pollution

Minimizing energy use is also part of living sustainably. Fossil fuels such as petroleum, natural gas, and coal supply most of the energy used by developed countries. Burning these nonrenewable fuels contributes to global warming and acid rain. Extracting and transporting fossil fuels add environmental costs. For example, oil that escapes from ocean-drilling operations harms aquatic species. Natural gas that leaks from wells and pipes contributes to global warming. Even nuclear energy production, which produces no carbon dioxide, has occasional accidents that allow dangerous radioactive material to escape into the environment.

Alternative Energy Reducing greenhouse gas emissions will be a challenge. However, international efforts are underway to increase the efficiency of processes that require fossil fuel, to shift to alternative energy sources such as solar and wind power, and to develop innovative ways to capture and store carbon dioxide before it leaves a power plant.

Solar technologies convert sunlight into electrical energy either through photovoltaic panels or through mirrors that concentrate solar radiation. This electrical energy can be used immediately or stored for later use. Solar energy systems must be integrated into homes, businesses, and existing electrical grids, typically as an additional or backup energy source. More individual residents and businesses are opting to install solar panels on rooftops across the United States. Utilities, too, are building large solar power plants to provide energy to all customers connected to the grid.

Solar energy is a clean, renewable, and essentially inexhaustible source of energy. However, there are downsides. Industrial-scale solar farms can pose a threat to birds that sometimes mistake the array of solar panels or mirrors at such facilities for a lake (**Figure 16-22**).

FIGURE 16-22 ▽
A large solar farm can produce more than 200 million kWh of energy per year.

FIGURE 16-23
The Horse Hollow Wind Energy Center spans 47,000 acres of land in central Texas.

Wind energy is the process by which the wind is used to generate electricity or mechanical power. Mechanical power can be used for such things as grinding grain or pumping water, or a generator can convert the mechanical power into electricity. Wind turns the blades of a turbine around a rotor, which spins a generator, which generates electricity.

Wind is another clean, renewable, inexhaustible source of energy. However, wind farms require miles of open land (**Figure 16-23**), are quite large and loud, and can be dangerous to flying animals.

Waste to Energy Energy recovery from waste is the conversion of nonrecyclable waste materials into usable heat, electricity, or fuel. This process is often called waste to energy. Confined and controlled burning of solid waste destined for landfills can recover energy from the waste-burning process. This generates a renewable energy source and reduces carbon emissions by offsetting the need for energy from fossil sources and reduces methane generation from landfills.

Reduce, Reuse, Recycle Nonrenewable mineral resources are used in electronic devices such as phones, computers, and televisions. Reducing consumption by fixing existing products is a sustainable resource use, as is recycling. Reuse and recycling reduce the need for extracting nonrenewable resources, and they also help keep material out of landfills. In 2020, the United States recycled 69 million tons of material that would otherwise have ended up in landfills.

Finding alternative building materials such as engineered timber and metal composites are becoming more common in new construction projects. Composite materials such as fiber-reinforced plastic and alternative metal alloys are gaining popularity in commercial construction as well. Composites can be more durable than steel, and repairing damaged composite components is often less costly and requires less heavy machinery.

SEP **Design Solutions** *What are two ways you can reduce your impact on the ecosystem in which you live?*

Managing Ecosystem Degradation and Habitat Loss

Land and habitat preservation can seem beyond an individual's ability, but it is not. There are many things that individuals can do, from reducing, reusing, and recycling their own materials to planting trees and butterfly gardens. On a larger scale, individuals can form groups that are actively involved at the local, national, and even global levels to help support environmental causes. It is important to protect ecosystems because they provide a number of important services. These **ecosystem services** can be divided into four categories:

- **Provisioning Services** These are the material benefits we get from ecosystems, such as food, fuel, water, and wood.

- **Supporting Services** These are the services that are necessary for all other ecosystem services, such as providing living spaces for species.

- **Regulating Services** These services include ecosystem processes such as water filtration by wetlands and crop pollination by insects.

- **Cultural Services** These are the intrinsic benefits we receive from ecosystems, such as natural spaces for recreational activities, as well as their aesthetic and inspirational aspects.

Reversing Land Degradation There are many rehabilitation strategies designed to address ecosystem degradation:

- development of large-scale composting programs to replenish organic soil to restore overgrazed land

- reforestation by planting trees to restore forests and habitats

- building terraces on steep land for crop cultivation to prevent soil erosion from rainfall runoff and increase water retention on the slopes of hills and mountains (**Figure 16-24**)

FIGURE 16-24 ▼
Building terraces allows farmers to cultivate rice on the steep hillsides in Mu Cang Chai, Vietnam.

Restoring Habitats In the United States, most of the protected land resources are undeveloped lands with various forms of protection status. These include national conservation areas, national parks, national forests, national wildlife refuges, and wildernesses. Worldwide, many biodiverse regions have been protected in ways that benefit local people. Ecosystems that are damaged by overuse need more than conservation measures to sustain biodiversity.

Ecological restoration is the process of renewing a natural ecosystem that has been degraded or destroyed. For example, artificial reefs are being used to help restore coral reefs damaged by human activity. Consider also the ecological restoration occurring in Louisiana's coastal wetlands. These ecosystems are being destroyed by upstream dams that hold back sediments that should replace sediment the marshes lose to the sea. Channels cut through the marshes for oil exploration and extraction have encouraged erosion, and the rising sea level threatens to drown existing plants. Restoration efforts now underway in Sabine National Wildlife Refuge have the goal of reversing some of those losses (**Figure 16-25a**).

As more roads and buildings continue to create barriers across natural lands, more habitats will become fragmented. This fragmentation forces animals to migrate to unfamiliar territory or prevents them from accessing their migratory routes entirely. In some places, engineers and ecologists have developed **wildlife corridors** designed to help local migratory species to navigate between human-constructed barriers such as roads and housing developments. These corridors, such as the one shown in **Figure 16-25b**, help to divert animals from crossing highways, busy roads, and other areas where their traditional migratory patterns intersect.

SEP **Design Solutions** *How might engineers have broken down the larger problem of habitat fragmentation into smaller problems to work on?*

FIGURE 16-25 ▸
Restoring marsh (a) in areas that had become open water increases animal abundance and overall species richness of the area. Wildlife corridors (b) have been designed to mitigate the effects of habitat fragmentation and allow animals to pass safely from area to area.

CITIZEN SCIENCE Documenting Earth's existing biodiversity and monitoring the effects of climate change and other human-caused factors are enormous undertakings. Scientists need to know the locations and sizes of a species' population in order to monitor changes in its range and numbers. Given the vast number of existing species, gathering such information is a task too big to be accomplished by scientists alone.

Fortunately, modern technology makes it easy to crowdsource data—to gather and organize information collected independently by a large number of individuals. Anyone with a camera can photograph organisms they encounter and then upload information about their sighting to an online database. Researchers then access this information.

Consider the iNaturalist project, an online social network for sharing information about biodiversity. The goal of iNaturalist is to foster a public appreciation of biodiversity, while also gathering scientifically valuable biodiversity data. The iNaturalist app allows users to upload photos of organisms they observe, along with the time and location of the observation. Users do not need to know exactly what they saw; in fact, they are encouraged to post unknown organisms.

Members of the iNaturalist community, which includes individuals with specialized expertise, collaborate in identifying the species in the uploaded photos. The resulting data are made available to anyone who is interested.

Since its launch in 2008, iNaturalist has collected more than 86 million observations documenting sightings of over 345,000 different species from locations throughout the world. To learn more about iNaturalist, visit iNaturalist.org or download the iNaturalist app.

Citizen scientists provide valuable data to scientists through their observations of the organisms around them.

Maintaining Biodiversity

Why should we protect biodiversity? From a selfish standpoint, doing so is an investment in our future. Healthy ecosystems are essential to the survival of our species. Other organisms produce the oxygen we breathe and the food we eat. They remove excess carbon dioxide from the air and decompose and detoxify wastes. Plants take up rain and hold soil in place, preventing erosion and reducing the risk of flooding. Wild species produce medically valuable compounds that we are still discovering. Wild relatives of crop plants are reservoirs of genetic diversity that plant breeders draw on to protect and improve crops.

There are ethical reasons to preserve biodiversity too. All living species are the result of an ongoing evolutionary process that stretches back billions of years. Each species has a unique combination of traits, and extinction removes that collection of traits from the world forever. The more diverse a biological system is, the greater is its capacity to recover from damage. This applies at all levels of life.

Go Online SIMULATION

Saving the Reefs Go online to evaluate solutions for the restoration of coral reef habitats.

16.4 REVIEW

1. **Identify** Describe two alternative energy resources.

2. **Synthesize** How might an increase in green spaces contribute to sustainability?

3. **Evaluate** What are some design considerations that would need to be evaluated when deciding on alternative materials or rehabilitation strategies?

MODELING HUMAN-CAUSED CHANGES IN THE ENVIRONMENT

SEP **Develop and Use a Model** How does a human-caused environmental change affect biodiversity?

Environmental change, including change due to human activity, can cause changes in populations, which affect a region's biodiversity. Human-caused habitat destruction can also disrupt ecosystems and threaten the survival of some species. In this activity, you will model how construction of a dam affects a species of beetles living in an area.

The construction of a dam drastically changes the environment around it.

Materials

- white poster board or sheet of paper
- color markers
- green beads (10)
- brown beads (10)
- yellow beads (10)
- blue construction paper
- scissors

Procedure

In this investigation, you will model the effects of a dam on a population of beetles living in a valley. The beetles will be represented by green, brown, and yellow beads.

1. On the white poster board, use the markers to draw an image of a river with banks on either side. One side of the river has a more desert-like habitat, while the other side of the river has a more forested habitat.

2. Distribute the different-colored beads onto the image. Each bead represents a group of similarly colored beetles. Do not put any beetles on the river. Place beads of all colors on both sides of the river. You do not need to use a specific number of each colored bead or even all the beads. If you think a bead of specific color would have an easier time surviving in a location, put more beads of that color there.

3. Count and record the number of beads on each side of the river. Keep the beads on the image, and do not move them.

A dam built downriver causes an artificial lake to form around the riverbed, causing areas to become flooded.

4. To model this lake, use the scissors to cut out the lake from the blue construction paper. You can make the lake whatever shape you want it to be.

5. Overlay the lake on the drawing of the river. To do this, start at one of the sides. As you place the lake on the river, remove the beads underneath it. This represents the beetles that died as a result of the formation of the lake.

6. Count and record the remaining beads on each side of the river.

Results and Analysis

1. **Represent Data** Make a data table that shows the number of each colored beetle on each side of the river before and after the dam was built.

2. **Analyze** How did the dam affect the beetle population? Consider the number and type of beetles affected.

3. **Analyze** How did the dam affect the biodiversity of the beetle population? Explain your reasoning.

4. **Predict** What changes might occur within the beetle populations on the drier side of the lake compared to those on the forested side of the lake after 5, 25, and 50 years?

5. **Predict** What might happen to the beetle populations if the river and the lake dried up?

TYING IT ALL TOGETHER
TRACKING TUSKLESS ELEPHANTS

WHY DO NEW SPECIES EMERGE WHILE OTHER SPECIES DISAPPEAR?

In this chapter, you learned how human activity can lead to changes in the biodiversity of an ecosystem. The Case Study described how ivory poaching has resulted in an increased proportion of tuskless female elephants in Mozambique's Gorongosa National Park. Savanna elephants first reproduce at about 12 years old and give birth every three to four years. The offspring of tuskless mothers are twice as likely to be female than male, and not a single tuskless male elephant has been seen in the park for over five decades. These clues directed scientists looking for the genetic origins of tusklessness to investigate X-linked genes involved in tooth and gum formation that may be lethal if inherited by male offspring.

In this activity, you will apply genetic and evolutionary principles to make predictions regarding an elephant population. Work individually or in a group to complete these steps.

Develop a Model

1. Suppose all the males in an elephant population have tusks and half of the females are tuskless. If the gene for tusklessness is linked to the X chromosome, recessive, and lethal to male offspring, how frequently would you expect the trait of tusklessness to occur in the population after three generations?

Construct an Explanation

2. Under what conditions could the presence of the gene for tusklessness in an elephant population lead to speciation?

3. Under what conditions could the presence of the gene for tusklessness in an elephant population lead to extinction?

4. African forest elephants, such as the one shown in **Figure 16-26**, take almost twice as long to reach reproductive age, with five to six years between offspring. The graph shows projected forest elephant population growth modeled using the natural birth and death rates of forest elephants in Dzanga, Central African Republic. How would the effects of poaching on forest elephant populations compare to savanna elephant populations? Explain your reasoning.

FIGURE 16-26 ▽

African forest elephants can be identified by their smaller size and downward-pointing tusks. The graph compares the projected growth rates of savanna and forest elephant populations.

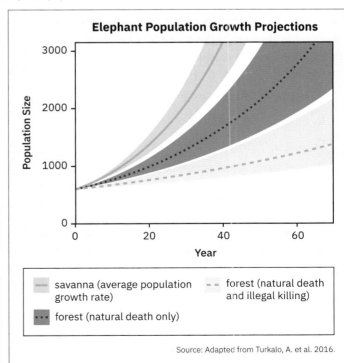

REVIEW KEY CONCEPTS

1. Identify Which situations can lead to speciation? Select all correct answers.

A. A physical barrier separates a population into two new populations.

B. Interbreeding takes place between individuals from two different populations.

C. Some individuals breed at a different time than others in the same population.

D. Increases in flooding change soil conditions in part of the habitat of a plant population.

E. Females from one population respond to courtship displays of males from a different population.

2. Contrast How is allopatric speciation different from sympatric speciation?

3. Describe Which phrase would best describe the fossil record of a line of related organisms that followed a punctuated equilibrium model of evolution?

A. small, incremental changes at a constant rate over long periods of time

B. long periods of little change interspersed with short periods of large changes

C. short periods of little change interspersed with long periods of small, incremental changes

D. short periods of small, incremental changes interspersed with long periods of large changes

4. Identify Which human impact on biodiversity most directly prevents wildlife from accessing resources needed for their survival?

A. capture of animals for the pet trade

B. introduction of nonnative species to new areas

C. degradation and fragmentation of natural areas

D. overharvesting of species through hunting and fishing

5. Predict Which factors would increase the vulnerability of a species to extinction? Select all correct answers.

A. The reproduction rate of the species is very high.

B. The species is preyed upon by an invasive species.

C. The species is endemic to a small geographic area.

D. The species can easily migrate to new geographic areas.

E. The species is harvested by humans for food, medicine, or other uses.

6. Explain Why does the number of species on Earth increase after a mass extinction event ends?

7. Identify What factors contribute to a country's per capita ecological footprint? Select all correct answers.

A. carbon emissions

B. form of government

C. natural resource usage

D. total land area

E. waste produced

8. Cause and Effect Which outcomes would be expected if humans significantly reduced greenhouse gas emissions? Select all correct answers.

A. Acid rain would diminish.

B. The rate of global warming would decrease.

C. Fewer renewable energy sources would be used.

D. Changes in rainfall and storm patterns would be observed.

E. The ecological footprints of developed countries would increase.

9. Classify Identify whether each action contributes to sustainable or unsustainable living.

• reducing food waste

• recycling electronic components

• leaving lights on when not in use

• converting natural areas into strip mines

• spraying crops with large amounts of pesticides

• switching from nonrenewable to renewable energy sources

• switching from biodegradable to plastic packaging

• using irrigation systems that deliver water directly to plant roots

10. Identify Which strategies can help reverse land degradation and deforestation? Select all correct answers.

A. using terraced land for growing crops

B. encouraging vehicle off-roading activities

C. opening public lands to cattle and sheep grazing

D. restricting commercial development using zoning laws

E. finding alternatives to wood in manufacturing and construction

CRITICAL THINKING

11. Justify A biologist hypothesizes that adaptive radiation of predator animals will follow an increase in prey diversification. Does this seem to be a reasonable hypothesis? Explain.

12. Predict Climate change is expected to increase the rate at which species migrate into new ecosystems. Explain what effect this will have on the extinction rate of native populations in those ecosystems.

13. Relate What is the relationship between industrialization and habitat destruction? How important is it for people to understand this relationship? Explain your reasoning.

14. NOS Science Knowledge What social and economic benefits do humans enjoy as a result of preserving biodiversity?

MATH AND ENGLISH LANGUAGE ARTS CONNECTIONS

Read the following passage. Use evidence from the passage to answer the question.

As land plants evolved from aquatic ancestors, they benefitted from several key innovations and subsequent adaptive radiations. The most recent of these innovations was the evolution of flowers. Flowers are reproductive structures that provide attractions for pollinators as well as protection for fertilized embryos. Data show the relative distribution of species belonging to the flowering plants compared to those belonging to nonflowering plant groups.

Plant type	Terrestrial plant groups	Relative distribution (%)
nonflowering plants	bryophytes and others	10.3
	gymnosperms	0.3
flowering plants	angiosperms	89.4

1. Evaluate a Science or Technical Text Evaluate whether the data support the claim in the text that flowers were a key innovation during the evolution of land plants. Explain your reasoning.

2. Argue From Evidence Using facts provided in the table, state and support a claim about the importance of sustaining biodiversity in ecosystems.

Facts about Freshwater Ecosystems	
contain 0.01% of Earth's water	support 33% of vertebrates and 10% of all animal species
occupy < 1% of Earth's surface	trap and break down pollutants, toxins, and heavy metals

Read the following passage. Use evidence from the passage to answer the question.

Before Europeans colonized North America, the Florida panther (*Puma concolor coryi*) was abundant throughout the southeastern United States. Currently, scientists estimate that only 120 to 230 adult panthers remain in the wild, with their current range restricted to southern Florida. In the 36 years from 1981 to 2017, the leading cause of death for Florida panthers was vehicular collisions. Before 2000, the rate of panther roadkill was four or fewer per year. Since 2000, the rate has increased substantially, with a high of 34 in 2016.

3. Cite Textual Evidence Propose a solution to aid in the restoration efforts for the Florida panther. Cite information from the text to support your answer.

► REVISIT HUMMINGBIRD EVOLUTION

Gather Evidence In this chapter, you have seen how changing environmental conditions lead to an increase in the individuals of some species, the emergence of new species, and the extinction of other species. In Section 16.1, you learned about the mechanisms of speciation. In Section 16.2, you learned about factors that lead to extinction. In Sections 16.3 and 16.4, you learned about the impact humans have on the environment and ways that this impact can be reduced.

1. How are changing environmental conditions affecting populations of hummingbirds?

2. What other questions do you have about how hummingbirds became adapted to their environment? What else do you need to know to understand hummingbird speciation?

EVOLUTION AND CHANGING ENVIRONMENTS

CHAPTER 14
EVIDENCE FOR EVOLUTION
How do we know how species have evolved?

- Common ancestry and biological evolution are supported by multiple lines of evidence including the fossil record, developmental patterns, anatomical structures, and DNA sequences.

- Fossils are typically found in sedimentary rock. The most recent fossils are found above layers that contain older fossils.

- Homologous structures are derived from a common ancestor. Analogous structures evolved independently in different lineages.

- Evolutionary relationships can be determined by comparing amino acid or nucleotide sequences from different organisms.

CHAPTER 15
THE THEORY OF EVOLUTION
Why do populations evolve over time?

- Natural selection is one process that drives evolution. The four principles of natural selection are competition, heritable genetic variation, overproduction, and adaptation.

- Natural selection acts on genetic variations. An advantageous trait helps individuals survive and reproduce.

- Directional selection, stabilizing selection, and disruptive selection are three ways that natural selection can change the distribution of a trait in a population.

- Other mechanisms that can lead to the evolution of populations include gene flow, genetic drift, and sexual selection.

CHAPTER 16
SURVIVAL IN CHANGING ENVIRONMENTS
Why do new species emerge while other species disappear?

- Changes in environmental conditions may result in population increases, speciation, or extinction.

- Engineering solutions, such as optimizing renewable resources, can be used to reduce the negative effects of human activities on the environment and biodiversity.

Go Online	**VIRTUAL INVESTIGATION**

Hummingbirds on the Move
How did hummingbirds become adapted to their environments?

Go into the field and gather evidence about hummingbird adaptations.

HOW DID HUMMINGBIRDS BECOME ADAPTED TO THEIR ENVIRONMENTS?

Argue From Evidence In this unit, you learned that evolution occurs in populations of species over time as they adapt to changes in their environment. The diversity of hummingbirds is one example of how certain species are able to rapidly expand into open ecological niches.

Using DNA data, scientists constructed a family tree for hummingbirds and their closest relatives. They determined that the branch leading to hummingbirds arose about 40 million to 50 million years ago. That is when they split from their sister group, the swifts and treeswifts. Scientists think that this likely occurred in Europe or Asia. Hummingbird fossils that date back 30 million to 45 million years ago have been found in Germany, France, and Poland.

If hummingbirds first evolved in Eurasia, how did they get to South America? Scientists hypothesize that ancestral hummingbirds likely migrated across the Bering Land Bridge, which once connected Asia to Alaska. They traveled from there down to what is now South America. Over the course of 22 million years—a relatively short period of evolutionary time—a common ancestor gave rise to the 338 species of hummingbirds that exist today. Hummingbirds returned to North America around 12 million years ago, and others began to inhabit the Caribbean around five million years ago. Research indicates that new species of hummingbirds continue to arise, though at a much slower pace than they have in the past. Scientists estimate that over the next several million years, the total number of hummingbird species could double as they maximize the number of ecological niches available to them.

 Claim Make a claim about how climate change may affect hummingbird speciation in the future.

 Evidence Use the evidence you gathered throughout the unit to support your claim.

 Reasoning To help illustrate your claim, develop a model that illustrates how changes in a hummingbird's environment could affect its ability to survive and reproduce.

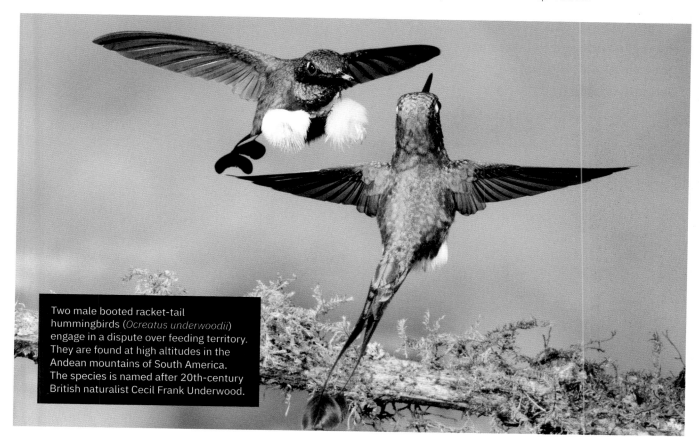

Two male booted racket-tail hummingbirds (*Ocreatus underwoodii*) engage in a dispute over feeding territory. They are found at high altitudes in the Andean mountains of South America. The species is named after 20th-century British naturalist Cecil Frank Underwood.

LABORATORY SAFETY AND PROCEDURES

Working Safely in the Laboratory

Working in the lab will help you master both the content of biology and the processes of science. But the laboratory can be a dangerous place if safety rules are not followed. You must be responsible for your safety and the safety of others.

General Safety Rules Study these symbols and the warnings or guidelines they represent in the lab. Look for them in each lab to indicate a safety risk to you and your fellow students where you should use extra caution.

| Eye Safety | Lab Clothing | Skin Safety | Fire Safety |

| Sharps Safety | Glassware Safety | Chemical Safety | Biohazard Safety |

| Plant Safety | Animal Safety | Cleanup Handwashing | Cleanup Disposal |

1. Thoroughly read each lab several times before you begin. Follow instructions exactly. Ask your teacher if you have questions.

2. Only perform authorized activities. Do not work in the lab or handle equipment without supervision.

3. Use safety equipment specified in each lab.
   - Wear safety goggles when working with chemicals, burners, or any substance that might get into your eyes.
   - Wear the appropriate gloves when handling any toxic or hazardous agents.
   - Wear a lab apron or lab coat when working with chemicals or heated substances.
   - When using lab equipment and chemicals, keep your hands away from your body, mouth, eyes, and face.

4. Never eat or drink in the lab. Do not inhale chemicals or taste them.

5. Use caution with liquids. If a spill occurs, immediately ask your teacher for the proper cleanup procedure. Never pour chemicals or other substances into a sink or trash can.

6. Tie back chin-length or longer hair.

7. Remove or tie back any loose clothing or jewelry that can hang down and come in contact with chemicals or a flame. Avoid wearing sandals or other open-toed shoes.

8. Know the locations of safety showers and eyewashes and how to use them.

9. Wash your hands with soap and water after performing an investigation.

Injury	Response
cuts and abrasions	Stop the bleeding by applying direct pressure. Call your teacher immediately.
fainting	Leave the person lying down. Loosen any tight clothing. Call your teacher immediately. Keep people away.
solid foreign matter in the eye	Close or cover the eye. Call your teacher immediately.
poisoning	Note the suspected substance. Call your teacher immediately.
spills on skin	Flush with large amounts of water or use the safety shower. Call your teacher immediately.
chemical splashes in the eye	Use the eyewash to flush with plenty of water. Call your teacher immediately.

Heating and Fire Safety

1. Maintain a clean work area and keep all materials away from flames. Store backpacks, coats, and other personal items away from the immediate lab bench area.

2. Use only heat-resistant glassware for heating. Prior to using glassware, check for chips or cracks and notify your teacher of any damaged glassware. Never heat glassware that is not thoroughly dry. Use a wire screen to protect glassware from any flame.

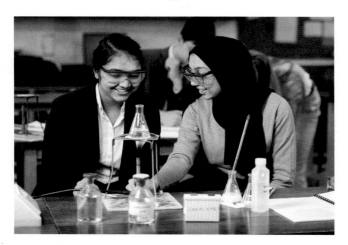

3. Never reach across a flame.

4. Ask your teacher how to use a Bunsen burner. Never leave a heat source unattended.

5. Point the opening of a test tube or bottle that is being heated away from you and others.

6. Never heat a liquid in a closed container. The increase in pressure may cause the container to break, injuring you or others.

7. Hot glass looks like cold glass. Before touching a container that has been heated, hold the back of your hand close to the container. If you can feel heat, the container is too hot to handle. Use a clamp, tongs, heat-resistant gloves, or a hot pad to move the container.

8. If a fire breaks out or your clothing catches fire, smother it with a fire blanket or roll on the ground. NEVER RUN.

Working With Chemicals and Tools

1. Use materials only from properly labeled containers. Read chemical labels carefully.

2. Discard extra chemicals as your teacher directs. Notify your teacher if chemicals are splashed or spilled.

3. When diluting acids, always add acid to water. Never pour water into acid.

4. Do not discard matches or other solid materials in the sink.

5. Use a lubricant when inserting glass tubing or thermometers through stoppers. Protect your hand with a paper towel or a folded cloth.

6. Be careful when handling sharp objects such as pins and dissecting probes.

Handling Living Organisms

1. Treat all living things with respect. Your teacher will instruct you on how to handle each organism that is brought into the classroom. Do not touch any organism without permission. Many plants are poisonous or have thorns, and even tame animals may bite or scratch if alarmed.

2. Animals should be handled only when necessary. If an animal is excited or frightened, pregnant, feeding, or with its young, special handling is required.

3. Treat all microorganisms as if they were harmful. Use antiseptic procedure as directed by your teacher when working with microbes. Dispose of microbes as your teacher directs.

4. Clean your hands thoroughly after handling any organism or object that has been in contact with an organism.

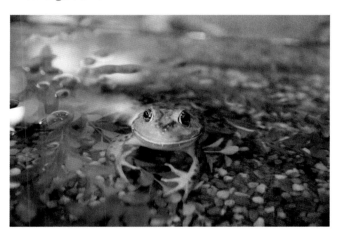

5. Wear gloves when handling any animal. Report animal bites, scratches, or stings to your teacher at once.

Cleaning Up the Laboratory

1. After working in the lab, clean your work area, and return all equipment to its proper place.

2. Turn off all faucets and burners. Check that you have turned off the gas jet as well as the burner.

3. Dispose of chemicals and other materials as directed by your teacher.

4. Wash your hands thoroughly before leaving the lab.

Practice *Describe how you and your classmates would stay safe in each of the following situations.*

1. An investigation displays these safety symbols at the beginning:

2. Your team is to design your own plan to test various cleaning materials in a forensics investigation.

3. Your team is about to carry out an investigation into the effect of heat on a few chemical reactions.

4. One of your teammates accidently cuts a finger with a knife while cutting carrots for an investigation.

5. It is the period before lunch, and you are testing the breakdown rates of digestive enzymes on various food materials, including mints, crackers, and small cakes.

Skills for Using Laboratory Equipment

The laboratory equipment you will encounter in biology investigations may require a little practice to help you make clear observations and collect useful data.

Using a Compound Microscope Review the parts of a typical microscope used in biology investigations and their functions for the best viewing experience and care of the microscope.

Clean the lenses with lens paper only. Other types of paper may scratch the lens. Be careful not to touch the lenses with your fingers, which can leave smudges.

When finished viewing, lower the stage, click the low power objective into position, and remove the slide. Switch off any light source and cover the microscope.

1. **Eyepiece** Contains a magnifying lens you look through. Keep both eyes open as you look through the eyepiece to avoid eyestrain.

2. **Arm** Supports the body tube. Place the arm toward you during viewing. To move the microscope, grasp the microscope here and place another hand under the base.

3. **Stage** Supports the slide. Place the area of the slide to be viewed over the hole and secure the slide with the stage clips.

4. **Coarse Adjustment Knob** Focuses the image under low power. Use this adjustment knob first to raise the low-power or shortest objective about 2 cm above the stage before placing the object on the stage. Then use this knob to bring the object into focus.

5. **Fine Adjustment Knob** Sharpens the image under high and low magnification. Only use this adjustment when the high-power or longest objective is in place. Using the coarse adjustment knob can easily crash the high-power objective into the slide, breaking the slide and damaging the objective.

6. **Base** Supports the microscope. Place one hand under the base while the other is on the arm when moving the microscope.

7. **Body Tube** Connects the eyepiece to the revolving nosepiece.

8. **Revolving Nosepiece** Holds and turns the objectives into viewing position. Gently turn the revolving nosepiece in either direction to click an objective into place.

9. **Objectives** Allow varying powers of magnification with lenses. Choose the low-power or shortest objective first. After using the coarse and then fine adjustment to focus on the slide, turn the revolving nosepiece to change to medium or high power.

10. **Stage Clips** Holds a slide in place. Gently push each end of the slide under the clips.

11. **Diaphragm** Regulates the amount of light passing up toward the eyepiece. Use the lever or dial to open or close the diaphragm.

12. **Light Source** Produces light or reflects light up toward the eyepiece. Adjust the source to direct as much light as possible through the lenses.

Stereomicroscopes These microscopes are designed to view larger specimens at lower magnification (usually 6× to 50×) and are common in biology laboratories. They have many of the same features as compound microscopes. The main difference is that they have binocular eyepieces for viewing with both eyes at the same time for greater depth perception.

Making a Wet Mount Slide

1. Obtain a clean microscope slide and a coverslip.

2. Using tweezers, place the specimen in the middle of the slide. The specimen must be thin enough for light to pass through it.

3. Place a drop of water on the specimen.

4. Hold a clean coverslip by its edges and place it at one edge of the drop of water. Slowly lower the coverslip until it lies flat on top of the specimen and the water. Lowering the coverslip from one side to the other minimizes or eliminates air bubbles under the coverslip. If air bubbles are present, gently tap the surface of the coverslip with a pencil eraser. You will not be able to see a specimen through an air bubble.

5. If you have too much water on the slide, touch the edge of a paper towel to the edge of the coverslip. This will draw off extra water, force air out of the mount, and further flatten the wet mount.

coverslip ———— lower slowly

Staining a Wet Mount Specimen
A stain may be added to a wet mount slide to make the specimen on the slide more visible. Follow these steps to stain a wet mount.

1. Collect a drop of stain with a dropper or pipette.

2. Add one drop of stain at the edge of the coverslip.

— dropper
— slide
— coverslip

3. Hold a small piece of paper towel or lens paper with forceps. Touch the paper to the edge of the coverslip opposite the stain. The paper causes the stain to be drawn under the coverslip, staining the specimen.

paper towel or lens paper

Using a Graduated Cylinder
A graduated cylinder is used to measure the volume of a liquid. A graduated cylinder is a cylindrical container marked with lines from bottom to top. Most have lines indicating milliliters (mL), although the volume of graduated cylinders ranges from 10 mL to 4 liters (L). To use a graduated cylinder properly, follow these steps.

1. Place the cylinder on a flat, level surface.

2. Move your head so that your eye is level with the surface of the liquid.

3. Read the mark closest to the liquid level. In glass and some plastic cylinders, the surface of the liquid forms a curve called a meniscus. Read the mark closest to the bottom of the meniscus to determine the volume in a glass cylinder.

eye

Using a Triple Beam Balance A triple beam balance is used to find the mass of objects in grams (g). On one side of the balance is the pan where the object to be massed is placed. The other side of the balance is made up of a set of beams ending in a pointer that points toward a scale. Each beam has a mass, or rider, that slides along the beam. When the pointer is aligned with 0 on the scale, the masses on the beams equal the mass of the object on the pan. Follow these steps to properly mass an object.

1. Set the balance to zero by sliding all the riders back to the zero point.

2. Check that the pointer on the right swings an equal distance above and below the zero point on the scale. If the swing is unequal, turn the adjustment knob until the swing is equal.

3. Place the object to be massed on the pan. Slide the rider with the largest mass along its beam until the pointer drops below zero. Then move that rider back a notch. Repeat the process on the second beam.

4. The 1-gram slider goes from 0 to 10 g. Marks between each whole number show portions of a gram. Each mark represents 0.1 g. Push the 1-g slider until the pointer points directly at the zero on the scale.

5. Add the masses indicated on the three beams to find the mass of the object. To get the most precise measurement, count the increments past the nearest whole number on the 1-g slider. If the mass is pointing between two marks, add a value of 0.05 to your measurement.

Massing Chemicals Never pour chemicals directly on the pan of any scale. Instead, follow these steps:

1. To find the mass of an empty beaker, place it on the scale and wait until the mass is displayed.

2. Press the tare button. The display will reset to zero.

3. Pour the dry or liquid chemical into the beaker. The display will show the mass of the chemical without including the mass of the beaker.

   - If you remove the beaker to add the chemical, the display will show the mass of the beaker as a negative number. When you place the beaker containing the chemical back onto the scale, the display will show only the mass of the chemical in the beaker.

If you are using a balance, calculate the mass of the chemical by subtracting the mass of the empty beaker from the combined mass of the beaker and chemical.

Practice *Check your understanding of how to use laboratory equipment.*

1. Why should you use a compound microscope's coarse adjustment knob only with the low-power objective?

2. Why would you place the coverslip by its edges onto the water drop instead of dropping it down from the top?

3. Why is it important to read the measurement of fluid in a graduated cylinder directly from the side?

4. How would a measurement be affected if you did not zero out the riders and the pointer of a triple beam balance before taking a measurement?

5. Why should you mass dry chemicals by putting them in a beaker first instead of directly on the scale?

DATA ANALYSIS GUIDE

Experimental Design and Data Collection

Scientists investigate natural phenomena by conducting experiments. Often, the scientist has a question about the phenomenon. The question could relate to the phenomenon's cause or effect or what happens during the event. Pondering the phenomenon, the scientist develops a *hypothesis,* or prediction about the answer to the question. Then, the scientist outlines an experimental plan or series of actions that will determine if the prediction is correct.

Plans allow scientists to collect data in organized ways that can be analyzed, such as in **Figure 1**. In a scientific experiment, the *independent variable* is a factor that differs among the experimental groups. For example, a scientist might apply different amounts of nitrogen per hectare (2.47 acres) to groups of crop plants to investigate how this nutrient affects plant height. In this experiment, the amount of nitrogen the plants receive is the independent variable. The height of the plants is the *dependent variable*; it is the observed or measured result of the experiment. The scientist's hypothesis predicts how the independent variable will affect the dependent variable.

Figure 1 A scientist measures the growth of plants in both the experimental group and the control group as evidence for the conclusion drawn from the data.

Another part of an experiment is a *control group*. In **Table 1**, the group of plants that received 0.0 kg/ha of nitrogen is the control group. Including a control group allows a scientist to compare the experimental groups, in which the independent variable was altered, to the control group, in which the independent variable was not altered.

Table 1. Amount of Nitrogen and Plant Growth

Nitrogen applied (kg/ha)	Plant height (cm)
0.0	27.4
37.5	37.2
75.0	41.9
112.5	42.3
150.0	43.5
187.5	44.1

Factors other than the independent variable should ideally be kept constant across all groups in an experiment. For example, the plant groups used in the nitrogen study should all receive the same amount of rainfall, sunlight, and nutrients. This type of consistency, however, does not always occur. So, it is crucial for scientists to identify possible sources of error in an experiment. Sources of error include mistakes made by humans, issues with equipment used to make measurements, and natural variations that cannot be avoided.

One way to account for unwanted variation in scientific experiments is to repeat the experiment many times. In the nitrogen study, the scientist would probably study many large areas of plants instead of only a few small areas. Using a large sample size decreases the likelihood that the results of the experiment happened by chance.

In the process of conducting experiments, scientists record observations and measurements called data. Scientists use tools such as data tables and computer programs to organize data. This organization makes it possible for scientists to analyze data from an experiment and draw conclusions about its results. **Table 1** shows how data from the nitrogen experiment mentioned earlier might be organized. The changes in the independent variable and dependent variables are clearly indicated, and the units of measurement are included.

The data collected during an experiment may be qualitative or quantitative. The data collected in the nitrogen experiment is *quantitative data* because it is expressed as numbers. Data that is not easily expressed as numbers, such as the data in **Table 2**, is called qualitative data.

Table 2. Colors of Common Substances

Substance	Color
ammonia	off-white
salt water	clear
water	clear
milk	white
lemon juice	yellow

Practice *Consider how a scientist would carry out an investigation of the effects of carbonic acid on a species of algae.*

The scientist wants to know how increasing levels of carbonic acid in ocean water affect the number of algae present in the water. Write a plan for this investigation that includes an independent variable, a dependent variable, a control group, and one or more experimental groups. Draw one or more data tables that the scientist could use to organize observations or measurements collected in the investigation.

Units of Measurement

Quantitative data collected during an experiment should always contain units of measurement. Including units allows people to understand the meaning of the data and possibly repeat the experiment. Scientists use a system of units called the International System (or SI from the French *Système International*) to ensure that scientists around the world use consistent units of measurement. SI, which is based on the metric system of units, was developed to replace multiple measurement systems with a single, standardized system.

Table 3 shows the seven basic units of the SI system. The base unit for mass is kilogram. The prefix *kilo-* means 1000, or 10^3. So, a kilogram is equivalent to 1000 grams. When using a graduated cylinder to measure volume, you might record your measurements in milliliters (mL). The prefix *milli-* means 0.001, or 10^{-3}. So, 1 milliliter is 1/1000th of a liter. **Table 4** shows other prefixes used with SI units.

Table 3. Base Units of the SI System

Measurement	Base unit
length	meter (m)
mass	kilogram (kg)
time	second (s)
electric current	ampere (A)
temperature	kelvin (K)
light intensity	candela (cd)
amount of substance	mole (mol)

Table 4. Prefixes Used with SI Base Units

Prefix	Symbol	Meaning	Order of magnitude
giga-	G	1,000,000,000	10^9
mega-	M	1,000,000	10^6
kilo-	k	1000	10^3
hecto-	h	100	10^2
deka-	da	10	10^1
	base unit	1	10^0
deci-	d	0.1	10^{-1}
centi-	c	0.01	10^{-2}
milli-	m	0.001	10^{-3}
micro-	μ	0.000001	10^{-6}
nano-	n	0.000000001	10^{-9}

Practice *Convert each measurement below by writing the equivalent measurement for the unit that is shown.*

1. 100 km = _____ Gm

2. 61976.569 cm = _____ nm

3. 89 mm = _____ hm

4. 30856775814913673 m = _____ Mm

5. 16.09344 hm = _____ cm

6. 149.5981 Gm = _____ km

7. 5.5 km = _____ mm

8. 2.5426924 cm = _____ dam

9. 2.2633485173216473 mm = _____ μm

10. 5 nm = _____ km

Scientific Notation

The numbers we must work with in scientific measurements are often very large or very small; thus it is convenient to express them using powers of 10. For example, the number 1,300,000 can be expressed as 1.3×10^6, which means multiply 1.3 by 10 six times, or

$$1.3 \times 10^6 = 1.3 \times 10 \times 10 \times 10 \times 10 \times 10 \times 10$$

$10^6 = 1$ million

A number written in scientific notation always has the form:

a number (between 1 and 10) times
the appropriate power of 10

To represent a large number such as 20,541 in scientific notation, we must move the decimal point in such a way as to achieve a number between 1 and 10 and then multiply the result by a power of 10 to compensate for moving the decimal point. In this case, we must move the decimal point four places to the left.

$$2\,0\,5\,4\,1$$
$$4\ 3\ 2\ 1$$

to give a number between 1 and 10.

$$2.0541$$

To compensate for moving the decimal point four places to the left, we must multiply by 10^4. Thus

$$20{,}541 = 2.0541 \times 10^4$$

As another example, the number 1985 can be expressed as 1.985×10^3. To end up with the number 1.985, which is between 1 and 10, we had to move the decimal point three places to the left. To compensate for that, we must multiply by 10^3. Some other examples are given below.

Number	Exponential notation
5.6	5.6×10^0 or 5.6×1
39	3.9×10^1
943	9.43×10^2
1126	1.126×10^3

So far, we have considered numbers greater than 1. How do we represent a number such as 0.0034 in exponential notation? First, to achieve a number between 1 and 10, we start with 0.0034 and move the decimal point three places to the right.

$$0.0034$$
$$1\,2\,3$$

This yields 3.4. Then, to compensate for moving the decimal point to the right, we must multiply by a power of 10 with a negative exponent, in this case, 10^{-3}. Thus

$$0.0034 = 3.4 \times 10^{-3}$$

In a similar way, the number 0.00000014 can be written as 1.4×10^{-7}, because going from 0.00000014 to 1.4 requires moving the decimal point seven places to the right.

In dealing with exponents, you must first learn to enter them into your calculator. First the number is keyed in and then the exponent. There is a special key that must be pressed just before the exponent is entered. This key is often labeled EE or exp. For example, the number 1.56×10^6 is entered as follows:

Press	Display	
1.56	1.56	
EE or exp	1.56	00
6	1.56	06

To enter a number with a negative exponent, use the change-of-sign key, usually marked $+/-$, after entering the exponent number. For example, the number 7.54×10^{-3} is entered as follows:

Press	Display	
7.54	7.54	
EE or exp	7.54	00
3	7.54	03
$+/-$	7.54	-03

Once a number with an exponent is entered into your calculator, the mathematical operations are performed exactly the same as with a "regular" number. For example, the numbers 1.0×10^3 and 1.0×10^2 are multiplied as follows:

Press	Display	
1.0	1.0	
EE or exp	1.0	00
3	1.0	03
$\times$	1	03
1.0	1.0	
EE or exp	1.0	00
2	1.0	02
$=$	1	05

Practice *Complete the table by converting each measurement to either scientific notation or the equivalent number.*

Number	Number in scientific notation
0.000045	
1,750,539	
	3.92174×10^5
	1.8×10^{-4}
	8.43×10^{-8}

Accuracy and Precision

Accuracy refers to how close a measurement is to the accepted value. For example, a tool used to check the accuracy of triple beam balances might have a mass of exactly 50.0 g. The closer a measurement is to this accepted mass, the greater the accuracy of the measurement. Precision refers to how consistent a set of measurements is. The first target in **Figure 2** represents both accuracy and precision. The darts on this target are on the bullseye (accurate) and close together (precise).

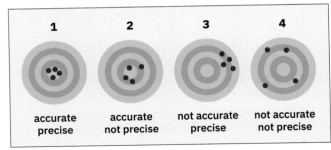

1	2	3	4
accurate precise	accurate not precise	not accurate precise	not accurate not precise

▲ **Figure 2** The targets represent varying degrees of accuracy and precision.

In a similar way, **Table 5** shows data collected by group 1, which are both accurate and precise. Group 1's measurements are very close to the accepted mass of 50.0 g, and they are very similar to one another. The next target represents less precision than the first. Similarly, group 2's data are less precise than group 1's data. The third target, like group 3's data, reflects precision but not accuracy. All the measurements are similar, but they are far from the accepted value of 50.0 g. The fourth target and the data gathered by group 4 show neither accuracy nor precision; the data are neither correct nor consistent.

Table 5. Measurements of Mass

Group 1: Mass (g)	Group 2: Mass (g)	Group 3: Mass (g)	Group 4: Mass (g)
50.1	48.6	75.0	12.1
50.0	49.5	74.9	80.4
49.9	50.3	75.1	73.2
49.8	51.1	75.0	24.6
50.2	47.0	75.2	19.7

One way to determine the accuracy of a measurement is to calculate percent error, which can be found using the following formula:

$$\% \text{ Error} = \frac{|\text{ experimental value} - \text{accepted value }|}{\text{accepted value}} \times 100\%$$

For example, if the accepted value was 50.0 g and a measurement gathered during an experiment (the experimental value) was 49.3 g, the percent error would be calculated as follows:

$$\% \text{ Error} = \frac{|\ 49.3 \text{ g} - 50.0 \text{ g}|}{50.0 \text{ g}} \times 100\%$$

$\% \text{ Error} = 1.4\%$

Thus, the percent error is 1.4 percent, which is small, indicating an accurate measurement.

Practice *Four groups conducted multiple trials to collect data of an object that has an accepted value of 80.00 g.*
Determine which group's data were both accurate and precise, which group's were accurate but not precise, which group's were precise but not accurate, and which group's were neither accurate nor precise. Explain your reasoning.

Group 1: Mass (g)	Group 2: Mass (g)	Group 3: Mass (g)	Group 4: Mass (g)
19.36	120.00	80.16	77.76
128.64	119.84	80.00	79.20
117.12	120.16	79.84	80.48
39.36	120.00	79.68	81.76
31.52	120.32	80.32	75.20

Graph Construction and Analysis

Once data from an experiment have been collected and organized, the data are analyzed to determine what conclusions can be made. This analysis may involve mathematical calculations, graphing, or statistical analysis.

Most graphs follow certain guidelines. For one, a graph has both an x-axis and a y-axis. The number values on both axes may be positive or negative. The title of a graph should describe the data displayed on the graph. To determine the scale for each axis, it is useful to identify the maximum and minimum values in the data set. For example, the minimum value in the first column of **Table 6** is 15 seconds, and the maximum value is 90 seconds. Thus, as shown in **Figure 3**, the scale for the x-axis extends from 0 to 100 and is divided by increments of 20. The scale for the y-axis is determined in the same way.

Table 6. Exercise and Heart Rate

Time exercising (s)	Heart rate (bps)
30	74
15	71
60	86
45	82
75	91
90	99

▼ **Figure 3** The range of measurements represented by the collected data helps determine the scale of each axis.

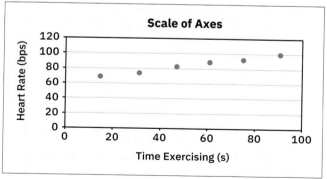

A graph may have multiple y-axes or multiple x-axes. **Figure 4** shows a graph with two y-axes. When interpreting this type of graph, pay careful attention to which set of points corresponds to which axis. On this graph, the purple line corresponds to the scale shown on the right y-axis. The orange line corresponds to the scale shown on the left y-axis.

▼ **Figure 4** Each axis on a graph shows different scales.

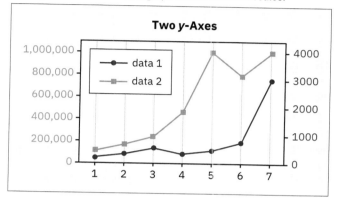

When points are plotted on a graph, a mathematical relationship between the points may be present. An equation may be used to show the relationship among the points. **Figure 5** shows a graph where the points form a straight line. The equation for a straight line (a linear equation) can be represented in the general form

$$y = mx + b$$

where y is the dependent variable, x is the independent variable, m is the slope, and b is the intercept with the y-axis.

To illustrate the characteristics of a linear equation, $y = 3x + 4$ is plotted in **Figure 5**. For this equation, $m = 3$ and $b = 4$. Note that the y-intercept occurs when $x = 0$. In this case the y-intercept is 4, as can be seen from the equation ($b = 4$).

The slope of a straight line is defined as the ratio of the rate of change in y to that in x:

$$m = \Delta y / \Delta x$$

For the equation $y = 3x + 4$, y changes three times as fast as x (because x has a coefficient of 3). So the slope in this case is 3. This can be verified from the graph. For the triangle shown in **Figure 5**,

$$\Delta y = 50 - 14 = 36 \text{ and } \Delta x = 15 - 3 = 12$$

So

$$\text{slope} = \Delta y / \Delta x = 36 / 12 = 3$$

This example illustrates a general method for obtaining the slope of a line from the graph of that line. Simply draw a triangle with one side parallel to the y-axis and the other side parallel to the x-axis, as shown in **Figure 5**. Then determine the lengths of the sides to get Δy and Δx, respectively, and compute the ratio $\Delta y / \Delta x$.

▼ **Figure 5** Direct relationships occur when both variables increase or decrease at the same time.

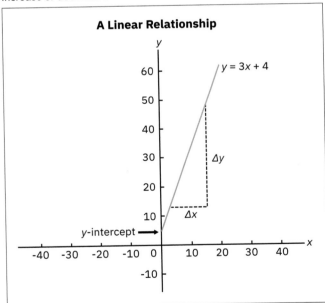

The relationship shown in **Figure 5** is also a direct relationship because, as one variable increases, the other variable increases. A direct relationship is also present when one variable decreases and the other decreases.

In an inverse relationship, as one variable increases, the other decreases, or vice versa. **Figure 6** shows a line that represents an inverse relationship. Sometimes the points on a graph do not form a neat line. But it may be appropriate to find a line of best fit. **Figure 6** shows a scatter plot with a line of best fit. When finding a line of best fit, it is also possible to calculate an R^2 value. This value tells you how well the line of best fit works as a predictor of y (if given x).

▼ **Figure 6** A line of best fit is similar to an average of the data.

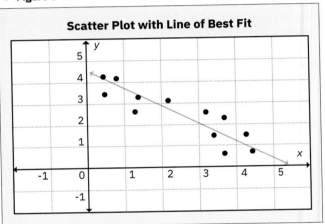

Sometimes, there is a nonlinear relationship between the points on a graph. **Figure 7** shows such a graph. An equation may still be used to represent the relationship between the points, but the equation is different from the equation used to represent linear relationships.

▼ **Figure 7** A line of best fit is similar to an average of the data.

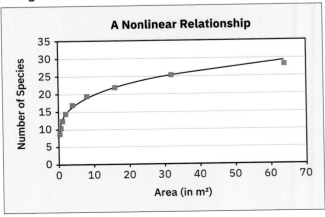

Another type of graph used to represent data is a bar graph. This type of graph is best for data that can be placed in separate groups or categories. **Figure 8** shows a bar graph. The lines extending from the ends of the bars are error bars. These shows the calculated error associated with each data point. The error may represent a standard or range shown by the data or a degree of uncertainty.

Error may also be represented as a number plus or minus some amount. For example, the range of values for the 46.6 ± 5.0 can be calculated as follows:

$$\text{maximum: } 46.6 + 5.0 = 51.6$$
$$\text{minimum: } 46.6 - 5.0 = 41.6$$

▼ **Figure 8** Possible errors related to data collection may be shown by the extensions on the bars.

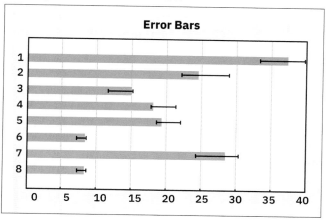

In some cases, the scales on the *x*-axis and/or *y*-axis may be in the form of a logarithmic scale. This means the values on the scale represent powers of 10. **Figure 9** shows a graph that uses a logarithmic scale on the *y*-axis. This type of graph is best for representing very large or very small numbers or numbers that vary by large amounts. Using a logarithmic scale can also make it easier to identify trends on a graph. In this case, the graph shows how, at first, the population size grows slowly and then grows very quickly over regular time intervals.

▼ **Figure 9** Very small and very large numbers are often shown with a logarithmic scale.

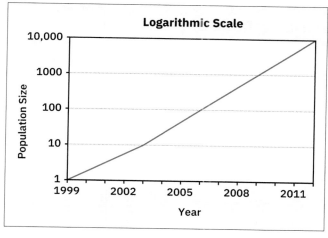

Practice *Describe the two graphs. Explain what each shows and what conclusions you might draw.*

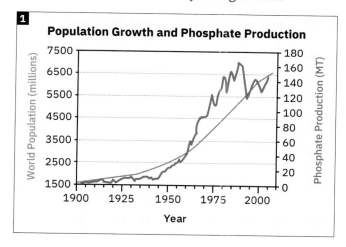

THE PERIODIC TABLE AND BIOCHEMISTRY

Periodic Table of the Elements

The periodic table displays all chemical elements arranged in order of increasing atomic number (the number of protons in the nucleus). Atomic number increases across a row, or period. The elements in each column, or group, share some properties. More than 90 of the elements occur naturally on Earth. Scientists have made the other elements by smashing atoms together at very high speeds, and they continue to make more.

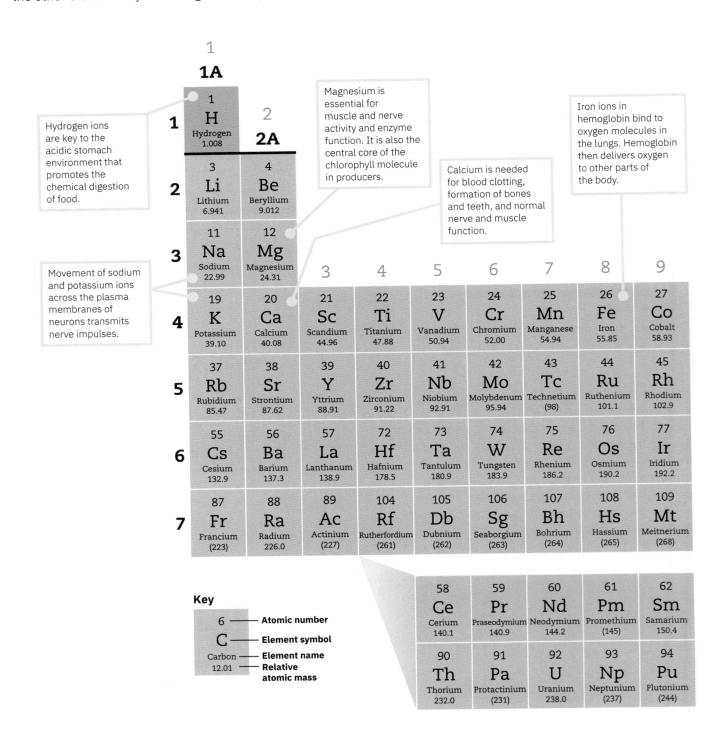

Hydrogen ions are key to the acidic stomach environment that promotes the chemical digestion of food.

Magnesium is essential for muscle and nerve activity and enzyme function. It is also the central core of the chlorophyll molecule in producers.

Calcium is needed for blood clotting, formation of bones and teeth, and normal nerve and muscle function.

Iron ions in hemoglobin bind to oxygen molecules in the lungs. Hemoglobin then delivers oxygen to other parts of the body.

Movement of sodium and potassium ions across the plasma membranes of neurons transmits nerve impulses.

Key

6 — Atomic number
C — Element symbol
Carbon — Element name
12.01 — Relative atomic mass

In this periodic table, metals are shaded blue, metalloids green, and nonmetals orange. Hydrogen, shaded brown, does not belong to any group, and its properties are not similar to those of the group 1A elements below it.

Some sets of elements have their own names. Group 1A is known as the alkali metals; group 2A, the alkaline earth metals; group 7A, the halogens; and group 8A, the noble gases. Elements 57 through 71 are the lanthanides (also called rare earth elements), and elements 89 through 103 are the actinides. Most of these elements typically are extracted from the sixth and seventh rows of the table for display purposes.

Carbon is key in the organic compounds that make up all life on Earth.

Nitrogen is a component of amino acids, which form proteins. Living things cannot function without proteins.

Oxygen is needed in aerobic cellular respiration (the breakdown of glucose molecules) that produces ATP and provides energy for many processes in living cells.

Phosphorus forms the backbone of DNA and RNA molecules and has a major role in the conversion of oxygen into energy. The breakdown of phosphorus-containing compounds ATP and ADP releases energy for cell metabolism.

The thyroid uses iodine to make the hormone thyroxine, which regulates rates of growth, development, and chemical activities.

18 / 8A
2 / He / Helium / 4.003

13 / 3A	14 / 4A	15 / 5A	16 / 6A	17 / 7A
5 / B / Boron / 10.81	6 / C / Carbon / 12.01	7 / N / Nitrogen / 14.01	8 / O / Oxygen / 16.00	9 / F / Fluorine / 19.00	10 / Ne / Neon / 20.18
13 / Al / Aluminum / 26.98	14 / Si / Silicon / 28.09	15 / P / Phosphorus / 30.97	16 / S / Sulfur / 32.07	17 / Cl / Chlorine / 35.45	18 / Ar / Argon / 39.95

10	11	12						
28 / Ni / Nickel / 58.69	29 / Cu / Copper / 63.55	30 / Zn / Zinc / 65.38	31 / Ga / Gallium / 69.72	32 / Ge / Germanium / 72.59	33 / As / Arsenic / 74.92	34 / Se / Selenium / 78.96	35 / Br / Bromine / 79.90	36 / Kr / Krypton / 83.80
46 / Pd / Palladium / 106.4	47 / Ag / Silver / 107.9	48 / Cd / Cadmium / 112.4	49 / In / Indium / 114.8	50 / Sn / Tin / 118.7	51 / Sb / Antimony / 121.8	52 / Te / Tellurium / 127.6	53 / I / Iodine / 126.9	54 / Xe / Xenon / 131.3
78 / Pt / Platinum / 195.1	79 / Au / Gold / 197.0	80 / Hg / Mercury / 200.6	81 / Tl / Thallium / 204.4	82 / Pb / Lead / 207.2	83 / Bi / Bismuth / 209.0	84 / Po / Polonium / (209)	85 / At / Astatine / (210)	86 / Rn / Radon / (222)
110 / Ds / Darmstadtium / (271)	111 / Rg / Roentgenium / (272)	112 / Cn / Copernicium / (285)	113 / Nh / Nihonium / (286)	114 / Fl / Flerovium / (289)	115 / Mc / Moscovium / (289)	116 / Lv / Livermorium / (293)	117 / Ts / Tennessine / (294)	118 / Og / Oganesson / (294)

63 / Eu / Europium / 152.0	64 / Gd / Gadolinium / 157.3	65 / Tb / Terbium / 158.9	66 / Dy / Dysprosium / 162.5	67 / Ho / Holmium / 164.9	68 / Er / Erbium / 167.3	69 / Tm / Thulium / 168.9	70 / Yb / Ytterbium / 173.0	71 / Lu / Lutetium / 175.0
95 / Am / Americium / (243)	96 / Cm / Curium / (247)	97 / Bk / Berkelium / (247)	98 / Cf / Californium / (251)	99 / Es / Einsteinium / (252)	100 / Fm / Fermium / (257)	101 / Md / Mendelevium / (258)	102 / No / Nobelium / (259)	103 / Lr / Lawrencium / (260)

Organic Molecules

All organisms take up carbon compounds from the environment and use them to build the molecules of life. Biological molecules are made up of carbon, hydrogen, nitrogen, and a few other elements. Carbon is the key element. Organic molecules have monomers, or single units of sugars, fatty acids, amino acids, and nucleotides, as building blocks. These monomers bond to form polymers, such as DNA, cellulose, and proteins. Biological molecules can be quite large polymers whose structure and function arise from the order, orientation, and interaction of its subunits.

> **See Chapter 5: Molecules in Living Systems** *for more information about organic molecules.*

Carbohydrates Carbohydrates are organic compounds made of carbon, hydrogen, and oxygen. The monomer in **Figure 1**, glucose, is one of two building blocks of most common carbohydrates, such as amylose. These compounds are involved in cellular metabolism, releasing energy that organisms need to survive. Complex carbohydrates can have chains of hundreds to thousands of monomers.

▼ **Figure 1** Glucose forms the basis of complex carbohydrates.

Lipids Lipids are comprised of fats, oils, and waxes that are relatively insoluble, or difficult to dissolve, in water. Composed mainly of carbon, hydrogen, and oxygen atoms, lipids function primarily to store energy. Typically, lipids are made up of one or more hydrocarbon chains such as that shown in **Figure 2** and are attached to a single functional group that includes oxygen.

▼ **Figure 2** The fatty acid stearic acid displays the general structure of a lipid.

Amino Acids and Proteins Amino acids are small organic compounds with the general structure shown in **Figure 3a**. In most amino acids, all three groups are covalently bonded to the same carbon atom. Cells make the thousands of different proteins they need from only 20 amino acid monomers. Each type of amino acid has a different side-chain R group that determines its bonding pattern in secondary and tertiary protein structures. R groups fall into four categories based on their overall polarity or distribution of charge.

Proteins generally contain 50 to 1000 amino acids linked together by covalent bonds called peptide bonds. The order of the bonded amino acids dictates a given protein's unique primary structure, as shown in **Figure 3b**. Proteins perform many cellular functions, such as the structural components of cells and their neighbors in multicellular organisms. Proteins also serve as enzymes that speed up countless chemical reactions and as the many regulatory proteins that control signals between and within cells.

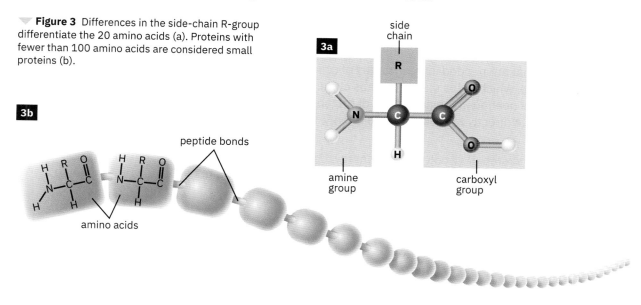

▼ **Figure 3** Differences in the side-chain R-group differentiate the 20 amino acids (a). Proteins with fewer than 100 amino acids are considered small proteins (b).

3a

side chain

3b

peptide bonds

amino acids

amine group

carboxyl group

Nucleotides and Nucleic Acids

Nucleotides can act alone to carry energy or act as monomers linked together to form the nucleic acids DNA and RNA, as shown in **Figure 4**. DNA and RNA code for protein synthesis and transmission of hereditary characteristics, and they control cell activities in all living things. Sugars and phosphate groups make the backbone of each strand. A DNA molecule forms when two such strands coil in the shape of a double helix. Information coded in DNA molecules is recorded in the sequence of the four nucleotide bases—adenine (A), thymine (T), guanine (G), and cytosine (C).

▼ **Figure 4** Millions of linked nucleotides form a strand of DNA or linear chromosome.

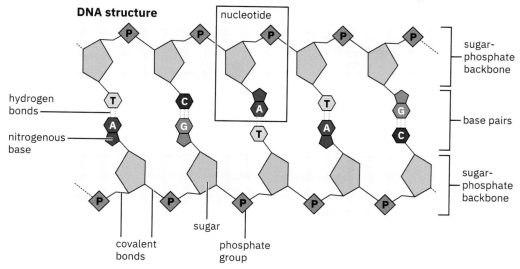

DNA structure

nucleotide

sugar-phosphate backbone

hydrogen bonds

nitrogenous base

base pairs

sugar-phosphate backbone

covalent bonds

sugar

phosphate group

CELLULAR PROCESSES

Cellular Respiration

Section 6.3 provides an overview of the process of cellular respiration and describes the three major stages—glycolysis, the Krebs cycle, and the electron transport chain. The models in this section outline key steps in each of the stages of cellular respiration.

Glycolysis Glycolysis takes place in the cytoplasm of cells and makes two very important contributions. First, glycolysis produces some energy in the form of ATP as well as electron carrier molecules (NADH) that are needed in later stages of cellular respiration. Second, glycolysis produces pyruvate, which helps start the Krebs cycle. The Krebs cycle, in turn, produces molecules that are needed in the next stage of metabolism to produce even more ATP. Cells cannot use glucose directly to produce more energy, so pyruvate is an important intermediate molecule.

As shown in **Figure 1**, the first step of glycolysis uses energy. Using some energy in this step allows the cell to gain more energy later. Each glucose molecule gets split into two, so each subsequent reaction will happen twice for each glucose molecule.

▶ **Figure 1** Glycolysis is anaerobic (does not require oxygen). Its product, pyruvate, can be used to start the process of aerobic respiration in the Krebs cycle (Figure 2) or the anaerobic process of fermentation (Figure 4).

glucose

ATP

ATP

ADP + P_i

ADP + P_i

1 fructose 1,6-bisphosphate (unstable)

1 The cell converts glucose to fructose 1,6-bisphosphate in a series of reactions, using two ATP molecules in the process.

2 The six-carbon molecule splits into two molecules, each with three carbons and one phosphate group.

This is the first step that starts to yield energy as NADH is then used in the electron transport chain.

3 Each three-carbon molecule gives two electrons and one H⁺ to an NAD⁺, turning NAD⁺ into NADH. The three-carbon molecule also gets another phosphate group.

$NAD^+ + P_i$

$NAD^+ + P_i$

e⁻ e⁻ NADH

e⁻ e⁻ NADH

ADP + P_i

ADP + P_i

ATP

ATP

With this happening for two molecules, the cell has now regained the energy that it spent in the first step.

4 One of the phosphate groups is transferred to an ADP to make it an ATP.

ADP + P_i

ADP + P_i

ATP

ATP

pyruvate

pyruvate

For every glucose molecule, the cell gains two ATP for energy. The cell also gains two NADH molecules that can be used in the electron transport chain to produce even more ATP.

5 The second phosphate group is also transferred to an ADP to make it an ATP.

Acetyl-CoA Formation The two molecules of pyruvate move into a mitochondrion. Follow steps 1 and 2 in **Figure 2** to see how Coenzyme A helps form acetyl-CoA, the starting molecule for the Krebs cycle.

Krebs Cycle Steps 3 through 8 in **Figure 2** detail the Krebs cycle, which starts when a four-carbon oxaloacetate molecule combines with the two-carbon acetyl-CoA to form a six-carbon molecule of citric acid. So, the cycle is sometimes called the citric acid cycle. The steps of the Krebs cycle harvest H^+ ions and their companion electrons from the participating molecules while removing carbon atoms that are no longer useful.

In one turn of the Krebs cycle, two carbon atoms enter in the form of acetyl-CoA and two molecules of carbon dioxide are released. This restores the four-carbon oxaloacetate molecule, so it is ready to begin another turn of the cycle. Four electron carrier molecules are produced: three NADH and one $FADH_2$. One molecule of ATP is produced.

Other important products result from the Krebs cycle, namely the electron carrier molecules NADH and $FADH_2$. These molecules are needed by the cell in the next stage of cellular respiration, the electron transpot chain, where they help the cell produce many more ATP molecules. Additional products formed during the Krebs cycle are also used in the biosynthesis of amino acids and fatty acids.

▼ **Figure 2** Glycolysis produces two pyruvate molecules. Therefore, the Krebs cycle repeats twice for every glucose molecule that enters glycolysis.

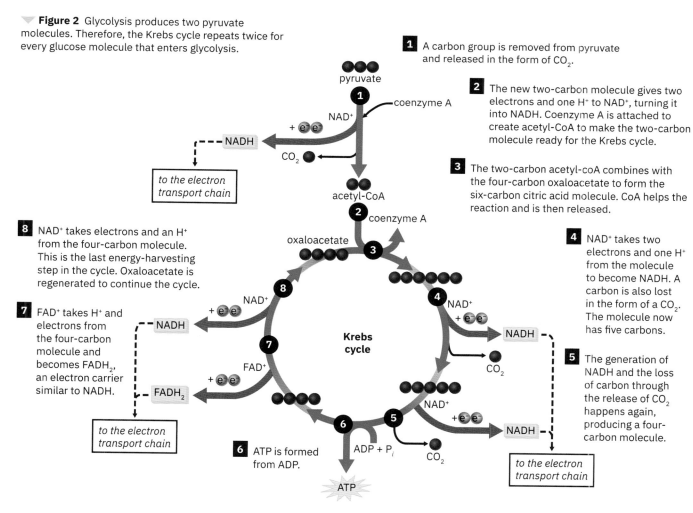

1 A carbon group is removed from pyruvate and released in the form of CO_2.

2 The new two-carbon molecule gives two electrons and one H^+ to NAD^+, turning it into NADH. Coenzyme A is attached to create acetyl-CoA to make the two-carbon molecule ready for the Krebs cycle.

3 The two-carbon acetyl-coA combines with the four-carbon oxaloacetate to form the six-carbon citric acid molecule. CoA helps the reaction and is then released.

4 NAD^+ takes two electrons and one H^+ from the molecule to become NADH. A carbon is also lost in the form of a CO_2. The molecule now has five carbons.

5 The generation of NADH and the loss of carbon through the release of CO_2 happens again, producing a four-carbon molecule.

6 ATP is formed from ADP.

7 FAD^+ takes H^+ and electrons from the four-carbon molecule and becomes $FADH_2$, an electron carrier similar to NADH.

8 NAD^+ takes electrons and an H^+ from the four-carbon molecule. This is the last energy-harvesting step in the cycle. Oxaloacetate is regenerated to continue the cycle.

pyruvate

coenzyme A

NAD^+

$+ e^- e^-$

NADH

CO_2

to the electron transport chain

acetyl-CoA

coenzyme A

oxaloacetate

Krebs cycle

NAD^+
$+ e^- e^-$
NADH
CO_2

NAD^+
$+ e^- e^-$
NADH
CO_2

to the electron transport chain

NAD^+
$+ e^- e^-$
NADH

FAD^+
$+ e^- e^-$
$FADH_2$

to the electron transport chain

ADP + P_i

ATP

Electron Transport Chain The electron transport chain shown in **Figure 3** uses the electron carriers NADH and $FADH_2$ that were produced in the Krebs cycle to make ATP for the cell. For each starting molecule of glucose, two ATP were produced during glycolysis and two ATP were produced during two turns of the Krebs cycle. In the electron transport chain, 26 to 28 ATP are produced through a process that moves hydrogen ions (H^+) across the inner membrane of the mitochondrion. This process of moving a chemical component to set up a concentration gradient that can power the production of ATP is called chemiosmosis. Here, it is the movment of ions across a membrane.

The set of proteins that make up the electron transport chain, as well as the chemiosmosis protein ATP synthase, are embedded in the inner membrane of the mitochondria. The membrane separates the mitochondrial matrix from the intermembrane space, preventing molecules, ions (like H^+), and electrons from moving across freely. The inner membrane acts as a dam, holding more H^+ on one side than the other. The electron transport chain and chemiosmosis are like a hydropower plant, harnessing the flow of the electrons and H^+ (from the more concentrated side to the less concentrated side) for energy to power the production of ATP.

The electron transport chain takes the electrons from NADH and $FADH_2$ to supply energy for setting up the H^+ concentration gradient. In doing so, NAD^+ and FAD are released so that they can be used again in glycolysis and the Krebs cycle.

In the last step, oxygen acts as the final electron acceptor. Because the electron transport chain requires oxygen to function, cellular respiration is often called "aerobic respiration."

▼ **Figure 3** The electron transport chain produces the most ATP and can be thought of as the "payoff" stage of cellular respiration.

1 NADH and $FADH_2$ donate electrons that move from the mitochondrial matrix to the inner membrane's electron transport chain. The newly formed NAD^+ and FAD can be used again where needed.

4 Hydrogen ions move from where they are highly concentrated in the intermembrane space back out into the mitochondrial matrix. The hydrogen ions can only pass through special channels created by the protein ATP synthase. As the H^+ moves through the ATP synthase, it spins like a rotor. The energy of the motion adds a phosphate group to ADP to produce ATP.

2 As electrons flow through the proteins in the electron transport chain towards the intermembrane space, the proteins use the energy to pump H^+ from the mitochondrial matrix to the intermembrane space.

3 In the last step of the chain, the electrons combine with two H^+ and half of an oxygen molecule to create H_2O. Creating H_2O keeps the concentration of electrons in the intermembrane space low, maintaining the concentration gradient that drives electrons to move through the electron transport chain.

Fermentation

If the cell has enough oxygen, the NADH made from glycolysis is constantly being turned back into NAD^+ as it is used in the electron transport chain. However, if no oxygen is present, the electron transport chain cannot function, so the NADH cannot drop off its electrons and H^+ there. That means NAD^+ is not being regenerated for the cell to use in glycolysis, so glycolysis cannot occur.

Figure 4 shows fermentation, a way to turn NADH back into NAD^+ by moving the electrons and H^+ from NADH onto the pyruvate molecules formed from glycolysis. This process does not produce ATP on its own, and it turns the pyruvate into molecules that are hard for the cell to use. Fermentation products can also be toxic in large quantities. However, fermentation can keep glycolysis going so that at least some ATP is being generated.

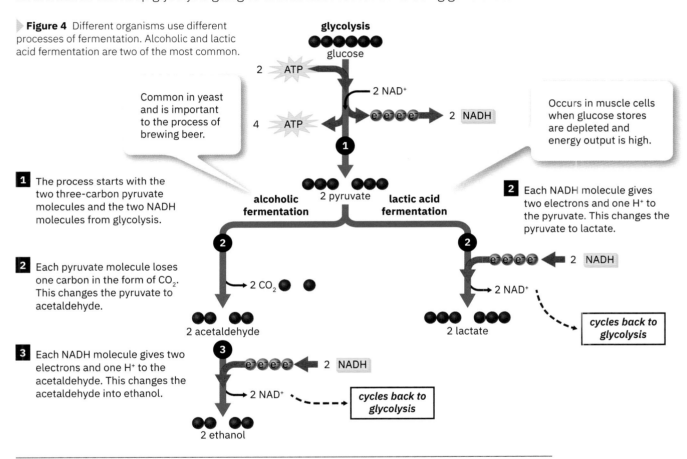

▶ **Figure 4** Different organisms use different processes of fermentation. Alcoholic and lactic acid fermentation are two of the most common.

Common in yeast and is important to the process of brewing beer.

Occurs in muscle cells when glucose stores are depleted and energy output is high.

1 The process starts with the two three-carbon pyruvate molecules and the two NADH molecules from glycolysis.

2 Each pyruvate molecule loses one carbon in the form of CO_2. This changes the pyruvate to acetaldehyde.

3 Each NADH molecule gives two electrons and one H^+ to the acetaldehyde. This changes the acetaldehyde into ethanol.

2 Each NADH molecule gives two electrons and one H^+ to the pyruvate. This changes the pyruvate to lactate.

Practice *Refer to the processes in cellular respiration as you answer these questions.*

1. How many total ATP can be produced from one glucose molecule? Trace the processes from glycolysis through the Krebs cycle and end with the electron transport chain. Hint: assume that the electrons from one NADH can power the production of 2.5 ATP from chemiosmosis and that one $FADH_2$ can power the production of 1.5 ATP.

2. How is fermentation an "alternate pathway" for cellular respiration. Why is it helpful to the cell even though no ATP is produced through the fermentation process?

3. Heterotrophic organisms such as humans must take in food molecules for energy. Autotrophs such as plants can make their own food through photosynthesis. Does this mean that autotrophs do not need to carry out cellular respiration? Explain.

Photosynthesis

Section 6.3 provides an overview of the process of photosynthesis and summarizes it as a series of light-dependent and light-independent reactions. The models in this section detail key steps in those two series.

Light-Dependent Reactions The light-dependent reactions shown in **Figure 5** can be thought of as similar to the electron transport chain in cellular respiration. Both use energy from moving electrons to gradually create a gradient, or area that is strongly positive with a high concentration of H^+, across a membrane. At the end, that gradient is used to turn ADP into ATP. The main difference is that instead of using electrons and energy from breaking down molecules of glucose (stored in molecules that carry energy and electrons, like NADH and $FADH_2$), light-dependent reactions take electrons from water and use energy from light to power the process.

Another difference is that in cellular respiration, the electron transport chain and ATP synthesis are at the end of the entire respiration process. But in light-dependent reactions, the electron transport chain and ATP synthesis occur in the first part of photosynthesis.

▼ **Figure 5** Chloroplasts contain stacks of disk-shaped thylakoids surrounded by a fluid called stroma. The thylakoid membrane holds chlorophylls and protein complexes used in the light-dependent reactions.

1 An electron is taken from H_2O by photosystem II. This turns water into two H^+ (which are released into the thylakoid compartment) and half of an O_2, which combines with an oxygen atom from another H_2O molecule and is released as O_2 byproduct.

2 Photosystem II uses energy from sunlight to give the electron more energy. This is known as excitation of the electron.

3 The excited electron is then moved from photosystem II to an electron transport chain in the thylakoid membrane.

4 As the electron moves through the molecules in the electron transport chain, the molecules use the movement of the electron to pump H^+ through the membrane, from the outer stroma into the inner thylakoid compartment.

5 Once the electron gets to the end of the transport chain, it is transferred to photosystem I, which uses light energy to excite it again.

6 The excited electron moves from photosystem I to a second electron transport chain in the thylakoid membrane.

7 The electron is moved to an NADP$^+$ on the stroma side of the membrane. They combine with an H^+ to form NADPH. NADPH and NADP$^+$ also hold and let go of electrons and H^+.

8 Energy released as the electron moves through this second chain is used to pump H^+ into the thylakoid compartment. This causes a concentration gradient, with a higher concentration of H^+ on the thylakoid compartment side than on the stroma side.

9 H^+ flow through the ATP synthase molecule, from the high-concentration thylakoid compartment side to the low-concentration stroma side. The energy from the flow of H^+ is used by the ATP synthase molecule to turn ADP into ATP.

Light-Independent Reactions **Figure 6** shows the light-independent reactions, often called the Calvin cycle after one of its pioneering researchers. Energy from the ATP produced in the light-dependent reactions of photosynthesis is used to "fix" carbon by creating carbon molecules out of CO_2, in what can be thought of almost as a "reverse Krebs cycle."

The Calvin cycle is unusual in that multiples of each molecule are needed to complete a full cycle. In the first half of the cycle, three five-carbon molecules are used to create six three-carbon molecules. However, only one of those three-carbon molecules is released to be used to form glucose. The other five three-carbon molecules are combined to create three five-carbon molecules that are needed to re-start the process. Eighteen carbon atoms are involved in the balanced version of the cycle.

▶ **Figure 6** The sugar molecules created by the Calvin cycle can be used as building blocks to create other molecules the cell needs. The sugar molecules are also used in cellular respiration to produce energy for plant cells.

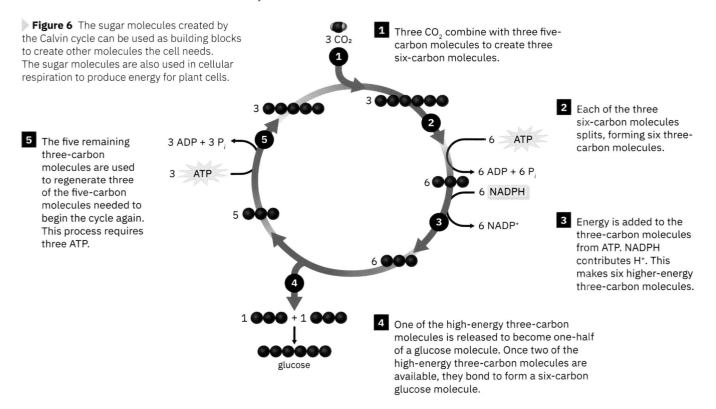

1 Three CO_2 combine with three five-carbon molecules to create three six-carbon molecules.

2 Each of the three six-carbon molecules splits, forming six three-carbon molecules.

3 Energy is added to the three-carbon molecules from ATP. NADPH contributes H⁺. This makes six higher-energy three-carbon molecules.

4 One of the high-energy three-carbon molecules is released to become one-half of a glucose molecule. Once two of the high-energy three-carbon molecules are available, they bond to form a six-carbon glucose molecule.

5 The five remaining three-carbon molecules are used to regenerate three of the five-carbon molecules needed to begin the cycle again. This process requires three ATP.

Practice *Refer to the processes involved in photosynthesis as you answer these questions.*

1. The light-dependent reactions convert light energy to chemical energy. Where does the light energy come from? What form of chemical energy is produced? How is this useful to the cell?

2. Plants take in carbon dioxide and water from the environment to make sugar building blocks, and they release oxygen back into the environment, as shown in the equation.

$$6CO_2 + 6H_2O \rightarrow C_6H_{12}O_6 + 6O_2$$

Identify the place in the light-dependent or light-independent reaction where each input and output of the process is important.

CLASSIFICATION AND RELATEDNESS OF SPECIES

Taxonomic Systems Over Time

For thousands of years, people sought to bring order to the vast array of life on Earth. Of course, at that time, classification extended only to those organisms visible to the naked eye. Of those organisms, most people focused on classifying plants according to their medicinal properties. Aristotle is considered the first to classify animals as well.

In the 1500s, optical lenses enabled a closer look at the structure of organisms, and taxonomic efforts progressed. In the mid-1700s, Carolus Linnaeus built on the work of earlier taxonomists to develop the nomenclature, or naming system, that is still used today with some modifications. Linnaeus grouped species into genera as Aristotle did. However, based on similarities, he then grouped genera into orders, orders into classes, and classes into kingdoms. Today, the most widely accepted taxonomic levels are reflected in **Table 1**, with domain being the most general and species the most specific. As significant differences have been discovered, organisms have been reclassified and new levels of classification have been inserted, such as groups, superorders, and subphyla.

Figure 1 The species name *Balaenoptera musculus* refers to the blue whale and no other living thing.

Table 1. Classification of the Blue Whale, *Balaenoptera musculus*

Level	Classification	Description
domain	Eukarya	complex cell structures enclosed within membranes
kingdom	Animalia	animals
phylum	Chordata	chordates (possessing a nerve cord)
subphylum	Vertebrata	vertebrates (with backbone and spinal column)
class	Mammalia	mammals
order	Cetacea	whales and dolphins
suborder	Mysticeti	baleen whales (possessing baleen plates instead of teeth)
family	Balaenopteridae	rorquals (possessing pleated throat grooves)
genus	*Balaenoptera*	finback whales
species	*Balaenoptera musculus*	blue whale

Current advancements in technology enable taxonomists to use a variety of genetic tools to determine relatedness among species. Findings based on similarities in DNA and protein sequences, ribosomal RNA, and mitochondrial DNA enable a more detailed picture of relatedness. Therefore, taxonomic classification is an ever-changing science. The snapshot shown in **Figure 2** is one way scientists currently classify the relatedness of life on Earth. New discoveries and different ways of looking at the data could change scientists' understanding of relatedness in the future.

Figure 2 The three domains of life have a common ancestor.

Bacteria

Archaea

Eukarya

protist

fungus

plant

animal

Phylogenetics and Relatedness

With advancements in biotechnology, scientists began to look at taxonomic relationships more as evolutionary pathways that provided evidence of common ancestry and how lineages diverged. Research into molecular and cellular structure also led to the conclusion that species grouped into the domain Eukarya were more closely related to species in domain Archaea than to those in domain Bacteria.

The representation shown in **Figure 3** was developed in 2009 using ribosomal RNA (rRNA) sequences because these sequences occur in all cells and organelles. They are also the most conserved large sequences in nature. Although much has been learned since 2009, scientists still agree on the evolutionary relationships shown in **Figure 3** and described in the boxes below.

Domain Bacteria All bacteria are prokaryotes and unicellular, but they are extremely diverse. They vary in shape, with some being rodlike and others being spherical. Still others are curved, forming shapes from commas to spirals. They differ in their modes of nutrition or how they obtain energy as well. They may be phototrophic, chemotrophic, autotrophic, or heterotrophic. They also vary greatly in growth requirements related to temperature, pH, oxygen, and osmotic pressure. The cell wall varies somewhat in bacteria, but in nearly all species it is made of a large molecule called peptidoglycan. This layer's thickness determines whether species are Gram-positive or Gram-negative. Bacteria are extremely important ecologically, both to the environment and to the individual organisms with which they form symbiotic relationships.

Domain Archaea All archaea are prokaryotic and unicellular, but they are also extremely diverse. They can be found in the most extreme habitats on Earth, such as hydrothermal vents, extremely acidic or salty soils, hot springs, and anerobic environments. Most archaea, however, are simply spread throughout the environment. Much of what scientists know about archaea comes from isolating and analyzing nucleic acids from the environment rather than from cultures grown in labs, which is extremely difficult to do. Such studies show that the organization of DNA around histone proteins connects archaea more closely to eukaryotes than bacteria. Another distinguishing factor is that while the cell walls of archaea vary in structure, none contain peptidoglycan. Also, the RNA involved in transcription and the process of protein synthesis is much more like that of eukaryotes than bacteria.

Domain Eukarya Eukaryotes can be unicellular or multicellular, but cells of all organisms in this diverse group have a membrane-bound nucleus. While eukaryotes are broadly divided into four kingdoms—Protista, Fungi, Plantae, and Animalia—their evolutionary relationships are not as neatly defined. Protista is no longer considered a valid grouping given its lack of a unifying characteristic. In fact, any given protist may be more closely related to fungi, plants, or animals than to other protists. Therefore, this text uses the system of classifying eukaryotes into supergroups, a level between domain and kingdom. **Figure 4** below shows one way scientists look at eukaryote supergroups.

▼ **Figure 4** Using supergroups better depicts the evolutionary relationships of eukaryotes than earlier kingdom classification systems.

excavates	SAR supergroup	CCTH supergroup	archaeplastids	amoebozoans	opisthokonts
euglenoids, trypanosomes	brown algae, paramecia, radiolaria	haptophyte algae, algae-like cryptophytes	plants, red algae, green algae	slime molds, amoebas	animals, fungi, choanoflagellates

common eukaryotic ancestor

Bacteria

Acidobacteria
Actinobacteria
TM7
Cyanobacteria
chloroplast
Chlorobi
Firmicutes
Proteobacteria
Thermotogae
WS6
mitochondria
Verrucomicrobia
Gemmatimonadetes
OP1 1
Bacteroidetes
Chloroflexi
BRC1

Origin

Fungi
Animals
Choanoflagellates
Red Algae
Plants
Stramenopiles
Alveolates
Acanthamoebae
Euglenozoa
Heterolobosea
BOL3
BAQ1
Crenarchaeota

Archaea

Euryarchaeota

Trichomonads
Diplomonads

rRNA sequence change

Unresolved branching order

Eucarya

Source: Fig. 3., A Molecular ToL based on rRNA sequence comparisons. From Norman R. Pace, "Mapping the Tree of Life: Progress and Prospects," *Microbiology and Molecular Biology Reviews*, December 1, 2009. (c) 2009 The American Society for Microbiology. Reprinted with permission.

Depicting Relatedness

Given that the vast array of life on Earth arose from a single common ancestor, the challenge becomes how to depict that relatedness and how to change the depiction given ongoing discoveries. The ability to computer-analyze huge molecular datasets feeds this challenge. For example, recent work has resulted in an even newer idea that the six supergroups of eukaryotes should be divided further into eleven or as many as fourteen groups, as shown in **Figure 5**. Time will tell how other scientists will react and whether they reach consensus.

▼ **Figure 5** Follow the pathways to determine which supergroups are more closely related. For example, this model shows that scientists think Ancyromonadida are more closely related to Amoebozoa than to Telonemia.

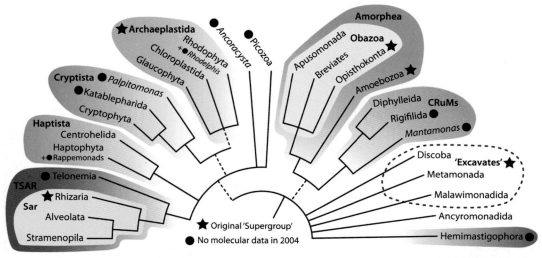

Trends in Ecology & Evolution

The diagram shown in **Figure 5** refers to a small section of a circular tree diagram, such as the one shown in **Figure 6a**. A circular evolutionary tree is often used to show relatedness among hundreds or thousands of species. The center of the diagram denotes the root, or earliest common ancestor. Each branching point indicates the common ancestor from which others in the connected sections evolved. The innermost point of the circle is farthest back in time and the branches flow outward toward more recent times. Other styles of trees, such as those in **Figure 6b** and **Figure 6c**, are typically used for showing relationships among fewer species. A self-contained branching section of a tree represents a clade, a grouping that includes a common ancestor and all the descendants. In any style of tree, the time scale can vary greatly between branches.

▼ **Figure 6** A circular tree (a), a diagonal tree (b), and a square-corner tree (c).

One challenge of depicting relatedness is that we have data for relatively few species. Of the estimated 8.7 million plant and animal species on Earth, only about 1.2 million have been identified and described. Overall, scientists have sequenced the genomes of about 3500 complex life forms. Researchers at the University of Texas used data from approximately 3000 species to create the tree of life in **Figure 7**, which includes all three domains and illustrates the complexity of showing relatedness of all living things. Most of the species in this diagram represent plants, animals, fungi, and protists. Yet, along with the millions of complex species yet to be described, a recent study estimates that between 0.8 and 1.6 million prokaryotic species exist, of which approximately 200,000 have been sequenced. Only a few of these are included in the dataset for this tree. Use **Figure 8** to find out more about a few of the species represented here.

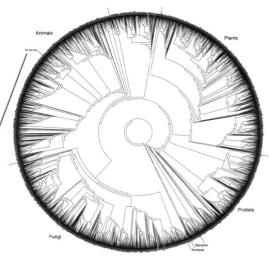

Source: From Elizabeth Pennisi, "Modernizing the Tree of Life," Science, 300(5626), June 13, 2003, pp. 1692-1697. Figure: Roundabout. Credit: David M. Hillis, Derrick Zwicki, and Robin Gutell, University of Texas, Austin. Reprinted with permission from AAAS and David M. Hillis.

▼ **Figure 7** Use a strong magnifier to identify other species cataloged here that have a relatively close relationship to *Homo sapiens*.

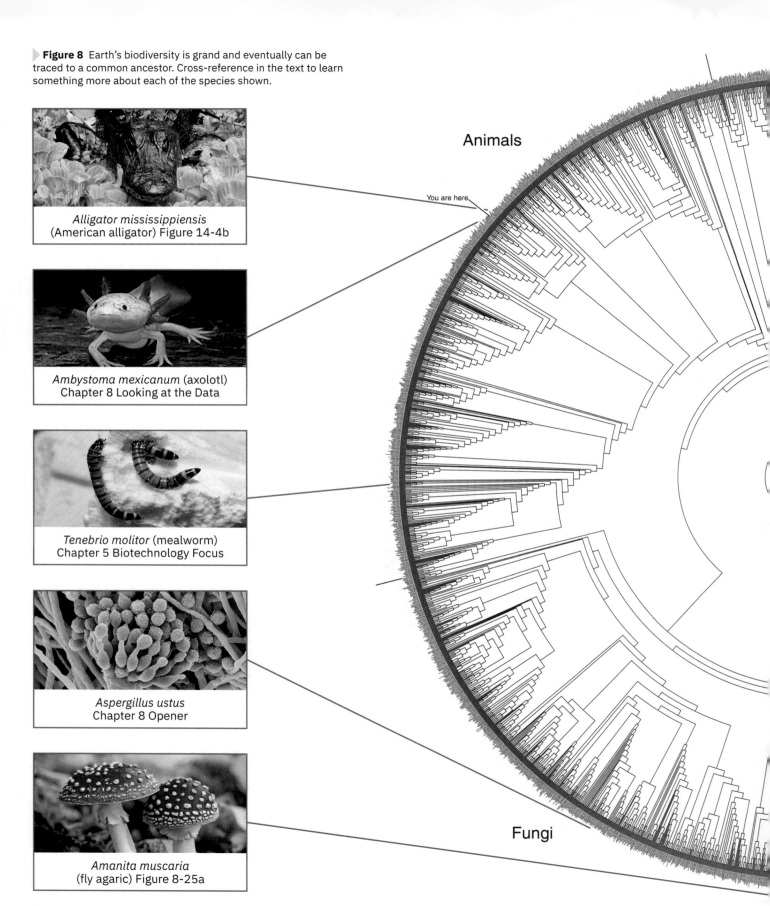

Figure 8 Earth's biodiversity is grand and eventually can be traced to a common ancestor. Cross-reference in the text to learn something more about each of the species shown.

Alligator mississippiensis
(American alligator) Figure 14-4b

Ambystoma mexicanum (axolotl)
Chapter 8 Looking at the Data

Tenebrio molitor (mealworm)
Chapter 5 Biotechnology Focus

Aspergillus ustus
Chapter 8 Opener

Amanita muscaria
(fly agaric) Figure 8-25a

Animals

You are here.

Fungi

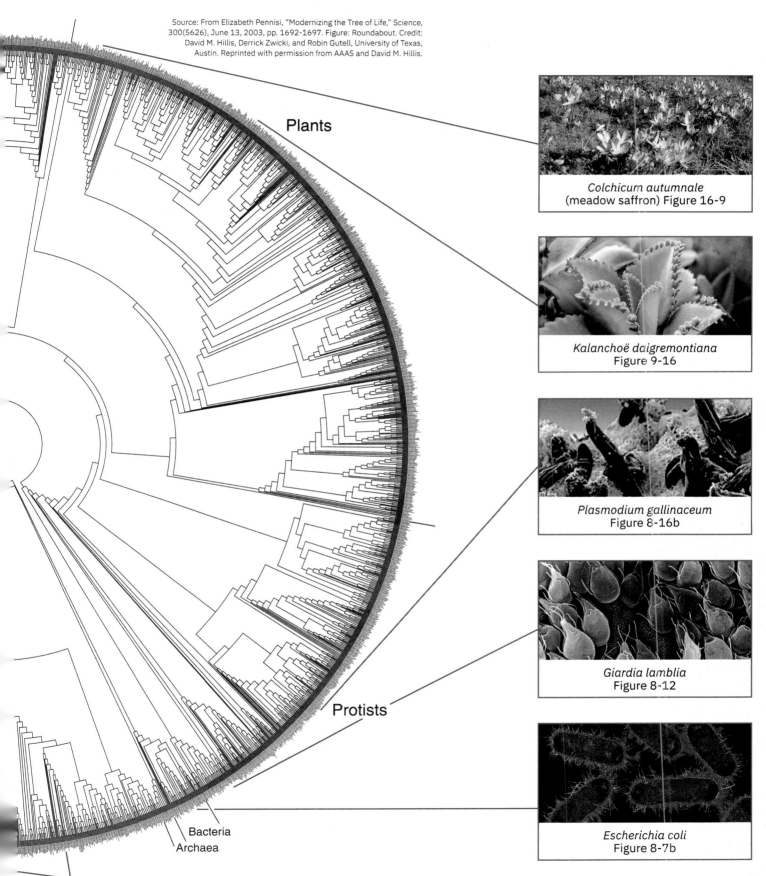

Source: From Elizabeth Pennisi, "Modernizing the Tree of Life," Science, 300(5626), June 13, 2003, pp. 1692-1697. Figure: Roundabout. Credit: David M. Hillis, Derrick Zwicki, and Robin Gutell, University of Texas, Austin. Reprinted with permission from AAAS and David M. Hillis.

Plants

Protists

Bacteria
Archaea

Colchicum autumnale
(meadow saffron) Figure 16-9

Kalanchoë daigremontiana
Figure 9-16

Plasmodium gallinaceum
Figure 8-16b

Giardia lamblia
Figure 8-12

Escherichia coli
Figure 8-7b

Diversity of Life

It's hard to imagine the incredible variation among Earth's life forms, much less show it in a snapshot. Use **Table 2** to compare the basic characteristics of the domains and kingdoms. Then, get a glimpse of this vast array in the images and cross-reference to other parts of the text to find out more.

Table 2. Comparison of domain and kingdom characteristics.

Domain	Kingdom	Characteristics				
		Cell type	Cell structure	Body type	Nutrition	Examples
Bacteria	Eubacteria	prokaryotic	cell wall of peptidoglycan	unicellular	autotrophic and heterotrophic	*Micrococcus luteus, Dietzia kunjamensis, Treponema pallidum*
Archaea	Archaebacteria	prokaryotic	cell wall with no peptidoglycan	unicellular	autotrophic and heterotrophic	Halophilic archaea, *Sulfolobus* archaea
Eukarya	Protista	eukaryotic	mixed	unicellular and multicellular	autotrophic and heterotrophic	diatoms, foraminifera, slime molds
Eukarya	Plantae	eukaryotic	cell wall of cellulose	unicellular and multicellular	autotrophic	liverworts, spruce, trilliums
Eukarya	Fungi	eukaryotic	cell wall of chitin	unicellular and multicellular	heterotrophic	bread mold, violet webcap, bleeding Hydnellum
Eukarya	Animalia	eukaryotic	no cell wall	multicellular	heterotrophic	spotted jelly, garden snail, puffins

Bacteria

See Chapter 8: *Find out more about bacteria in Section 8.1.*

Archaea

See Chapter 8: *Find out more about archaea in Section 8.1.*

Protists

See Chapter 8: *Find out more about protists in Section 8.2.*

Plants

See Chapter 9: *Find out more about plants in Section 9.1.*

Fungi

See Chapter 8: *Find out more about fungi in Section 8.3.*

Animals

See Chapter 10: *Find out more about animals in Section 10.1.*

GLOSSARY

A

abiotic factor a nonliving factor in an ecosystem, such as temperature, wind, soil, and sunlight
  factor abiótico factor inerte de un ecosistema, como la temperatura, el viento, el suelo y la luz solar

acid a substance that releases hydrogen ions in water
  ácido sustancia que libera iones de hidrógeno en el agua

activation energy minimum amount of energy required to start a reaction
  energía de activación cantidad mínima de energía que se necesita para provocar una reacción

activator a transcription factor that increases the rate of transcription when it binds to a promoter or enhancer
  activador factor de la transcripción que aumenta la tasa de transcripción al unirse a un promotor o potenciador

active site an area of an enzyme that accepts a substrate and catalyzes its breakdown or its reaction with another substrate
  sitio activo área de una enzima que acepta un sustrato y cataliza su descomposición o su reacción con otro sustrato

active transport energy-requiring mechanism in which a transport protein pumps a solute across a cell membrane against the solute's concentration gradient
  transporte activo mecanismo que requiere energía, donde una proteína de transporte bombea un soluto a través de una membrana celular en dirección opuesta al gradiente de concentración del soluto

adaptation a heritable trait that improves an organism's chances of surviving and producing offspring
  adaptación rasgo hereditario que mejora las posibilidades de que un organismo sobreviva y produzca descendencia

adaptive immunity a set of immune defenses that can be tailored to specific pathogens as an organism encounters them during its lifetime; characterized by self/nonself recognition, specificity, diversity, and memory
  inmunidad adaptativa conjunto de defensas inmunitarias que se adaptan a patógenos específicos a medida que los organismos los encuentran durante su vida; se caracterizan por el reconocimiento de lo propio y lo ajeno, la especificidad, la diversidad y la memoria

adaptive radiation a pattern of macroevolution in which a lineage undergoes a burst of genetic divergences that gives rise to many species
  radiación adaptativa patrón macroevolutivo en el que un linaje experimenta un aumento explosivo de divergencias genéticas que da origen a muchas especies

adenosine triphosphate (ATP) a nucleotide that consists of an adenine base, a ribose sugar, and three phosphate groups; functions as a subunit of RNA and as a coenzyme in many reactions; important energy carrier
  adenosín trifosfato (ATP) nucleótido compuesto de una base de adenina, un azúcar ribosa y tres grupos de fosfato; funciona como subunidad del ARN y como coenzima en muchas reacciones; es un importante portador de energía

adhesion an attraction between molecules of different substances
  adhesión atracción entre las moléculas de sustancias diferentes

aerobic cellular respiration a type of cellular respiration that requires oxygen
  respiración aeróbica celular tipo de respiración celular que requiere oxígeno

allele one form of a gene with slightly different DNA sequence; may encode different versions of the gene's product
  alelo forma de un gen con una secuencia de ADN ligeramente distinta; puede codificar distintas versiones del producto del gen

allele frequency the proportion of one allele relative to all the alleles for that trait in a population's chromosomes
  frecuencia alélica en los cromosomas de una población, la proporción de un alelo en relación con todos los alelos de una característica dada

alternative splicing a post-translational RNA modification process in which exons are joined in different combinations
  empalme alternativo proceso de modificación postraducción en el cual los exones se unen en distintas combinaciones

altruism a behavior that benefits others at the expense of the individual performing it
  altruismo comportamiento que beneficia a otros a expensas del individuo que lo lleva a cabo

amino acid a small organic compound that consists of a carboxyl group, an amine group, and a characteristic side group (R), all typically bonded to the same carbon atom; monomer of proteins
  aminoácido pequeño compuesto orgánico que consta de un grupo carboxílico, un grupo amino y un grupo característico adjunto (R), los cuales están unidos al mismo átomo de carbono; monómero de proteínas

analogous structure a body structure that is similar in function or appearance to another in a different lineage but not similar in origin or development
  estructura análoga estructura que es similar en función o aspecto a otra de un linaje distinto, pero que no es similar en origen ni desarrollo

anaphase a stage of mitosis during which sister chromatids separate and move toward opposite spindle poles
  anafase etapa de la mitosis durante la cual las cromátidas hermanas se separan y se mueven hacia polos opuestos del huso

antibody a y-shaped antigen receptor protein made by B cells; immunoglobulin; e.g., IgA, IgG, IgE, IgM, IgD
  anticuerpo proteína receptora de antígenos que tiene forma de Y y está hecha de células B; inmunoglobulina; p. ej., IgA, IgG, IgE, IgM, IgD

anticodon a set of three nucleotides that base-pairs with an mRNA codon in a tRNA
  anticodón conjunto de tres nucleótidos que se emparejan en la base con un codón de ARNm en un ARNt

antigen a molecule or particle that the immune system recognizes as nonself; its presence in the body triggers an immune response

    antígeno molécula o partícula que el sistema inmune reconoce como ajena; su presencia en el cuerpo desencadena una respuesta inmune

apex consumer a consumer at the top trophic level that eats other consumers but is not typically consumed by others

    consumidor ápice consumidor que está en el nivel trófico más alto y que se come a otros consumidores, pero generalmente sin que los otros se lo coman

apoptosis a predictable, controlled process of cell self-destruction; programmed cell death

    apoptosis proceso predecible y controlado de autodestrucción celular; muerte celular programada

artificial selection the selection by humans of traits that are desirable in plants or animals and breeding only those individuals that possess the desired traits

    selección artificial selección por parte de los seres humanos de rasgos deseables en plantas o animales mediante el cruce exclusivo de aquellos individuos que poseen los rasgos deseados

asexual reproduction a reproductive mode of eukaryotes by which offspring arise from a single parent only

    reproducción asexual modo reproductivo de los eucariotas en el que la descendencia surge de un solo progenitor

atom the fundamental unit of which elements are composed

    átomo unidad fundamental de la cual se componen los elementos

ATP see adenosine triphosphate

    ATP ver adenosín trifosfato

autotroph an organism that makes its own food from abiotic sources, such as sunlight or inorganic materials; also known as a producer

    autótrofo organismo que produce su propio alimento a partir de fuentes abióticas, como luz solar o materiales inorgánicos; conocido también como *productor*

B

background extinction the continuous, low-level extinction of species that has been evident throughout much of the history of life

    extinción de fondo la extinción continua y de bajo nivel de especies que ha sido evidente a lo largo de una gran parte de la historia de la vida

bacteriophage a type of virus that infects bacteria

    bacteriofago tipo de virus que infecta bacterias

base a substance that accepts hydrogen ions in water

    base sustancia que acepta iones de hidrógeno en el agua

binary fission a method of asexual reproduction in which one prokaryotic cell divides into two identical descendant cells

    fisión binaria método de reproducción asexual en el cual una célula procariota se divide en dos células descendientes idénticas

biodiversity the variety and variability of life on Earth; a region's biodiversity is measured at three levels: the genetic diversity within species, species diversity, and ecosystem diversity

    biodiversidad variedad y variabilidad de la vida en la Tierra; la biodiversidad de una región se mide en tres niveles: la diversidad genética dentro de las especies, la diversidad de especies y la diversidad de ecosistemas

biogeochemical cycle a process by which matter cycles from the living world to the nonliving physical environment and back again; examples of biogeochemical cycles include the carbon cycle, the nitrogen cycle, and the phosphorus cycle

    ciclo biogeoquímico proceso a través del cual la materia transita entre el mundo vivo, el entorno físico no vivo y de regreso al mundo vivo; los ciclos del carbono, del nitrógeno y del fósforo son ciclos biogeoquímicos

biogeography the study of patterns in the geographic distribution of species and communities

    biogeografía el estudio de patrones en la distribución geográfica de especies y comunidades

bioinformatics the use of computational tools for analyzing and interpreting biological data

    bioinformática uso de herramientas computacionales para analizar e interpretar datos biológicos

biological engineer an engineer that uses principles of biology to design solutions to problems

    ingeniero biológico ingeniero que aplica los principios de la biología para diseñar soluciones a problemas

biology the scientific study of life

    biología el estudio científico de la vida

biomass the total dry mass of all the living organisms within a given area at a specific time

    biomasa el total de masa seca de todos los organismos vivos dentro de un área dada en un momento específico

biomass pyramid a model depicting the total dry mass of all the living organisms at each trophic level within a given area at a specific time

    pirámide de biomasa modelo que muestra el total de masa seca de todos los organismos vivos de cada nivel trófico dentro de un área dada en un momento específico

biome a region characterized by its climate and dominant vegetation

    bioma región que se caracteriza por su clima y vegetación dominante

biosphere all of Earth's organisms and the regions where organisms live

    biosfera todos los organismos de la Tierra y las regiones donde los organismos viven

biotic factor a living thing in an ecosystem

    factor biótico un ser vivo en un ecosistema

biotic potential a measure of how much a population could grow under ideal conditions; measured by its per capita growth rate as determined only by the reproductive characteristics of the species

    potencial biótico medida de cuánto podría crecer una población bajo condiciones ideales; se mide por su crecimiento per cápita, que se determina únicamente por las características reproductivas de la especie

bottleneck effect a reduction in population size so severe that it reduces genetic diversity; a type of genetic drift

    efecto de cuello de botella reducción tan drástica del tamaño de la población que reduce la diversidad genética; tipo de deriva genética

bulb a short plant stem covered with overlapping scales that stores reserve energy during unfavorable growth conditions; the lower portion of a bulb gives rise to new roots

    bulbo tallo corto de una planta cubierto con escamas superpuestas y que almacena energía de reserva durante condiciones de crecimiento desfavorables; en la parte baja de un bulbo se generan raíces nuevas

C

capsid the protein shell containing the genetic material of a virus

    cápside envoltura de proteína que contiene el material genético de un virus

carbohydrate an organic compound that consists of carbon, hydrogen, and oxygen

    carbohidrato compuesto orgánico de carbono, hidrógeno y oxígeno

carpel the reproductive organ of a flower that produces the female gametophyte; consists of an ovary, stigma, and usually a style

    carpelo órgano reproductivo de una flor que produce el gametofito femenino; está compuesto por un ovario, un estigma y un estilo

carrying capacity the maximum number of individuals that a population's environment can support indefinitely

    capacidad de carga número máximo de individuos que el medio ambiente de una población puede soportar de manera indefinida

catalyst a substance that regulates the speed at which a chemical reaction occurs without affecting the end point of the reaction and without being used up as a result of the reaction

    catalizador sustancia que regula la rapidez de una reacción química sin afectar el final de la reacción y sin ser consumido como resultado de la reacción

catastrophism the principle stating that infrequent catastrophic geologic events alter the course of Earth history, in contrast to the principle of gradualism

    catastrofismo principio según el cual los sucesos geológicos catastróficos e infrecuentes alteran el curso de la historia de la Tierra, en contraste con el principio de gradualismo

cell differentiation a process by which cells become specialized during development; occurs as different cells in an embryo begin to use different subsets of their DNA

diferenciación celular proceso por el cual las células se especializan durante el desarrollo; ocurre cuando las células de un embrión empiezan a usar diferentes subconjuntos de su ADN

cell membrane a lipid bilayer that encloses the cytoplasm; separates a cell from its external environment

    membrana celular una bicapa lipídica que encierra el citoplasma; separa a la célula de su ambiente externo

cellular respiration a process that harvests energy from an organic molecule to store it in the usable form of ATP

    respiración celular proceso que cosecha la energía de una molécula orgánica para almacenarla como ATP que se puede usar

cellulose a complex carbohydrate that consists of parallel chains of glucose monomers

    celulosa carbohidrato complejo compuesto de cadenas paralelas de monómeros de glucosa

centromere a constricted region where sister chromatids attach to each other

    centrómero región restringida donde se unen las cromátidas hermanas

character a quantifiable, heritable trait such as the number of segments in a backbone or the nucleotide sequence of ribosomal RNA

    carácter rasgo cuantificable y hereditario, como el número de segmentos que hay en la columna vertebral o la secuencia de nucleótidos de ARN ribosomal

charge a property of matter that results in electrical forces; like charges repel, and opposite charges attract

    carga propiedad de la materia que resulta en fuerzas eléctricas; las cargas iguales se repelen y las cargas opuestas se atraen

chemical bond a force that holds atoms in a molecule or substance together

    enlace químico fuerza que une los átomos de una molécula o sustancia

chemical reaction a process in which substances change into different substances through the breaking and forming of chemical bonds

    reacción química proceso en el que las sustancias se convierten en otras sustancias al romperse y formarse enlaces químicos

chemoautotroph an organism that uses carbon dioxide as its carbon source and obtains energy by oxidizing inorganic molecules

    quimioautótrofo organismo que usa dióxido de carbono como fuente de carbono y oxida moléculas inorgánicas para obtener energía

chemoheterotroph an organism that obtains energy and carbon by breaking down organic compounds

    quimioheterótrofo organismo que descompone compuestos orgánicos para obtener energía y carbono

chemosynthesis a process by which sugars are made by organisms that use chemicals as an energy source rather than sunlight

    quimiosíntesis proceso en el que organismos producen azúcares utilizando productos químicos como fuente de energía en lugar de luz solar

chitin a nitrogen-containing polysaccharide that composes fungal cell walls and arthropod exoskeletons

    quitina polisacárido que contiene nitrógeno y compone las paredes celulares de los hongos y los exoesqueletos de los artrópodos

chloroplast an organelle of photosynthesis in plants and photosynthetic protists; light-dependent reactions occur at its inner thylakoid membrane; light-independent reactions, in the stroma

    cloroplasto orgánulo de la fotosíntesis en plantas y protistas fotosintetizadores; en su membrana tilacoide interior se dan reacciones que dependen de la luz; las reacciones que son independientes de la luz ocurren en el estroma

choanoflagellate the protist group most closely related to animals

    coanoflagelados el grupo protista más cercano a los animales

chordate an animal with an embryo that has a notochord, dorsal nerve cord, pharyngeal gill slits, and a tail that extends beyond the anus

    cordado animal cuyo embrión tiene notocorda, tubo neural hueco en la posición dorsal, hendiduras branquiales y cola que se extiende más allá del ano

chromosome a structure that consists of DNA together with associated proteins; carries part or all of a cell's genetic information

    cromosoma estructura que consta de ADN y proteínas asociadas; contiene una parte o toda la información genética de una célula

chytrid a fungus with flagellated spores

    quítrido hongo con esporas flageladas

clade a group of taxa whose members share one or more defining derived traits

    clado grupo de taxones cuyos miembros comparten uno o más rasgos derivados

cladistics a system of classification that arranges organisms by shared characteristics and inferred evolutionary relationships

    cladística sistema de clasificación que ordena los organismos por características compartidas y relaciones evolutivas inferidas

cladogram an evolutionary tree diagram that visually summarizes a hypothesis about how a group of clades are related

    cladograma diagrama evolutivo ramificado que resume visualmente una hipótesis sobre las relaciones entre un grupo de clados

clone a genetic copy of an organism

    clon copia genética de un organismo

club fungus a fungus that produces spores on club-shaped structures during sexual reproduction

    basidiomiceto hongo que produce esporas con estructuras que tienen forma de botella durante la reproducción sexual

clumped distribution a population distribution pattern in which individuals are closer to one another than would be predicted by chance alone

distribución agrupada patrón de distribución de la población en el que los individuos están más cerca de lo que se podría predecir por azar únicamente

codominance an effect in which the full and separate phenotypic effects of two alleles are apparent in heterozygous individuals

    codominancia efecto en el que los efectos fenotípicos totales y separados de dos alelos son aparentes en individuos heterocigotos

codon a nucleotide base triplet that codes for an amino acid or stop signal during translation in an mRNA

    codón triplete de bases de nucleótidos que, durante la traducción de un ARNm, codifica un aminoácido o una señal de parada

coevolution the joint evolution of two closely interacting species; a macroevolutionary pattern in which each species is a selective agent for traits of the other

    coevolución evolución conjunta de dos especies que interactúan de manera cercana; patrón macroevolutivo en el que cada especie es un agente selectivo de los rasgos de la otra

cohesion an attraction between molecules of the same substance

    cohesión atracción entre moléculas de la misma sustancia

cohesion-tension theory an explanation of how transpiration creates a tension that pulls a cohesive column of water upward through xylem

    teoría de la cohesión-tensión explicación de cómo la transpiración crea una tensión que jala una columna cohesiva de agua hacia arriba a través de la xilema

colonial organism an organism composed of many similar cells, each capable of living and reproducing on its own

    organismo colonial organismo compuesto por muchas células similares, cada una de las cuales es capaz de vivir y reproducirse por su cuenta

community the collection of populations of all species in a defined area

    comunidad conjunto de poblaciones de una especie en un área definida

competition a ecological relationship in which two organisms try to obtain the same resource

    competencia relación ecológica en la cual dos organismos tratan de obtener el mismo recurso

complementary a strand in which the base of each nucleotide pairs, through hydrogen bonding with a partner base on another strand of DNA

    complementaria hebra en la cual la base de cada nucleótido se empareja, por medio de un enlace de hidrógeno, con una base asociada de otra hebra de ADN

constraint a factor that limits the possible solutions that could be developed to solve a problem

    restricción factor que limita las soluciones posibles que se pueden desarrollar para resolver un problema

consumer an organism that gets its energy and nutrients from eating other organisms

    consumidor organismo que come otros organismos para obtener energía y nutrientes

control center the body system that gathers information from sensory receptors and sends information to the body's effectors; the main control center in vertebrates is the nervous system

    centro de control sistema del cuerpo que reúne información de los receptores sensoriales y envía información a los efectores del cuerpo; el centro de control principal de los vertebrados es el sistema nervioso

convergent evolution the independent evolution of similar structures that carry on similar functions in two or more organisms of widely different, unrelated ancestry

    evolución convergente evolución independiente de estructuras similares que cumplen con funciones similares en dos o más organismos de ascendencia notoriamente distinta y no relacionada

covalent bond a type of chemical bond in which two atoms share electrons

    enlace covalente tipo de enlace químico en el cual dos átomos comparten electrones

CRISPR a method of editing DNA using an RNA sequence and nuclease enzyme

    CRISPR método de edición de ADN en el que se usa una secuencia de ARN y enzima nucleasa

criterion a standard that an engineering solution must meet to be considered successful

    criterio estándar que una solución de ingeniería debe cumplir para ser considerada exitosa

cuticle a waxy covering over the epidermis of the aboveground portion of land plants that reduces water loss from plant surfaces

    cutícula cubierta cerosa sobre la epidermis de la parte aérea de las plantas terrestres que reduce la pérdida de agua en la superficie de las plantas

cytokinesis a process in which a eukaryotic cell divides in two after mitosis or meiosis; cytoplasmic division

    citocinesis proceso en el que una célula eucariota se divide en dos después de la mitosis o meiosis; división citoplásmica

cytoplasm a semifluid substance enclosed by a cell's plasma membrane

    citoplasma substancia semilíquida contenida por la membrana plasmática de una célula

cytoskeleton a network of microtubules, microfilaments, and intermediate filaments that support, organize, and move eukaryotic cells and their internal structures

    citoesqueleto red de microtúbulos, microfilamentos y filamentos intermedios que apoyan, organizan y mueven a las células eucariotas y sus estructuras internas

D

decomposer an organism that breaks down decaying organic matter into simpler compounds that other organisms can use

    descomponedor organismo que descompone materia orgánica deteriorada, reduciéndola a compuestos más simples que les sirven a otros organismos

deforestation the removal of forest without adequate replanting

    deforestación tala de bosques sin reforestación adecuada

denature to modify the molecular structure, and therefore the structure, of a protein

    desnaturalizar modificar la estructura molecular y, por tanto, la estructura de una proteína

density-dependent factor a factor that slows the growth of a population by causing an increase in death rate or a decrease in birth rate as the size of the population increases

    factor dependiente de la densidad factor que reduce el crecimiento de la población al causar un aumento en la tasa de mortalidad o una reducción en la tasa de natalidad a medida que aumenta el tamaño de la población

density-independent factor a factor for which the likelihood of occurrence and the magnitude of its effect is not influenced by the density of the affected population

    factor independiente de la densidad factor en el que la densidad de la población afectada no influye en la probabilidad de que algo suceda ni en la magnitud de su efecto

deoxyribonucleic acid (DNA) the nucleic acid that carries hereditary information in its sequence; double helix structure consists of two chains (strands) of deoxyribonucleotides (adenine, guanine, thymine, cytosine)

    ácido desoxirribonucleico (ADN) el ácido nucleico que contiene la información hereditaria en su secuencia; estructura de doble hélice que consiste en dos cadenas (hebras) de desoxirribonucleótidos (adenina, guanina, timina, citosina)

derived trait a character that is present in a clade under consideration, but not in any of the clade's ancestors

    rasgo derivado rasgo que está presente en un clado bajo consideración, pero que no está presente en los antepasados del clado

desertification the conversion of grassland or woodland to desert

    desertificación la conversión de un pastizal o bosque en desierto

detritus dead particulate organic matter

    detrito materia orgánica particulada muerta

diffusion the spontaneous spreading of molecules or atoms through a fluid or gas

    difusión la propagación espontánea de moléculas o átomos por medio de un fluido o gas

directional selection a mode of natural selection in which forms of a trait at one end of a range of variation are adaptive

    selección direccional modo de selección natural en el cual las formas de un rasgo en un extremo de un rango de variación son adaptativas

disruptive selection a mode of natural selection in which forms of a trait at both ends of a range of variation are adaptive, and intermediate forms are selected against

    selección disruptiva modo de selección natural en el que las formas de un rasgo a ambos extremos de un rango de variación son adaptativas y se selecciona contra las formas intermedias

DNA see deoxyribonucleic acid

ADN ver ácido desoxirribonucleico

DNA cloning a set of laboratory methods that uses living cells to mass produce specific DNA fragments

clonación de ADN conjunto de métodos de laboratorio en el que se usan células vivas para producir en serie fragmentos específicos de ADN

DNA ligase an enzyme that seals strand breaks or gaps in double-stranded DNA

ADN ligasa enzima que sella rupturas o brechas en las hebras del ADN de doble cadena

DNA polymerase an enzyme that carries out DNA replication; it uses a DNA template to assemble a complementary strand of DNA

ADN polimerasa enzima que lleva a cabo la replicación del ADN; usa un cebador de ADN para ensamblar una hebra complementaria de ADN

DNA profiling identifying an individual by analyzing the unique parts of his or her DNA

perfil de ADN o huella genética identificación de un individuo mediante el análisis de las partes únicas de su ADN

dominant an allele that is always expressed when it is present

dominante alelo que siempre se expresa cuando está presente

E

ecological disturbance an event of intense environmental stress that occurs over a relatively short time period and causes a large change in the affected ecosystem

perturbación ecológica suceso de estrés ambiental intenso que ocurre en un período relativamente corto y causa un cambio grande en el ecosistema afectado

ecological footprint the area of Earth's surface required to sustainably support a particular level of development and consumption

huella ecológica el área de la superficie de la Tierra que se necesita para mantener un nivel determinado de desarrollo y consumo de manera sostenible

ecological niche an organism's role within its habitat; it includes how an organism utilizes materials in its environment as well as how it interacts with other organisms

nicho ecológico el papel de un organismo dentro de su hábitat; incluye la manera en que un organismo usa los materiales de su medio ambiente y su manera de interactuar con otros organismos

ecological pyramid a model that shows the distribution of energy and matter at each trophic level in a food chain or food web

pirámide ecológica modelo que muestra la distribución de energía y materia en cada nivel trófico de una cadena o red alimenticia

ecological restoration the process of assisting in the recovery of an area in an effort to restore an ecosystem that has been damaged or destroyed

restauración ecológica el proceso de apoyar la recuperación de un área en un esfuerzo por restaurar un ecosistema que ha sido dañado o destruido

ecological succession the sequence of changes in a plant community over time

sucesión ecológica secuencia de cambios en una comunidad de plantas a lo largo del tiempo

ecosystem a biological community interacting with its environment

ecosistema comunidad biológica que interactúa con su medio ambiente

ecosystem service a benefit people derive from ecosystems

servicio de ecosistema beneficio que la gente obtiene de los ecosistemas

effector a muscle or gland that acts in response to instructions from the nervous system

efector músculo o glándula que actúa en respuesta a instrucciones del sistema nervioso

electron a negatively charged subatomic particle that moves around the nucleus of an atom

electrón partícula subatómica con carga negativa que se mueve alrededor del núcleo de un átomo

electron transport chain the final step of aerobic respiration which produces most of the ATP; occurs at the inner mitochondrial membrane in eukaryotes, and the infoldings of the inner cell membrane in prokaryotes

cadena de transporte de electrones paso final de la respiración aeróbica que produce la mayoría del ATP; ocurre en la membrana mitocondrial interna en eucariotas y en los pliegues internos de la membrana celular de los procariotas

element a pure substance that consists only of atoms with the same characteristic number of protons

elemento sustancia pura que consta solo de átomos que tienen el mismo número característico de protones

embryo splitting a natural process in which the developing cells of an early embryo split spontaneously; both halves develop independently into identical twins

división de embriones proceso natural en el cual las células en desarrollo de un embrión temprano se dividen de manera espontánea; ambas partes se desarrollan de manera independiente como gemelos idénticos

endangered species a species that faces extinction in all or a part of its range

especie en peligro especie que está en riesgo de extinción en su totalidad o en parte de su zona de distribución

endemic species a species that occurs only in the area in which it evolved

especie endémica especie que ocurre solo en el área donde evolucionó

endergonic a reaction that requires a net input of free energy

reacción endergónica reacción que requiere una entrada neta de energía libre

endocytosis the process by which a cell takes in a small amount of extracellular fluid (and its contents) by the ballooning inward of the plasma membrane

    endocitosis proceso por el cual una célula introduce una pequeña cantidad de fluido extracelular (y su contenido) a través del englobamiento de la membrana plasmática hacia su interior

endophyte a fungal organism that lives within a plant host; many are symbiotes

    endófito organismo fúngico que vive dentro de una planta hospedadora; muchos son simbiontes

endoplasmic reticulum a membrane-enclosed organelle that is a system of sacs and tubes extending from the nuclear envelope; smooth ER makes phospholipids, stores calcium, and has additional functions in some cells; ribosomes on the surface of rough ER make proteins

    retículo endoplásmico orgánulo contenido dentro de una membrana que es un sistema de sacos y tubos que salen de la envoltura nuclear; el RE liso produce fosfolípidos, almacena calcio y tiene funciones adicionales en algunas células; los ribosomas en la superficie del RE rugoso producen proteínas

endospore resistant resting stage of some soil bacteria

    endospora etapa de reposo resistente en ciertas bacterias del suelo

endosymbiont an organism that lives inside another organism and does not harm it

    endosimbionte organismo que vive dentro de otro organismo sin causarle daño

endosymbiont theory a theory that mitochondria and chloroplasts evolved from bacteria that entered and lived inside a host cell

    teoría de la endosimbiosis teoría según la cual las mitocondrias y los cloroplastos evolucionaron de una bacteria que ingresó y vivió dentro de una célula hospedadora

energy pyramid a model that shows the energy that flows through each trophic level in a given ecosystem

    pirámide de energía modelo que muestra la energía que fluye por cada nivel trófico de un ecosistema dado

engineering the application of scientific and mathematical ideas to design solutions to problems

    ingeniería la aplicación de ideas científicas y matemáticas para diseñar soluciones a problemas

enzyme a biological catalyst such as a protein that speeds up a reaction without being changed by it

    enzima catalizador biológico, como una proteína, que acelera una reacción sin cambiarla

enzyme-substrate complex an enzyme with substrates bound at its active sites

    complejo enzima-sustrato enzima con sustratos unidos a sus sitios activos

epigenetic a heritable and stable change in gene expression that occurs through chromosomal changes rather DNA sequence changes

    epigenético cambio estable y hereditario en expresión génica que ocurre a través de cambios cromosómicos y no a través de cambios en la secuencia de ADN

equilibrium a state in which forward and reverse reactions proceed at equal rates

    equilibrio estado en el que las reacciones directas e inversas suceden a velocidades iguales

eukaryote any single-celled or multicellular organism whose cells contain a distinct, membrane-bound nucleus; a protist, fungus, plant, or animal

    eucariota cualquier organismo unicelular o multicelular cuyas células contienen un núcleo diferenciado cubierto por una membrana; protista, hongo, planta o animal

eusocial an animal species that lives in a multigenerational group in which many sterile workers cooperate in all tasks essential to the group's welfare; only a few members of the group produce offspring

    eusocial especie animal que vive en un grupo multigeneracional en el que muchos trabajadores estériles cooperan en todas las labores esenciales para el bienestar del grupo; solo unos cuantos miembros del grupo producen crías

evolution the cumulative genetic change in a population of organisms from generation to generation; leads to differences among populations and explains the origin of all of the organisms that exist today or have ever existed

    evolución cambio genético acumulativo en una población de organismos de una generación a la siguiente; conduce a diferencias entre poblaciones y explica el origen de todos los organismos que existen o que han existido

exergonic a reaction that ends with a net release of free energy

    reacción exergónica reacción que termina con una liberación de energía libre neta

exocytosis a process by which a cell expels a vesicle's contents to extracellular fluid

    exocitosis proceso por el cual una célula expulsa los contenidos de una vesícula hacia el fluido extracelular

exon a nucleotide sequence that remains in an RNA after post-transcriptional modification

    exón secuencia nucleotídica que permanece en el ARN después de una modificación postranscripcional

exponential growth a population growth pattern in which a population grows at a constant rate of increase over a period of time; exponential growth produces a characteristic J-shaped curve

    crecimiento exponencial patrón de crecimiento de población en el que una población crece a un ritmo que va en aumento constante durante un período de tiempo; el crecimiento exponencial produce una curva característica en forma de J

extinction the disappearance of a species; occurs when the last individual of a species dies

    extinción desaparición de una especie; ocurre cuando muere el último individuo de una especie

F

facilitated diffusion a passive transport mechanism in which a solute follows its concentration gradient across a membrane by moving through a transport protein

difusión facilitada mecanismo de transporte pasivo en el que un soluto sigue su gradiente de concentración a través de una membrana al moverse por medio de una proteína de transporte

fatty acid an organic molecule with a polar carboxyl functional group "head" and a long nonpolar hydrocarbon "tail"

ácido graso molécula orgánica con una "cabeza" carboxílica polar y una "cola" hidrocarbonada no polar

feedback the process by which the outputs of a system influence the system's behavior

retroalimentación proceso mediante el cual las salidas de un sistema influyen en el comportamiento del sistema

feedback mechanism a change within a system that intensifies the conditions that caused its occurrence (positive feedback) or causes a response that reverses the change (negative feedback)

mecanismo de retroalimentación cambio dentro de un sistema que intensifica las condiciones que causaron su ocurrencia (retroalimentación positiva) o causa una respuesta que revierte el cambio (retroalimentación negativa)

fermentation the anaerobic glucose-breakdown pathway that produces ATP without the use of electron transfer chains

fermentación trayectoria de descomposición anaeróbica de la glucosa que produce ATP sin el uso de cadenas de transferencia de electrones

fitness a measure of an individual's ability to survive and produce offspring relative to other members of its population

aptitud física medida de la capacidad de un individuo para sobrevivir y producir descendencia en comparación con el resto de los miembros de su población

flower a specialized reproductive shoot of a flowering plant (angiosperm)

flor brote reproductivo especializado de una planta con flores (angiosperma)

fluid mosaic model the model of a cell membrane as a two-dimensional fluid of mixed composition

modelo de mosaico fluido modelo de una membrana celular como un fluido bidimensional de composición mixta

food web a complex system of feeding relationships in an ecosystem

red alimentaria sistema complejo de relaciones de alimentación en un ecosistema

fossil the physical evidence of an organism that lived in the ancient past

fósil evidencia física de un organismo que vivió en el pasado antiguo

fossil fuel the combustible deposits in the Earth's crust; fossil fuels are composed of the remnants of prehistoric organisms that existed millions of years ago; examples include oil, natural gas, and coal

combustible fósil depósitos combustibles en la corteza de la Tierra; los combustibles fósiles están compuestos de los restos de organismos prehistóricos que existieron hace millones de años; entre ellos están el petróleo, el gas natural y el carbón

founder effect a reduction in genetic variation that results from a small population colonizing a new area; a type of genetic drift

efecto fundador reducción en la variación genética que resulta cuando una población pequeña coloniza un espacio nuevo; tipo de deriva genética

functional group a group of atoms that, when added to a hydrocarbon, gives the compound a particular property

grupo funcional grupo de átomos que, al ser agregados a un hidrocarburo, le dan al compuesto una propiedad particular

fungus (plural *fungi*) a single-celled or multicellular eukaryotic consumer that digests food outside the body, then absorbs the resulting breakdown products; has chitin-containing cell walls

hongo consumidor eucariota unicelular o multicelular que digiere alimentos fuera del cuerpo para luego absorber los productos descompuestos resultantes; sus paredes celulares contienen quitina

G

gamete a mature, haploid reproductive cell; e.g., a sperm or an egg

gameto célula reproductiva haploide madura; p. ej., un espermatozoide o un óvulo

gametophyte generation the stage in the life cycle of a plant during which the plant's cells undergo mitosis to produce gametes

generación de gametofitos etapa en el ciclo de vida de una planta durante la cual sus células producen gametos a través de la mitosis

gel electrophoresis a technique for separating DNA fragments according to length using an electric field generated in a semi-solid gel

electroforesis en gel técnica de separación de fragmentos de ADN de acuerdo con su longitud a través de un campo eléctrico generado en un gel semisólido

gene a chromosomal DNA sequence that encodes an RNA or protein product

gen secuencia de ADN cromosómico que codifica un producto de ARN o proteína

gene drive a gene capable of inserting itself into other chromosomes and spreading through a population

impulso genético gen capaz de insertarse en otros cromosomas y distribuirse en una población

gene expression the multistep process by which the information in a gene guides assembly of an RNA or protein product; includes transcription and translation

    expresión génica proceso de varias etapas en el que la información de un gen guía el ensamblaje de un producto de ARN o proteína; incluye la transcripción y traducción

gene flow the movement of alleles between populations

    flujo genético movimiento de alelos entre poblaciones

gene pool all the alleles of all the genes in a population; a pool of genetic resources

    acervo génico todos los alelos de todos los genes de una población; acervo de recursos genéticos

gene therapy a treatment method for a genetic defect or disorder by transferring a normal or modified gene into the affected individual

    terapia génica método de tratamiento para un defecto o trastorno genético por medio de la transferencia de un gen normal o modificado al individuo afectado

genetic drift a change in allele frequency due to chance alone

    deriva genética cambio en la frecuencia alélica que se da solamente por azar

genetic engineering a process by which an individual's genome is altered deliberately, in order to change its phenotype

    ingeniería genética proceso por el cual el genoma de un individuo es alterado deliberadamente con el fin de cambiar su fenotipo

genetically modified organism (GMO) an organism deliberately modified by genetic engineering

    organismo modificado genéticamente (OMG) organismo deliberadamente modificado a través de la ingeniería genética

genome an organism's complete set of genetic material

    genoma conjunto completo de material genético de un organismo

genomics the study of whole-genome structure and function

    genómica el estudio de la estructura y función del genoma completo

genotype the particular set of alleles that is carried by an individual's chromosomes

    genotipo el conjunto particular de alelos que llevan los cromosomas de un individuo

genus (plural *genera*) a group of species that share a unique set of traits; also the first part of a species name

    género grupo de especies que comparten un conjunto único de rasgos; también es la primera parte del nombre de una especie

glomeromycete a fungus that partners with plant roots; its hyphae grow inside cell walls of root cells

    glomeromycetes hongos que se asocian con las raíces de las plantas; sus hifas crecen dentro de las paredes celulares de las células de las raíces

glucose a simple sugar with the chemical formula $C_6H_{12}O_6$; often serves as a carbohydrate monomer with a ring structure

    glucosa azúcar simple con la fórmula química $C_6H_{12}O_6$; puede servir como monómero de carbohidrato con estructura de anillo

glycogen a complex carbohydrate that consists of highly branched chains of glucose monomers

    glucógeno carbohidrato complejo que consiste en cadenas de monómeros de glucosa muy ramificadas

glycolysis a set of reactions that convert glucose to two pyruvate for a net yield of two ATP and two NADH

    glicólisis conjunto de reacciones que convierten la glucosa en dos piruvatos para un rendimiento neto de dos ATP y dos NADH

Golgi body a membrane-enclosed organelle that modifies proteins and lipids, then sorts the finished products into vesicles; shaped like a stack of pancakes

    aparato de Golgi orgánulo contenido en una membrana, que modifica proteínas y lípidos y luego ordena los productos terminados en vesículas; tiene la forma de una pila de discos

gradualism in biology, the idea that evolutionary change of a species is because of a slow, steady accumulation of changes over time; in geology, the principle that geologic changes result from slow processes rather than sudden events

    gradualismo en biología, la idea de que el cambio evolutivo en una especie se debe a la acumulación lenta y estable de cambios en el tiempo; en la geología, el principio según el cual los cambios geológicos son el resultado de procesos lentos en lugar de sucesos repentinos

gravitropism a directional response to gravity

    gravitropismo respuesta direccional a la gravedad

greenhouse effect the natural warming of the lower atmosphere by greenhouse gases

    efecto invernadero calentamiento natural de la atmósfera inferior por gases invernadero

greenhouse gas a gas, such as carbon dioxide, methane, or water vapor, that warms the lower atmosphere

    gas invernadero gases como el dióxido de carbono, el metano o el vapor de agua, que calientan la atmósfera inferior

H

habitat the natural environment or place where an organism, population, or species lives

    hábitat medio ambiente natural o lugar donde vive un organismo, población o especie

habitat fragmentation the break up of a continuous habitat into smaller pockets by the intrusion of human alterations to the land (e.g., buildings, roads)

    fragmentación del hábitat rompimiento de un hábitat continuo en secciones más pequeñas como consecuencia de alteraciones humanas a la tierra (p. ej., edificios, caminos)

half-life the characteristic time it takes for half of a quantity of a radioisotope to decay

    vida media tiempo típico que tarda media cantidad de radioisótopo en descomponerse

halophile an organism adapted to life in a highly salty environment

    halófilo organismo adaptado a la vida en un medio ambiente muy salado

heliotropism a directional change in position in response to the changing angle of the sun throughout the day

    heliotropismo cambio de dirección en respuesta al ángulo cambiante de la luz del sol durante el día

heterotroph an organism that gets its energy and nutrients from eating other organisms; also known as a consumer

    heterótrofo organismo que obtiene su energía y nutrientes al comerse a otros organismos; también conocido como consumidor

heterozygous possessing two different alleles of the same gene

    heterocigoto que posee dos alelos del mismo gen

histone a type of protein that associates with DNA and structurally organizes eukaryotic chromosomes

    histona tipo de proteína que se asocia con el ADN y organiza estructuralmente los cromosomas eucariotas

homeostasis a process in which organisms keep their internal conditions within tolerable ranges by sensing and responding appropriately to change

    homeostasis proceso en el que organismos mantienen sus condiciones internas dentro de rangos tolerables al sentir cambios y responder adecuadamente a ellos

homologous chromosome in a nucleus, one of a pair of chromosomes that have the same length, shape, and genes

    cromosoma homólogo en un núcleo, cada miembro de un par de cromosomas que tienen la misma longitud, forma y genes

homologous structure a body structure similar to another in a different lineage because the structure evolved in a common ancestor

    estructura homóloga estructura corporal que es similar a una de otro linaje debido a que la estructura evolucionó en un ancestro común

homozygous possessing a pair of identical alleles

    homocigoto que posee un par de alelos idénticos

hormone one of many chemical messengers in multicellular organisms that usually travels in body fluids to target cells, where it combines with receptors and affects some aspect of metabolism, growth, or reproduction

    hormona uno de muchos mensajeros químicos en organismos multicelulares que normalmente viajan en fluidos corporales hacia células objetivo, donde se combinan con receptores y afectan algún aspecto del metabolismo, el crecimiento o la reproducción

hydrocarbon a substance made entirely of carbon and hydrogen

    hidrocarburo sustancia compuesta completamente de carbono e hidrógeno

hydrogen bond a force of attraction between a hydrogen atom in one molecule and a highly attractive atom in another molecule

    enlace de hidrógeno fuerza de atracción entre un átomo de hidrógeno y un átomo altamente atractivo de otra molécula

hydrotropism a directional growth of plant roots in response to water

    hidrotropismo crecimiento direccional de las raíces de una planta en respuesta al agua

hyperaccumulator a plant that can take up and store high concentrations of metals from soil or water

    planta hiperacumuladora planta que puede absorber y almacenar altas concentraciones de metales del suelo o agua

hypertonic a solution with a solute concentration greater than that of the solution with which it is compared

    hipertónica solución con una concentración de soluto mayor que la solución con la cual se le compara

hypha (plural *hyphae*) one filament in a fungal mycelium

    hifa filamento en un micelio fúngico

hypotonic a solution with a solute concentration less than that of the solution with which it is compared

    hipotónica solución con una concentración de soluto menor que la solución con la cual se le compara

I

immunity the body's ability to resist and fight infections

    inmunidad la capacidad del cuerpo para resistir y combatir infecciones

incomplete dominance an inheritance pattern in which one allele is not fully dominant over another, so the heterozygous phenotype is an intermediate blend between the two homozygous phenotypes

    dominancia incompleta patrón de herencia en el que un alelo no es completamente dominante sobre otro, por tanto, el fenotipo heterocigoto es una combinación intermedia entre los dos fenotipos homocigotos

index fossil a fossil that dates the layers where it is found because it came from an organism that is abundantly preserved in rocks, was widespread geographically, and existed as a species or genus for only a relatively short time

    fósil índice fósil que data las capas del sitio donde fue encontrado porque viene de un organismo preservado en abundancia en las rocas, que estuvo geográficamente esparcido y existió como especie o género por un tiempo relativamente corto

inflammation a part of innate immunity: a local response to tissue damage or infection; characterized by redness, warmth, swelling, and pain

    inflamación parte de la inmunidad innata: respuesta local a daños a tejidos o infección; se caracteriza por enrojecimiento, calor, hinchazón y dolor

inheritance the transmission of DNA to offspring

    herencia transmisión de ADN a la descendencia

initiator tRNA a type of tRNA that delivers amino acids to a ribosome during translation
  ARNt iniciador tipo de ARNt que distribuye aminoácidos a un ribosoma durante la traducción

innate immunity a set of immediate, general responses (complement activation, phagocytosis, inflammation, fever) that defend the body from infection in multicellular organisms
  inmunidad innata conjunto de respuestas inmediatas generales (activación de complemento, fagocitosis, inflamación, fiebre) que defiende al cuerpo de la infección en organismos multicelulares

instinctive behavior an innate response to a simple stimulus
  comportamiento instintivo respuesta innata ante un estímulo simple

insulator a region of DNA that, upon binding a transcription factor, can block the effect of a silencer or enhancer on a neighboring gene
  aislador región del ADN que, al unirse a un factor de transcripción, puede bloquear el efecto de un silenciador o potenciador en un gen vecino

intermediate disturbance hypothesis a hypothesis that states that species richness is greatest when physical and biological disturbances are moderate in their intensity or frequency
  hipótesis de la perturbación intermedia hipótesis según la cual la riqueza de especies es mayor cuando las perturbaciones físicas y biológicas son de intensidad y frecuencia moderada

interphase the period in the life cycle of a cell in which there is no visible mitotic division; period between mitotic divisions in which cell performs normal growth and metabolic functions
  interfase período en el ciclo de vida de una célula en el que no hay división mitótica visible; período entre divisiones mitóticas durante el cual la célula desempeña funciones normales de metabolismo y crecimiento

interphase in a eukaryotic cell cycle, the interval during which a cell grows, roughly doubles the number of its cytoplasmic components, and replicates its DNA in preparation for division
  interfase en una célula eucariota, el intervalo durante el cual una célula crece, duplica aproximadamente el número de sus componentes citoplásmicos y replica su ADN para prepararse para la división

intron a nucleotide sequence that intervenes between exons and is removed during post transcriptional modification
  intrón secuencia de nucleótidos que interviene entre exones y es retirada durante la modificación postranscripcional

invasive species a non-native species that outcompetes and threatens the existence of native organisms in an ecosystem
  especie invasiva especie no nativa, más competitiva y que amenaza la existencia de organismos nativos en un ecosistema

invertebrate an animal that does not have a backbone
  invertebrado animal que no tiene columna vertebral

ion an atom that has a different number of electrons than protons
  ion átomo que tiene un número de electrones diferente del de protones

ionic bond a type of chemical bond formed by the force of attraction between oppositely charged ions
  enlace iónico tipo de enlace químico formado por la fuerza de atracción entre iones de carga opuesta

isotonic a solution with identical concentrations of solute and solvent molecules
  isotónico solución con concentraciones idénticas de moléculas de soluto y solvente

isotope a variation of an element with the same number of protons (or the same atomic number) but a different number of neutrons (and thus a different atomic mass) than another variation of the same element
  isótopo variación de un elemento que tiene el mismo número de protones (o el mismo número atómico) pero un número diferente de neutrones (y, por tanto, una masa atómica diferente) que otra variación del mismo elemento

K

keystone species a species that has a disproportionately large effect on community structure relative to its abundance
  especie clave especie que, en comparación con su abundancia, tiene un efecto desproporcionadamente grande sobre la estructura de una comunidad

Krebs cycle a cyclic pathway that harvests energy from acetyl–CoA; part of aerobic respiration; also called citric acid cycle
  ciclo de Krebs trayectoria cíclica que cosecha energía del acetil-CoA; parte de la respiración aeróbica; también conocido como ciclo del ácido cítrico

L

learned behavior a behavior that is modified by experience
  comportamiento aprendido comportamiento modificado por la experiencia

lichen a composite organism consisting of a fungus and green algae or cyanobacteria
  liquen organismo compuesto que consta de un hongo y un alga o cianobacteria

life history a pattern that describes how an individual organism uses resources and energy for growth, survival, and reproduction over the course of its lifetime
  historia de vida patrón que describe la manera en que un organismo individual usa recursos y energía para crecer, sobrevivir y reproducirse a lo largo de su vida

light-dependent reactions the first stage of photosynthesis that requires the presence of light; light energy is converted to chemical energy in the form of ATP and NADPH
  reacciones dependientes de la luz primera etapa de la fotosíntesis que requiere la presencia de luz; la energía luminosa se convierte en energía química en forma de ATP y NADPH

light-independent reactions the second stage of photosynthesis that does not directly require light; use ATP and NADPH to build sugar molecules such as glucose from carbon dioxide and water.

reacciones no dependientes de la luz segunda etapa de la fotosíntesis que no requiere de luz directa; usa ATP y NADPH para construir moléculas de azúcar; p. ej., glucosa a partir de dióxido de carbono y agua

lignin a material that strengthens cell walls of vascular plants

lignina material que fortalece las paredes celulares de las plantas vasculares

lipid a fatty, oily, or waxy organic compound that is partly or completely nonpolar

lípido compuesto orgánico graso, aceitoso o ceroso que es parcial o completamente no polar

logistic growth a population growth pattern in which a population grows slowly at first, followed by a period of exponential growth before leveling off at a stable size; logistic growth produces a characteristic S-shaped curve

crecimiento logístico patrón de crecimiento de la población en el que la población crece lentamente al principio, seguido por un período de crecimiento exponencial antes de nivelarse al alcanzar un tamaño estable; el crecimiento logístico produce una curva típica en forma de S

lysogenic pathway the replication pathway of a bacteriophage in which viral DNA becomes integrated into the host's chromosome and is passed to the host's descendants

ciclo lisogénico trayectoria de replicación de un bacteriófago en la cual el ADN se integra al cromosoma del anfitrión y es transmitido a los descendientes del anfitrión

lysosome an enzyme-filled vesicle that breaks down cellular wastes and debris

lisosoma vesícula llena de enzima que descompone desperdicios celulares y desechos

lytic pathway the replication pathway of a bacteriophage in which a virus immediately replicates in its host and kills it

ciclo lítico trayectoria de replicación de un bacteriófago en la cual un virus se replica dentro de su anfitrión y lo mata

M

macroevolution evolutionary patterns and trends on a larger scale than microevolution; e.g., adaptive radiation, coevolution

macroevolución patrones evolutivos y tendencias a una escala mayor que la de la microevolución; por ejemplo, la radiación adaptativa, la coevolución

mark-recapture sampling a method in which a sample group of members of a population are captured and marked; the proportion of marked organisms in a second group, captured at a later time, is used to estimate the size of the population

muestreo de marca y recaptura método en el que un grupo muestra de los miembros de una población es capturado y marcado; la proporción de organismos marcados en un segundo grupo, capturado en un momento posterior, se usa para estimar el tamaño de la población

mass extinction a sudden, catastrophic event during which a significant percentage of all life-forms on Earth become extinct

extinción masiva suceso repentino y catastrófico en el que se extingue un porcentaje significativo de todas las formas de vida en la Tierra

meiosis division of the cell nucleus that produces haploid cells; produces gametes in animals and spores in plants

meiosis división del núcleo celular que produce células haploides; produce gametos en animales y esporas en plantas

meristem a zone of undifferentiated parenchyma cells, the divisions of which give rise to new tissues during plant growth

meristemo zona de células de parénquima indiferenciadas, cuyas divisiones dan lugar a nuevos tejidos durante el crecimiento de la planta

metabolism all of the enzyme-mediated reactions in a cell

metabolismo todas las reacciones mediadas por enzimas de una célula

metaphase a stage of mitosis at which all chromosomes are aligned midway between spindle poles

metafase etapa de la mitosis en la cual todos los cromosomas se alinean en la línea media del huso

methanogen a prokaryotic organism that produces methane gas (CH_4) as a metabolic by-product

metanógeno organismo procariota que produce gas metano (CH_4) como producto secundario de su metabolismo

microarray a laboratory tool used to detect the expression of thousands of DNA sequences at the same time

microarreglo herramienta de laboratorio que detecta la expresión de miles de secuencias de ADN al mismo tiempo

microevolution changes in allele frequencies that occur within a population over successive generations

microevolución cambios en la frecuencia alélica que ocurren dentro de una población a lo largo de generaciones sucesivas

mitochondrion (plural *mitochondria*) a double-membraned organelle that produces ATP by aerobic respiration in eukaryotes

mitocondria orgánulo de doble membrana que produce ATP a través de la respiración celular en los eucariotas

mitosis a division of the cell nucleus resulting in the distribution of a complete set of chromosomes to each daughter cell; occurs in stages (prophase, metaphase, anaphase, and telophase); basis of body growth, tissue repair, and (in some organisms) asexual reproduction

    mitosis división del núcleo celular que resulta en la distribución de un juego completo de cromosomas a cada célula hija; ocurre en etapas (profase, metafase, anafase y telofase); es la base del crecimiento del cuerpo, reparación de tejidos y (en algunos organismos) de la reproducción asexual

mitotic spindle a temporary structure consisting of microtubules that moves chromosomes during mitosis

    huso mitótico estructura temporal que consiste en microtúbulos que mueve los cromosomas durante la mitosis

model a tool for representing an idea or an explanation, or an analagous system that can be used to test a hypothesis

    modelo herramienta para representar una idea o explicación, o un sistema análogo que sirve para probar una hipótesis

molecule a collection of atoms bonded together that behave as a unit

    molécula colección de átomos enlazados que se comportan como unidad

monomer a molecule that is used as a subunit of a larger molecule

    monómero molécula que se usa como subunidad de una molécula más grande

monosaccharide a simple carbohydrate molecule that is often a monomer for a complex carbohydrate; also referred to as a simple sugar

    monosacárido molécula de carbohidrato simple que a menudo es un monómero para un carbohidrato complejo; también se conoce como azúcar simple

mutagen any physical or chemical agent that is capable of producing mutations

    mutágeno cualquier agente físico o químico que es capaz de producir mutaciones

mutation a permanent change in the DNA sequence of a chromosome

    mutación cambio permanente en la secuencia de ADN de un cromosoma

mycelium mass of threadlike filaments (hyphae) that make up the body of a multicellular fungus

    micelio masa de filamentos filiformes (hifas) que forman el cuerpo de un hongo multicelular

mycorrhiza (plural *mycorrhizae*) a mutually beneficial partnership between a fungus and a plant root

    micorriza asociación mutuamente benéfica entre un hongo y la raíz de una planta

N

natural resource a natural material used by humans, such as water, forests, animals, and minerals

    recurso natural material natural usado por humanos, como el agua, los bosques, los animales y los minerales

natural selection a major mechanism of evolution: the differential survival and reproduction of individuals of a population based on differences in shared, heritable traits; outcome of environmental pressures

    selección natural uno de los mecanismos principales de la evolución: la supervivencia y reproducción diferenciales entre individuos de una población según las distinciones de los rasgos hereditarios que comparten; es el resultado de presiones ambientales

near-uniform distribution a population distribution pattern in which individuals are more evenly spaced than would be expected by chance

    distribución casi uniforme patrón de distribución de una población en el cual los individuos están espaciados de manera más pareja de lo que se esperaría por azar

negative feedback mechanism a change that causes a response that reverses the change; important mechanism of homeostasis

    mecanismo de retroalimentación negativa cambio que genera una respuesta que revierte el cambio; mecanismo importante de la homeostasis

neutral an atom with exactly the same number of electrons as protons; it carries no charge

    neutral átomo que tiene exactamente el mismo número de electrones que de protones; no lleva carga

neutron a neutral subatomic particle that occurs in the nucleus of an atom

    neutrón partícula subatómica que ocurre en el núcleo de un átomo

node in a phylogenetic tree, represents a common ancestor

    nodo en un árbol filogenético, representa un ancestro común

non-native species a species that evolved in one community and later became established in a different one

    especie no nativa especie que evolucionó en una comunidad y más adelante se estableció en otra distinta

nonenveloped virus a virus particle in which its outermost layer is the protein capsid

    virus sin envoltura partícula de virus en la cual la capa exterior es la proteína cápside

nonpoint source a source of water pollution that is widespread in the environment

    contaminación difusa fuente de contaminación de agua que está extendida en el medio ambiente

nonpolar a chemical bond or molecule in which charge is distributed evenly

    no polar enlace químico o molécula cuya carga está distribuida de manera pareja

nonrenewable resource a natural resource that cannot be replenished at the same rate at which it is used

    recurso no renovable recurso natural que no puede ser reabastecido a la misma tasa que se usa

nonvascular plant a plant that does not have xylem and phloem; a bryophyte such as a moss

    planta no vascular planta que no tiene xilema ni floema; una briófita, como un musgo

nucleic acid polymer of nucleotides; DNA or RNA

    ácido nucleico polímero de nucleótidos; ADN o ARN

nucleotide a molecule that consists of a monosaccharide ring bonded to a nitrogen-containing base and one, two, or three phosphate groups

    nucleótido molécula que consta de un anillo monosacárido unido a una base que contiene nitrógeno y uno, dos o tres grupos fosfato

nucleus of an atom, central core area occupied by protons and neutrons; of a eukaryotic cell, organelle with a double membrane that holds the cell's DNA

    núcleo de un átomo, el área central ocupada por protones y neutrones; de una célula eucariota, un orgánulo de doble membrana que contiene el ADN de la célula

O

oncogene a gene that helps transform a normal cell into a tumor cell

    oncogén gen que ayuda a transformar una célula normal en una célula tumoral

operator a DNA binding site for a repressor; part of an operon

    operador el sitio donde un represor se une al ADN; parte de un operón

operon a group of genes together with a promoter–operator DNA sequence that controls their transcription

    operón grupo de genes unidos a una secuencia promotora-operadora que controla su transcripción

organ a structure that consists of tissues engaged in a collective task in multicellular organisms

    órgano estructura compuesta de tejidos que cumplen una función colectiva en los organismos multicelulares

organ system a set of interacting organs that carry out a particular body function in multicellular organisms

    sistema de órganos conjunto de órganos que interactúan para llevar a cabo una función corporal específica en los organismos multicelulares

organelle a structure that carries out a specialized metabolic function inside a cell

    orgánulo estructura que desempeña una función metabólica especializada dentro de una célula

organic compound a chemical compound that consists mainly of carbon and hydrogen

    compuesto orgánico compuesto químico que está formado principalmente por carbono e hidrógeno

osmosis the diffusion of water across a selectively permeable membrane; occurs in response to a difference in solute concentration between the fluids on either side of the membrane

    ósmosis difusión del agua a través de una membrana selectivamente permeable; ocurre en respuesta a una diferencia en concentración del soluto los entre fluidos que hay a cada lado de una membrana

ovary in flowering plants, the enlarged base of a carpel, inside which one or more ovules form and eggs are fertilized; in animals, the egg-producing gonad

    ovario en las plantas con flores, la base agrandada del carpelo, dentro del cual se forman uno o más óvulos y son fertilizados; en los animales, la gónada que produce óvulos

ovule a seed plant reproductive structure in which the female gametophyte forms and develops; matures into a seed after fertilization

    óvulo estructura reproductiva de las plantas espermatofitas donde se desarrolla y forma el gametofito femenino; madura en forma de semilla después de la fertilización

P

parenchyma a simple plant tissue composed of living, thin-walled cells; has various specialized functions such as photosynthesis

    parénquima tejido simple en las plantas; está compuesto de células vivas con paredes delgadas; tiene varias funciones especializadas, como la fotosíntesis

passive transport a membrane-crossing mechanism that requires no energy input

    transporte pasivo mecanismo de movimiento a través de membranas que no requiere energía

pathogen disease-causing agent (virus or cellular organism

    patógeno agente que causa enfermedad (virus u organismo celular)

pellicle an outer layer of plasma membrane and elastic proteins that protects and gives shape to many unwalled, single-celled protists

    película capa exterior formada por membrana plasmática y proteínas elásticas que protege y da forma a muchos protistas unicelulares que no cuentan con paredes

per capita growth rate the rate of change in population size, expressed in terms of the increase in population per existing individual; may be calculated by subtracting the population's per capita death rate from its per capita birth rate

    tasa de crecimiento per cápita tasa de cambio en el tamaño de la población, expresada en términos del aumento en la población en relación con los individuos existentes; se calcula restando la tasa de mortalidad per cápita de la población de su tasa de natalidad per cápita

peristalsis wavelike smooth muscle contractions that propel food through the digestive tract

    peristalsis contracciones musculares como ondas que impulsan el alimento por el tracto digestivo

peroxisome an enzyme-filled vesicle that breaks down fatty acids, amino acids, and toxic substances

    peroxisoma vesícula llena de enzimas que descompone ácidos grasos, aminoácidos y sustancias tóxicas

petal a modified, often brightly colored, leaf of a flower

    pétalo hoja modificada y a veces colorida de una flor

pH a measure of the number of hydrogen ions in a water-based fluid

    pH medida del número de iones de hidrógeno que tiene un fluido basado en agua

phenotype an individual's observable traits

    fenotipo rasgos observables de un individuo

pheromone a chemical that serves as a communication signal between members of an animal species

    feromona químico que sirve como señal de comunicación entre miembros de una especie animal

phloem a complex vascular tissue of plants; its living sieve elements compose sieve tubes that distribute sugars through the plant body; each sieve element has an associated companion cell that provides it with metabolic support

    floema tejido vascular complejo que tienen las plantas; sus elementos cribosos vivientes componen tubos cribosos que distribuyen azúcares a lo largo del cuerpo de la planta; cada elemento criboso tiene una célula acompañante que le da apoyo metabólico

phosphate group a functional group that consists of a phosphorus atom bonded to four oxygen atoms

    grupo fosfato grupo funcional que consta de un átomo de fósforo unido a cuatro átomos de oxígeno

photoautotroph an organism that obtains carbon from carbon dioxide and energy from light

    fotoautótrofo organismo que obtiene carbono del dióxido de carbono y energía de la luz

photoheterotroph an organism that obtains carbon from organic compounds and energy from light

    fotoheterótrofo organismo que obtiene carbono de compuestos orgánicos y energía de la luz

photoperiodism a biological response to seasonal changes in the relative lengths of day and night

    fotoperiodismo respuesta biológica a cambios estacionales en la duración relativa del día y la noche

photosynthesis the biological process that captures light energy and transforms it into the chemical energy of organic molecules (such as glucose), which are made from carbon dioxide and water; used by plants, algae, and several kinds of bacteria

    fotosíntesis proceso biológico que captura energía luminosa y la transforma en la energía química de moléculas orgánicas (como la glucosa), que se componen de dióxido de carbono y agua; este proceso lo siguen las plantas, las algas y varios tipos de bacterias

phototropism a directional response to light
    fototropismo respuesta direccional a la luz

phylogenetic analysis a group of methods to estimate relatedness between organisms by comparing genetic sequences

    análisis filogenético grupo de métodos para estimar el nivel de relación entre organismos mediante la comparación de sus secuencias genéticas

phylogeny an evolutionary history of a species or group of species

    filogenia historia evolutiva de una especie o grupo de especies

phytoplankton a community of tiny drifting or swimming photosynthetic organisms

    fitoplancton comunidad de diminutos organismos fotosintéticos que flotan o nadan

phytoremediation the use of plants to extract chemical contaminants from soil or water

    fitorremediación uso de plantas para extraer contaminantes químicos del suelo o el agua

pioneer species a species whose traits allow it to colonize new or newly vacated habitats

especie pionera especie cuyos rasgos le permiten colonizar hábitats nuevos o recientemente desocupados

plot sampling a sampling method in which the number of members of a population occupying a sample area or volume of their range is counted directly in order to estimate the size of the population

    muestreo de parcelas método de muestreo en el cual el número de integrantes de una población que ocupa un área de muestra o volumen de muestra de su rango se cuenta directamente para estimar el tamaño de la población

pluripotent the capability of stem cells to develop into any of the cell types present in an organism

    pluripotente capacidad de las células madre de desarrollarse como cualquier tipo de célula presente en un organismo

point source a single, easily identifiable source of water pollution

    fuente puntual fuente única de contaminación del agua que es fácil de identificar

polar a chemical bond or molecule in which charge is distributed unevenly

    polar enlace químico o molécula cuya carga está distribuida de manera despareja

pollen grain a walled, immature male gametophyte of a seed plant

    grano de polen en las plantas que producen semillas, un gametofito masculino que tiene pared externa

pollination the arrival of pollen on a stigma or other pollen-receiving reproductive part of a seed plant

    polinización en las plantas que producen semillas, la llegada del polen a un estigma u otra parte reproductiva receptora de polen

pollutant a harmful substance released into the environment by human activities

    contaminante sustancia dañina liberada al ambiente por actividades humanas

polymer a molecule that consists of repeated monomers
    polímero molécula que está compuesta de monómeros repetidos

polymerase chain reaction (PCR) laboratory method that rapidly generates many copies of a specific section of DNA

    reacción en cadena de la polimerasa (PCR, en inglés) método de laboratorio que genera muchas copias de un segmento específico de ADN de manera rápida

polysaccharide a molecule formed by three or more simple sugar molecules (monosaccharides)

    polisacárido molécula formada por tres o más moléculas de azúcar simple (monosacáridos)

population a group of individual organisms of the same species that interbreed with one another

    población grupo de organismos individuales de la misma especie que se reproducen entre sí

population density the average number of individuals in a population per unit area or volume

    densidad de población número promedio de individuos que tiene una población por unidad de área o volumen

population distribution the location of individuals in a population relative to one another

    distribución de la población la ubicación de individuos en una población en relación con los otros individuos

population size the total number of individuals in a population

    tamaño de población número total de individuos que tiene una población

positive feedback mechanism a response that intensifies the conditions that caused its occurrence

    mecanismo de retroalimentación positiva respuesta que intensifica las condiciones que causaron que sucediera

predation an ecological relationship in which one species captures, kills, and eats another

    depredación relación ecológica en la cual una especie captura, mata y se come a otra

pressure flow theory an explanation of how a difference in turgor between sieve elements in source and sink regions pushes sugar-rich fluid through a sieve tube

    hipótesis de flujo de presión explicación de cómo una diferencia de turgencia entre elementos cribosos en regiones de fuente y sumidero impulsa fluidos ricos en azúcar a través de un tubo criboso

primer a short, single strand of DNA or RNA that base-pairs with a specific DNA sequence and serves as an attachment point for DNA polymerase

    partidor hebra de ADN o ARN simple y corta que se aparea con una secuencia específica de ADN y sirve como punto de unión para la ADN polimerasa

prion an infectious protein

    prion proteína infecciosa

producer an organism that makes its own food from abiotic sources, such as sunlight or inorganic materials

    productor organismo que produce su propio alimento a partir de fuentes abióticas como luz solar o materiales inorgánicos

product a molecule that is produced by a reaction

    producto molécula que se produce por una reacción

prokaryote an informal term for a single-celled organism without a nucleus; a bacterium or archaeon

    procariota término informal para referirse a un organismo unicelular que no tiene núcleo; bacteria o arquea

promoter a sequence that is a site where RNA polymerase binds and begins transcription in DNA

    promotor secuencia que es un sitio donde el ARN polimerasa se une y comienza la transcripción en el ADN

prophase stage of mitosis during which chromosomes condense and become attached to a newly forming spindle

    profase etapa de la mitosis en la que los cromosomas se condensan y se unen a un huso recién formado

protein a large, complex organic compound composed of amino acid subunits; proteins are the principal structural components of cells

    proteína compuesto orgánico complejo grande que se compone de subunidades de aminoácidos; las proteínas son el principal componente estructural de las células

proteome the study of all the proteins encoded by a genome within a specific context

    proteoma el estudio de todas las proteínas codificadas por un genoma dentro de un contexto específico

protist a common term for a eukaryote that is not a plant, animal, or fungus

    protista término común para un eucariota que no es una planta, animal u hongo

proto-oncogene a gene that, by mutation, can become an oncogene

    protooncogén gen que, por mutación, se convierte en oncogén

proton a positively charged subatomic particle that occurs in the nucleus of an atom

    protón partícula subatómica con carga positiva que se encuentra en el núcleo de un átomo

pseudopod a temporary protrusion that helps some eukaryotic cells move and engulf prey

    pseudópodo protuberancia temporal con la que ciertas células eucariotas se mueven y envuelven a sus presas

punctuated equilibrium the concept that evolution has periods of inactivity (i.e., periods of little or no change within a species) followed by very active phases, so that major adaptations or clusters of adaptations appear suddenly in the fossil record

    equilibrio puntuado concepto que establece que la evolución tiene períodos de inactividad (es decir, períodos de poco o ningún cambio dentro de una especie) seguidos por fases muy activas, de tal manera que las grandes adaptaciones o cúmulos de adaptaciones aparecen repentinamente en el registro fósil

pyramid of numbers a model that compares the relative number of individual organisms at each trophic level

    pirámide de números modelo en que se compara el número relativo de organismos individuales a cada nivel trófico

pyruvate a three-carbon product of glycolysis

    piruvato producto de la glicólisis que contiene tres átomos de carbono

R

radioisotope an isotope with an unstable nucleus

    radioisótopo isótopo con un núcleo inestable

radiometric dating a method of estimating the age of a rock or fossil by measuring the content and proportions of a radioisotope and its daughter elements

    datación radiométrica método para estimar la edad de un fósil o roca a través de la medición del contenido y proporciones de sus elementos hijos

random distribution a population distribution pattern that occurs when occurs when resources are distributed uniformly through the environment, and proximity to others neither benefits nor harms individuals

    distribución aleatoria patrón de distribución que ocurre cuando los recursos están uniformemente distribuidos en el medio ambiente y su proximidad con otros ni beneficia ni daña a los individuos

range the geographical area in which a population of organisms lives
  rango área geográfica en la cual vive una población de organismos

reactant a molecule that enters a reaction and is changed by participating in it
  reactante molécula que entra en una reacción y cambia al participar en ella

recessive an allele that is not expressed in the heterozygous state
  recesivo alelo que no se expresa en el estado heterocigoto

recombinant DNA a DNA molecule that consists of genetic material from two or more organisms
  ADN recombinante molécula de ADN que consiste en material genético de dos o más organismos

renewable resource a natural resource that can be replenished at the same rate at which it is used
  recurso renovable recurso natural que puede ser reabastecido al mismo ritmo en que se usa

replication the process by which a cell duplicates all of its DNA before it divides
  replicación proceso a través del cual una célula duplica todo su ADN antes de dividirse

repressor a transcription factor that slows or stops transcription
  represor factor de transcripción que detiene o reduce la velocidad de la transcripción

reproductive cloning a laboratory procedure such as SCNT that produces animal clones from a single somatic cell
  clonación reproductiva procedimiento de laboratorio, como SCNT, que produce clones animales a partir de una sola célula somática

reproductive isolation the end of gene flow between populations; part of speciation
  aislamiento reproductivo el fin del flujo genético entre poblaciones; parte de la especiación

reservoir an organism that can be infected with pathogens transmissible to humans
  reservorio organismo que puede ser infectado con patógenos transmisibles a los humanos

resilience in ecology, the ability of an ecological community to regain its original structure and function following a disturbance
  resiliencia en la ecología, la capacidad de una comunidad ecológica para recuperar su estructura y función originales después de una perturbación

resistance in ecology, the ability of an ecological community to remain unchanged when affected by a disturbance
  resistencia en la ecología, la capacidad de una comunidad ecológica de permanecer inalterada al ser afectada por una perturbación

restriction enzyme an enzyme that cuts DNA wherever a specific nucleotide sequence occurs
  enzima de restricción enzima que corta el ADN en cualquier lugar donde ocurre una secuencia nucleótida específica

retrovirus an RNA virus that uses the enzyme reverse transcriptase to produce viral DNA in a host cell
  retrovirus virus ARN que usa la enzima transcriptasa inversa para producir ADN viral en una célula anfitriona

rhizome a fleshy plant stem that grows horizontally along or under the ground
  rizoma la parte carnosa del tallo de una planta que crece horizontalmente a lo largo o debajo del suelo

ribonucleic acid (RNA) a single-stranded nucleic acid molecule that functions mainly in protein synthesis from DNA templates
  ácido ribonucleico (ARN) molécula de ácido nucleico de cadena sencilla que funciona principalmente en la síntesis de proteínas a partir de moldes de ADN

RNA see ribonucleic acid
  ARN ver ácido ribonucleico

RNA interference a mechanism in which RNA molecules interfere with gene expression by preventing translation of specific messenger RNAs
  ARN interferente mecanismo donde las moléculas de ARN interfieren con la expresión génica al prevenir la traducción de ARNs mensajeros específicos

RNA polymerase an enzyme that carries out transcription
  ARN polimerasa enzima que lleva a cabo la transcripción

root system the organ system of a plant that absorbs water and dissolved minerals; roots generally grow below ground
  sistema de raíces sistema de órganos de una planta que absorbe agua y minerales disueltos; las raíces generalmente crecen bajo tierra

S

sac fungus a fungus that forms spores in a sac-shaped structure during sexual reproduction; sac fungi are the most diverse fungal group
  ascomicetos hongos que durante la reproducción sexual forman esporas en una estructura en forma de bolsa; los ascomicetos son los más diversos del grupo fúngico

seed an embryo sporophyte of a seed plant packaged with nutritive tissue inside a protective coat
  semilla embrión esporófito de una semilla con tejido nutritivo dentro de una capa protectora

selective gene expression the expression of differing subsets of an organism's genes by different cells
  expresión génica selectiva expresión de diferentes subconjuntos de genes de un organismo por células diferentes

selective permeability a characteristic of a cell membrane in which some substances are able to cross it more easily than others
  permeabilidad selectiva característica de una membrana celular en la cual unas sustancias son más capaces de atravesarla que otras

sensory receptor a cell or cell component that responds to a specific stimulus, such as temperature or light
  receptor sensorial célula o componente celular que responde a un estímulo específico, como la temperatura o luz

sepal one of a set of green, leaflike portions of a plant that serve as the outer covering of unopened flowers

> **sépalo** parte de un conjunto de porciones verdes que parecen hojas de una planta; funcionan como cobertura de flores que no se han abierto

sexual reproduction reproductive mode by which offspring arise from two parents and inherit genes from both

> **reproducción sexual** modo reproductivo en el que la descendencia procede de dos progenitores y hereda genes de ambos

sexual selection a mode of natural selection in which some individuals out reproduce others of a population because they are better at securing mates

> **selección sexual** modo de selección natural donde unos individuos se reproducen más que otros en la población porque son mejores para conseguir parejas

shoot system the organ system of a plant consisting of stems, leaves, and reproductive organs; generally the aboveground parts of a plant

> **sistema de brotes** sistema de órganos de una planta que está compuesto de tallos, hojas y órganos reproductivos; generalmente, son las partes de la planta que están arriba de la tierra

SI system the internationally standardized system of measurements

> **sistema internacional** sistema de medidas estandarizado internacionalmente

sieve elements the living cells that make up sugar conducting sieve tubes of phloem; each sieve tube consists of a stack of sieve elements that meet end-to-end at sieve plates

> **elementos cribosos** células vivas que componen los tubos cribosos de floema que conducen el azúcar; cada tubo criboso consta de una pila de elementos cribosos que se unen de extremo a extremo en las placas cribosas

sieve tube the sugar-conducting tube of phloem; consists of stacked sieve elements

> **tubo criboso** tubo del floema que conduce el azúcar; está compuesto de elementos cribosos amontonados

silencer a DNA sequence where a repressor may bind to prevent RNA polymerase from transcribing a gene

> **silenciador** secuencia de ADN a la que un represor se puede unir para evitar que el ARN polimerasa transcriba un gen

single nucleotide polymorphism (SNP) a one-nucleotide DNA sequence variation carried by a measurable percentage of a population

> **polimorfismo de nucleótido único (SNP, en inglés)** variación de secuencia de ADN de un nucleótido que lleva un porcentaje medible de una población

sister chromatid one of two identical DNA molecules of a duplicated eukaryotic chromosome, attached at the centromere

> **cromátida hermana** cada una de las dos moléculas idénticas de ADN de un cromosoma eucariota duplicado, unida por el centrómero

sister group the two lineages that emerge from a node on a cladogram

grupo hermano cada uno de los dos linajes que surgen de un nodo en un cladograma

solute a dissolved substance

> **soluto** sustancia diluida

solution a uniform mixture of solute completely dissolved in solvent

> **solución** mezcla uniforme de un soluto completamente disuelto en un solvente

solvent a liquid in which other substances dissolve

> **solvente** líquido en el que otras sustancias se disuelven

somatic cell nuclear transfer (SCNT) a reproductive cloning method in which the DNA of a donor's body cell is transferred into an enucleated egg; produces clones of the donor

> **transferencia nuclear de células somáticas (SCNT, en inglés)** método de clonación reproductiva en el cual el ADN de la célula del cuerpo donador es transferido a un óvulo desnucleado; produce clones del donador

sori (singular *sorus*) clusters of spore-producing capsules on a fern leaf

> **soros** cúmulos de cápsulas productoras de esporas en la hoja de un helecho

speciation the emergence of a new species

> **especiación** surgimiento de nuevas especies

species a group of organisms with similar structural and functional characteristics that in nature breed only with one another and have a close common ancestry; a group of organisms with a common gene pool

> **especie** grupo de organismos con características estructurales y funcionales similares que en la naturaleza se aparean únicamente entre sí y tienen ascendencia común cercana; grupo de organismos con un acervo genético común

species evenness the relative abundance of each species in a community

> **igualdad de especies** abundancia relativa de cada especie en una comunidad

species richness the number of different species in a community

> **riqueza de especies** número de especies diferentes en una comunidad

spore a reproductive cell that gives rise to individual offspring in plants, algae, fungi, and certain protozoa

> **espora** célula reproductiva que produce descendientes individuales en plantas, algas, hongos y ciertos protozoarios

sporophyte generation the stage in the life cycle of a plant during which the plant's cells undergo meiosis to produce spores

> **generación esporófita** etapa en el ciclo de vida de una planta durante la cual las células producen esporas a través de meiosis

stabilizing selection a mode of natural selection in which an intermediate form of a trait is adaptive, and extreme forms are selected against

> **selección estabilizadora** modo de selección natural donde una forma intermedia de un gen es adaptativa y se selecciona en contra de formas extremas

stamen the reproductive organ of a flower that consists of a pollen-producing anther and, in most species, a filament

    estambre órgano reproductivo de una flor, que consta de una antera productora de polen y, en la mayoría de las especies, un filamento

starch a complex carbohydrate that does not dissolve readily in water; main form of stored sugars in plants

    almidón carbohidrato complejo que no se disuelve fácilmente en agua; forma principal de azúcares almacenados en plantas

stem cell a cell that can divide to produce more stem cells or differentiate into a specialized cell type

    célula madre célula que puede dividirse para producir más células madre o diferenciarse en un tipo de célula especializada

stigma the upper part of the carpel of a flower; adapted to receive pollen

    estigma parte superior del carpelo de una flor; adaptado para recibir polen

stolon a stem that branches from a plant's main stem and grows horizontally on, or just under, the ground

    estolón tallo que brota del tallo principal de la planta y crece horizontalmente sobre la tierra o justo debajo de esta

stomata (singular *stoma*) tiny gaps between pairs of guard cells in a plant's epidermis; allow internal tissues to exchange gases with the air; can be closed to prevent water loss

    estomas pequeños huecos entre pares de células de guarda en la epidermis de una planta; permiten que los tejidos internos intercambien gases con el aire; se pueden cerrar para evitar la pérdida de agua

style the tube that connects the ovary to the stigma of a flower

    estilo tubo que conecta el ovario con el estigma de una flor

substrate a molecule that an enzyme acts upon and converts to a product; reactant in an enzyme-catalyzed reaction

    sustrato molécula sobre la cual una enzima actúa y la convierte en producto; reactante en una reacción catalizada por enzimas

survivorship curve a plot that shows how many individuals born during the same interval remain alive over time

    curva de supervivencia gráfica que muestra cuántos individuos que nacen en el mismo intervalo permanecen vivos a lo largo del tiempo

sustainability a way of using resources to meet human needs without deep impacts to the environments that produce those resources

    sostenibilidad forma de usar recursos para satisfacer necesidades humanas sin impacto profundo en los medioambientes que producen esos recursos

symbiosis a close ecological relationship in which one species lives in or on another species in a commensal, mutualistic, or parasitic relationship

    simbiosis relación ecológica cercana donde una especie vive dentro de otra especie o sobre ella, en una relación comensal, mutualista o parasitaria

system a combination of interacting parts that form a complex whole

    sistema combinación de partes que interactúan y forman una entidad compleja

T

taxonomy the science of naming, describing, and classifying organisms

    taxonomía ciencia de nombrar, describir y clasificar organismos

telophase a stage of mitosis during which chromosomes arrive at opposite spindle poles, decondense, and become enclosed by a new nuclear envelope

    telofase etapa de la mitosis durante la cual los cromosomas llegan a polos opuestos del huso, se descondensan y se encapsulan en una nueva envoltura nuclear

tension in transpiration, the continuous negative pressure created by evaporation of water from the surface of a leaf or stem

    tensión en la transpiración, la presión negativa continua creada por la evaporación del agua de la superficie de una hoja o tallo

thermophile an organism adapted to life at a very high temperature

    termófilo organismo adaptado a la vida a temperaturas muy altas

thigmotropism plant movement or growth in a direction influenced by contact

    tigmotropismo movimiento o crecimiento de una planta en una dirección por influencia del contacto

threatened species a species whose population is low enough for it to be at risk of becoming extinct, but not low enough that it is in imminent danger of extinction

    especie amenazada especie cuya población es suficientemente baja para que esté en riesgo de extinción, pero no lo suficientemente baja para enfrentar peligro inminente de extinción

thylakoid a flat membranous sac occuring in stacks inside the chloroplast; where light energy is converted into ATP and NADPH used in carbohydrate synthesis

    tilacoide saco plano y membranoso que se presenta en pilas dentro del cloroplasto; sitio donde la energía luminosa se convierte en el ATP y NADPH que se usan en la síntesis de carbohidratos

trace fossil the physical evidence from the ancient past of an organism's activities

    icnofósiles evidencia física del pasado antiguo de las actividades de un organismo

tracheid a component of xylem; a tapered cell that dies when mature; pitted walls that remain interconnect with other tracheids to form water-conducting tubes

    traqueida componente del xilema; célula estrecha que muere cuando madura; paredes picadas que permanecen interconectadas con otras traqueidas para formar tubos conductores de agua

trade-off a compromise in the solution to a problem where one feature, quality, or factor is favored at the cost of another
    compensación compromiso en la solución a un problema donde una característica, cualidad o factor es favorecido a expensas de otro

trait a characteristic inherited by an offspring from its parent
    rasgo característica heredada por un descendiente de parte de un progenitor

transcription the process in which enzymes use DNA as a template to assemble RNA; part of gene expression
    transcripción proceso en el que las enzimas usan ADN como modelo para ensamblar ARN; parte de la expresión génica

transcription factor a regulatory protein that influences transcription by binding directly to DNA; e.g., an activator or repressor
    factor de transcripción proteína reguladora que influye sobre la transcripción al unirse directamente al ADN; por ejemplo, un activador o represor

transcriptome the study of all the messenger RNA molecules in a genome
    transcriptoma estudio de todas las moléculas de ARN mensajero en un genoma

transgenic a genetically modified organism that carries a gene from a different species
    transgénico organismo modificado genéticamente que lleva un gen de una especie diferente

translation the process in which a polypeptide chain is assembled from amino acids in the order specified by an mRNA
    traducción proceso en el que una cadena de polipéptidos es ensamblada a partir de aminoácidos en el orden especificado por un ARNm

transpiration the evaporation of water from aboveground plant parts
    transpiración evaporación del agua en plantas que viven encima del suelo

trophic level the group of organisms in an ecosystem which occupy the same level in a food chain
    nivel trófico grupo de organismos de un ecosistema que ocupan el mismo lugar en una cadena alimenticia

tropism a directional movement toward or away from a stimulus that triggers it
    tropismo movimiento direccional hacia o en contra de un estímulo que desencadena ese movimiento

tuber a fleshy storage structure made from the stem of a plant; may grow buds on its surface that potentially develop into new plants
    tubérculo estructura carnosa de almacenamiento hecha del tallo de una planta; muchos tienen brotes en su superficie que potencialmente se desarrollan para convertirse en plantas nuevas

U

uniformitarianism a geologic principle that states geologic processes operate consistently throughout time

uniformismo principio geológico que establece que los procesos geológicos operan de manera consistente a lo largo del tiempo

V

vaccine a preparation introduced into the body in order to elicit immunity to a specific antigen
    vacuna preparación introducida al cuerpo para despertar inmunidad a un antígeno específico

vacuole a large, fluid-filled vesicle that isolates or breaks down waste, debris, toxins, or food
    vacuola vesícula grande, llena de fluido, que aísla o descompone desechos, toxinas o alimentos

variolation a practice of deliberately infecting a person with a pathogen in the hope they develop a mild infection and acquire natural immunity
    variolización práctica de infectar a una ersona con un patógeno de manera deliberada con la esperanza de desarrollar una infección ligera y obtener inmunidad natural

vascular plant a plant that has xylem and phloem
    planta vascular planta que tiene xilema y floema

vascular tissue the plant tissue that carries water and nutrients through the plant body
    tejido vascular el tejido de la planta que transporta agua y nutrientes por todo el cuerpo de la planta

vector in biotechnology, a molecule that can carry foreign DNA into host cells; in epidemiology, an organism that transmits an infectious pathogen to another organism
    vector en la biotecnología, una molécula que puede transportar ADN foráneo a una célula anfitriona; en la epidemiología, un organismo que transmite un patógeno infeccioso a otro organismo

vertebrate an animal with a backbone
    vertebrado animal con columna vertebral

vesicle a saclike, membrane enclosed organelle; different kinds store, transport, or break down their contents
    vesícula orgánulo contenido en una membrana con forma de saco; distintos tipos almacenan, transportan o descomponen sus contenidos

vessel a water-conducting tube consisting of a stack of xylem cells that meet end to end at perforation plates
    vaso tubo conductor de agua que consiste en una pila de células del xilema que se unen de extremo a extremo en las placas de perforación

vestigial structure an evolutionary remnant of a formerly functional structure
    estructura vestigial resto evolutivo de una estructura que antes era funcional

viral envelope an outer membrane of a virus particle derived from the host cell in which it formed
    envoltura vírica membrana externa de una partícula de virus derivada de la célula anfitriona donde se formó

viral particle a virus that is not inside a host cell
    partícula viral virus que no está dentro de una célula anfitriona

W

wildlife corridor an area of habitat that connects wildlife populations separated by human activities or structures

corredor ecológico área de hábitat que conecta poblaciones de fauna separadas por actividades o estructuras humanas

X

xylem a complex vascular tissue of plants; cell walls of its dead tracheids and vessel elements form tubes that distribute water and mineral ions through the plant body

xilema tejido vascular complejo en las plantas; las paredes celulares de traqueidas muertas y elementos de los vasos forman tubos que distribuyen agua e iones minerales por el cuerpo de la planta

Z

zooplankton a community of tiny drifting or swimming heterotrophic organisms

zooplancton comunidad de diminutos organismos heterotróficos que flotan o nadan

zygote the first cell of a new individual

cigoto la primera célula de un individuo

zygote fungus a fungus that forms a thick-walled zygospore during sexual reproduction

zygomycota hongo que forma una zigospora con paredes gruesas durante la reproducción sexual

Page numbers in **bold** indicate key terms.
An *f* refers to a figure; *t* refers to a table.

ACKNOWLEDGEMENTS

National Geographic Learning gratefully acknowledges the contributions of the following National Geographic Explorers and affiliates to our program:

Katie Amato, Biological anthropologist

Diva Amon, Deep-sea biologist

Christopher C. Austin, Biologist

Carter Clinton, Biological anthropologist

Nicole Colón Carrión, Biologist and ecologist

Camila Espejo, Veterinarian

Holly Fearnbach, Zoologist

Andrian Gajigan, Biochemist

Pablo Garcia Borboroglu, Marine biologist and penguin conservationist

Stanley Gehrt, Urban wildlife researcher

Shane Gero, Marine biologist

David Gruber, Marine biologist

Federico Kacoliris, Biologist

Brenda Larison, Biologist

Heather Joan Lynch, Quantitative ecologist

Emily Otali, Primatologist

Robert A. Raguso, Biologist

Kristen Ruegg, Biologist

Pardis Sabeti, Computational biologist

Çağan Şekercioğlu, Ornithology professor

Anusha Shankar, Ecologist

Daniel Streicker, Infectious disease ecologist

Varun Swamy, Ecologist

Gerard Talavera, Evolutionary biologist

Rosa Vásquez Espinoza, Chemical biologist and Amazon conservationist

Branwen Williams, Oceanographer and climate scientist

Kimberly Williams-Guillén, Conservationist

Robert Wood, Roboticist

Rae Wynn-Grant, Carnivore ecologist

National Geographic Learning gratefully acknowledges the contributions of the following National Geographic Photographers to our program:

Ary Bassous

Annie Griffiths

Melissa Groo

Charlie Hamilton James

Frans Lanting

David Liittschwager

Ian Nichols

Thomas Peschak

Jim Richardson

Gabby Salazar

Joel Sartore

Babak Tafreshi

Stefano Unterthiner

Edson Vandeira

Ami Vitale

Shannon Wild

PHOTOGRAPHIC CREDITS

Shutterstock.com; (tr) Wesdotphotography/Alamy Stock Photo; **100-101** (spread)© Edson Vandeira/National Geographic Image Collection; **103** Nature Picture Library/Alamy Stock Photo; **107** © NOAA ONMS/Ocean Exploration Trust; **108-109** (spread) © M. Oeggerli/Pathology, University Hospital Basel and School of Life Sciences, FHNW.; **111** (tc) Courtesy of Katie R. Amato; (bl) Juniors Bildarchiv GmbH/Alamy Stock Photo; (br) Courtesy of Katie R. Amato; **112** © Klaus Nigge/National Geographic Image Collection; **113** Tom & Pat Leeson/Science Source; **121** © Jennifer Hayes/National Geographic Image Collection; **122** Phil Degginger/Alamy Stock Photo; **123** Hans Heinz/Shutterstock.com; **126** © Jasper Doest/National Geographic Image Collection; **135** © Jim Richardson/National Geographic Image Collection; **136** (t) © Lvcas Fiat/Projeto Mantis; (tl) © Stephanie King/University of Michigan; **142** Paul Gunning/Science Source; **143** Jonathan Plant/Alamy Stock Photo; **145** (bl) Cyril Ruoso/JH Editorial/Minden Pictures; (br) Ritvars/Shutterstock.com; **148** Vojce/iStock/Getty Images; **149** Courtesy of Argonne National Laboratory; **151** Steve Gschmeissner/Science Photo Library/Getty Images; **153** Biophoto Associates/Science Source; **155** Jennifer Waters/Science Source; **156** (bl) Don W. Fawcett/Science Source; (br) Biophoto Associates/Science Source; **157** (cl) Keith R. Porter/Science Source; (bl) Dr. Kari Lounatmaa/Science Source; **159** Eye of Science/Science Source; **160-161** (spread) © Charlie Hamilton James/National Geographic Image Collection; **164** (bl) Dennis Kunkel Microscopy/Science Source; (bc) Dennis Kunkel Microscopy/Science Source; (br) Dennis Kunkel Microscopy/Science Source; **165** Hermann Schillers, Prof. Dr. H. Oberleithner, University Hospital Of Muenster/Science Source; **169** Izabella Joubert/EyeEm/Getty Images; **173** inset Steve Gschmeissner/Science Source; (tl) Richard T. Nowitz/Science Source; (tr) Nicolas Asfouri/AFP/Getty Images; inset Andrew Syred/Science Source; (bl) NOAA; **176** (t) © Gil S. Jacinto; (tl) Courtesy of Andrian Gajigan; **177** (bl) Jenson/Shutterstock.com; (br) © University of Bordeaux, CNRS, Centre de Recherche Paul Pascal/T. Beneyton; **180** Dr Paul Andrews, University Of Dundee/Science Source; **181** (bl) Pictorial Press Ltd/Alamy Stock Photo; (br) BSIP/Universal Images Group/Getty Images; **185** From "Expression of the epidermal growth factor receptor (EGFR) and the phosphorylated EGFR in invasive breast carcinomas." http://breast-cancer research.com/content/10/3/R49; **186** Robert Henno/Alamy Stock Photo; **188** (bc) Don. W. Fawcett/Science Source; (br) Andrew Syred/Science Source; **190** (tl) Ed Reschke/Photolibrary/Getty Images; (tr1) Michael Abbey/Science Source; (tr2) Michael Abbey/Science Source; (cl1) Ed Reschke/Stone/Getty Images; (cl2) (cr1) (cr2) (br) Michael Abbey/Science Source; **192** Dr Torsten Wittmann/Science Source; **193** (cl) Nature Picture Library/Alamy Stock Photo; (cr) Christopher Biggs/Shutterstock.com; (bl) GFC Collection/Alamy Stock Photo; (br) Ondrej Vavra/Shutterstock.com; **194** (cl) Roger J. Bick & Brian J. Poindexter/UT-Houston Medical School/Science Source; (c) SPL/Science Source; (cr) SPL/Science Source; (bl) Steve Gschmeissner/Science Source; (br) Daniel Schroen, Cell Applications Inc/Science Source; **196** (cl) © Triarch/Visuals Unlimited, Inc.; (cr) © Biodisc/Visuals Unlimited, Inc.; (bl) Dr. Keith Wheeler/Science Source; (br) Emilio Ereza/Alamy Stock Photo; **197** © David Liittschwager/National Geographic Image Collection; **198** (t) © Dr. Manuel Ruiz-Aravena; (tl) © Dr. Manuel Ruiz-Aravena; **199** Dr. Gopal Murti/Science Source; **203** Dennis Kunkel Microscopy/Science Source; **204-205** (spread) Brian Overcast/Alamy Stock Photo; **207** (t) Courtesy of Varun Swamy; (bl) Pete Oxford/Minden Pictures; (br) Courtesy of Varun Swamy; **208** Dennis Kunkel Microscopy/Science Source; **209** NASA; **213** (cl) Frank Fox/Science Source; (cr) Charles V. Angelo/Science Source; **214** (tl) James Cavallini/Science Source; (tr) CNRI/Science Source; (bl) © Heide Schulz-Vogt/Leibniz Institute for Baltic Sea Research; (br) Eye of Science/Science Source; **216** (cl) Stem Jem/Science Source; (cr) Juniors Bildarchiv GmbH/Alamy Stock Photo; **217** Ralph White/Corbis Documentary/Getty Images; **220** Ami Images/Science Source; **221** (cl) Eye of Science/Science Source; (bl) Biophoto Associates/Science Source; **222** © Brian Skerry/National Geographic Image Collection; **223** (tl) M. I. Walker/Science Source; (tr) BSIP SA/Alamy Stock Photo; (bl) Frank Fox/Science Source; **224** (cl) London School of Hygiene & Tropical Medicine/Science Source; (cr) Matthijs Wetterauw/Alamy Stock Photo; **225** (tl) M. I. Walker/Science Source; (tr) Udeyismail/Shutterstock.com; (cl) Eye of Science/Science Source; **226** Science History Images/Alamy Stock Photo; **229** (t) Eye of Science/Science Source; (br) Professor Sir David Read FRS; **230** (t) Prisma/Dukas Presseagentur GmbH/Alamy Stock Photo; (br) Ed Reschke/Photodisc/Getty Images; **231** Reza Saputra/iStock/Getty Images; **232** Michel Viard/Jacana/Science Source; **233** (tl) Arie v.d. Wolde/Shutterstock.com; (cr) Galina Bondarenko/Shutterstock.com; (bl) © Dennis, David M./Animals Animals; (br) JerHetrick/Shutterstock.com; **235** (cl) Paul Starosta/Stone/Getty Images; (cr) Akira Kaede/Photographer's Choice RF/Getty Images; (bl) Andrew Syred/Science Source; (br) © Etienne Littlefair/Minden Pictures; **238** Biozentrum, University of Basel/Science Source; **239** Petit Format/Science Source; **241** (tl) Cellou Binani/AFP/Getty Images; (tr) CAMR/A. Barry Dowsett/Science Source; (bl) James Cavallini/Science Source; **243** © Gabriele Galimberti/National Geographic Image Collection; **244** (t) © Ronan Donovan; (tl) Courtesy of Emily Otali; **245** NASA; **248** United States Forest Service; **249** Vasilis Ververidis/Alamy Stock Photo; **251** Scott Camazine/Science Source; **252** (bl) Nichole Casebolt/Shutterstock.com; (bc1) ShadeDesign/Shutterstock.com; (bc2) Memitina/iStock/Getty Images; (br) Gloomy Photography/Shutterstock.com; **253** Dr. Keith Wheeler/Science Source; **254** AntiMartina/E+/Getty Images; **255** (cl) Wild Horizon/Universal Images Group/Getty Images; (c) Amit kg/Shutterstock.com; (cr) Kamomeen/Shutterstock.com; **256** Nick Garbutt/Steve Bloom Images/Alamy Stock Photo; **257** Dr. Keith Wheeler/Science Source; **259** Power and

Syred/Science Source; **262** © Babak Tafreshi/National Geographic Image Collection; **263** Little Dinosaur/Moment/Getty Images; **264** (tl) Jeff Holcombe/Shutterstock.com; (tc) Ed Reschke/Stone/Getty Images; (tr) Tami Ruble/Alamy Stock Photo; **265** Rieger Bertrand/Hemis/Alamy Stock Photo; **267** Andrew E Gardner/Shutterstock.com; **268** Aimpol Buranet/Shutterstock.com; **269** (cl) Blickwinkel/Alamy Stock Photo; (cr) MichaelGrantPlants/Alamy Stock Photo; (bl) FotoDuets/Shutterstock.com; (br) Inga Gedrovicha/Shutterstock.com; **270** (t) © Robert Raguso; (c) © Yash Sondhi; (bl) Martin Shields/Alamy Stock Photo; (br) Franz Krenn/Okapia/Science Source; **273** Ornitolog82/iStock/Getty Images; **274** DieterMeyrl/E+/Getty Images; **275** Eric Mischke/EyeEm/Getty Images; **276** Panther Media GmbH/Alamy Stock Photo; **277** © ANP/Hollandse Hoogte/Ko Hage; **280** Buiten-Beeld/Alamy Stock Photo; **281** Daniel Ruthrauff/USGS; **282** (cl) Dennis Sabo/Shutterstock.com; (cr) Ozgur Kerem Bulur/Shutterstock.com; (bl) Kurit Afshen/Shutterstock.com; (br) MarieHolding/iStock/Getty Images; **283** (tl) Ifish/E+/Getty Images; (tc) Selim Kohen/500px/Getty Images; (tr) Pulse/The Image Bank/Getty Images; **285** HeritagePics/Alamy Stock Photo; **286** Lightspruch/iStock/Getty Images; **289** Eye of Science/Science Source; **290** Eye of Science/Science Source; **291** James Oliver/Digital Vision/Getty Images; **293** In Green/Shutterstock.com; **295** All Canada Photos/Alamy Stock Photo; **296** Blickwinkel/Alamy Stock Photo; **297** Steve Bloom Images/Alamy Stock photo; **298** Blickwinkel/Alamy Stock Photo; **299** (cl) Scott Camazine/Science Source; (br) Sylvain Cordier/Stockbyte/Getty Images; **300** Tony Wu/Minden Pictures; **301** All Canada Photos/Alamy Stock Photo; **302** Jim Brandenburg/Minden Pictures; **303** Stan Tekiela Author/Naturalist/Wildlife Photographer/Getty Images; **304** Paul Souders/Stone/Getty Images; **305** © Stefano Unterthiner/National Geographic Image Collection; **306** (t) © John Durban/Holly Fearnbach; (tl) Courtesy of Holly Fearnbach; **307** Winfried Wisniewski/The Image Bank/Getty Images; **311** © Félix Colón Ruíz; **312-313** (spread) CDC/Science Source; **315** (t) © Daniel Streicker/National Geographic Image Collection; (bl) © Daniel Streicker/National Geographic Image Collection; (br) Courtesy of Daniel Streicker; **316** James Schwabel/Alamy Stock Photo; **317** Frank Fox/Science Source; **320** Science & Society Picture Library/SSPL/Getty Images; **324** (t) National Park Service; (tl) © Carter Clinton/National Geographic Image Collection; **325** © Melissa Groo/National Geographic Image Collection; **327** Professor Oscar Miller/Science Source; **329** (cl) Don W. Fawcett/Science Source; (bl) Biology Pics/Science Source; **343** (bl) Hans Verburg/Alamy Stock Photo ; (br) Risto0/istock/Getty Images; **346** Dora Zett/Shutterstock.com; **347** Ressormat/Shutterstock.com; **349** (bl) Omikron/Science Source; (br) Biophoto Associates/Science Source; **357** (t) RichardSeeley/Istock/Getty Images; (tr) © Neil Losin; **361** Hermann Eisenbeiss/Science Source; **368-369** (spread) © Shannon Wild; **371** John Kaprielian/Science Source; **372** (tl) Richard P Long/Alamy Stock Photo; (tc) Harvey Wood/Alamy Stock Photo; (tr) Wayne Hutchinson/Alamy Stock Photo; **373** Grossemy Vanessa/Alamy Stock Photo; **375** (tl) Jim Cumming/Shutterstock.com; (tr) Colleen Gara/Moment/Getty Images; **377** © Susan Bronson; **380** © Revive & Restore; **381** Kristel Richard/NaturePL/Science Source; **386** Eurelios/Science Source; **390-393** (spread) © Ary Bassous; **393** (bl) Pascal Goetgheluck/Science Source; (br) KorradolYamsattham/Istock/Getty Images; **394** Reuters/Alamy Stock Photo; **395** (tl) © University of Exeter; (tr) Slowmotiongli/Istock/Getty Images; **397** The Asahi Shimbun/Getty Images; **401** Frederic J. Brown/AFP/Getty Images; **402** IanDagnall Computing/Alamy Stock Photo; (tr) Dennis Kunkel Microscopy/Science Source; **403** (t) © Pardis Sabeti; (tr) © Chiun-Kai Shih/National Geographic Image Collection; **406** Science Photo Library/Alamy Stock Photo; **409** Tchandrou Nitanga/AFP/Getty Images; **414** Freder/E+/Getty Images; **417** © Bauer et al./The Genetics Society of America; **421** Xinhua News Agency/Getty Images; **422-433** (spread) © Nelson, Alan G./Animals Animals; **425** (t) Courtesy of Anusha Shankar; (b) Courtesy of Anusha Shankar; **426** Parkol/Shutterstock.com; **427** © Trustees of the Natural History Museum, London; **429** (cl) Chris Packham/Minden Pictures; (cr) Sduben/iStock/Getty Images; **432** (bl) Steph111/iStock/Getty Images; (bc) Chris Mattison/Minden Pictures; (br) Ondrej Prosicky/Alamy Stock Photo; **435** (cl) Age Fotostock Spain, S.L./Alamy Stock Photo; (cr) Science History Images/Alamy Stock Photo; (bl) Francois Gohier/Science Source; (br) Nature Picture Library/Alamy Stock Photo; **437** © Pete Mcbride/National Geographic Image Collection; **438** (cl) Historic Collection/Alamy Stock Photo; (cr) The Natural History Museum/Alamy Stock Photo; (bl) Sinclair Stammers/Science Source; (br) Ted Kinsman/Science Source; **440** Francois Gohier/Science Source; **444-445** (spread) © Annie Griffiths/National Geographic Image Collection; **446** (bl) Sinclair Stammers/Science Source; (bc) © Catherine May; (br) Oxford Scientific/The Image Bank/Getty Images; **448** (cl) Joao Ponces/Alamy Stock Photo; (cr) MriyaWildlife/iStock/Getty Images; (bc) Breck P. Kent/Animals Animals; **452** (t) lumen-digital/Shutterstock.com ; (tl) © Brenda Larison; **456** (tc) Eye of Science/Science Source; **457** (bl) Dmitry Bezrukov/iStock/Getty Images; **459** (bl) Its About Light/Design Pics/Getty Images; (bc) Mike Powles/Stone/Getty Images; (br) Tier Und Naturfotografie J und C Sohns/Photographer's Choice RF/Getty Images; **460** (tl) B.A.E. Inc./Alamy Stock Photo; (tr) Jose A. Bernat Bacete/Moment/Getty Images; (bl) Millard H. Sharp/Science Source; (br) © George Grall/National Geographic Image Collection; **461** (bl) Arterra/Universal Images Group/Getty Images; (br) © Eduardo Mayoral Alfaro; **464** Robert Alexander/Archive Photos/Getty Images; **467** Elena Shavlovska/Shutterstock.com; **473** © Gabby Salazar/National Geographic Image Collection; **474** (tr) Rick & Nora Bowers/Alamy Stock Photo; (cr) Karel Bock/iStock/Getty Images; **477** Juergen & Christine Sohns/Minden Pictures; **478** All Canada Photos/Alamy Stock Photo; **479** Imageplotter/Alamy Stock Photo; **480** (t) © Christopher Austin; (tl) Courtesy of Christopher Austin;

484 Peter Chadwick/Gallo Images ROOTS RF collection/Getty Images;
486 (bl) Cavan Images/Getty Images; (br) David Madison/Photodisc/Getty
Images; 487 Aaron Geddes Photography/Moment/Getty Images; 488 (tr) ©
Arthur Anker; (cr) © Arthur Anker; 489 (tl) Johannes Melchers/Minden
Pictures; (cl) NPS Photo/Alamy Stock Photo; (cl) Robby Kohley/USFWS; (c)
Researchgate/U.S. Geological Survey; (cr) Michael Walther/Alamy Stock
Photo; (cr) Photo Resource Hawaii/Alamy Stock Photo; 490 (tl) Carmen
Hauser/Shutterstock.com; (tr) The Natural History Museum/Alamy Stock
Photo; 493 AYImages/iStock/Getty Images; 494-495 (spread) © Ami Vitale/
National Geographic Image Collection; 496 (bl) Byron Jorjorian/Alamy Stock
Photo; (br) Dante Fenolio/Science Source; 497 NOAA; 499 (t) © Çağan
Şekercioğlu; (tr) © Rebecca Hale/National Geographic Image Collection;
503 Magnus Larsson/iStock/Getty Images; 504 Bloomberg Creative/Getty
Images; 506 Alf Manciagli/Shutterstock.com; 507 Sue Cunningham
Photographic/Alamy Stock Photo; 508 Imaginechina Limited/Alamy Stock
Photo; 510 Alaska Stock/Alamy Stock Photo; 511 Henglein and Steets/
Cultura/Getty Images; 512 © Joel Santore/National Geographic Image
Collection; 513 Jung Getty/Moment/Getty Images; 514 (cr) Ken Hurst/
Alamy Stock Photo; (bc) Steve_Gadomski/iStock/Getty Images; 515 Erik
Reis/Alamy Stock Photo; 516 Ahei/iStock/Getty Images; 517 Jwngshar
Narzary/EyeEm/Getty Images; 521 (bc) Hal Beral/Corbis/Getty Images;
524 (cl) Adrian Sherratt/Alamy Stock Photo; (br) Imran Khan's Photography/
Shutterstock.com; 525 (bl) Lacey Barber/Shutterstock.com; 526 (br)
Winston Link/Shutterstock.com; (bl) Jon Rehg/Shutterstock.com;
546 Eco2drew/iStock/Getty Images Plus/Getty Images; 547 (tl) Steve
Gschmeissner/Science Photo Library/Getty Images; (tr) Power and Syred/
Science Source; (cl) Andrew Syred/Science Source; (cr) Roberto Sorin/
Shutterstock.com; (bl) Kimberly Boyles/Shutterstock.com; (br) Christian
Puntorno/Shutterstock.com; 549 © Norman R. Pace/American Society For
Microbiology; 550 © Burki, F. Roger, A. J., Brown, M. W., & Simpson, A. G. B.
(2020). "Review: The New Tree of Eukaroytes." Trends in Ecology &
Evolution, 35(1), p. 48; 551 (bc) © David M. Hillis, Derrick Zwickl, and Robin
Gutell, University of Texas/The American Association for the Advancement
of Science; 552 (tl1) Chris Mattison/Minden Pictures; (tl2) Paul Starosta/
Stone/Getty Images; (cl1) BSIP/Universal Images Group/Getty Images;
(cl2) Jonathan Plant/Alamy Stock Photo; (cl3) Dennis Kunkel Microscopy/
Science Source; (c) Dennis Kunkel Microscopy/Science Source; (cr) Eye of
Science/Science Source; (bl1) Dennis Kunkel Microscopy/Science Source;
(bl2) Arie v.d. Wolde/Shutterstock.com; (bc) Steve Gschmeissner/Science
Source; (br) Eye of Science/Science Source; 553 (tl) Micro Discovery/Corbis
Documentary/Getty Images; (tc) Steve Gschmeissner/Science Source; (tr1)
Ed Reschke/Stone/Getty Images; (tr2) AYImages/iStock/Getty Images; (tr3)
Aimpol Buranet/Shutterstock.com; (cl1) Fatahdijava/Shutterstock.com;
(cl2) Greg Dimijian/Science Source; (c1) Mike Pellinni/Shutterstock.com;
(c2) Drew Rawcliffe/Shutterstock.com; (cr1) Malachi Jacobs/Shutterstock.
com; (cr2) Julija Kumpinovica/Shutterstock.com; (cr3) BSIP SA/Alamy Stock
Photo; (cr4) Ami Images/Science Source; (bl) Silvergull/Shutterstock.com;
(bc) Poirot55/Shutterstock.com; (br1) CatalinT/Shutterstock.com; (br2) Eye
of Science/Science Source.